Post-Traumatic Stress Disorder

Post-Traumatic Stress Disorder

Basic Science and Clinical Practice

Edited by

Priyattam J. Shiromani

Harvard Medical School, Department of Neurology, VA Boston Healthcare System, West Roxbury, MA

Terence M. Keane

National Center for Post-Traumatic Stress Disorder, VA Boston Healthcare System, Boston MA

Joseph E. LeDoux

New York University, Center for Neural Science, New York, NY

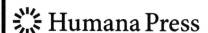 Humana Press

Editors

Priyattam J. Shiromani
Harvard Medical School
Department of Neurology
VA Boston Healthcare System
West Roxbury, MA

Terence M. Keane
National Center for Post-Traumatic
 Stress Disorder
VA Boston Healthcare System
Boston MA

Joseph E. LeDoux
New York University,
Center for Neural Science,
New York, NY

ISBN 978-1-60327-328-2   e-ISBN 978-1-60327-329-9
DOI: 10.1007/978-1-60327-329-9

Library of Congress Control Number: 2008942054

springer.com

Preface

Post-traumatic stress disorder or PTSD is a psychiatric condition that can occur in anyone who has experienced a life-threatening or violent event. The trauma can be due to war, terrorism, torture, natural disasters, accidents, violence, or rape. PTSD was once associated exclusively with military service and characterized by the terms "shell shock" and "battle fatigue." However, now it is recognized that PTSD can occur in any traumatic situation and can afflict children as well as adults. Studies across cultures, languages, and races suggest that PTSD is a universal response to exposure to traumatic events.

In the U.S. population, the prevalence rate of PTSD is approximately 8%, with the rate for women more than twice that for men *(1)*. In the aftermath of Hurricane Katrina, the prevalence of PTSD in the New Orleans metro area (hardest hit by the hurricane) was 30.3% compared to 12.5% in the remainder of the hurricane area *(2)*. Among U.S. military personnel, a study *(3)* found that during the 1991 Gulf War symptoms of PTSD were evident in 6.2% of the deployed troops versus 1.1% of the nondeployed peers. Importantly, 10 years later the rate of PTSD among deployed veterans (Operation Enduring Freedom-Operation Iraqi Freedom; OEF-OIF) was three times higher than in the nondeployed peers. In the Iraq War, a U.S. Army study found that 12.9% of the soldiers suffered from PTSD *(4)*. Not all individuals exposed to a life-threatening event develop PTSD, indicating significant individual differences in coping with the stressful event. However, prior history of trauma may increase the risk for PTSD *(5)*, suggesting an additive effect of stress.

The brain's response to trauma and stress, also termed the "fight-or-flight" response, was first described by Walter Cannon in 1915 *(6)*. Its purpose is to mobilize the body to action and protect us from danger. The cascade of chemicals unleashed during a fight-or-flight response acts on specific brain regions, in particular the hippocampus and amygdala, which are parts of the limbic system related to emotion, memory, and cognition. The amygdala is especially vulnerable because it is here that a fearful association of the event is processed and stored.

Individuals with PTSD have memories of the event that they relive again and again (i.e., flashbacks, nightmares, preoccupation with thoughts or images of the events of war); they avoid people and places associated with the trauma, becoming distressed at cues or reminders of the experience (e.g., the anniversary of the event); and they are hyperaroused (difficulty sleeping, trouble concentrating, hypervigilant).

In the past few years, there has been a tremendous growth in our under-standing of PTSD. Relevant brain areas have been identified; there are animal models to study the disease; there are sound evaluation methods; and large-scale clinical trials are under way to examine the effectiveness of psychological and pharmacological treatments. In this text, we have invited experts to review the current state of knowledge regarding PTSD, including treatment strategies, both pharmacological and psychological. The collection of reviews in this book covers epidemiological findings, neurobiology and neurophysiology, brain imaging, and treatment strategies.

We would like to thank Richard Lansing at Humana Press for recognizing the need for this book, Amanda Quinn and Joseph Albert André for assistance with the publication process.

P. J. Shiromani
Terence M. Keane
Joseph LeDoux

REFERENCES

1. Kessler, R. C., Sonnega, A., Bromet, E., Hughes, M., and Nelson, C. B. (1995) Post-traumatic stress disorder in the National Comorbidity Survey. Arch Gen Psychiatry 52, 1048–1060.
2. Galea, S., Brewin, C. R., Gruber, M., Jones, R. T., King, D. W., King, L. A., McNally, R. J., Ursano, R. J., Petukhova, M., and Kessler, R. C. (2007) Exposure to hurricane-related stressors and mental illness after Hurricane Katrina. Arch Gen Psychiatry 64(12), 1427–1434.
3. Toomey, R., Kang, H. K., Karlinsky, J., Baker, D. G., Vasterling, J. J., Alpern, R., Reda, D. J., Henderson, W. G., Murphy, F. M., Eisen, S. A. (2007) Mental health of US Gulf War veterans 10 years after the war. Br J Psychiatry 190, 385–393.
4. Hoge, C. W., Castro, C. A., Messer, S. C., McGurk, D., Cotting, D. I., and Koffman, R. L. (2004) Combat duty in Iraq and Afghanistan, mental health problems, and barriers to care. N Engl J Med 351, 13–22.
5. King, D. W., King, L. A., Foy, D. W., and Gudanowski, D. M. (1996) Prewar factors in combat-related posttraumatic stress disorder: structural equation modeling with a national sample of female and male Vietnam veterans. J Consult Clin Psychol 64, 520–531.
6. Cannon, W. (1915) Bodily Changes in Pain, Hunger, Fear and Rage: An Account of Recent Researches into the Function of Emotional Excitement. Appleton.New York:

About the Editors

P. J. Shiromani, Ph.D., is an associate professor of neurology at Harvard Medical School and senior research scientist at the VA Boston Healthcare System, where he is the director of the Molecular Sleep Laboratory. Dr. Shiromani's research identifies the neural circuitry underlying sleep and wakefulness and how the brain shifts between states of consciousness. He has pioneered the use of molecular tools to identify key neurons regulating sleep. His current research effort uses gene transfer to rescue the neurodegenerative sleep disorder narcolepsy. In recognition of his research, he has received the Young Investigator Award from the Sleep Research Society. He is the author of more than 100 research articles in leading scientific journals. His research has been supported by the National Institutes of Health (NIH) and by the Veterans Administration. He has served as chair of an NIH review group and as a regular member of several NIH review groups. He was the first editor of the *Sleep Research Society Bulletin*.

Terence M. Keane, Ph.D., is associate chief of staff for research and development, VA Boston Healthcare System; director, National Center for PTSD, Behavioral Sciences Division; professor and vice chair of research and psychiatry, Boston University School of Medicine. He is recognized internationally as a leading expert on trauma and PTSD, authoring numerous books and research articles in peer-reviewed journals.

Joseph E. LeDoux, M.D., is university professor and Henry and Lucy Moses Professor of Science, New York University; director, Center for the Neuroscience of Fear and Anxiety; and director, Emotional Brain Institute. He is the author of hundreds of research articles in scholarly journals and books (*The Emotional Brain*, Simon & Schuster; and *Synaptic Self*, Viking Press). LeDoux's work focuses on the study of the neural basis of emotions, especially fear and anxiety. Central to emotional processing is the amygdala, a brain area that LeDoux and his collaborators study extensively. Using an array of methods, including neuroanatomical, electrophysiological, neurochemical, molecular, and behavioral approaches, he has contributed to the understanding of emotional learning and memory. For more information, visit www.cns.nyu.edu/ledoux. Over the course of his career, LeDoux has received a number of awards, including the Fyssen Foundation International Prize, the Hoch Award, the Jean-Louis Signoret Prize, and consecutive MERIT Awards and Research Scientist Awards from the American National Institute of Mental Health. LeDoux sits on the editorial board of several journals and has given the Society for Neuroscience Presidential Lecture. He is a Fellow of the American Association for the Advancement of Science, a Fellow of the New York Academy of Sciences, and a Fellow of the American Academy of Arts and Sciences. LeDoux is also a member of the Amygdaloids, a band of scientists who play original songs about mind and brain and mental disorders, the lyrics of which are often inspired by his research. Since the Amygdaloids formed in 2006, they have played at Madison Square Garden, the John F. Kennedy Center, the 92nd Street Y, and numerous rock clubs in New York City. Their first CD, Heavy Mental, was released in 2007, and they are working on a second CD tentatively titled *Brainstorm*. Information about the band is available at www.cns.nyu.edu/ledoux/amygdaloids and at www.myspace.com/amygdaloids.

Contents

Preface.. v

About the Editors vii

Contributors xi

1 Post-Traumatic Stress Disorder: Definition, Prevalence,
    and Risk Factors.. 1
    Terence M. Keane, Brian P. Marx, and Denise M. Sloan

Amygdala and Fear

2 The Amygdala and the Neural Pathways of Fear............................... 23
    Jacek Dębiec and Joseph LeDoux

3 Physiology of the Amygdala: Implications for PTSD 39
    Donald G. Rainnie and Kerry J. Ressler

4 Counteracting Molecular Pathways Regulating the Reduction
    of Fear: Implications for the Treatment of Anxiety Diseases 79
    Andre Fischer and Li-Huei Tsai

5 Memory in PTSD: A Neurocognitive Approach 105
    Mieke Verfaellie and Jennifer J. Vasterling

Animal Models of Post-Traumatic Stress Disorder

6 Toward Animal Models of Post-Traumatic Stress Disorder 133
    Hagit Cohen and Gal Richter-Levin

7 PTSD: From Neurons to Networks.. 151
    Rajnish P. Rao, Aparna Suvrathan, Melinda M. Miller,
    Bruce S. McEwen, and Sumantra Chattarji

Post-Traumatic Stress Disorder and Arousal

8 Arousal Neurons in the Brain 187
    Priyattam J. Shiromani and Carlos Blanco-Centurion

9 Hyperarousal and Post-Traumatic Stress Disorder:
    A Role for the Hypocretin System 201
    Matt Carter and Luis de Lecea

10 The Locus Coeruleus-Noradrenergic System and Stress:
    Implications for Post-Traumatic Stress Disorder 213
    Craig W. Berridge

11 Effect of Stress on Sleep and Its Relationship
    to Post-Traumatic Stress Disorder 231
    L. D. Sanford and X. Tang

Stress Hormones in Post-Traumatic Stress Disorder

12 Stress Hormones and PTSD 257
    Rachel Yehuda

13 Low Basal Cortisol and Startle Responding as Possible
    Biomarkers of PTSD: The Influence of Internalizing
    and Externalizing Comorbidity 277
    **Mark W. Miller, Erika J. Wolf, Laura Fabricant,
    and Nathan Stein**

Brain Imaging in Post-Traumatic Stress Disorder

14 Functional Neuroimaging in Post-Traumatic Stress Disorder 297
    Israel Liberzon and Sarah N. Garfinkel

15 The Amygdala in Post-Traumatic Stress Disorder 319
    Lisa M. Shin

Treatment Strategies

16 Pharmacologic Treatment of PTSD 337
    Murray A. Raskind

17 Guided Imagery as a Therapeutic Tool in Post-Traumatic
    Stress Disorder 363
    **Jennifer L. Strauss, Patrick S. Calhoun,
    and Christine E. Marx**

18 Virtual Reality Exposure Therapy for Combat-Related PTSD 375
    **Albert Rizzo, Greg Reger, Greg Gahm, JoAnn Difede,
    and Barbara O. Rothbaum**

Index 401

Contributors

CRAIG W. BERRIDGE, PhD • *Department of Psychology, University of Wisconsin-Madison, 1202 West Johnson Street, Madison, WI 53706*

CARLOS BLANCO-CENTURION, PhD • *Department of Neurology, VA Boston Healthcare System and Harvard Medical School, 1400 Veterans of Foreign Wars Parkway, West Roxbury, MA 02132*

PATRICK S. CALHOUN, PhD • *508 Fulton Street, Mental Health Service Line (116A), Durham, North Carolina, 27705*

MATT CARTER, BSc • *Department of Psychiatry and Behavioral Sciences, Stanford University, 701B Welch Road, Palo Alto, CA 94304*

SUMANTRA CHATTARJI, PhD • *National Centre for Biological Sciences, Tata Institute of Fundamental Research, Bellary Road, Bangalore 560 065, India*

HAGIT COHEN, PhD • *Beer-Sheva Mental Health Center, The State of Israel Ministry of Health, Anxiety and Stress Research Unit, Faculty of Health Sciences, Ben-Gurion University of the Negev, Beer-Sheva, 84170, Israel*

JACEK DEBIEC, MD, PhD • *Center for Neural Science, New York University, 4 Washington Place, Room 809, New York, NY 10003*

LUIS DE LECEA, PhD • *Department of Psychiatry and Behavioral Sciences, Stanford University, 701B Welch Road, Palo Alto, CA 94304*

JOANN DIFEDE, PhD • *Weill Cornell Medical College, New York Presbyterian Hospital, 525 East 68th Street, Box 200, New York, NY 10021*

LAURA FABRICANT, BA • *National Center for PTSD (116B-2), VA Boston Healthcare System, 150 South Huntington Avenue, Boston, MA 02130*

ANDRE FISCHER, PhD • *European Neuroscience Institute, Laboratory for Aging and Cognitive Diseases, Grisebach Strasse 5, D-37077 Goettingen, Germany*

GREG GAHM, PhD • *Telehealth and Technology, Madigan Army Medical Center, Madigan Annex, Building 9933A, Fort Lewis, WA 98431*

SARAH N. GARFINKEL, PhD • *Department of Psychiatry, University of Michigan, Rachel Upjohn Building, Room 2753, 4250 Plymouth Road, Box 5765, Ann Arbor, MI 48109-2700*

TERENCE M. KEANE, PhD • *National Center for PTSD (116B-2), VA Boston Healthcare System, 150 South Huntington Avenue, Boston, MA 02130*

JOSEPH LEDOUX, MD • *Center for Neural Science, New York University, 4 Washington Place, Room 809, New York, NY 10003*

ISRAEL LIBERZON, MD • *Department of Psychiatry, University of Michigan, Rachel Upjohn Building, Room 2753, 4250 Plymouth Road, Box 5765, Ann Arbor, MI 48109-2700*

BRIAN P. MARX, PhD • *National Center for PTSD (116B-2), VA Boston Healthcare System, 150 South Huntington Avenue, Boston, MA 02130*

CHRISTINE E. MARX, MD, MA • *508 Fulton Street, Mental Health Service Line (116A), Durham, NC 27705*

BRUCE S. MCEWEN, PhD • *Laboratory of Neuroendocrinology, Rockefeller University, 1230 York Ave, New York, NY 10065*

MARK W. MILLER, PhD • *National Center for PTSD (116B-2), VA Boston Healthcare System, 150 South Huntington Avenue, Boston, MA 02130*

MELINDA M. MILLER • *Rockefeller University, 1230 York Ave, New York, NY 10065*

DONALD G. RAINNIE, PhD • *Emory University, Department of Psychiatry, Yerkes National Primate Center, 954 Gatewood Road, Atlanta, GA 30329*

RAJNISH P. RAO, PhD • *National Centre for Biological Sciences, Tata Institute of Fundamental Research, Bellary Road, Bangalore 560 065, India*

MURRAY A. RASKIND, MD • *VA Puget Sound Health Care System, 1660 South Columbian Way, S116-6 East, Seattle, WA 98105*

GREG REGER, PhD • *Telehealth and Technology, Madigan Army Medical Center, Madigan Annex, Building 9933A, Fort Lewis, WA 98431*

KERRY J. RESSLER, MD, PhD • *Yerkes Research Center, 954 Gatewood Drive, Atlanta, GA 30319*

GAL RICHTER-LEVIN, PhD • *The Institute for the Study of Affective Neuroscience (ISAN), The Brain and Behavior Research Center, Department of Psychology and Department of Neurobiology and Ethology, University of Haifa, Haifa, 31905 Israel*

ALBERT RIZZO, PhD • *USC Institute for Creative Technologies, Department of Psychiatry and School of Gerontology, 552 Crane Boulevard, Los Angeles, CA 90065*

BARBARA O. ROTHBAUM, PhD, ABPP • *Emory University School of Medicine, 1256 Briarcliff Road, Building A, Third Floor, Atlanta, GA 30322*

LARRY D. SANFORD, PhD • *Department of Pathology and Anatomy, Eastern Virginia Medical School, 700 Olney Road, Norfolk, VA 23501*

LISA M. SHIN, PhD • *Department of Psychology, Tufts University, 490 Boston Avenue, Medford, MA 02155*

PRIYATTAM J. SHIROMANI, PhD • *Department of Neurology, VA Boston Healthcare System and Harvard Medical School, 1400 Veterans of Foreign Wars Parkway, West Roxbury, MA 02132*

DENISE M. SLOAN, PhD • *National Center for PTSD (116B-2), VA Boston Healthcare System, 150 South Huntington Avenue, Boston, MA 02130*

NATHAN STEIN, PhD • *National Center for PTSD (116B-2), VA Boston Healthcare System, 150 South Huntington Avenue, Boston, MA 02130*

JENNIFER L. STRAUSS, PhD • *508 Fulton Street, HSR&D (152), Durham, NC 27705*

APARNA SUVRATHAN • *National Centre for Biological Sciences, Tata Institute of Fundamental Research, Bellary Road, Bangalore 560 065, India*

XIANGDONG TANG, PhD • *Department of Pathology and Anatomy, Eastern Virginia Medical School, P.O. Box 1980, 700 Olney Road, Norfolk, VA 23501*

LI-HUEI TSAI, MD, PhD • *Howard Hughes Medical Institute, Picower Institute for Learning and Memory, Department of Brain and Cognitive Sciences, MIT, 46 Vassar Street, Cambridge, MA 02139*

JENNIFER J. VASTERLING, PhD • *Psychology Service (116B), VA Boston Healthcare System, 150 South Huntington Avenue, Boston, MA 02130*

MIEKE VERFAELLIE, PhD • *Memory Disorders Research Center (151A), VA Boston Healthcare System, 150 South Huntington Avenue, Boston, MA 02130*

ERIKA J. WOLF, MA • *National Center for PTSD (116B-2), VA Boston Healthcare System, 150 South Huntington Avenue, Boston, MA 02130*

RACHEL YEHUDA, PhD • *James J. Peters Veterans Affairs Medical Center, 130 West Kingsbridge Road, 526 OOMH PTSD 116-A, Bronx, NY 10468*

1

Post-Traumatic Stress Disorder: Definition, Prevalence, and Risk Factors

Terence M. Keane, Brian P. Marx, and Denise M. Sloan

CONTENTS

INTRODUCTION
DEFINITION AND DIAGNOSTIC CRITERIA FOR PTSD
PREVALENCE OF PTSD
AN ETIOLOGICAL MODEL OF PTSD
RISK FACTORS FOR PTSD
MODELING THE PREDICTION OF PTSD
REFERENCES

Abstract

In this chapter, we provide the definition and diagnostic criteria for post-traumatic stress disorder (PTSD). Next, the prevalence data for this disorder are reviewed, with a particular focus on how prevalence rates vary with demographic characteristics (e.g., gender) and trauma type. The literature on risk and resilience factors for the development and maintenance of PTSD is then discussed. The chapter concludes with a discussion of contemporary statistical methods that may be used to advance our knowledge and understanding of PTSD.

Key Words: Demographic, epidemiology, meta-analyses, refugees, risk factor.

From: *Post-Traumatic Stress Disorder: Basic Science and Clinical Practice*
Edited by: P. J. Shiromani et al., DOI: 10.1007/978-1-60327-329-9_1
© Humana Press, a part of Springer Science+Business Media, LLC 2009

INTRODUCTION

The global war on terrorism and the military actions in Iraq and Afghanistan (i.e., Operation Iraqi Freedom and Operation Enduring Freedom) represent significant risks to the mental health of the American forces assigned to these regions. Coupled with the impact of the terrorist attacks on the Pentagon and the World Trade Center (WTC), the diagnosis of post-traumatic stress disorder (PTSD) is currently receiving increased attention in both the scientific and popular literature. This chapter seeks to provide a current understanding of the nature of the diagnosis, its prevalence across a variety of different populations, and risk factors associated with developing it. In addition, we present an overview of an etiological model for PTSD previously proposed (1,2). We, finally, summarize the literature on structural equation modeling in PTSD, a statistical approach that has contributed greatly to our understanding of the associations and predictive value of many of the key variables underlying the development of PTSD.

Our ultimate understanding of this condition, to include its biological and psychological substrates, is premised on the use of a common definitional framework across scientific and clinical venues. Great progress in the field was stimulated by the inclusion of the diagnosis of PTSD in the psychiatric nomenclature in 1980 and by several attempts to strengthen the operational criteria employed to define cases and noncases of people who have PTSD (3). Our goal here is to contribute to continued investigation of scientific research on this topic that blends the best in behavioral science with the most contemporary models and methods of measuring and understanding the biological and physiological parameters associated with PTSD (4).

DEFINITION AND DIAGNOSTIC CRITERIA FOR PTSD

In its current conception, the Diagnostic and Statistical Manual of Mental Disorders (DSM) defines PTSD as stemming from an event in which one is exposed to serious threat of injury or death and then experiences extreme fear, helplessness, or horror. Three symptom clusters define the disorder. In addition to recurrent and intrusive recollections and dreams of the event, the reexperiencing cluster includes the experience of flashback episodes in which an individual experiences a recurrence of at least a portion of the trauma. Hyperarousal symptoms are characterized by an enhanced startle reaction and difficulty sleeping, concentrating, and controlling anger as well as hypervigilance for danger and a sense of a foreshortened future. Extreme distress and avoidance of cues or reminders of the trauma, as well as an inability to remember aspects of the event, also can accompany this disorder. Additional avoidance symptoms include emotional numbing, described as an inability to feel any positive emotions, such as love, contentment, satisfaction, or happiness.

The interpersonal, psychosocial, physical health, and societal consequences of PTSD contribute to the overall costs of developing this condition. People with PTSD are more likely to divorce, report trouble raising their children, engage in intimate partner aggression, experience depression and other psychological problems, report poorer life satisfaction and physical health problems, become involved with the legal system, earn less, and change jobs frequently (5–9). These findings suggest that PTSD constitutes a major public health challenge for this nation and the world and highlight the importance of our complete understanding of the biological, psychological, and social factors associated with this condition. This review outlines our achievements to date in understanding the characteristics of PTSD and its prevalence, course, and treatment. Further, we provide a heuristic model for understanding the development of PTSD while specifying future directions for scientific work.

PREVALENCE OF PTSD

Initially, PTSD was considered a relatively rare condition, and traumatic events were considered extreme life stressors that were outside the range of normal human experience (10). Epidemiological studies, however, have since documented high prevalence rates of exposure to traumatic events in the general population and confirmed that PTSD occurs following a wide range of extreme life events (11–13). Most important, though, are the consistent findings indicating that, although exposure to potentially traumatic events is common, development of PTSD is relatively rare. Elucidation of the factors responsible for some people developing PTSD while others exposed to similar threatening events do not may inform our understanding of key variables in the etiology of this condition.

PTSD in the U.S. Population

Perhaps the most complete general U.S. population studies are those conducted by Kessler and colleagues. In the original National Comorbidity Survey (NCS) (12), 5,877 individuals aged 15 to 54 years in a nationally representative sample were interviewed using a structured diagnostic interview. An overall lifetime PTSD prevalence rate of 7.8% was found, with rates for women (10.4%) more than twice that for men (5.0%). Trauma exposure estimates indicated that about 60% of men and 51% of women were exposed to one or more traumatic events. In the National Comorbidity Survey Replication (NCS-R) (13), 5,692 individuals in a nationally representative sample were interviewed and had an overall lifetime PTSD prevalence rate of 6.8% detected.

Compared with the NCS and NCS-R, similar or slightly higher PTSD rates were obtained in selected, specialized samples. For instance, among 21- to 30-year-old members of a Detroit area health maintenance organization (HMO), 40% reported experiencing a trauma, and 9.5% met PTSD criteria (11.3% of women and 5.6% of men) (11). Similarly, among former Miami-Dade public school students aged 18–23 years, 11.5% met lifetime PTSD criteria (15.5% of women and 7.5% of men) (14). Further, among two American Indian tribes, lifetime PTSD rates were 14.2% and 16.1%, while past year rates were 4.8% and 5.8%, respectively, with higher rates consistently found among women compared with men (15).

Other studies focused on sexual assault and criminal victimization of women. For example, in a nationally representative sample of 4,008 women, Kilpatrick,

Edmunds, and Seymour (*16*) found that 13% reported a completed rape. Of those who were raped, lifetime and current PTSD rates were 32% and 12%, respectively. Similarly, using a national probability sample, Resnick, Kilpatrick, Dansky, Saunders, and Best (*17*) estimated that 36% of women had been criminally victimized, with 14.3% experiencing attempted rape or molestation and 12.7% experiencing a completed rape. They estimated lifetime and current PTSD rates to be 12% and 5%, respectively. Among those who were exposed to criminal victimization, rates of lifetime and current PTSD were 26% and 10%, respectively.

Clearly, the prevalence of exposure to traumatic events in the United States is far more common than anticipated in 1980 when the diagnosis of PTSD was incorporated into the diagnostic nomenclature. Even more surprising are findings indicating that the rate of current PTSD in the general population falls only behind major depression, attention deficit/hyperactivity disorder, specific phobia, and social anxiety disorder, making it the fifth most common psychiatric condition in the United States (*13*).

PTSD Among U.S. Combatants

Soldiers sent to fight wars and to keep peace are among those most at risk for trauma exposure and the development of PTSD. Despite the high frequency of military action and war worldwide, few countries have ever estimated the psychological toll of war. The major exception to this was the National Vietnam Veterans Readjustment Study (NVVRS) (*8*), which included a representative sample of 1,632 Vietnam theater veterans (VTVs), a matched sample of 716 Vietnam era veterans (VEVs), and 668 civilian comparison subjects. Of VTVs, 64% were exposed to trauma in their lives, compared with 48% of VEVs and 45% of civilians. More than 15% of male VTVs and 9% of female VTVs met criteria for current PTSD, and 30% of male VTVs and 27% of female VTVs met criteria for lifetime PTSD. Notably, the direction of this gender difference is opposite that of the civilian samples reviewed here, likely attributable to the different roles women had in the military at that time, the different types of stressors to which they were exposed, and the higher educational level of women in the study. In all cases, PTSD prevalence rates for VTVs were five to ten times higher than those found for the VEVs and civilians.

Litz, Orsillo, Friedman, Ehlich, and Batres (*18*) examined a sample of 3,461 active duty peacekeeping military troops who served in Somalia. Shortly after their return to the United States, 8% of these soldiers reported PTSD, a rate that did not differ for men and women. Eighteen months after their return, 6.5% of a subsample of 1,040 veterans met criteria for delayed-onset PTSD (*19*).

Several studies examined the impact of service in recent wars in the Persian Gulf. For instance, Wolfe, Brown, and Kelley (*20*) conducted a longitudinal study of 2,344 Gulf War I veterans and found PTSD prevalence rates of 4% for men and 9% for women. Studies using smaller convenience and reservist samples found PTSD rates in the range of 16–19% (*21,22*). Among soldiers deployed during Operation Iraqi Freedom (OIF) and Operation Enduring Freedom (OEF), Hoge et al. (*23*) found that 6.2% of the Army soldiers met screening criteria for PTSD after deployment to Afghanistan, and 12.9% met criteria after deployment to Iraq. Among the Marine Corps soldiers deployed to Iraq, 12.2% met screening criteria for PTSD.

With the elevated prevalence rates of PTSD among combatants, as well as findings indicating that PTSD symptoms among Vietnam veterans typically do not remit (*24*), additional studies of combatants will be a national priority for an indefinite period of time. Further substantiating the course and nature of combat-related PTSD is the detailed study of the military's testing of mustard gas on soldiers during World War II. While this testing was not commonly known until the 1990s, fully 32% of those exposed continued to exhibit full PTSD symptomatology a half century later (*25*).

One study by Vasterling, Proctor, Amoroso, Kane, Heeren, and White (*26*) contributed to our understanding of the specific consequences of war zone exposure. Prior studies utilized cross-sectional designs to compare prevalence rates among exposed and nonexposed samples. The Neurocognition Deployment Health Study was able to examine 961 Army troops prior to and following their deployment to OIF. Measures of sustained attention, verbal learning, and visual spatial memory were impaired as a function of their service. Reaction time measures improved. These findings remained true even when depressive and PTSD symptoms were statistically controlled. These findings support the notion that the trauma exposure of war affects psychological functioning broadly, crossing the emotional and cognitive domains of functioning.

Refugees

Fazel, Wheeler, and Danesh (*27*) summarized the refugee data across multiple studies, including a total of 5,499 adult refugees resettled in Western countries. They found substantial variability in prevalence rates (ranging from 3% to 44%). When restricting analyses to more rigorously designed studies including at least 200 participants, the average PTSD prevalence rate was 9%. This conclusion is different from that of De Girolamo and McFarlane (*28*), who summarized 12 studies of refugees and reported that half of the studies had a PTSD rate equal to or higher than 50%. Several factors likely account for such variability in PTSD rates across studies, including the nature of the sample and the trauma experienced, the length of time since the trauma, and the lack of PTSD measures validated among refugee samples (*29–31*).

PTSD in Disaster Contexts

There is a burgeoning literature suggesting that a wide range of natural and human-made disasters can lead to the development of chronic PTSD. Green and colleagues found that 44% of survivors of the collapse of the Buffalo Creek

Dam in West Virginia in the late 1970s met criteria for PTSD, and 28% of the sample still met diagnostic criteria 14 years later (*32,33*). Similarly, McFarlane (*34*) studied the effects of Australian brush fires on a sample of firefighters. The PTSD prevalence rates at 4, 11, and 29 months postdisaster were estimated at 32%, 27%, and 30%, respectively.

In recent years, concern regarding the psychological consequences of terrorist attacks has increased substantially. In a review of studies reporting PTSD prevalence rates following terrorist attacks, Gidron (*35*) reported a mean rate of 28%. However, these studies varied greatly in subject sampling and in the timing of assessments.

Following the September 11, 2001, terrorist attacks on the WTC, telephone and Web-based methodologies were employed to examine levels of resultant PTSD symptoms throughout the United States. Rates of PTSD generally were higher based on regional proximity to the attacks. For example, Schlenger et al. (*36*) found the prevalence of probable PTSD to be 11.2% in the New York City metropolitan area but much lower in Washington, D.C. (2.7%), other metropolitan areas (3.6%), and the remainder of the country (4.0%). In a sample of adults residing in an area of Manhattan closest to the WTC, 7.5% reported symptoms consistent with a PTSD diagnosis, and 20.0% of a subsample residing closest to the WTC reported such symptoms (*37*).

These are just a few of the many different types of disasters examined to date. Overall, the epidemiological literature strongly suggests that various types of disasters contribute substantially to the development of PTSD.

AN ETIOLOGICAL MODEL OF PTSD

As with all psychiatric conditions, there is no single cause of PTSD. Yet, identification of the precipitating event or proximal cause is relatively straightforward. Keane and Barlow (*2*) proposed a triple vulnerability model of PTSD etiology based on theoretical descriptions of anxiety and fear. The three components of vulnerability are *(1)* preexisting psychological variables, *(2)* preexisting biological variables, and *(3)* the experience of a traumatic event. Unlike specific phobia, for which true alarms, false alarms, or (less often) simple transmission of information may develop into a specific phobic reaction, PTSD is hypothesized to emerge from one special chain of events. Intense basic emotions, such as true alarms (but also including rage or distress resulting from the overwhelming effects of traumatic events), lead to learned alarms. Learned alarms occur during exposure to situations that symbolize or resemble an aspect of the traumatic event, such as anniversaries of the trauma and thoughts, feelings, and memories of the event. As in any phobic reaction, the development of learned alarms can result in persistent avoidance of stimuli associated with the trauma. These are defining features of PTSD in the DSM-IV (*3*).

The pure experience of alarm or other intense emotions is not sufficient for the development of PTSD. Much as in other disorders, one must develop anxiety or the sense that these events, including one's own emotional reactions to them, are proceeding in an unpredictable, uncontrollable manner. When negative affect emerges, anxious apprehension and preoccupation with the traumatic event begins, and collateral PTSD symptoms appear such as intrusive thoughts, emotional numbing and avoidance, and arousal.

The presence and severity of the various PTSD symptoms may be moderated to some extent by coping skills and social support. In PTSD, evidence already exists that these variables play a prominent role in determining whether the disorder develops.

RISK FACTORS FOR PTSD

Although many people experience traumatic events, the majority do not develop PTSD; individuals who experience the same or a similar stressor may or may not develop the disorder. The identification of the factors that might account for these differences can assist in our understanding of the etiology of the disorder and in the development of preventive approaches for people who are at highest risk for developing the disorder. Potential PTSD risk factors can be divided into three major categories: *(1)* preexisting factors inherent to the individual; *(2)* factors related to the traumatic event, including one's immediate response during the trauma; and *(3)* events that occur following the trauma. Although the last category may not be considered "causal" risk factors, such variables may help us better understand the commonly found severe, chronic cases of PTSD (*38*).

A Priori Factors

Discriminating the predisposition for developing PTSD from the predisposition for exposure to traumatic events represents a methodological and interpretive challenge. This issue is profoundly important for accurately identifying those variables that contribute to the development of PTSD. We begin to address this issue by examining preexisting factors that are related to trauma exposure and the development of PTSD.

Familial Psychopathology

Early fear conditioning research in animals suggests that there may be a genetic component associated with variability in sensitivity to environmental stress (*39*). Although studies of such a mechanism in humans do not exist, several twin and family studies have examined the heritability of PTSD.

Using the Vietnam Veteran Twin Registry, heritability factors were observed for exposure to combat (*40,41*) and PTSD symptoms (*41*). Despite an apparent genetic link for experiencing certain classes of traumatic events (*42,43*), genetic influences on trauma exposure do not appear to be shared with those influencing the development of PTSD when the trauma is combat (*44*). For noncombat interpersonal violence, there appears to be some association between genetic influences on trauma exposure and genetic influences in the development of PTSD (43). Unfortunately, these studies used questionnaire data, thus deferring strong conclusions. In perhaps the most elegant study of genetic contributions to the development of PTSD, Orr and colleagues (45) used a wide variety of laboratory tasks (e.g., physiological reactivity, ERP) and standardized diagnostic tools in an attempt to elucidate the parameters that might underlie PTSD. They found little evidence of an inherited component for PTSD.

To help clarify conflicting results, Ozer, Best, Lipsey, and Weiss (46) recently applied meta-analysis to nine twin and family studies. They concluded that, overall, family history of psychopathology predicted a small but significant amount of variance of PTSD (average weighted effect size of $r = .17$). Interestingly, family history was more strongly related to PTSD when the traumatic experience involved noncombat, interpersonal violence than when it was combat or an accident. Similarly, in their earlier meta-analysis of 11 studies examining family history of psychopathology, Brewin, Andrews, and Valentine (47) found an average weighted effect size of $r = .13$, with the same effect found in military and civilian samples. These effect sizes are small, and it appears that unique environmental contributors to the development of PTSD are significantly stronger than any genetic influences measured to date (48).

The results of twin and family studies demonstrating genetic factors associated with PTSD suggest that genes influencing this risk may be identified. However, only a few genetic marker studies have been conducted, and there are, unfortunately, inconsistent results. Investigators examined allelic associations at the D2 dopamine receptor gene (DRD2), as it has previously been associated with other psychiatric disorders. Comings and colleagues (49,50) found associations between DRD2 and PTSD, but Gelernter et al. (51) did not. Thus, despite fairly consistent findings of a small association between familial psychopathology and the development of PTSD, the actual mechanism accounting for this association (either genetic or environmental) is far from clear.

Demographic Factors

Gender

Early epidemiological studies found relationships between demographic variables and exposure to trauma and between demographics and the development of PTSD. For example, we know that PTSD prevalence varies as a function of the type of trauma experienced; we also know that men are more likely to be exposed to a traumatic event during their lives; yet, we also know that women are more likely to develop PTSD. Some have hypothesized that this heightened rate of PTSD is a function of the types of events to which women are exposed (e.g., sexual assault). However, even when controlling for gender differences in types of traumas, women appear to remain at greater risk for developing PTSD than men (12,52). Similar gender differences in PTSD prevalence rates have been found in a variety of samples (e.g., Kosovar Albanians) (53), yet the average weighted effect size across studies is small ($r = .13$) (47), and elucidating the mechanisms (i.e., psychological or biological) involved in these differences surely requires additional scientific study.

Age

Age at the time of a traumatic event is frequently seen as an important determinant of response, with the very young and the very old seen as carrying additional risk for disorder on exposure. Interestingly, among women in the NCS, no relationship existed between age and PTSD, and only a small positive relationship between age and exposure to traumatic events was found. In contrast, among men there was a strong positive correlation between age and PTSD, but this was due to increasing exposure to traumatic events over the life span (12). Across 29 studies, Brewin et al. (46) found that the average weighted effect of age on PTSD was minimal ($r = .06$).

Race

The data regarding race as a risk factor are complicated by great variability across data sets. For instance, in the NVVRS (8), PTSD prevalence rates were highest among Hispanic veterans and higher among African American veterans than the aggregate of Caucasian, Asian, and Native American veterans. These findings were largely, but not entirely, due to differences in rates of combat exposure. In the NCS, Kessler et al. (12) compared racial/ethnic groups and found that Caucasian and Hispanic participants reported higher rates of trauma exposure, whereas African American, Asian American, and Native American participants reported higher rates of PTSD following such exposures.

Using clinical interview data from the Hawaii Vietnam Veterans Project, Friedman, Schnurr, Sengupta, Holmes, and Ashcraft (54) reported that veterans of Japanese ancestry had lower odds of a current PTSD diagnosis compared with Caucasian veterans from the NVVRS data set, even after adjusting for age and combat exposure. Finally, in a sample of American Indian Vietnam veterans, Beals et al. (55) found that the American Indian sample had higher rates of current and lifetime PTSD than Caucasian participants of the NVVRS. Yet, when exposure to atrocities and violence was included in a multivariate model, ethnicity no longer predicted current or lifetime PTSD. Overall, racial/ethnic status does not appear to provide consistent differences in PTSD prevalence, and this variability across studies may be due to race/ethnicity not being a strong predictor of PTSD. Of note, Brewin et al.'s (47) meta-analysis found that the effect of racial/ethnic status as a predictor of PTSD was small ($r = .05$), with larger effect sizes found for socioeconomic status (SES; $r = .14$) and education ($r = .10$), variables often associated with racial/ethnic status in Western societies.

Marital Status

Few large-scale studies examined the relation between marital status and PTSD prevalence. In the NCS (12), marriage appeared to confer some level of protection when one was exposed to a traumatic event, even when holding trauma exposure constant in the analyses. In contrast, in Breslau, Peterson, Poisson, Schultz, and Lucia's (56) Detroit trauma survey, marital status was not significantly associated with PTSD after controlling the type of trauma that the participants rated worst. As with other predictors of PTSD, the mechanisms for these associations are not yet known.

Prior Trauma and Life Adversity

Increasing evidence suggests that prior life trauma and cumulative adversity may increase risk of PTSD following a later trauma. Brewin et al. (47) found small effect sizes for childhood abuse ($r = .14$), other previous trauma ($r = .12$), and other adverse childhood factors ($r = .19$). Ozer et al. (46) also conducted a meta-analysis of prior trauma and found a small but significant effect size ($r = .17$). This effect did not vary based on the time elapsed since the trauma or if the trauma occurred in childhood or as an adult. However, the effect size did vary according to whether the prior trauma resulted from an accident, combat, or noncombat interpersonal violence ($r = .12$, $r = .18$, and $r = .27$, respectively). Interestingly, ethnic groups often differ in terms of distal and proximal life adversity, and variability in life adversity appears to decrease the relationship between ethnicity and PTSD, suggesting that race/ethnicity and other demographic differences may be markers for histories of unequal levels of life adversity (14).

Together, these studies suggest that prior trauma and life adversity may sensitize people to later traumas. With a fairly large degree of variability across study samples, it is possible that some individuals (e.g., nurses, firefighters) develop adaptive coping skills that may protect them from adverse responses to future traumas. Further, Bowman and Yehuda (57) suggested that if normal stress hormones (e.g., cortisol) are activated over prolonged periods of time, brain physiology and anatomy may be altered, leading to a depletion of hormones, resulting in an inadequate physiological response to later trauma exposure. Additional research on this as a possible biological mechanism is clearly needed.

Psychopathology Prior to the Trauma

Several studies have identified the prior existence of a psychiatric condition as a risk factor for the development of PTSD. For example, a recent prospective study of 2,949 Gulf War veterans indicated that PTSD symptoms more strongly predicted symptoms of depression over 2 years than vice versa (58). In both Brewin et al.'s (47) and Ozer et al.'s (46) meta-analyses, psychiatric history was found to confer only a small degree of risk for the development of PTSD ($r = .11$ and .17, respectively). However, when Ozer et al. examined a subset of studies that specifically examined prior depression, the degree of risk increased significantly ($r = .32$).

The presence of psychopathology such as an addictive disorder or conduct disorder may also lead to exposure to traumatic events themselves (11,12). This complex relationship is fundamental to our understanding of the effects of traumatic events and PTSD. Careful assessment of the precipitating variables that contribute to a particular psychological condition can provide meaningful information about which condition to treat first when intervening with patients with multiple comorbid psychological disorders (59).

In an important prospective study of risk for developing PTSD, Bryant and Guthrie (60) measured maladaptive cognitions of student firefighters during their training and prior to deployment. Pretrauma catastrophic thinking strongly predicted (24% of the variance) the level of PTSD symptomatology 20 months after training was completed, indicating that a tendency to catastrophize about aversive events is a risk factor for the eventual development of PTSD.

The Traumatic Event Itself

Characteristics of the event itself, not surprisingly, predict the development and severity of PTSD. Most theoretical models suggest the presence of a dose-response model of PTSD that sees symptom severity as a function of traumatic event severity. Yet, operationally defining severity for various traumatic events is a complex task. Peritraumatic variables measured to date include a range of factors, such as physiology, affect, and cognitions that occur during the trauma, as well as particular aspects of the type of traumatic event.

Trauma Severity

Numerous studies defined the severity of a traumatic event in a variety of creative ways and found a significant association with PTSD severity. For example, across 49 studies Brewin et al. (47) found an average weighted effect size of $r = .23$ for the association between trauma severity and PTSD severity. In addition, Norris, Kaniasty, Conrad, Inman, and Murphy (61) suggested that severity is a strong predictor of PTSD cross-culturally.

Some studies examined proxies for traumatic event severity and then related them to severity of PTSD. For example, in survivors of the Oklahoma City bombing, suffering physical injuries was strongly related to PTSD symptoms 6 months later (62). In addition, among an Australian national sample, Rosenman (63) found that experiencing combat and rape or molestation were events that were especially likely to increase one's odds of developing PTSD. Finally, in their sample of Mexican adults, Norris et al. (64) found that exposure to violence in childhood was related to the chronicity of PTSD.

Perceived Life Threat and Peritraumatic Emotional Response

Across 12 studies, Ozer et al. (46) found a small-to-medium average weighted effect size of $r = .26$ for the strength of the relationship between perceived life threat and PTSD. Interestingly, the strength of the relationship was higher in studies with more time elapsed between the traumatic event and the assessment of PTSD; moreover, in a recent study perceived life threat was associated with maintenance of PTSD (65).

Ozer et al. (*46*) separately examined the relationship between peritraumatic emotional response (e.g., fear, helplessness, horror, guilt, shame) and PTSD and found a similar effect size across five studies ($r = .26$). Notably, Tucker, Pfefferbaum, Nixon, and Dickson (*62*) suggested that feeling nervous or afraid, expecting to die, and being upset by how others reacted during the Oklahoma City bombing explained 67% of the variance in PTSD symptoms 6 months later. Peritraumatic emotional distress also predicted the chronicity of PTSD symptoms (*64*). Interestingly, in their study of Somalia peacekeepers, Gray, Bolton, and Litz (*19*) found that negative perceptions of the mission were associated with immediate and chronic post-traumatic symptomatology.

Individual differences in peritraumatic emotional response may be due to differences in the meaning assigned to stressful events. Dunmore, Clark, and Ehlers (*66*) found that cognitions, such as negative beliefs about oneself and the world, measured shortly after the trauma were risk factors for PTSD severity 6 and 9 months later, even after controlling for the severity of the event. As reviewed by Bowman and Yehuda (*57*), several retrospective and cross-sectional studies found associations between cognitive beliefs and PTSD severity. Such cognitions included negative appraisals of trauma symptoms, low self-efficacy, and external locus of control.

Peritraumatic Dissociation

Peritraumatic dissociation includes an altered sense of time, "blanking out," and feeling disconnected from one's body (*67*). Across 16 studies, Ozer et al. (*46*) found a medium average weighted effect size ($r = .35$) for the strength of the relationship between peritraumatic dissociation and PTSD. Although the strength of this relationship did not differ according to the type of trauma experienced, it did vary as a function of the time elapsed between the trauma and symptom measurement, the type of sample, and the method of symptom assessment. Peritraumatic dissociation has also been found to play a role in the maintenance of PTSD (*65*).

To better understand this relationship, Gershuny, Cloitre, and Otto (*68*) examined the role that cognitions of panic (i.e., fears of death or losing control) might play in the association between peritraumatic dissociation and PTSD. They found that retrospectively reported fears of death and losing control during the trauma mediated the relationship between peritraumatic dissociation and PTSD. They suggest that peritraumatic dissociation might be part of the panic process, and the cognitive elements of panic may override the dissociative elements in their relative importance for PTSD development. These researchers noted that these cognitions may elicit dissociation.

Halligan, Michael, Clark, and Ehlers (*69*) studied survivors of a recent physical or sexual assault. They found that peritraumatic dissociation may lead to the disorganized trauma memories that are characteristic of PTSD. They also found that degree of disorganization in trauma memories and negative appraisals of that disorganization, as well as negative appraisals of intrusive memories, predicted PTSD symptoms over the course of 6 months; this was true even after controlling for actual memory characteristics and depressive symptoms. Overall, cognitive variables such as cognitive processing during the trauma, trauma memory disorganization, persistent dissociation, and negative interpretations of trauma memories each predicted PTSD symptoms beyond objective and subjective measures of stressor severity.

Clearly, cognitive factors and their relationship to reports of peritraumatic dissociation are important areas of future inquiry. Yet, this work is centered on the accurate measurement of peritraumatic dissociation. For example, Marshall and Schell (70) found that individuals' recall of peritraumatic dissociation within days of the trauma differed markedly from their recall at 3- and 12-month follow-ups, and baseline dissociation did not predict subsequent PTSD symptom severity after controlling for initial symptom severity. Thus, it is possible that the cognitive factors inherent in Ehlers and Clark's (71) model and found in the Bryant and Guthrie (60) prospective study may ultimately prove most important to the prediction of PTSD.

Post-Trauma Factors

Very few studies actually include the assessment of post-trauma factors in terms of their contribution to the development and maintenance of PTSD. Social support is the one exception. Across 11 studies, Ozer et al. (46) found that perceived social support following the trauma event was associated with PTSD symptoms, with an average effect size falling in the small-to-medium range ($r = -.28$). This effect was strongest among studies in which more time elapsed between the trauma and the assessment. Similarly, Brewin et al. (47) found an average weighted effect size in the medium range ($r = -.40$) across 11 studies for the relationship between social support and PTSD symptoms. In both meta-analyses, this relationship was stronger among military/combat samples. Further, among Vietnam veterans, Schnurr, Lunney, and Sengupta (65) found that emotional sustenance and instrumental assistance, both at homecoming and currently, in addition to current levels of social support decreased the odds of lifetime PTSD; all variables except homecoming and current levels of assistance decreased the odds of chronic PTSD. Recently, King, Taft, King, Hammond, and Stone (72) examined the directionality of the relationship between PTSD and social support among a sample of Gulf War I veterans examined on multiple occasions. Using structural equation modeling and a cross-lagged panel design, they found that PTSD symptoms more strongly predicted subsequent social support than did social support predict subsequent PTSD symptoms. These findings support the idea that interpersonal problems associated with PTSD negatively influence one's support resources. Clearly, further work is needed to replicate these findings across samples and to examine the nature of this relationship.

MODELING THE PREDICTION OF PTSD

To begin to disentangle associations found in risk factor analyses, multivariate analytic methods such as structural equation modeling (SEM) are used to simultaneously examine interrelationships among several predictors of PTSD. In a series of studies, Daniel and Lynda King and their colleagues applied SEM to a wide variety of theoretically driven variables in the NVVRS data set to understand the relationship of various factors to the prediction of PTSD following the Vietnam War. In the first of their series of studies, war zone stressor variables of atrocities/abusive violence, perceived threat, and malevolent war zone environment had direct effects on PTSD outcome, with malevolent environment exerting the largest effect. Traditional combat exposure had an indirect effect, influencing the development of PTSD primarily through the perceived threat that individuals reported (73).

Next, King, King, Foy, and Gudanowski (74) examined demographic variables, prewar factors (i.e., family environment, childhood antisocial behavior, maturity at entry to Vietnam, and prior trauma exposure) and war zone stressor variables as predictors of PTSD. In separate models for men and women, they found that war zone stressors were important contributors to PTSD, but additional variance was attributable to the prewar factors, particularly for men. Prior history of trauma and age at entry to Vietnam were important factors for men; for women, only prior trauma history contributed to the development of PTSD.

King, King, Fairbank, Keane, and Adams (75) then examined hardiness, structural social support, functional social support, and recent stressful life events as possible factors predicting PTSD. When examined together with the war zone stressor variables, all four variables had direct effects on PTSD development for men. For women, structural support did not predict PTSD development.

In the final report of their series of studies, King, King, Foy, Keane, and Fairbank (76) aggregated the pretrauma risk factors, the war zone stressors, and the post-trauma resilience-recovery variables to more comprehensively understand how these variables interrelate in the development of PTSD. Remarkably, these three categories of variables predicted 72% of the variability in PTSD among women and 70% among men. Prewar trauma exposure, exposure to abusive violence and life threat during the war, as well as postwar life stressors and functional social support were the strongest predictors of PTSD for women. Among the men, the key variables were the same as for women, plus younger age at entry to Vietnam, the malevolent war zone environment, and structural social support. While future studies should examine constitutional, physiological, and hereditary factors, the level of variance accounted for in these studies without the inclusion of biological variables is quite impressive.

REFERENCES

1. Barlow, D. (2002) Anxiety and Its Disorders: The Nature and Treatment of Anxiety and Panic. 2nd ed. New York: Guilford.
2. Keane, T. M., and Barlow, D. H. (2002) Posttraumatic stress disorder. Barlow, D. H., ed., Anxiety and Its Disorders. 2nd ed. New York: Guilford: 418–53.
3. American Psychiatric Association. (1994) Diagnostic and Statistical Manual of Mental Disorders. 4th ed. Washington, DC: American Psychiatric Association.

4. Keane, T. M. (2008) Posttraumatic stress disorder: future directions in science and practice. J Rehab Res Dev 45, vii–ix.

5. Schnurr, P. P., and Green, B. L. (2004) Understanding relationships among trauma, posttraumatic stress disorder, and health outcomes. In: Schnurr, P. P., and Green, B. L., Trauma and Health: Physical Health Consequences of Exposure to Extreme Stress. Washington, DC: American Psychological Association: 217–43.

6. Jordan, B. K., Marmar, C. R., Fairbank, J. A., et al. (1992) Problems in families of male Vietnam veterans with posttraumatic stress disorder. J Consult Clin Psychol 60, 916–26.

7. Koss, M. P., Koss, P. G., and Woodruff, W. J. (1991) Deleterious effects of criminal victimization on women' health and medical utilization. Arch Intern Med 151, 342–47.

8. Kulka, R. A., Schlenger, W. E., Fairbank, J. A., et-al. (1990) Trauma and the Vietnam War Generation: Report of Findings from the National Vietnam Veterans Readjustment Study. New York: Brunner/Mazel.

9. Walker, E. A., Katon, W., Russo, J., Ciechanowski, P., Newman, E., and Wagner, A. W. (2003) Health care costs associates with posttraumatic stress disorder symptoms in women. Arch Gen Psychiatry 60, 369–74.

10. American Psychiatric Association. (1980) Diagnostic and Statistical Manual of Mental Disorders. 3rd ed. Washington, DC: American Psychiatric Association.

11. Breslau, N., Davis, G. C., Andreski, P., and Peterson, E. (1991) Traumatic events and posttraumatic stress disorder in an urban population of young adults. Arch Gen Psychiatry 48, 216–22.

12. Kessler, R. C., Sonnega, A., Bromet, E., Hughes, M., and Nelson, C. B. (1995) Posttraumatic stress disorder in the National Comorbidity Survey. Arch Gen Psychiatry 52, 1048–60.

13. Kessler, R. C., Berglund, P., Demler, O., Jin, R., and Walters, E. E. (2005) Lifetime prevalence and age of onset distributions of DSM-IV disorders in the National Comorbidity Survey Replication. Arch Gen Psychiatry 62, 592–602.

14. Lloyd, D. A., and Turner, R. J. (2003) Cumulative adversity and posttraumatic stress disorder: evidence from a diverse community sample of young adults. Am Orthopsychiatry 73, 381–91.

15. Beals, J., Manson, S. M., Whitesell, N. R., Spicer, P., Novins, D. K., and Mitchell, C. M. (2005) Prevalence of DSM-IV disorders and attendant help-seeking in two American Indian reservation populations. Arch Gen Psychiatry 62, 99–108.

16. Kilpatrick, D. G., Edmunds, C. N., and Seymour, A. K. (1992) Rape in America: A Report to the Nation. Arlington, VA: National Victim Center.

17. Resnick, H. S., Kilpatrick, D. G., Dansky, B. S., Saunders, B. E., and Best, C. L. (1993) Prevalence of civilian trauma and posttraumatic stress disorder in a representative national sample of women. J Consult Clin Psychol 61, 984–91.

18. Litz, B. T., Orsillo, S. M., Friedman, M., Ehlich, P., and Batres, A. (1997) Posttraumatic stress disorder associated with peacekeeping duty in Somalia for U.S. military personnel. Am J Psychiatry 154, 178–84.

19. Gray, M. J., Bolton, E. E., and Litz, B. T. (2004) A longitudinal analysis of PTSD symptom course: delayed-onset PTSD in Somalia peacekeepers. J Consult Clin Psychol 72, 909–13.

20. Wolfe, J., Brown, P. J., and Kelley, J. M. (1993) Reassessing war stress: exposure and the Persian Gulf War. J Soc Issues 49, 15–31.

21. Perconte, S. T., Wilson, A. T., Pontius, E. B., Dietrick, A. L., and Spiro, K. J. (1993) Psychological and war stress symptoms among deployed and non-deployed reservists following the Persian Gulf War. Mil Med 158, 516–21.

22. Sutker, P. B., Uddo, M., Brailey, K., and Allain, A. N. (1993) War-zone trauma and stress-related symptoms in Operation Desert Shield/Storm ODS returnees. J Soc Issues 49, 33–50.

23. Hoge, C. W., Castro, C. A., Messer, S. C., McGurk, D., Cotting, D. I., and Koffman, R. L. (2004) Combat duty in Iraq and Afghanistan, mental health problems, and barriers to care. N Engl J Med 351, 13–22.

24. Schnurr, P. P., Lunney, C. A., Sengupta, A., and Waelde, L. C. (2003) A descriptive analysis of PTSD chronicity in Vietnam veterans. J Trauma Stress 16, 545–53.

25. Schnurr, P. P., Ford, J. D., Friedman, M. J., Green, B. L., Dain, B. J., and Sengupta, A. (2000) Predictors and outcomes of posttraumatic stress disorder in World War II veterans exposed to mustard gas. J Consult Clin Psychol 68, 258–68.

26. Vasterling, J., Proctor, S., Amoroso, P., Kane, R., Heeren, T., and White, R. (2006) Neuropsychological outcomes of army personnel following deployment to the Iraq war. JAMA 296, 519–529.

27. Fazel, M., Wheeler, J., and Danesh, J. (2005) Prevalence of serious mental disorder in 7,000 refugees resettled in Western countries: a systematic review. Lancet 365, 1309–14.

28. De Girolamo, G., and McFarlane, A. C. (1996) The epidemiology of PTSD: A comprehensive review of the international literature. In: Marsella, A. J., Friedman, M. J., Gerrity, E. T., and Scurfield, R. M., , Ethnocultural Aspects of Posttraumatic Stress Disorder: Issues, Research, and Clinical Applications. Washington, DC: American Psychological Association: 33–85.

29. Charney, M. E., and Keane, T. M. (2007) Psychometric analysis of the Clinician Administered PTSD Scale (CAPS)-Bosnian Translation. Cultural Diversity Ethnic Minority Psychol 13, 161–68.

30. Hollifield, M., Warner, T. D., Lian, N., et al. (2002) Measuring trauma and health status in refugees: a critical review. JAMA 288, 611–21.

31. Keane, T. M., Kaloupek, D. G., and Weathers, F. W. (1996) Ethnocultural considerations in the assessment of PTSD.In:Marsella, A. J., Friedman, M. J., Gerrity, E. T., and Scurfield, R. M., eds. Ethnocultural Aspects of Posttraumatic Stress Disorder: Issues, Research, and Clinical Applications. Washington, DC: American Psychological Association: 183–205.

32. Green, B. L., Lindy, J. D., Grace, M. C., et al. (1990) Buffalo Creek survivors in the second decade: stability of stress symptoms. Am J Orthopsychiatry 60, 43–54.

33. Green, B. L., Grace, M. C., Lindy, J. D., Gleser, G. C., Leonard, A. C., and Kramer, T. L. (1990) Buffalo Creek survivors in the second decade: comparison with unexposed and nonlitigant groups. J Appl Soc Psychol 20, 1033–50.

34. McFarlane, A. (1989) The aetiology of post-traumatic morbidity: predisposing, precipitating and perpetuating factors. Br J Psychiatry 154, 221–228.

35. Gidron, Y. (2002) Posttraumatic stress disorder after terrorist attacks: a review. J Nerv Ment Dis 190, 118–21.

36. Schlenger, W. E., Caddell, J. M., Ebert, L., et al. (2002) Psychological reactions to terrorist attacks: findings from the National Study of Americans' Reactions to September 11. JAMA 288, 581–88.

37. Galea, S., Ahern, J., Resnick, H., et al. (2002) Psychological sequelae of the September 11 terrorist attacks in New York City. N Engl J Med 346, 982–87.

38. Bromet, E., Sonnega, A., and Kessler, R. C. (1998) Risk factors for DSM-III-R posttraumatic stress disorder: findings from the National Comorbidity Survey. Am J Epidemiol 147, 353–61.

39. Anisman, H., Grimmer, L., Irwin, J., Remington, G., and Sklar, L. S. (1979) Escape performance after inescapable shock in selectively bred lines of mice: response maintenance and catecholamine activity. J Comp Physiol Psychol 93, 229–41.

40. Lyons, M. J., Goldberg, J., Eisen, S. A., et al. (1993) Do genes influence exposure to trauma? A twin study of combat. Am J Med Genet 48, 22–27.

41. True, W. R., Rice, J., Eisen, S. A., et al. (1993) A twin study of genetic and environmental contributions to liability for posttraumatic stress symptoms. Arch Gen Psychiatry 50, 257–64.

42. Koenen, K. C., Harley, R., Lyons, M. J., et al. (2002) A twin registry study of familial and individual risk factors for trauma exposure and posttraumatic stress disorder. J Nerv Ment Dis 190, 209–18.

43. Stein, M. B., Jang, K., Taylor, S., Vernon, P. A., and Livesley, W. J. (2002) Genetic and environmental influences on trauma exposure and posttraumatic stress disorder symptoms: a twin study. Am J Psychiatry 159, 1675–81.

44. Roy-Byrne, P., Arguelles, L., Vitek, M. E., et al. (2004) Persistence and change of PTSD symptomatology: a longitudinal co-twin control analysis of the Vietnam Era Twin Registry. Soc Psychiatry Psychiatr Epidemiol 39, 681–85.

45. Orr, S. P., Metzger, L. J., Lasko, N. B., et al. (2003) Physiological responses to sudden, loud tones in monozygotic twins discordant for combat exposure: association with posttraumatic stress disorder. Arch Gen Psychiatry 60, 283–88.

46. Ozer, E. J., Best, S. R., Lipsey, T. L., and Weiss, D. S. (2003) Predictors of posttraumatic stress disorder and symptoms in adults: a meta-analysis. Psychol Bull 129, 52–73.

47. Brewin, C. R., Andrews, B., Valentine, J. D. (2000) Meta-analysis of risk factors for posttraumatic stress disorder in trauma-exposed adults. J Consult Clin Psychol 68, 748–66.

48. McLeod, D. S., Koenen, K. C., Meyer, J. M., et al. (2001) Genetic and environmental influences on the relationship among combat exposure, posttraumatic stress disorder symptoms, and alcohol use. J Trauma Stress 14, 259–75.

49. Comings, D. E., Comings, B. G., Muhleman, D., et al. (1991) The dopamine D2 receptor locus as a modifying gene in neuropsychiatric disorders. JAMA 266, 1793–1800.

50. Comings, D., Muhleman, D., and Gysin, R. (1996) Dopamine D-sub-2 receptor (DRD2) gene and susceptibility to posttraumatic stress disorder: a study and replication. Biol Psychiatry 40, 368–372.

51. Gelernter, J., Southwick, S., Goodson, S., Morgan, A., Nagy, L., and Charney, D. S. (1999) No association between D2 dopamine receptor DRD2: "A" system alleles, or DRD2 haplotypes, and posttraumatic stress disorder? Biol Psychiatry 45, 620–25.

52. Breslau, N., Chilcoat, H. D., Kessler, R. C., Peterson, E. L., and Lucia, V. C. (1999) Vulnerability to assaultive violence: further specification of the sex difference in posttraumatic stress disorder. Psychol Med 29, 813–21.

53. Cardozo, B., Bilukha, O., Gotway, C., Wolfe, M., Gerber, M., and Anderson, M. (2005) Mental health of women in postwar Afghanistan. J Womens Health 14, 285–93.

54. Friedman, M. J., Schnurr, P. P., Sengupta, A., Holmes, T., and Ashcraft, M. (2004) The Hawaii Vietnam Veterans Project: is minority status a risk factor for posttraumatic stress disorder? J Nerv Ment Dis 192, 42–50.

55. Beals, J., Manson, S. M., Shore, J. H., et al. (2002) The prevalence of posttraumatic stress disorder among American Indian Vietnam veterans: disparities and context. J Trauma Stress 15, 89–97.

56. Breslau, N., Peterson, E. L., Poisson, L. M., Schultz, L. R., and Lucia, V. C. (2004) Estimating posttraumatic stress disorder in the community: lifetime perspective and the impact of typical traumatic events. Psychol Med 34, 889–98.

57. Bowman, M. L., and Yehuda, R. (2004) Risk factors and the adversity-stress model. In: Rosen, G. M., , Posttraumatic Stress Disorder: Issues and Controversies. New York: Wiley: 15–38.

58. Erickson, D., Wolfe, J., King, D., King, L., and Sharkansky, E. (2001) Posttraumatic stress disorder and depression symptomatology in a sample of Gulf War veterans: a prospective analysis. J Consult Clin Psychol 69, 41–49.

59. Najavits, L. M. (2000) Seeking Safety: A Cognitive Behavioral Treatment for Substance Abuse and PTSD. New York: Guilford.

60. Bryant, R. A., and Guthrie, R. M. (2005) Maladaptive appraisals as a risk factor for post-traumatic stress. Psychol Sci 16, 749–52.

61. Norris, F. H., Kaniasty, K., Conrad, M. L., Inman, G. L., and Murphy, A. D. (2002) Placing age differences in cultural context: a comparison of the effects of age on PTSD after disasters in the United States, Mexico, and Poland. J Clin Geropsychol 8, 153–73.

62. Tucker, P., Pfefferbaum, B., Nixon, S. J., and Dickson, W. (2000) Predictors of post-traumatic stress symptoms in Oklahoma City: exposure, social support, peri-traumatic response J Behav Health Serv Res 27, 406–16.

63. Rosenman, S. (2002) Trauma and posttraumatic stress disorder in Australia: findings in the population sample of the Australian National Survey of Mental Health and Wellbeing. Aust N Z J Psychiatry 36, 515–20.

64. Norris, F. H., Murphy, A. D., Baker, C. K., and Perilla, J. L. (2003) Severity, timing, and duration of reactions to trauma in the population: an example from Mexico. Biol Psychiatry 53, 769–78.

65. Schnurr, P. P., Lunney, C. A., and Sengupta, A. (2004) Risk factors for the development versus maintenance of posttraumatic stress disorder. J Trauma Stress 17, 85–95.

66. Dunmore, E., Clark, D. M., and Ehlers, A. (2001) A prospective investigation of the role of cognitive factors in persistent posttraumatic stress disorder PTSD after physical or sexual assault. Behav Res Ther 39, 1063–84.

67. Marmar, C., R., Weiss, D. S., Schlenger, W. E., et al. (1994) Peritraumatic dissociation and posttraumatic stress in male Vietnam theater veterans. Am J Psychiatry 151, 902–7.

68. Gershuny, B. S., Cloitre, M., and Otto, M. W. (2003) Peritraumatic dissociation and PTSD severity: do event-related fears about death and control mediate their relation? Behav Res Ther 41, 157–66.

69. Halligan, S. L., Michael, T., Clark, D. M., and Ehlers, A. (2003) Posttraumatic stress disorder following assault: the role of cognitive processing, trauma memory, and appraisals. J Consult Clin Psychol 71, 419–31.

70. Marshall, G. N., and Schell, T. L. (2002) Reappraising the link between peritraumatic dissociation and PTSD symptom severity: evidence from a longitudinal study of community violence survivors. J Abnorm Psychol 111, 626–36.

71. Ehlers, A., and Clark, D. M. (2000) A cognitive model of posttraumatic stress disorder. Behav Res Ther 38, 319–45.

72. King, D. W., Taft, C. T., King, L. A., Hammond, C., and Stone, E. R. (2007) Directionality of the association between social support and posttraumatic stress disorder: a longitudinal investigation. J Appl Soc Psychol 36, 2980–92.

73. King, D. W., King, L. A., Gudanowski, D. M., and Vreven, D. L. (1995) Alternative representations of war zone stressors: relationships to posttraumatic stress disorder in male and female Vietnam veterans. J Abnorm Psychol 104, 184–96.

74. King, D. W., King, L. A., Foy, D. W., and Gudanowski, D. M. (1996) Prewar factors in combat-related posttraumatic stress disorder: structural equation modeling with a national sample of female and male Vietnam veterans. J Consult Clin Psychol 64, 520–31.

75. King, L. A., King, D. W., Fairbank, J. A., Keane, T. M., and Adams, G. A. (1998) Resilience-recovery factors in post-traumatic stress disorder among female and male Vietnam veterans: hardiness, postwar social support, and additional stressful life events. J Personal Soc Psychol 74, 420–34.

76. King, D. W., King, L. A., Foy, D. W., Keane, T. M., and Fairbank, J. A. (1999) Posttraumatic stress disorder in a national sample of female and male Vietnam veterans: risk factors, warzone stressors, and resilience-recovery variables. J Abnorm Psychol 108, 164–70.

Amygdala and Fear

2

The Amygdala and the Neural Pathways of Fear

Jacek Dębiec and Joseph LeDoux

CONTENTS

INTRODUCTION
THE INTRA-AMYGDALA MICROCIRCUITRY OF FEAR
SYNAPTIC PLASTICITY AND ITS MOLECULES
FEAR MEMORIES: THE QUESTION OF PERSISTENCE
EXTINCTION OF FEAR: THE POWER OF CORRECTIVE
    EXPERIENCE
ACTIVELY COPING WITH FEAR
FROM ANIMAL TO HUMAN AMYGDALA
CONCLUSIONS
REFERENCES

Abstract

Fear and anxiety are evolutionarily developed responses to perceived or anticipated threat. They involve behavioral, autonomic, and endocrine alterations aimed at increasing an organism's chances of survival. Excessive or uncontrolled fear and anxiety may lead to anxiety disorders. Animal and human studies indicate the critical role of the amygdala in adaptive and maladaptive fear. Recent advances elucidating the organization of the neural circuitry and molecular mechanisms of fear provide new insights in normal as well as pathological fear. In this chapter, we review the microcircuitry of the amygdala with a special emphasis on its relevance to fear processing and fear learning. We also discuss recent developments in understanding the basic molecular mechanism of fear. Finally, we address some of the implications of amygdala research for developing novel therapeutic approaches to maladaptive fear and anxiety.

From: *Post-Traumatic Stress Disorder: Basic Science and Clinical Practice*
Edited by: P. J. Shiromani et al., DOI: 10.1007/978-1-60327-329-9_2
© Humana Press, a part of Springer Science+Business Media, LLC 2009

Key Words: Amygdala, anxiety, extinction, fear, fear conditioning, learning, memory, memory consolidation, memory reconsolidation, synaptic plasticity.

INTRODUCTION

Research on neural mechanisms of fear and anxiety has advanced significantly in recent decades. Animal models have been particularly useful in characterizing the microanatomy as well as the cellular and molecular mechanisms of fear and anxiety. More recently, animal studies have been complemented by a growing body of human research, especially involving functional imaging. Both avenues of investigation point at the key role of the amygdala in processing fear.

Fear is a natural, evolutionarily developed response to environmental threats. It includes autonomic and endocrine changes supporting defensive behaviors, such as fighting, fleeing, or immobility (freezing). Physiological adjustments allow increased blood flow and energy supply to skeletal muscles and the brain. These alterations support actions aimed at increasing the organism's chances of survival. Information about natural threats have been evolutionarily hardwired into animal brains, which appear to selectively respond to relevant environmental factors, such as sights, sounds, or odors of common predators; specific social behaviors of conspecifics; and painful or intense stimuli (e.g., sound of thunder, etc.). These natural factors elicit innate fear. However, an individual has to learn through experience about a variety of other possible threats. While innate pre-programmed fear reactions are inherited, acquired fear responses result from a capacity of an organism to learn and remember cues associated with danger experienced throughout life. Whereas fear is considered to be a response to an actual danger and is typically triggered by specific stimuli, anxiety is a state of preparation for a predicted threat, which can be real or imaginary.

Maladaptive fear and anxiety occur in anxiety disorders. Although anxiety disorders may involve innate mechanisms that unfold during life, such as a tendency for extreme shyness (1), fear learning contributes significantly to many anxiety pathologies (2–6). Thus, defining neural networks as well as cellular and molecular pathways underlying fear learning is crucial for better understanding of pathogenesis of anxiety disorders and for development of new treatment approaches.

One of the most commonly and successfully used experimental models of fear learning is Pavlovian fear conditioning (7). In this procedure, a neutral event (a conditioned stimulus, CS), such as tone, is paired with an aversive event (an unconditioned stimulus, US), such as a mild electric shock (Fig. 1) (6,8,9). Once the CS and the US are paired, the CS acquires an ability to elicit behavioral, autonomic, and endocrine fear responses. These responses are expressed automatically on subsequent exposures to the CS. Fear conditioning has been observed in a variety of species, ranging from insects and worms to birds and mammals.

Animal studies using fear conditioning demonstrate a unique and powerful character of fear learning. First, fear conditioning occurs very quickly. Usually, a single pairing of the CS with the US is sufficient to establish a memory. Second, once learned, conditioned fear responses persist, often remaining throughout the

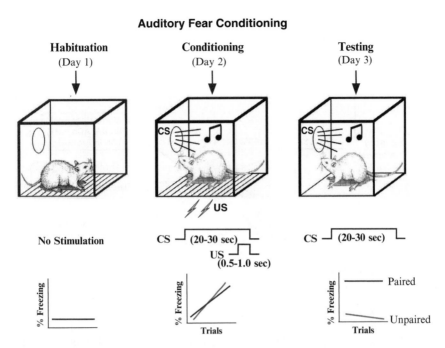

Fig. 1. Auditory fear conditioning. In auditory fear conditioning, a neutral stimulus (conditioned stimulus, CS), such as tone, is paired with an aversive event (unconditioned stimulus, US), often a mild electric shock to the foot pads. As a consequence, subsequent presentations of the CS trigger fear responses, such as immobility or freezing

life of an organism. Third, defensive responses to stimuli previously associated with aversive events may weaken or extinguish through experiences that show that the CS no longer predicts harm. However, the original conditioning can frequently be recovered either spontaneously or as a result of a new stressful experience months or years after it has been extinguished. Fourth, fear motivates other kinds of behaviors, such as approach and avoidance. Avoidance can be adaptive, but in anxiety disorders avoidance often takes on a maladaptive role, with the patient successfully avoiding fear and anxiety but at the expense of failing to perform routine life roles.

THE INTRA-AMYGDALA MICROCIRCUITRY OF FEAR

The amygdala was named by the nineteenth century German anatomist Karl Burdach for the almond-like (in Greek almond: *amygdale*) shape of one of its subregions *(10)*. Although the amygdala is a complex structure involved in a variety of functions, overwhelming evidence shows the critical role of the amygdala in fear *(6,11–18)*, as well as in fear and anxiety pathologies *(19–22)*. The role of the amygdala in fear is ubiquitous in vertebrate species *(6)*.

The amygdala is located bilaterally deep inside the temporal lobe. It consists of several distinct groups of cells organized in nuclei *(23)* (Fig. 2). The regions

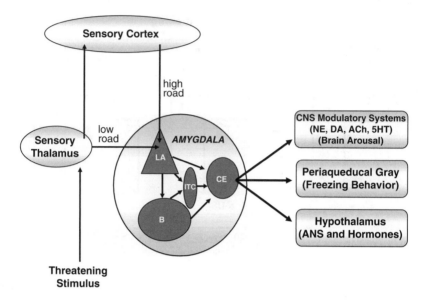

Fig. 2. Amygdala inputs, internal connections, and outputs. The amygdala consists of a group of nuclei. The nuclei most relevant to fear conditioning are the lateral (LA), basal (B), and central (CE) nuclei of the amygdala, as well as the subgroup of neurons known as intercalated cells (ITCs). The LA is the main sensory input area. It receives inputs from the thalamus and the cortex; thus, it is responsible for linking the CS with the US. The basal nucleus receives projections from the hippocampus and enthorhinal and polymodal associative cortices, areas that may convey information about the environmental context in which the fearful event is occurring. The CE is the common output area controlling expression of behavioral, autonomic, and endocrine fear responses. The LA is connected with the CE in direct and indirect (via the basal nucleus and the ITCs) ways. The ITCs have inhibitory control over the CE. Major identified neuromodulators involved in fear regulation include NE norepinephrine, DA dopamine, *ACh* acetylcholine, *5HT* 5-hydroxytryptophan (serotonin)

most relevant to fear conditioning are the lateral (LA), basal (B), and central (CE) nuclei, as well as a distinct subgroup of neurons known as the massa intercalata or intercalated cells (ITCs) *(6,18,23–26)*

The LA is considered to be a sensory gateway of the amygdala. It receives inputs from all sensory modalities, including visual, auditory, tactile, olfactory, and gustatory, as well as from fibers transmitting pain *(11)*. Although other amygdala nuclei also receive some sensory afferents, the LA is the main region where the sensory pathways converge. Studies using fear conditioning demonstrate that the LA is responsible for linking information about the neutral cue (CS) with that of the noxious stimulus (US). One of the most thoroughly investigated variants of fear conditioning is auditory fear conditioning, whereas a CS consists of a single tone. Fear conditioning studies reveal that auditory information reaches the LA through two distinct sensory inputs: thalamic and cortical *(6,11)*. The thalamic pathway conveys a rapid but imprecise auditory signal from extralemniscal areas, whereas the cortical pathway delivers a refined representation

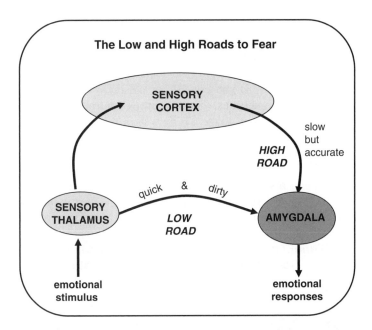

Fig. 3. Two roads to fear. Sensory information reaches the LA (lateral nucleus) through two independent sensory inputs: The "low road" or thalamic pathway provides the amygdala with a rapid but imprecise signal, while the "high road" delivers a more complex and detailed representation derived from cortical association areas responsible in humans for conscious processing. The two-road model of signal transmission illustrates how fear responses can be initiated (by the direct low road) before we are aware of the eliciting stimulus

from associative cortices, which in humans are responsible for conscious processing. This last pathway, however, includes additional synaptic connections, which results in longer transmission. The "two-roads" model of signal transmission is used to illustrate how fear responses can be triggered (by thalamic road) before we are aware of the initiating stimulus (Fig. 3) *(6)*.

While the lateral nucleus is believed to be the main sensory gateway, the central nucleus is considered to be the major output region *(27–29)*. The CE projects to brain stem regions and through these projections controls expression of fear responses, including some behavioral responses, such as freezing, as well as autonomic and endocrine reactions. In addition, the CE is responsible for activating amine modulatory systems, such as adrenergic, serotonergic, dopaminergic, and cholinergic systems *(11,18,23)* (Fig. 2).

The major input and output amygdala regions, the lateral and the central nuclei, respectively, are connected through direct and indirect routes *(23,30)*. The indirect routes are believed to be major communication channels between the both nuclei and involve connections from LA to the basal nucleus and the ITCs, both of which project to CE. The basal nucleus also receives inputs from the hippocampus and entorhinal and polymodal associative cortices and delivers information about the environmental context in which the threat is occurring *(23,24)*. In addition to fibers descending to the CE, the basal nucleus also projects to striatal areas. These outputs are believed to control instrumental behaviors *(23,31,32)*. The ITC network extends from the rostral amygdala to the anterior commissure *(33)* and consists of clusters of γ-aminobutyric acid (GABA) or GABA-ergic neurons. These neurons control the flow of activity from the LA and basal nucleus to the CE by way of forward inhibition *(34)*.

SYNAPTIC PLASTICITY AND ITS MOLECULES

Fear conditioning results in alterations in the strength of synaptic signaling in the amygdala (Fig. 4). Although synaptic plasticity occurs in other amygdala regions receiving some sensory inputs, such as the CE *(35)* and basal nucleus

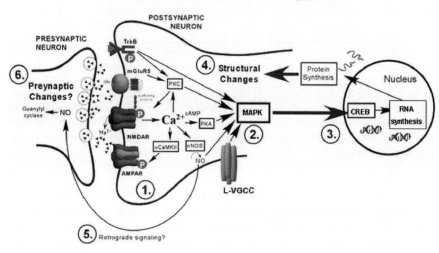

Fig. 4. Signal transduction pathways involved in fear conditioning in the lateral amygdala. Consolidation of fear conditioning is initiated by the activation of receptors at the postsynaptic neuron (1). This in turn triggers cascades of intracellular events that regulate the activity of mitogen-activated protein kinase (MAPK) (2). MAPK controls transcription factors, such as CREB (cyclic adenosine monophosphate response element-binding) proteins, which regulate transcription of certain genes (3). Gene activation leads to new RNA (ribonucleic acid) and new protein synthesis and thus structural changes in the postsynaptic neuron (4). Plausible mechanisms of retrograde signaling (5) from the postsynaptic neuron induce changes in the presynaptic neuron (6). cAMP cyclic adnosine monophosphate, NO nitric oxide, PKA protein kinase A, TrkB neurotrophic tyrosine kinase receptor 2, mGluR5 metabotropic glutamate 5 receptor, NMDR N-methyl D-aspartate receptor, AMPAR alpha-amino-3-hydroxy-5-methyl-4-isoxazolepropionic acid receptor, PKC protein kinase C, CaMKII calcium/calmodulin-dependent protein kinase II, NOS nitric oxide system. L-VGCC L-type voltage-gated calcium channel

(36), the main site of synaptic changes underlying learning and memory is the LA *(13,24,25,37–41)*. The LA is a site where the CS and the US pathways converge. Most of the inputs projecting onto the amygdala are excitatory and release glutamate binding to NMDA (*N*-methyl D-aspartate) and AMPA (α-amino-3-hydroxy-5-methyl-4-isoxazolepropionic acid) receptors localized on principal neurons. These neurons in turn transmit the information to other amygdala regions.

The cellular hypothesis of fear conditioning posits that relatively weak CS inputs become strengthened by the cooccurrence of the US, which is capable of eliciting robust responses in the LA. The activation of postsynaptic NMDA receptors on principal neurons by the CS signaling pathways in the context of the strong depolarization by the US inputs triggers calcium influx *(42)* (Fig. 4). This initiates cascades of intracellular processes involving second messengers and protein kinases, which lead to activation of transcription factors, gene expression, new protein synthesis, and synaptic alterations *(24,37,39–41)* Newly synthesized proteins strengthen synaptic connections. For example, it has been demonstrated that fear conditioning stimulates trafficking of AMPA receptors to synapses in LA *(43)*. The insertion of new glutamatergic receptors increases the postsynaptic response elicited by presynaptic inputs.

Synaptic plasticity and learning in the amygdala are regulated by a variety of modulatory systems. Identified neuromodulators include the catecholamines noradrenaline *(44–46)* and dopamine *(47,48)* as well as glucocorticoids *(49,50)*, serotonin *(51)*, nitric oxide *(52)*, BDNF (brain-derived neurotrophic factor) *(53)*, endocannabinoids *(54)*, neuropeptide Y *(55,56)*, and others. These neuromodulators may facilitate changes on principal neurons or inhibitory GABA-ergic interneurons or both.

FEAR MEMORIES: THE QUESTION OF PERSISTENCE

Synaptic changes triggered by experience lead to the consolidation of the new learning. However, before consolidation is completed, interference with any of the stages of underlying intracellular events, from activation of the receptors to new protein synthesis, impairs the memory. According to the standard view of memory consolidation *(57)*, once synaptic alterations are stabilized, memories become immune to interference.

The standard memory consolidation model has been successfully used in clinical studies. For example, it is well established that noradrenergic signaling enhances learning, especially emotional learning *(57)*, and two pilot studies have demonstrated that administration of the β-adrenergic receptor antagonist propranolol shortly after trauma decreases the risk of post-traumatic stress disorder (PTSD) *(58,59)*

The traditional view of consolidation, that once memories are consolidated they persist in an unaltered state *(57)*, was first challenged by studies in the 1960s showing that reactivation of a consolidated memory through retrieval renders this memory susceptible to amnesic treatments *(60–62)*. Recent studies

Reconsolidation Processes Enable Modification of the Memory

Destabilization of Memory

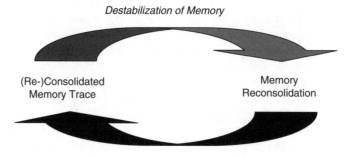

(Re-)Consolidated   Memory
Memory Trace   Reconsolidation

Re-stabilization of Memory

Fig. 5. Reconsolidation processes enable modification of the memory. Reactivation of the consolidated memory renders it labile and susceptible to interferences. This enables the modification of the existing memory trace by the circumstances accompanying the memory retrieval

ultimately challenged the consolidation theory, providing compelling evidence that memory reactivation triggers another round of synaptic plasticity, a phenomenon known as *memory reconsolidation* (Fig. 5) *(62–71)*. It has been demonstrated that reconsolidation of auditory fear conditioning in the LA involves NMDA receptor activation *(66,72)*, protein kinases *(73–75)*, expression of immediate early gene *Zif268 (76)*, and new protein synthesis *(63,77,78)* and is modulated by noradrenergic signaling *(45)*.

One of the implications of reconsolidation research is that even well-consolidated memories may be altered. In particular, a reconsolidation model may be helpful in developing new treatments of fear pathologies, such as PTSD or specific phobias *(62,65,69,70,79–81)*. Blocking reconsolidation may be helpful in attenuating learned fear responses and thus reducing the debilitating impact of traumatic experiences.

EXTINCTION OF FEAR: THE POWER OF CORRECTIVE EXPERIENCE

Learned fear responses may be attenuated by repeated exposure to the fear-arousing stimulus in a safe or neutral context *(82,83)*. This phenomenon, referred to as fear extinction, forms a theoretical basis of exposure therapies *(84–86)*. Extinction is a form of learning in which an organism learns that cues previously associated with a fearful event no longer predict danger. Extinction learning involves an interacting circuiting that includes the amygdala, medial prefrontal cortex, and the hippocampus *(87–96)*. Studies in humans have found involvement of the amygdala and prefrontal cortex in extinction *(97)*.

As a form of learning, extinction shares with fear conditioning similar molecular mechanisms. Specifically, glutamatergic signaling is required to initiate synaptic plasticity processes. Animal studies have demonstrated that enhancing glutamatergic stimulation by using the NMDA receptor agonist d-cycloserine facilitates extinction learning via the amygdala (98). This was further applied in human studies showing that exposure therapy in conjunction with d-cycloserine facilitates fear extinction (99–101).

ACTIVELY COPING WITH FEAR

Successfully extinguished fears often spontaneously recover or may be reinstated by a new traumatic event. Extinction learning is based on a passive exposure to fear-related stimuli. In contrast, a new study in rodents showed that active coping with fear may produce enduring reduction of fear. This new learning paradigm is referred to as *escape from fear* (102,103). In escape-from-fear learning, an organism learns to perform active behaviors that eliminate a fearful stimulus and thus reduce fear. The circuitry underlying escape-from-fear learning involves a circuit switch in the amygdala that, instead of transmitting signaling from the LA to the CE, directs information to the basal nucleus, which through its projections to the striatum and cortex controls actions (14). A recent study in humans using an active coping task found evidence for the involvement of not only the same emotion regulation circuit as extinction—the amygdala and medial prefrontal cortex—but also the striatum (Schiller D, Cain CK, Kuhlman K, LeDoux JE, Phelps EA, unpublished data). One implication of these findings is that therapies actively engaging patients may produce more enduring effects (104–106).

FROM ANIMAL TO HUMAN AMYGDALA

Recent studies using brain-imaging techniques have supported earlier animal research depicting the amygdala as a key structure involved in fear and anxiety (Fig. 6). The amygdala has been implied in adaptive fear (97,107,108) as well as in pathological fear and anxiety (21,109–112). In particular, the amygdala has been implied in PTSD (109–111) and phobias (112,113).

In addition, pharmacological approaches developed using animal models offer promising results in treating human fear and anxiety pathologies (58,59,81, 99,101).

CONCLUSIONS

Recent studies significantly advanced our knowledge about the organization of neural circuits and cellular and molecular mechanisms underlying fear and fear learning. This has been accomplished in major part thanks to the use of animal models, which allow insights into the microcircuitry and molecular mechanism of fear. Animal research forms a foundation for further human studies and provides clues about possible future therapeutic approaches.

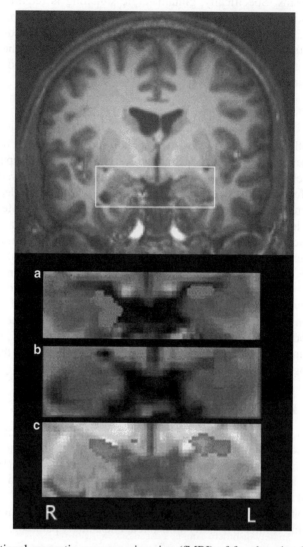

Fig. 6. Functional magnetic resonance imaging (fMRI) of fear learning in the human brain. *Top*: Structural magnetic resonance image (MRI) of the human brain (the box delineates an area containing the amygdala). **a** Conditioned fear: fMRI showing amygdala activation by the conditioned stimulus (CS) following pairing with the unconditioned stimulus (US). **b** Instructed fear: fMRI showing amygdala activation by a CS that was not directly paired with the US but instead the subjects were instructed about the US. **c** Observational fear learning: fMRI showing amygdala activation by a CS after the subjects observed someone else undergoing fear conditioning in which this CS was paired with a US. (Images provided by Elizabeth Phelps)

REFERENCES

1. Kagan, J., Reznick, J. S., and Snidman, N. (1988) Biological bases of childhood shyness. Science 240, 167–71.
2. Dollard, J., and Miller, N. E. (1950) Personality and Psychotherapy; An Analysis in Terms of Learning, Thinking, and Culture. New York: McGraw-Hill.
3. Eysenck, M. W. (1997) Anxiety and Cognition: A Unified Theory. Hove, U.K.: Erlbaum.
4. Bandura, A. (1986) Social Foundations of Thought and Action: A Social Cognitive Theory. Englewood Cliffs, NJ: Prentice Hall.
5. Rosen, J. B., and Schulkin, J. (1998) From normal fear to pathological anxiety. Psychol Rev 105, 325–50.
6. LeDoux, J. E. (1996) The Emotional Brain. New York: Simon and Schuster.
7. Pavlov, I. P. (1927) Conditioned Reflexes; An Investigation of the Physiological Activity of the Cerebral Cortex. Oxford, U.K.: Oxford University Press.
8. Bouton, M. E., and Bolles, R. C. (1980) Conditioned fear assessed by freezing and by the suppression of three different baselines. Anim Learn Behav 8, 429–34.
9. Fanselow, M. S. (1980) Conditional and unconditional components of postshock freezing. Pavlov J Biol Sci 15, 177–82.
10. Swanson, L. W., and Petrovich, G. D. (1998) What is the amygdala? Trends Neurosci 21, 323–31.
11. LeDoux, J. E. (2000) Emotion circuits in the brain. Annu Rev Neurosci 23, 155–84.
12. Davidson, R. J., Jackson, D. C., and Kalin, N. H. (2000) Emotion, plasticity, context, and regulation: perspectives from affective neuroscience. Psychol Bull 126, 890–909.
13. Maren, S. (2001) Neurobiology of Pavlovian fear conditioning. Annu Rev Neurosci 24, 897–931.
14. Cardinal, R.N., Parkinson, J.A., Hall, J., and Everitt, B.J. (2002) Emotion and motivation: The role of the amygdala, ventral striatum, and prefrontal cortex. Neurosci Biobehav Rev 26, 321–52.
15. McGaugh, J.L. (2004) The amygdala modulates the consolidation of memories of emotionally arousing experiences Annu Rev Neurosci 27, 1–28.
16. Paré, D. (2002) Mechanisms of Pavlovian fear conditioning: Has the engram been located? Trends Neurosci 25, 436–37; discussion 437–38.
17. Phelps, E.A., and LeDoux, J.E. (2005) Contributions of the amygdala to emotion processing: from animal models to human behavior. Neuron 48, 175–87.
18. Lang, P.J., and Davis, M. (2006) Emotion, motivation, and the brain: reflex foundations in animal and human research. Prog Brain Res 156, 3–29.
19. Rauch, S.L., Shin, L.M., and Wright, C.I. (2003) Neuroimaging studies of amygdala function in anxiety disorders. Ann N Y Acad Sci 985, 389–410.
20. Charney, D.S. (2004) Psychobiological mechanisms of resilience and vulnerability: implications for successful adaptation to extreme stress. Am J Psychiatry 161, 195–216.
21. Etkin, A., and Wager, T.D. (2007) Functional neuroimaging of anxiety: a meta-analysis of emotional processing in PTSD, social anxiety disorder, and specific phobia. Am J Psychiatry 164, 1476–88.
22. Liberzon, I., and Sripada, C.S. (2008) The functional neuroanatomy of PTSD: a critical review. Prog Brain Res 167, 151–69.
23. LeDoux, J.E. (2007) The amygdala. Curr Biol 17, R868–74.

24. Maren, S. (2005) Synaptic mechanisms of associative memory in the amygdala. Neuron 47, 783–86.
25. Fanselow, M.S., and Poulos, A.M. (2005) The neuroscience of mammalian associative learning. Annu Rev Psychol 56, 207–34.
26. Paré, D., Quirk, G.J., and LeDoux, J.E. (2004) New vistas on amygdala networks in conditioned fear. J Neurophysiol 92, 1–9.
27. Kapp, B.S., Whalen, P.J., Supple, W.F., and Pascoe, J.P. (1992) Amygdaloid contributions to conditioned arousal and sensory information processing. In: Aggleton, J.P., ed., The Amygdala: Neurobiological Aspects of Emotion, Memory, and Mental Dysfunction. New York: Wiley-Liss: 229–54.
28. Davis, M. (1992) The role of the amygdala in fear and anxiety. Annu Rev Neurosci 15, 353–75.
29. LeDoux, J.E. (1992) Emotion and the amygdala. In: Aggleton, J.P., ed., The Amygdala: Neurobiological Aspects of Emotion, Memory, and Mental Dysfunction. New York: Wiley-Liss: 339–51.
30. Pitkanen, A., Savander, V., and LeDoux, J.E. (1997) Organization of intra-amygdaloid circuitries in the rat: an emerging framework for understanding functions of the amygdala. Trends Neurosci 20, 517–23.
31. Everitt, B.J., Parkinson, J.A., Olmstead, M.C., Arroyo, M., Robledo, P., and Robbins, T.W. (1999) Associative processes in addiction and reward. The role of amygdala-ventral striatal subsystems. Ann N Y Acad Sci 877, 412–38.
32. Balleine, B.W., and Killcross, S. (2006) Parallel incentive processing: an integrated view of amygdala function. Trends Neurosci 29, 272–79.
33. Millhouse, O.E. (1986) The intercalated cells of the amygdala. J Comp Neurol 247, 246–71.
34. Paré, D., Royer, S., Smith, Y., and Lang, E.J. (2003) Contextual inhibitory gating of impulse traffic in the intra-amygdaloid network. Ann N Y Acad Sci 985, 78–91.
35. Samson, R.D., Duvarci, S., and Paré, D. (2005) Synaptic plasticity in the central nucleus of the amygdala. Rev Neurosci 16, 287–302.
36. Chapman, P.F., Ramsay, M.F., Krezel, W., and Knevett, S.G. (2003) Synaptic plasticity in the amygdala: comparisons with hippocampus. Ann N Y Acad Sci 985, 114–24.
37. Schafe, G.E., Nader, K., Blair, H.T., and LeDoux, J.E. (2001) Memory consolidation of Pavlovian fear conditioning: a cellular and molecular perspective. Trends Neurosci 24, 540–46.
38. Sah, P., Faber, E.S., Lopez De Armentia, M., and Power, J. (2003) The amygdaloid complex: anatomy and physiology Physiol Rev 83, 803–34.
39. Rodrigues, S.M., Schafe, G.E., and LeDoux, J.E. (2004) Molecular mechanisms underlying emotional learning and memory in the lateral amygdala. Neuron 44, 75–91.
40. Dityatev, A.E., and Bolshakov, V.Y. (2005) Amygdala, long-term potentiation, and fear conditioning. Neuroscientist 11, 75–88.
41. Sigurdsson, T., Doyère, V., Cain, C.K., and LeDoux, J.E. (2007) Long-term potentiation in the amygdala: a cellular mechanism of fear learning and memory. Neuropharmacology 52, 215–27.
42. Blair, H.T., Schafe, G.E., Bauer, E.P., Rodrigues, S.M., and LeDoux, J.E. (2001) Synaptic plasticity in the lateral amygdala: a cellular hypothesis of fear conditioning. Learn Mem 8, 229–42.
43. Rumpel, S., LeDoux, J., Zador, A., and Malinow, R. (2005) Postsynaptic receptor trafficking underlying a form of associative learning. Science 308, 83–88.
44. Huang, C.C., Wang, S.J., and Gean, P.W. (1998) Selective enhancement of p-type calcium currents by isoproterenol in the rat amygdala. J Neurosci 18, 2276–82.

45. Dębiec, J., and LeDoux, J.E. (2004) Disruption of reconsolidation but not consolidation of auditory fear conditioning by noradrenergic blockade in the amygdala. Neuroscience 129, 267–72.

46. Tully, K., Li, Y., Tsvetkov, E., and Bolshakov, V.Y. (2007) Norepinephrine enables the induction of associative long-term potentiation at thalamo-amygdala synapses. Proc Natl Acad Sci U S A 104, 14146–50.

47. Guarraci, F.A., Frohardt, R.J., Falls, W.A., and Kapp, B.S. (2000) The effects of intra-amygdaloid infusions of a d2 dopamine receptor antagonist on Pavlovian fear conditioning. Behav Neurosci 114, 647–51.

48. Kröner, S., Rosenkranz, J.A., Grace, A.A., and Barrionuevo, G. (2005) Dopamine modulates excitability of basolateral amygdala neurons in vitro. J Neurophysiol 93, 1598–1610.

49. Johnson, L.R., Farb, C., Morrison, J.H., McEwen, B.S., and LeDoux, J.E. (2005) Localization of glucocorticoid receptors at postsynaptic membranes in the lateral amygdala. Neuroscience 136, 289–99.

50. Duvarci, S., and Paré, D. (2007) Glucocorticoids enhance the excitability of principal basolateral amygdala neurons. J Neurosci 27, 4482–91.

51. Huang, Y.Y., and Kandel, E.R. (2007) 5-hydroxytryptamine induces a protein kinase a/mitogen-activated protein kinase-mediated and macromolecular synthesis-dependent late phase of long-term potentiation in the amygdala. J Neurosci 27, 3111–19.

52. Schafe, G.E., Bauer, E.P., Rosis, S., Farb, C.R., Rodrigues, S.M., and LeDoux, J.E. (2005) Memory consolidation of Pavlovian fear conditioning requires nitric oxide signaling in the lateral amygdala. Eur J Neurosci 22, 201–11.

53. Rattiner, L.M., Davis, M., and Ressler, K.J. (2005) Brain-derived neurotrophic factor in amygdala-dependent learning. Neuroscientist 11, 323–33.

54. Azad, S.C., Monory, K., Marsicano, G., et al. (2004) Circuitry for associative plasticity in the amygdala involves endocannabinoid signaling. J Neurosci 24, 9953–61.

55. Krysiak, R., Obuchowicz, E., and Herman, Z.S. (2000) Conditioned fear-induced changes in neuropeptide Y-like immunoreactivity in rats: the effect of diazepam and buspirone Neuropeptides 34, 148–57.

56. Cui, H., Sakamoto, H., Higashi, S., and Kawata, M. (2008) Effects of single-prolonged stress on neurons and their afferent inputs in the amygdala. Neuroscience 152, 703–12.

57. McGaugh, J.L. (2000) Memory—a century of consolidation Science 287, 248–51.

58. Pitman, R.K., Sanders, K.M., Zusman, R.M., et al. (2002) Pilot study of secondary prevention of posttraumatic stress disorder with propranolol. Biol Psychiatry 51, 189–92.

59. Vaiva, G., Ducrocq, F., Jezequel, K., et al. (2003) Immediate treatment with propranolol decreases posttraumatic stress disorder two months after trauma. Biol Psychiatry 54, 947–49.

60. Misanin, J.R., Miller, R.R., and Lewis, D.J. (1968) Retrograde amnesia produced by electroconvulsive shock after reactivation of a consolidated memory trace, Science 160, 554–55.

61. Schneider, A.M., and Sherman, W. (1968) Amnesia: a function of the temporal relation of footshock to electroconvulsive shock. Science 159, 219–21.

62. Sara, S.J. (2000) Retrieval and reconsolidation: toward a neurobiology of remembering. Learn Mem 7, 73–84.

63. Nader, K., Schafe, G.E., and LeDoux, J.E. (2000) Fear memories require protein synthesis in the amygdala for reconsolidation after retrieval. Nature 406, 722–26.

64. Dębiec, J., LeDoux, J.E., and Nader, K. (2002) Cellular and systems reconsolidation in the hippocampus. Neuron 36, 527–38.

65. Nader, K. (2003) Memory traces unbound. Trends Neurosci 26, 65–72.

66. Lee, J.L., Milton, A.L., and Everitt, B.J. (2006) Reconsolidation and extinction of conditioned fear: inhibition and potentiation. J Neurosci 26, 10051–56.

67. Suzuki, A., Josselyn, S.A., Frankland, P.W., Masushige, S., Silva, A.J., and Kida, S. (2004) Memory reconsolidation and extinction have distinct temporal and biochemical signatures. J Neurosci 24, 4787–95.
68. Alberini, C.M., Milekic, M.H., and Tronel, S. (2006) Mechanisms of memory stabilization and de-stabilization. Cell Mol Life Sci 63, 999–1008.
69. Dudai, Y. (2006) Reconsolidation: the advantage of being refocused. Curr Opin Neurobiol 16, 174–78.
70. Tronson, N.C., and Taylor, J.R. (2007) Molecular mechanisms of memory reconsolidation. Nat Rev Neurosci 8, 262–75.
71. Alberini, C.M. (2008) The role of protein synthesis during the labile phases of memory: revisiting the skepticism Neurobiol Learn Mem 89, 234–46.
72. Ben Mamou, C., Gamache, K., and Nader, K. (2006) NMDA receptors are critical for unleashing consolidated auditory fear memories. Nat Neurosci 9, 1237–39.
73. Duvarci, S., Nader, K., and LeDoux, J.E. (2005) Activation of extracellular signal-regulated kinase- mitogen-activated protein kinase cascade in the amygdala is required for memory reconsolidation of auditory fear conditioning. Eur J Neurosci 21, 283–89.
74. Doyère, V., Dębiec, J., Monfils, M.H., Schafe, G.E., and LeDoux, J.E. (2007) Synapse-specific reconsolidation of distinct fear memories in the lateral amygdala. Nat Neurosci 10, 414–16.
75. Tronson, N.C., Wiseman, S.L., Olausson, P., and Taylor, J.R. (2006) Bidirectional behavioral plasticity of memory reconsolidation depends on amygdalar protein kinase a. Nat Neurosci 9, 167–69.
76. Lee, J.L., Di Ciano, P., Thomas, K.L., and Everitt, B.J. (2005) Disrupting reconsolidation of drug memories reduces cocaine-seeking behavior. Neuron 47, 795–801.
77. Duvarci, S., & Nader, K. (2004) Characterization of fear memory reconsolidation. J Neurosci 24, 9269–75.
78. Dębiec, J., Doyère, V., Nader, K., and LeDoux, J.E. (2006) Directly reactivated, but not indirectly reactivated, memories undergo reconsolidation in the amygdala. Proc Natl Acad Sci U S A 103, 3428–33.
79. Dębiec, J., and Altemus, M. (2006) Toward a new treatment for traumatic memories. Cerebrum, Sep, 2–11.
80. Dębiec, J., and LeDoux, J.E. (2006) Noradrenergic signaling in the amygdala contributes to the reconsolidation of fear memory: treatment implications for PTSD. Ann N Y Acad Sci 1071, 521–24.
81. Brunet, A., Orr, S.P., Tremblay, J., Robertson, K., Nader, K., and Pitman, R.K. (2008) Effect of post-retrieval propranolol on psychophysiologic responding during subsequent script-driven traumatic imagery in post-traumatic stress disorder. J Psychiatr Res 42, 503–6.
82. Bouton, M.E. (1988) Context and ambiguity in the extinction of emotional learning: implications for exposure therapy. Behav Res Ther 26, 137–49.
83. Myers, K.M., and Davis, M. (2002) Behavioral and neural analysis of extinction. Neuron 36, 567–84.
84. Rudd, M.D., and Joiner, T. (1998) The role of symptom induction in the treatment of panic and anxiety. Identifiable domains, conditional properties, and treatment targets. Behav Modif 22, 96–107.
85. Shear, M.K., and Beidel, D.C. (1998) Psychotherapy in the overall management strategy for social anxiety disorder. J Clin Psychiatry 59(suppl 17), 39–46.
86. Foa, E.B. (2000) Psychosocial treatment of posttraumatic stress disorder. J Clin Psychiatry 61(suppl 5), 43–48; discussion 49–51.

87. Morgan, M.A., Romanski, L.M., and LeDoux, J.E. (1993) Extinction of emotional learning: contribution of medial prefrontal cortex. Neurosci Lett 163, 109–13.
88. Morgan, M.A., and LeDoux, J.E. (1995) Differential contribution of dorsal and ventral medial prefrontal cortex to the acquisition and extinction of conditioned fear in rats. Behav Neurosci 109, 681–88.
89. Milad, M.R., and Quirk, G.J. (2002) Neurons in medial prefrontal cortex signal memory for fear extinction. Nature 420, 70–74.
90. Sotres-Bayon, F., Bush, D.E., and LeDoux, J.E. (2004) Emotional perseveration: an update on prefrontal-amygdala interactions in fear extinction. Learn Mem 11, 525–35.
91. Sotres-Bayon, F., Cain, C.K., and LeDoux, J.E. (2006) Brain mechanisms of fear extinction: historical perspectives on the contribution of prefrontal cortex. Biol Psychiatry 60, 329–36.
92. Sotres-Bayon, F., Bush, D.E., and LeDoux, J.E. (2007) Acquisition of fear extinction requires activation of NR2B-containing NMDA receptors in the lateral amygdala. Neuropsychopharmacology 32, 1929–40.
93. Sotres-Bayon, F., Diaz-Mataix, L., Bush, D.E., and Ledoux, J.E. (2008) Dissociable roles for the ventromedial prefrontal cortex and amygdala in fear extinction: NR2B contribution. Cereb Cortex Jun 17 [Epub ahead of print].
94. Quirk, G.J., and Beer, J.S. (2006) Prefrontal involvement in the regulation of emotion: convergence of rat and human studies. Curr Opin Neurobiol 16, 723–27.
95. Corcoran, K.A., and Quirk, G.J. (2007) Recalling safety: cooperative functions of the ventromedial prefrontal cortex and the hippocampus in extinction. CNS Spectr 12, 200–6.
96. Ji, J., and Maren, S. (2007) Hippocampal involvement in contextual modulation of fear extinction. Hippocampus 17, 749–58.
97. Phelps, E.A., Delgado, M.R., Nearing, K.I., and LeDoux, J.E. (2004) Extinction learning in humans; role of the amygdala and vmpfc. Neuron 43, 897–905.
98. Walker, D.L., Ressler, K.J., Lu, K.T., and Davis, M. (2002) Facilitation of conditioned fear extinction by systemic administration or intra-amygdala infusions of d-cycloserine as assessed with fear-potentiated startle in rats. J Neurosci 22, 2343–51.
99. Ressler, K.J., Rothbaum, B.O., Tannenbaum, L., et al. (2004) Cognitive enhancers as adjuncts to psychotherapy: use of d-cycloserine in phobic individuals to facilitate extinction of fear. Arch Gen Psychiatry 61, 1136–44.
100. Davis, M. (2006) Neural systems involved in fear and anxiety measured with fear-potentiated startle. Am Psychol 61, 741–56.
101. Norberg, M.M., Krystal, J.H., and Tolin, D.F. (2008) A meta-analysis of d-cycloserine and the facilitation of fear extinction and exposure therapy. Biol Psychiatry 63, 1118–26.
102. Amorapanth, P., LeDoux, J.E., and Nader, K. (2000) Different lateral amygdala outputs mediate reactions and actions elicited by a fear-arousing stimulus. Nat Neurosci 3, 74–79.
103. Cain, C.K., and LeDoux, J.E. (2007) Escape from fear: a detailed behavioral analysis of two atypical responses reinforced by CS termination. J Exp Psychol Anim Behav Process 33, 451–63.
104. LeDoux, J.E., and Gorman, J.M. (2001) A call to action: overcoming anxiety through active coping. Am J Psychiatry 158, 1953–55.
105. van der Kolk, B.A., McFarlane, A.C., and Weisaeth, L. (eds.). (1996) Traumatic Stress: The Effects of Overwhelming Experience on Mind, Body, and Society. New York: Guilford Press.

106. Cloitre, M., Cohen, L.R. & Koenen, K.C. (2006) Treating Survivors of Childhood Abuse: Psychotherapy for the Interrupted Life. New York: Guilford Press.
107. LaBar, K.S., Gatenby, J.C., Gore, J.C., LeDoux, J.E., and Phelps, E.A. (1998) Human amygdala activation during conditioned fear acquisition and extinction: a mixed-trial fMRI study. Neuron 20, 937–45.
108. Morris, J.S., Ohman, A., and Dolan, R.J. (1998) Conscious and unconscious emotional learning in the human amygdala. Nature 393, 467–70.
109. Shin, L.M., Kosslyn, S.M., McNally, R.J., et al. (1997) Visual imagery and perception in posttraumatic stress disorder. A positron emission tomographic investigation. Arch Gen Psychiatry 54, 233–41.
110. Liberzon, I., Britton, J.C., and Phan, K.L. (2003) Neural correlates of traumatic recall in posttraumatic stress disorder. Stress 6, 151–56.
111. Shin, L.M., Orr, S.P., Carson, M.A., et al. (2004) Regional cerebral blood flow in the amygdala and medial prefrontal cortex during traumatic imagery in male and female Vietnam veterans with PTSD. Arch Gen Psychiatry 61, 168–76.
112. Schienle, A., Schafer, A., Walter, B., Stark, R., and Vaitl, D. (2005) Brain activation of spider phobics towards disorder-relevant, generally disgust- and fear-inducing pictures. Neurosci Lett 388, 1–6.
113. Phan, K.L., Fitzgerald, D.A., Nathan, P.J., and Tancer, M.E. (2006) Association between amygdala hyperactivity to harsh faces and severity of social anxiety in generalized social phobia. Biol Psychiatry 59, 424–29.

3 Physiology of the Amygdala: Implications for PTSD

Donald G. Rainnie and Kerry J. Ressler

CONTENTS

INTRODUCTION
MICROCIRCUITRY OF THE BASOLATERAL COMPLEX
SYNAPTIC TRANSMISSION IN THE BLC: GLUTAMATE
   AND GABA
NEUROCHEMICAL MODULATION OF BASOLATERAL
   AMYGDALA EXCITABILITY
ANIMAL STUDIES MODELING ASPECTS OF PTSD
SUMMARY
REFERENCES

Abstract

To survive in any environment, an organism needs to learn about places and things that may threaten its survival and to adapt its behavior accordingly. The existence of parallel neural systems that mediate acquisition and retrieval of aversive learning have been discovered through behavioral paradigms such as Pavlovian aversive conditioning. These neural systems encompass the amygdala, hippocampus, and perirhinal and prefrontal cortices. The normal physiological functions of these areas support the adaptive "fight-or-flight" response and are important evolutionarily conserved processes that enhance survival. Unfortunately, in human anxiety disorders, particularly with post-traumatic stress disorder (PTSD), this "normal" fear response system appears to be abnormally regulated and hyperactive in its function of identifying fearful stimuli and activating fear response circuitry. Although numerous areas are likely involved in the processes of fear learning and inhibition of fear and are similarly disrupted in PTSD, this chapter focuses on the neurochemistry, cellular organization, and neurophysiology of the basolateral complex (BLC) of the amygdala as it relates to the pathophysiology of PTSD. Many or even all of

From: *Post-Traumatic Stress Disorder: Basic Science and Clinical Practice*
Edited by: P. J. Shiromani et al., DOI: 10.1007/978-1-60327-329-9_3
© Humana Press, a part of Springer Science+Business Media, LLC 2009

these processes may be abnormal in the complex syndrome of PTSD, in which a previously experienced trauma is relived and reexperienced through traumatic fear memories. These memories are intrusive, often generalized to nonspecific cues, and are accompanied by a host of physiological reactions consistent with activation of the endogenous fear response. If possible, we highlight some of the physiological properties of the BLC that may contribute to the etiology of PTSD when their function is disrupted by acute intense trauma or chronic stress.

Key Words: Amygdala, extinction, PTSD, neurophysiology, stress.

INTRODUCTION

The principle brain regions implicated in the pathophysiology of post-traumatic stress disorder (PTSD) are the hippocampus, the prefrontal cortex (PFC), and the amygdala, each of which is critically involved in emotional memory formation. A feature of PTSD is sustained processing and elaboration of intrusive emotional memories. Recent findings suggest that neural activity in the amygdala may normally be under "top-down" inhibitory control by the PFC, and that a breakdown of this process could contribute to the psychopathology of PTSD (Fig. 1).

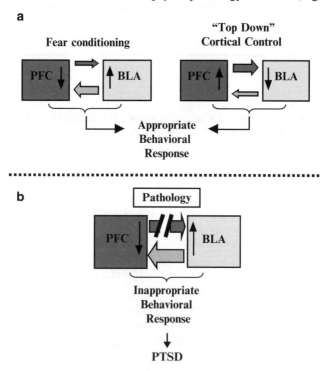

Fig. 1. Model showing the importance of the reciprocal interactions between the PFC (prefrontal cortex) and the BLC (basolateral complex) for control of emotional processing (**a**) and the pathological consequence of aberrant reciprocal interaction between these two areas (**b**). *BLA* basolateral nucleus, *PTSD* post-traumatic stress disorder

Although numerous areas are likely involved in the processes of fear learning and inhibition of fear and are similarly disrupted in PTSD, this chapter focuses on the neurochemistry, cellular organization, and neurophysiology of the amygdala as it relates to the pathophysiology of PTSD.

The amygdala is a heterogeneous structure located in the temporal lobe, which has been shown to be an essential component of the fear-learning neural network (1,2). Functional imaging studies in humans have shown that neural activity in the amygdala appears to increase during implicit and explicit recognition of affective stimuli, as well as during the acquisition of emotional memories (3–6). Significantly, recent data also implicate dysfunction of the amygdala in several psychiatric disorders of affective instability, such as depression(7), bipolar disorder (8), panic disorder (9), and PTSD (for review, see Refs. 10–12).

MICROCIRCUITRY OF THE BASOLATERAL COMPLEX

The amygdala is comprised of at least 12 subdivisions; each can be differentiated according to cytoarchitecture, afferent and efferent connections, and neurotransmitter content (13,14). The principal site of unimodal and multimodal sensory input into the amygdala is at the level of the basolateral complex (BLC). This pseudocortical complex is comprised of the lateral (LA), basolateral (BLA), and accessory basal (AB) nuclei (15). Recent animal studies focused attention on the LA as a critical site for the initial association of interoceptive and exteroceptive stimuli and as such may be the point at which fear learning occurs (16,17). However, evidence suggests that the location of fear learning is dependent on the stimulus modality. For example, olfactory fear conditioning would be expected to occur in the AB as this is the primary point of input from the olfactory cortex (18). Despite these subnuclei distinctions, the three subdivisions of the BLC express many of the same cell types, share a common neural circuitry, and are reciprocally connected (19). Hence, for the purposes of this chapter, we make no distinctions between the three subregions and refer to them collectively as the BLC.

Afferent Input to the Basolateral Complex

Sensory information converges in the amygdala at the level of the BLC, and it is generally agreed that this complex mediates cross-modal associations. However, many of the cortical and subcortical inputs selectively target subregions of the complex, and hence afferent information that reaches the lateral nucleus initially remains somewhat segregated from information that reaches the basal and accessory basal nuclei (20). Moreover, the complexity of intrinsic amygdala connections supports the notion that it is not a simple relay station for sensory information. Rather, the output of the nucleus depends heavily on the point of afferent input and hence the intrinsic pathway that is activated by this input (21). This notion is exemplified by recent experiments in rat that demonstrated that activation of the lateral nucleus by a conditioned stimulus (CS) triggers a conditioned response via its connections with the central nucleus and a conditioned avoidance response via its connections with the basal nucleus (1).

Neuronal Heterogeneity in the Basolateral Complex

It is generally agreed that neurons of the BLC in both rat and primate can be divided into two main classes: (1) large spine-dense, glutamate-containing, pyramidal neurons that provide the major extrinsic projections of the complex and (2) spine-sparse nonpyramidal cells that are presumed to be local circuit neurons and that contain γ-aminobutyric acid (GABA), cholineacetyltransferase (ChAT), and several different neuropeptides *(14,22–24)*.

BLC Projection Neurons

The primary output neurons of the BLC are glutamatergic pyramidal neurons *(14,25)*, and the firing pattern of these neurons presumably represents the engram of encoded information leaving the amygdala. For the purposes of most studies, these neurons are typically viewed as a single homogeneous cell group. However, recent evidence from electrophysiology and anatomical studies suggests that glutamatergic pyramidal neurons are a heterogeneous cell population.

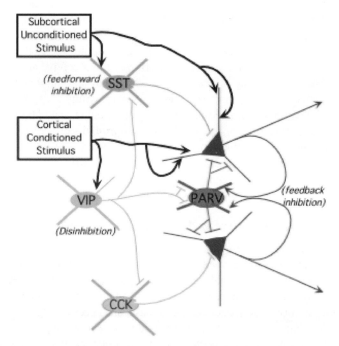

Fig. 2. Different subpopulations of basolateral complex (BLC) interneurons. Inhibitory GABA-ergic (γ-aminobutyric acid-ergic) interneurons of the BLC can be subdivided into the following nonoverlapping subpopulations: parvalbumin (PARV), interneurons containing the neurotransmitter somatostatin (SST), interneurons containing the neurotransmitter cholecystokinin (CCK), and calretinin and vasoactive intestinal peptide (VIP) immunoreactive interneurons

BLC Interneurons: Four Mutually Exclusive Subgroups

Inhibitory GABA-ergic interneurons of the BLC can be subdivided into the following nonoverlapping subpopulations: (1) parvalbumin (PARV) immunoreactive interneurons that are represented in approximately 40% of the total population (26–28); (2) interneurons containing the neurotransmitter somatostatin (SST), which represent approximately 20% of the total population (29,30); (3) interneurons containing the neurotransmitter cholecystokinin (CCK), which also represent approximately 20% of the total population (22,31); and (4) calretinin and vasoactive intestinal peptide (VIP) immunoreactive interneurons, which also represent approximately 20% of the total population (VIP)(32–34). A schematic representation of these subpopulations is shown in Fig. 2.

It is noteworthy that recent patch-clamp studies of PARV interneurons revealed that this cell population can be subdivided into two to four subgroups based on

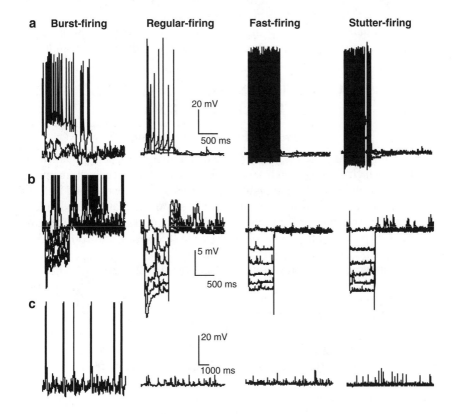

Fig. 3. Identification of four electrophysiologically distinct subtypes of basolateral complex (BLC) interneurons. Based on their action potential discharge pattern in response to depolarizing current injection (**a**), their voltage response to hyperpolarizing current injection (**b**), and their spontaneous synaptic activity (**c**), interneurons of the BLC can be subdivided into at least four subtypes: burst firing, regular firing, fast firing, and stutter firing. (From Rainnie et al., 2006, J Comp Neurol)

their physiological properties (*see* Fig. 3) (*35,36*). Significantly, these interneurons are coupled electrically by gap junctions (*37*), and the probability of coupling is highest when the PARV neurons have the same physiological properties (*38*). Hence, activation of PARV interneurons not only can regulate the synchronized firing of discrete clusters of projection neurons, but also can synchronize the firing of multiple overlapping clusters of BLA projection neurons when the need arises.

Because of their functional and anatomical diversity, activation of interneurons in the BLC is no longer perceived as simply preventing projection neurons from firing. It is now widely recognized that, at the cellular level, interneuron functions include governing action potential generation, firing pattern, membrane potential oscillations, and dendritic calcium spikes (*39–42*). At the network level, GABA-ergic interneurons are important in controlling synaptic strength and synchronizing neuronal population activity (*43–47*). Hence, far from simply inhibiting projection neurons, interneurons are a major driving force in establishing spatiotemporal encoding in the BLC. Consequently, neurotransmitters that either directly or indirectly modulate the activity of interneurons in the BLC can have a profound effect on the network excitability of this complex.

SYNAPTIC TRANSMISSION IN THE BLC: GLUTAMATE AND GABA

Postsynaptic Receptor Function

In a neural network like the BLC, whose major afferent input is glutamatergic (*48*) and in which there is a high level of feed-forward and feedback reciprocal connectivity between neighboring glutamatergic projection neurons and local circuit GABA-ergic interneurons (*49,50*), it is not surprising that the predominant synaptic activity observed in most neurons is a mixture of relatively fast excitatory and inhibitory postsynaptic potentials (EPSPs and IPSPs, respectively) (*51–57*).

Multiple studies have examined synaptic transmission in BLC projection neurons following activation of intrinsic or extrinsic afferents (*51–54,56,58*). Irrespective of the point of afferent stimulation, the most commonly observed postsynaptic waveform consists of a glutamatergic EPSP that is rapidly terminated by a dual-component GABA-ergic IPSP (*51,52*). Significantly, both the fast and slow IPSPs are blocked by local application of glutamate receptor antagonists, indicating that the evoked synaptic waveform in BLC projection neurons is a composite of a monosynaptic EPSP and disynaptic IPSPs.

Traditionally, this feed-forward disynaptic inhibition has been viewed simply as a mechanism for curtailing further action potential generation in projection neurons. However, it is becoming increasingly apparent that a key function of the feed-forward IPSP in the BLC is to limit the window for spike generation in projection neurons to the time interval (about 4 ms) between the onset of the EPSP and the onset of the fast IPSP (*59,60*). Minimizing the response window to excitatory afferent input in BLC projection neurons serves two functions. First, minimizing the response window ensures a high level of spike timing precision in the output stream of BLC projection neurons. Second, minimizing the response window also minimizes the potential for temporal summation of the afferent input onto BLC projection neurons, thereby creating a precise mechanism for postsynaptic coincidence detection in the afferent input stream.

Here, activity in two independent but convergent sensory streams would activate BLC projection neurons if they occurred within a 4-ms window, but not if the inter-spike interval between the afferent inputs was greater than 4 ms. This form of post-synaptic coincidence detection and subsequent entrainment of the firing activity of groups of BLC projection neurons has important ramifications for the integration and association of sensory stimuli during fear memory formation, consolidation, and extinction. Hence, anything that acts to expand the temporal window for spike activation would reduce the precision of coincidence detection and could lead to inappropriate sensory generalization similar to that observed in PTSD. As we show in this chapter, two animal models that are thought to display some of the behavioral traits found in patients with PTSD show deficits in the expression of the fast IPSP that could lead to significant cross-modal sensory generalization.

Presynaptic Receptor Function

Synaptic transmission in the BLC is also tightly regulated by a variety of ionotropic and metabotropic receptors located on presynaptic terminals. Perhaps the best-documented presynaptic regulator of synaptic release in the BLC is the $GABA_B$ receptor, which functions as an inhibitory autoreceptor at GABA-ergic terminals and an inhibitory heteroreceptor at glutamatergic terminals (61–64).

The importance of presynaptic $GABA_B$ receptors in regulating the normal input-output function of the BLC should not be underestimated. Activation of presynaptic $GABA_B$ receptors has been shown to mediate paired-pulse depression of the excitatory input onto BLC projection neurons in homosynaptic pathways (62,65) as well as heterosynaptic pathways (66). Significantly, genetic disruption of presynaptic $GABA_B$ receptors facilitates a switch from a heterosynaptic associative form of long-term potentiation (LTP) in cortical and subcortical pathways onto projection neurons to a homosynaptic nonassociative form of LTP (67). Hence, activation of presynaptic $GABA_B$ receptors on afferent sensory pathways may serve to constrain the induction of nonassociative LTP and may be a critical mechanism for the prevention of sensory generalization. As mentioned, sensory generalization is a significant component of PTSD, and it is possible that a malfunction or loss of presynaptic $GABA_B$ receptors may contribute to this condition. As we outline, alterations of presynaptic $GABA_B$ function have been observed in an animal model of PTSD.

Metabotropic glutamate receptors (mGluRs) also play a critical role in regulating glutamate release from afferent terminals. In the BLC, at least two pharmacologically distinct mGluRs have been shown to act as inhibitory autoreceptors on glutamatergic terminals. Here, both group II and group III mGluR agonists cause a dose-dependent reduction in the amplitude of the EPSP/current (C) recorded in BLC projection neurons (68–70). Activation of presynaptic group II mGluRs has also been shown to depotentiate LTP in afferent pathways to the BLC (71), suggesting that these receptors may be critically involved in regulating bidirectional synaptic plasticity in the BLC (depotentiation; *see* section on extinction).

As noted, presynaptic $GABA_B$ receptors work efficiently to regulate glutamate release in the BLC. However, presynaptic $GABA_B$ receptor function is dependent on the functional integrity of the GABA-ergic system, and if this becomes compromised, mGluR autoreceptor activation would act as a final brake to prevent overactivation of BLC projection neurons. It is notable, therefore, that the same animal model of PTSD that disrupts presynaptic $GABA_B$ receptor function enhances the sensitivity of presynaptic mGluRII receptors in the BLC *(72)*.

Interestingly, presynaptic ionotropic glutamate receptors also contribute to the regulation of synaptic transmission in the BLC. For example, activation of Glutamate receptor 5 (GluR5) kainate receptors bidirectionally modulate the strength of GABA-ergic transmission onto BLC projection neurons *(73)*. Here, low concentrations of the kainate receptor agonist (RS)-2-amino-3(3-hydroxy-5-tert-butylisoxazol-4-yl)propanoic acid (ATPA) facilitate GABA transmission, and high concentrations of ATPA attenuate GABA-ergic transmission. However, high-frequency afferent stimulation evokes a GluR5 receptor-mediated EPSP in BLC interneurons; hence, the exact mechanism leading to the ATPA-induced bidirectional plasticity remains unclear.

Finally, several groups have shown the existence of NMDA (*N*-methyl D-aspartate) receptors on axon terminals making asymmetric, presumed excitatory, contacts with projection neurons in the BLC *(74–76)*. Recent evidence suggests that presynaptic NMDA receptors may be involved in a novel form of coincidence detection *(77)*. Hence, Luthi and colleagues *(78)* showed that associative heterosynaptic LTP between cortical and thalamic inputs onto BLC projection neurons requires coincidence detection by presynaptic, but not postsynaptic, NMDA receptors, which results in a persistent increase in synaptic release from cortical afferents. Significantly, nonassociative LTP did not occur in the cortical pathway unless it was stimulated in the presence of a glutamate uptake blocker. These data suggest that glutamate release from the thalamic pathway directly activates presynaptic NMDA receptors on the cortical input, and that the efficiency of local glutamate transport system is a critical determinant of the specificity of sensory input. Consistent with this hypothesis, inhibition of glutamate transporters in the BLC also results in a loss of input pathway specificity and greatly facilitates heterosynaptic LTP between cortical and thalamic inputs *(79)*. Hence, a reduction in the efficiency of the glutamate transport system may also contribute to sensory generalization seen in PTSD.

Spontaneous Postsynaptic Potentials

Little is known about the normal pattern of synaptic activation in the BLC in awake behaving animals. However, recent evidence from in vivo studies in anesthetized rats and cats *(80,81)* and our own in vitro slices studies *(82)* (Jasnow and Rainnie, unpublished observations) suggest that the baseline activity of the BLC network is dominated by a pattern of slow, rhythmic, synaptic activity that functionally entrains BLC projection neuron firing activity at about 1 Hz. In the in vitro slice preparation, the rhythmic activity is characterized by the occurrence of high-amplitude, long-duration $GABA_A$ receptor-mediated IPSPs.

Significantly, BLC projection neurons and PARV interneurons are reciprocally connected by multiple perisomatic contacts *(83,84)*, and PARV interneurons can contact over 100 neighboring projection neurons. Previously, we had
shown that spontaneous, high-amplitude, GABA$_A$ receptor-mediated IPSPs
observed in BLC projection neurons occur at the same frequency (about 1
Hz) as the rhythmic burst firing seen in a subpopulation of PARV interneurons
(85,86), and that rhythmic inhibition in neighboring projection neurons is phase
locked at about 1 Hz. Moreover, Woodruff and Sah *(87)* showed that PARV
interneurons with similar intrinsic properties are coupled electrically via gap
junctions, suggesting that electrically coupled PARV interneurons can regulate

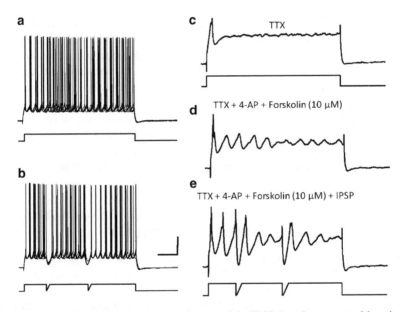

Fig. 4. Spontaneous inhibitory postsynaptic potentials (IPSPs) act in concert with an intrinsic membrane oscillation in basolateral complex (BLC) projection neurons to enhance
spike timing precision. **a** Repeated depolarizing current injection of constant amplitude
and duration evokes a series of action potential waveforms in a BLC projection neuron.
Superimposition of the voltage traces shows an increasing variance in the time to spike
onset that increases with time. **b** In the same neuron, introduction of an artificial IPSP
in the current injection trace markedly enhances the spike timing precision of the action
potential waveform such that action potentials following the second "IPSP" are almost
completely entrained. A similar response has been reported in the mouse BLC. **C** In the
presence of tetrodotoxin (TTX), to block action potential generation, the same depolarizing current injection as shown in **a** evokes a transient membrane potential oscillation
that rapidly terminates. However, application of the transient potassium channel blocker
4-aminopyridine (4-AP) and the nonselective adenylate cyclase activator forskolin revealed
an intrinsic theta frequency membrane oscillation that is maintained for the duration of the
depolarizing current injection (**d**). Introduction of the artificial IPSPs at 1 Hz significantly
facilitated the amplitude of the intrinsic membrane oscillation (**e**)

the firing activity of a large population of BLC projection neurons. Consistent with this hypothesis, synchronous oscillatory activity at theta and gamma frequencies in the BLC is dependent on gap junction activity *(88)*. Theta and gamma frequency oscillations in the BLC are thought to play a critical role in memory formation and recall *(89–92)*, hence rhythmic firing activity in PARV interneurons may be a critical factor in regulating fear memory formation and extinction. At the cellular level, rhythmic IPSPs act to synchronize BLC projection neuron firing activity by facilitating an intrinsic membrane oscillation that is present in the majority of BLC projection neurons (*see* Fig. 4). A similar response has been reported in the mouse BLC *(93)*.

These data raise two important issues. First, any neurotransmitter that modulates the frequency of spontaneous IPSPs in BLC projection neurons would have a significant impact on the frequency of synchronized oscillations in the BLC. Second, the sensitivity of the intrinsic membrane oscillation to adenylate cyclase activation suggests that synchronized firing in BLC projection neurons would be enhanced by neurotransmitters such as dopamine (DA), noradrenaline, and corticotrophin-releasing factor (CRF), all of which have been shown to raise cyclic adenosine monophosphate (cAMP) levels in the BLC. As mentioned, phase synchronization between oscillating BLC projection neurons and neurons in target structures is thought to facilitate memory consolidation and recall *(94,95)*. It is possible that acute intense trauma or prolonged stress may induce aberrant oscillatory activity in the BLC and thus faulty recall or extinction of fear memories.

NEUROCHEMICAL MODULATION OF BASOLATERAL AMYGDALA EXCITABILITY

Superimposed on the intrinsic neural network of the BLC is an array of intrinsic and extrinsic afferent fibers from such diverse sources as the brain stem monoamine systems and the cholinergic system of the basal forebrain *(96–99)*. Indeed, a high level of acetylcholinesterase staining is a defining feature of the BLC, in particular the BLA, that distinguishes it from the surrounding tissue. Monoaminergic fibers are also heterogeneously distributed throughout the amygdala. In the rat, serotonin (5HT) fibers show the highest overall degree of labeling in the BLC compared to surrounding regions, whereas DA and noradrenaline fibers have a more intermediate level of labeling. Significantly, serotonergic and dopaminergic terminals preferentially target the spines and dendrites of BLC projection neurons and the somatic region of PARV interneurons *(100,101)*, suggesting that these systems are ideally situated to modulate not only synaptic transmission but also oscillatory activity within the BLC.

Serotonin

Serotonin (5HT) release in the BLC is increased in response to physiological and psychological stressors *(102,103)*, suggesting that local 5HT release may modulate the behavioral response to stressful stimuli. 5HT receptor activation in the BLC has actions at both pre- and postsynaptic receptors and can effectively modulate the activity of both projection neurons and interneurons *(104)*. However, in general the net effect of 5HT release in the BLA is to reduce the overall excitability of the nucleus. The inhibitory action results from three distinct mechanisms: (1) a direct excitation of PARV interneurons mediated by $5HT_{2A/C}$ receptor activation resulting in an increased inhibitory drive onto BLA projection neurons, (2) a direct $5HT_{1A}$ receptor-mediated inhibition of a small subpopulation (20%) of projection neurons, and (3) an indirect reduction of the excitatory drive onto BLA projection neurons. These observations have been confirmed in vivo *(105,106)*, where 5HT has been shown to reduce single-unit firing activity in the BLC. Moreover, this action was blocked by $GABA_A$ receptor antagonists, suggesting that indirect activation of inhibitory interneurons was a key component of this response. Significantly, the initial response to 5HT release in the BLC is a twofold increase in the rate of spontaneous IPSPs observed in BLC projection neurons *(107)*, which could potentially change the frequency of synchronized oscillations in groups of projection neurons and hence change the degree of synchronization between reciprocally connected structures, such as the BLC and PFC.

However, given the diversity of 5HT receptors found in the BLC (summarized in Fig. 5), the response to 5HT is somewhat more complex than originally envisioned. For example, activation of $5HT_{1A}$ or $5HT_{2C}$ receptors has opposing effects on NMDA receptor-mediated excitatory postsynaptic potentials/

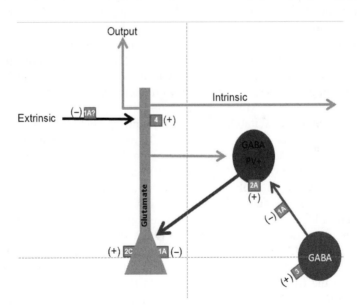

Fig. 5. The effects of 5HT in the BLC are complex, but the net function appears to be to reduce overall excitability. A schematic showing the relative distribution of 5HT receptors in the basolateral complex as determined by results obtained in electrophysiological studies. *GABA* γ-aminobutyric acid, + excitation, − inhibition

excitatory postsynaptic currents (EPSP/EPSCs) recorded in projection neurons *(108,109)*. Here, $5HT_{1A}$ receptor activation decreases NMDA receptor-mediated EPSCs, whereas $5HT_{2C}$ receptor activation enhances these same EPSCs. Consistent with this observation, activation of $5HT_{1A}$ receptors attenuates the acquisition of LTP in BLA projection neurons *(110,111)*, whereas activation of $5HT_{2C}$ or $5HT_4$ receptors facilitates LTP *(109,112)*.

Activation of presynaptic $5HT_{1A}$ receptors is also reported to attenuate stimulus-evoked glutamate release onto BLA projection neurons *(113)*. However, we now have compelling data suggesting that this response is most likely mediated by activation of $5HT_{1B/D}$ receptors (Rainnie, unpublished observations). A more consistent role for presynaptic $5HT_{1A}$ receptors is in the regulation of GABA release onto BLA interneurons. Here, $5HT_{1A}$ agonists acting at presynaptic receptors on GABA-ergic terminals act to reduce miniature Inhibitory Postsynaptic Current (IPSCs) recorded in BLA interneurons *(114,115)*. In contrast, activation of $5HT_3$ receptors increases the frequency of miniature IPSC (mIPSCs) in BLA interneurons *(116)*.

Dopamine

Dopamine (DA) is released into the amygdala during stressful situations such as fear conditioning and foot shock *(117–119)*, and subsequent DA receptor activation has been shown to enhance many affective-related behaviors (for review, *see* Refs. *120* and *121–123*). However, the cellular mechanisms contributing to the DA-induced facilitation of fear conditioning are still being elucidated.

In an elegant series of in vivo studies, Grace and colleagues demonstrated that some of the facilitatory effects of DA may be attributed to a pathway-specific modulation of afferent input into the BLC *(124–126)*. Hence, DA receptor activation attenuated short latency spikes evoked by stimulation of the PFC and medial dorsal thalamus (MD) thalamus while potentiating inputs from the sensory association cortex. Moreover, fear conditioning resulted in a CS-evoked increase in neuronal excitability and postsynaptic potentials (PSPs), an effect that could be blocked by the nonselective D1 receptor antagonist haloperidol. The assumption is that during fear conditioning, local DA release would act to uncouple the top-down inhibitory control of the BLC by the PFC, simultaneously facilitating synaptic plasticity in sensory afferent pathways.

Subsequent in vitro studies revealed that DA has multiple actions within the BLC. Hence, D1 receptor activation increases projection neuron excitability by decreasing an outward potassium current *(127)* and enhancing the nonspecific cation current I_h *(128)*. D1 receptor activation also increases the firing rate of a subpopulation of presumed PARV interneurons, thereby causing a concomitant increase in the frequency of spontaneous IPSPs observed in BLC projection neurons *(128,129)*. Conversely, two subsequent studies showed that DA inhibits interneurons of the BLC and intercalated cell groups that mediate feed-forward inhibition, resulting in a disinhibition of BLC projection neurons and a facilitation of LTP in sensory input pathways *(130,131)*.

At first glance, many of these actions seem paradoxical: Why increase the excitability of projection neurons and PARV interneurons while simultaneously inhibiting feed-forward inhibition? We would argue that these actions make perfect sense if the ultimate objective of local DA release is to facilitate cross-modal association between sensory inputs and simultaneously enhance synchronized oscillations in BLC projection neurons. This response is most likely the normal adaptive response to an acute stressor, but what happens when the stress is traumatic or chronic in nature? Hyperactivation of the mesolimbic dopaminergic system may result in a maladaptive response in which top-down inhibitory control of the BLC by the PFC is uncoupled, possibly by aberrant synchronization, and sensory generalization is facilitated.

Noradrenaline

Psychological and physiological stressors as well as emotional arousal all act to increase norepinephrine (NE) release in the amygdala *(132,133)*, and this action has been shown to be critical for the regulation of memory consolidation (for review, *see* Ref. *134*).

Stress and arousal would normally be expected to increase the activity of the BLC. However, in vivo recordings from the BLC indicate that spontaneous and evoked firing activity is markedly attenuated by local application of NE. This effect is mimicked by stimulation of the locus coeruleus *(135,136)* and blocked by systemic administration of α_1-adrenoceptor antagonists. Consistent with this observation, NE has been shown to facilitate spontaneous, evoked, and miniature IPSCs in BLC projection neurons, an effect that was also blocked by α_1-adrenoceptor antagonists *(137)*. Moreover, NE has also been shown to attenuate AMPA (α-amino-3-hydroxy-5-methyl-4-isoxazolepropionic acid)- and NMDA-mediated EPSPs and block the induction of LTP in the BLC, possibly via activation of α_2-adrenoceptors *(138,139)*. Although increased GABA release and decreased excitatory drive are consistent with the observation that NE can facilitate the extinction of fear conditioning *(140)*, a process that is thought to require increased inhibition *(141)*, it is somewhat inconsistent with the notion of arousal-induced activation of the BLC.

However, evidence suggests that activation of β-adrenoceptors in the BLC can have diametrically opposite actions on the excitability of BLC neurons. Hence, β-adrenoceptor activation can enhance both AMPA and NMDA receptor-mediated EPSPs *(142,143)*, attenuate $GABA_A$ receptor-mediated IPSPs, and facilitate the induction of associative LTP in the BLC *(144)*. Application of NE also increases the excitability of BLC projection neurons by blocking the expression of a slow after-hyperpolarizing potential (sAHP; *see* Ref. *145*).

At present, little is known about what regulates the differential activation of α-adrenoceptors versus β-adrenoceptors, but a shift in favor of the latter would significantly increase the chances of developing PTSD in the response to traumatic life events *(146,147)*.

Neuropeptides

Although interneurons of the BLC coexpress GABA and an assortment of neuropeptides, very little is known about the behavioral and cellular actions of peptide neurotransmitters in the BLC. Administration of CCK can induce panic-like reactions in healthy volunteers *(148)*, and local application of CCK excites BLC projection neurons *(148)*. It is noteworthy that CCK has been shown to facilitate the actions of DA in the mesolimbic pathway *(149,150)*. Although the interaction between these two transmitter systems has not been systematically examined in the BLC, it is interesting to note that both neurotransmitter systems increase the occurrence of spontaneous IPSPs in BLC projection neurons. It is possible that an abnormal synergistic interaction between the CCK and DA systems in the BLC contributes to the psychopathology of PTSD.

Two other stress-related neuropeptide transmitters have been shown to have significant and opposing effects on amygdala-dependent anxiety-like behaviors: CRF and neuropeptide Y (NPY). CRF is released into the amygdala in response to stress *(151)*, where it is thought to cause a time-dependent facilitation of memory consolidation *(152,153)* and initiate anxiogenic-like behaviors *(154,155)* via an action at CRF_1 receptors *(156)*. At the cellular level, CRF enhances BLC projection neuron excitability by decreasing the expression of a postburst sAHP *(157)* and causing a time-dependent facilitation of evoked EPSPs *(158)*. These most likely represent the normal adaptive response to an acute stressor. As outlined in this chapter, extreme or chronic stress can cause a prolonged disruption of the adaptive response to stress stimuli. Interestingly, local CRF_1 receptor activation in the BLC, which induces anxiogenic-like behavior, is also associated with increased c-fos expression in the subgroup of dorsal raphé serotonergic neurons that project back to the amygdala *(159)*. This most likely represents part of feedback neural circuitry that functions to regulate the intensity and duration of anxiety-like behaviors.

In a similar fashion, NPY has been postulated as a potential stress resiliency factor *(160,161)*, and low baseline levels of NPY are positively correlated with the occurrence of PTSD in combat veterans *(162)*. Although NPY antagonizes the behavioral manifestation of stress through actions at multiple brain regions *(163)*, it is significant that local injections of NPY into the BLC elicit anxiolytic-like behavioral responses *(164)*. In addition, pretreatment with NPY blocks the anxiogenic response evoked by local CRF injections or restraint stress *(165,166)*, and selective lesions of NPY interneurons in the BLC mimic the effects of local CRF injections *(167)*, suggesting that release of NPY from intrinsic sources acts to buffer against the anxiogenic effects of local CRF release. It is noteworthy that NPY colocalizes with SST in a subpopulation of interneurons, that both neuropeptides function to reduce the excitability of BLC projection neurons *(168,169)*, and that 50% of these neurons are lost in epilepsy *(170)*. It is possible that more subtle disruptions of the NPY/SST system could remove an essential buffer against the effects of extreme or chronic stress, thereby conferring a susceptibility to the development of PTSD.

Neuromodulators

There are numerous additional neuromodulators that affect amygdala functioning, including agents acting on the GABA system, such as the endogenous benzodiazepines, retrograde signaling molecules such as nitric oxide (NO), and growth factors such as brain-derived neurotrophic factor (BDNF). Space limitations prevent significant additional discussion of the myriad modulatory transmitters, so we only briefly discuss some of the effects of the endogenous cannabinoid system and cortisol.

Although it was long suspected that the active agent in marijuana, tetrahydrocannabinol (THC), acted on an endogenous receptor, this receptor was not identified and cloned until the 1990s. In 2002, Lutz and colleagues first published the creation of a targeted knockout line of mice that were deficient in the endogenous cannabinoid receptor, CB-1. These CB-1-deficient mice showed no effects on baseline acquisition, consolidation, or expression of fear. However, they had markedly impaired short-term and long-term extinction of fear. Treatment of wild-type mice with a CB-1 antagonist mimicked the phenotype of CB-1-deficient mice. In the BLC, CB-1 receptor activation has been shown to be crucially involved in long-term depression of GABA IPSPs *(171)*. In addition, the cannabinoid agonist WIN55212-2 potently inhibited the unit-firing activity of BLA projection neurons *(172)*. Although the microcircuitry of these effects has yet to be fully understood, it is notable that CB-1 antagonists prevent extinction of fear in rats as well as mice (as described in this chapter), and that pretreatment with a compound that enhances endogenous cannabinoid levels was found to enhance the extinction of fear *(173)*. Together, these data suggest that the endogenous cannabinoid system may be dysregulated in disorders of fear extinction, and possibly in PTSD, consistent with a model in which PTSD is in part a disorder of recovery from fear.

There is a long history of studies demonstrating cortisol and hypothalamic-pituitary-adrenal (HPA) axis dysregulation in PTSD. Significantly, glucocorticoid receptors (GRs) are found at relatively high levels in nonnuclear sites in BLC neurons and appear to have a high affinity for the postsynaptic densities of dendritic spines *(174)*, suggesting that activation of these receptors may play a critical role in regulating synaptic plasticity in the BLC. Consistent with this observation, glucocorticoids are reported to enhance fear memory by acting synergistically with noradrenergic receptor activation in the BLC *(175,176)*. From a physiological perspective, numerous direct effects of cortisol on amygdala functioning have been demonstrated. Notably, a recent study demonstrated that corticosterone application caused a time-dependent depolarization of the resting membrane potential of BLC projection neurons, increased their input resistance, and dramatically decreased spike frequency adaptation *(177)*. Corticosterone also caused a selective reduction in $GABA_A$-mediated IPSPs due to a positive shift in the GABA reversal potential. Moreover, a synergistic interaction between glucocorticoid and noradrenergic receptor activation in the BLC could further reduce GABA-ergic transmission. As noted, anything that functionally attenuates GABA-ergic transmission in the BLC has the potential to facilitate homosynaptic or heterosynaptic LTP and hence memory formation. Together these data suggest that glucocorticoids, in addition to their role in feedback regulation of the HPA axis, may directly affect amygdala excitability and overall function. Similar to the discussions here, it is conceivable that in PTSD, a disorder of demonstrated glucocorticoid dysregulation and amygdala dysfunction, these two are interrelated.

Cortisol has many effects throughout the brain. In addition, it appears that the biology of stress is at least in part due to dysregulation of the central nucleus of the amygdala (CeA) activity, specifically dysregulation of the CRF-producing neurons within the CeA *(178)*. Chronic stress leads to abnormal regulation and sensitization of CRF by the amygdala and hypothalamus. Intuitively, a disorder involving stress would involve overexcitation of the stress response system and would lead to predictions that there would be excess cortisol and insensitivity to cortisol feedback. That is what is found in major depressive disorder *(179)*. In contrast, recent work suggests that decreased basal cortisol and increased HPA feedback control may be present in PTSD *(180,181)*, although not all studies have consistently found this. The most parsimonious view of these data is that in PTSD the HPA axis is hypersensitive to both stress activation and feedback inhibition *(182,183)*. In this model, the cortisol system is hyperresponsive, leading to low levels of cortisol at baseline and to elevated levels of cortisol with stress.

Variants in genes regulating the HPA axis have been proposed as potential candidate genes for stress-related disorders. Several variants in the glucocorticoid receptor gene (*GR*, NR3C1 locus) have been reported to directly influence GR sensitivity as measured by the dexamethasone suppression test (DST) and a series of endocrinological and metabolic parameters *(184)*. Two *GR* gene polymorphisms were associated with a hypersensitivity to glucocorticoids, as observed by an increased response to the adrenocorticotropic hormone (ACTH)- and cortisol-suppressive effects of low-dose dexamethasone and a metabolic profile suggestive of GR hypersensitivity *(185,186)*. The largest genetic study of PTSD risk to date demonstrated a gene-environment effect of a gene involved in HPA axis regulation, *FKBP5*, a cochaperone of hsp90 that influences GR sensitivity and regulation. Recently, Binder and colleagues *(187)* demonstrated that multiple single-nucleotide polymorphisms spanning the *FKBP5* gene interacted with level of past child abuse to predict risk of PTSD following adult trauma. Notably, these polymorphisms did not have a direct effect on predicting risk of PTSD by themselves and did not interact with level of adult trauma. These results suggest that feedback regulation of the HPA axis may be particularly important during developmental critical periods, and that biological/genetic variants in genes regulating this system may interact with childhood environment to affect the nature of the stress response system during adulthood.

ANIMAL STUDIES MODELING ASPECTS OF PTSD

Although several different approaches have been proposed, we discuss three animal models that have proven particularly useful in examining some of the mechanisms that may contribute to the etiology of PTSD: Pavlovian fear conditioning (*see also* Chapter 2, this volume), the kindling model of epilepsy, and acute and chronic stress manipulations (*see also* Chapter 6, this volume).

Pavlovian Fear Conditioning

One well-founded model of PTSD in animals is classical (or Pavlovian) fear conditioning. The theory holds that during the exposure to a traumatic event the person undergoes an extreme form of fear conditioning, and that the later symptoms of PTSD are the manifestations of this conditioned fear response. Although simple fear conditioning is not sufficient to explain many of the complexities of PTSD, a broader perspective of conditioned fear, including generalization of cues, hyperexcitability, hyperarousal, intrusive fear memories, fear responsiveness, and a deficit in extinction of fear together may explain many of the symptoms. Furthermore, the neural circuitry underlying conditioned fear (*see* Chapter 2, this volume) provides one of the most well-studied circuits underlying a complex behavior.

The amygdala has long been implicated in learning and memory processes *(188–190)*. It has been shown to modulate fear learning and memory processes and is a possible site of plasticity underlying the storage of fear memories *(191,192)*. The amygdala receives highly processed sensory inputs into its lateral and basolateral nuclei *(193)*. These nuclei then project to the central nucleus, which in turn projects to hypothalamic and brain stem areas that directly mediate the telltale signs of fear in animals, such as increased heart rate, freezing, and increased startle response *(194)*. Studies of Pavlovian fear conditioning, in which learning is acquired by pairing a CS with an intrinsically aversive unconditioned stimulus (US), have provided the most detailed understanding of the amygdala's role in learning and memory to date. The neural circuitry of fear learning has been extensively mapped. It has been shown that fear conditioning leads to increases in synaptic strength between neurons of the thalamus and the BLC *(195,196)*. Rats receiving paired CS-US trials, but not those receiving unpaired trials, exhibited an increase in synaptic currents evoked in BLC neurons through stimulation of thalamic afferents *(195)*. In addition, direct in vivo measurements before and after fear conditioning showed that the field potentials triggered by the CS in the BLC increase after the CS is paired with shock *(196)*. This implies that fear conditioning induces a form of "behavioral LTP" in the BLC, supporting the idea that the amygdala utilizes synaptic changes to mediate fear-conditioned learning. Consistent with this hypothesis, fear conditioning has been shown to occlude the LTP in cortical pathways into the BLC *(197)*.

More recently, a variety of new studies have shed light on the physiological and synaptic mechanisms of fear conditioning. Some of the most interesting developments have been the nature of synaptic receptor modulation. In hippocampal models of LTP, it has been shown that stimulation leading to LTP results in part from switching from immature "silent" NMDA-dependent synapses to active AMPA-dependent mature synapses *(198,199)*.

Several studies have now confirmed similar events within the pathways that mediate conditioned fear in the BLC. Notably, it was found that NMDA transmission in the thalamo-BLC pathway is not potentiated after fear conditioning *(200)*. Moreover, the ability of nonselective and selective subunit antagonists to block NMDA-receptor-mediated EPSCs is reduced following fear conditioning. This correlates with a reduction in phosphorylated NR1, NR2A, and NR2B subunits.

In contrast, in naïve slices, it has been repeatedly found that LTP in both the tha-
lamo- and cortico-BLC pathways is NMDA- and L type voltage gated calcium
channel (L-VGCC)-dependent *(201)*.

In addition, Schroeder and Shinnick-Gallagher found that the stimulus frequency for synaptic potentiation is also switched during maintenance of fear
memory in the cortico-BLC pathway. Hence, fear conditioning attenuated
high-frequency stimulation-dependent LTP (HFS-LTP), but facilitated low-
frequency elicited potentiation. Moreover, HFS-LTP is NMDA receptor and
VGCC dependent in control animals and independent in fear-conditioned animals *(202)*. Notably, this group also found that synaptic alterations induced by
fear conditioning are evident in vitro 10 days after fear conditioning the animal.
At this delayed time point, synaptic transmission was facilitated, and HFS-LTP
of the cortical input into the LA was attenuated, presumably due to downregulation of the NMDA pathway and occlusion of LTP mechanisms *(203)*.

Recently, an elegant study involved genetically targeting amygdala with
recombinant AMPA receptors to specifically examine their incorporation with
fear learning *(204)*. Here, fear conditioning was seen to drive AMPA receptors
into the synapse of a large proportion of projection neurons in the BLC. However, fear memory was blocked if receptor incorporation was reduced by as little
as 10–20%. These data are consistent with the hypotheses that new amygdala-
dependent fear memories are in part dependent on insertion of new AMPA receptors into amygdala synapses. Notably, the results also suggest that fear memories
are encoded by widely distributed AMPA receptor trafficking in many amygdala
neurons, and this distributed neural "trace" appears to show little redundancy.

Work on specificity of inhibitory pathways is also consistent with this idea of
pathway specificity. Hence, theta burst stimulation of afferent inputs onto BLC
projection neurons produces an input-specific potentiation of IPSPs in the thalamic pathway, whereas the cortical input is unaffected *(205)*. Notably, this IPSP
potentiation was prevented by blockers of calcium-permeable AMPA receptors.
Moreover, the IPSP potentiation was mirrored by a potentiation of EPSPs in
BLC interneurons, an effect that was blocked by prior Pavlovian fear conditioning. These data suggest that during fear conditioning simultaneous activation of
cortical and thalamic pathways into the BLC causes a long-lasting attenuation
of feedforward IPSPs. These fear-conditioning data on the modulation of feed-
forward inhibition in the BLC are consistent with many of the studies discussed
in which regulation of GABA-dependent amygdala excitability may underlie
fear learning and possibly the etiology of PTSD.

Extinction of Conditioned Fear

Extinction of conditioned fear is also partly amygdala dependent *(206)*. A
deficit in normal extinction of conditioned fear provides another process that
may be abnormal in PTSD. Following the pairing of an aversive US to a neutral
CS, a conditioned fear response is established. If the neutral CS is then repeatedly presented in the absence of the US, a procedure known as *extinction training*, the result is an inhibition of the conditioned fear response to the neutral CS.

From an operational perspective, extinction may thus be defined as "a reduction in the strength or probability of a conditioned fear response as a consequence of repeated presentation of the CS in the absence of the UCS" *(207)*.

A variety of behavioral observations support the hypothesis that extinction is a form of learning and not "unlearning" or the forgetting of a conditioned association (reviewed in Ref. *208)*. Numerous studies have demonstrated that synaptic plasticity within the BLC is associated with extinction of fear, and that blockade of BLC function prevents normal extinction of conditioned fear (*209–219)*. Recent work from our group has shown that enhancing neural plasticity by enhancing NMDA function with D-cycloserine (DCS), a partial NMDA agonist, enhances amygdala-dependent extinction *(220)*. The central findings of this study were that both systemic and amygdala-specific administration of DCS dose-dependently enhanced extinction of previously conditioned fear but did not influence fear in rats that had not received extinction training. The general findings of this study have now been replicated by numerous groups for extinction of fear with startle and freezing and with extinction of appetitive cues, such as cocaine-conditioned place preference *(221–223)*. Collectively, data from rodent studies suggest that DCS, a drug already shown to be safe for use in humans, may have potential use in the facilitation of extinction-based therapies for human anxiety disorders *(224–226)*.

From a therapeutic standpoint, the behavior therapies for different anxiety disorders generally involve some form of extinction training *(227)*. This involves graded exposure to the feared object or event in the absence of any likely actual harm. This exposure may be imaginal in nature, with a narrative read or listened to by the patient, or in vivo, with the feared stimulus directly encountered by the patient. Notably, the Institute of Medicine has confirmed the efficacy for exposure-based psychotherapy treatment for PTSD (*see* Chapter 18, this volume), while finding that the current data are inadequate to determine the efficacy of medication treatment for PTSD (Institutes Of Medicine 2008, *266,267)*.

Understanding the role of the amygdala in the extinction of fear has direct translational importance to understanding and treating PTSD. Several very interesting results related to the physiological role of amygdala in extinction of fear have been described. Falls, Miserendino, and Davis initially elucidated the requirement for NMDA activation within the amygdala for the extinction of fear *(228)*. Interestingly, NMDA receptors are essential for the acquisition of both behavioral and neuronal correlates of conditioned fear and its extinction. In addition, 3(2-carboxypiperazine-4-yl)propyl-1-phosphinic acid (CPP) administered prior to extinction testing did not affect the expression of conditional single-unit activity but attenuated conditional freezing *(229)*.

One theory for the new inhibitory learning that occurs with extinction of fear is the process of learning conditional safety. Conditioned learning of a safety signal induced a long-lasting *depression* of CS-evoked activity in the BLC. In contrast, fear conditioning induced an *increase* in the CS-evoked field potential *(230)*. The idea of a depression or depotentiation during extinction of the excitatory potential created during fear acquisition has several additional neurochemical and neurophysiological correlates. Depotentiation has been proposed as a cellular mechanism for fear extinction. Hence, a unique form of depotentiation has been shown to reverse conditioning-induced potentiation at thalamic synapses onto BLC projection neurons *(231)*. Similarly, extinction returned the enhanced BLC efficacy to baseline and occluded depotentiation. Here, a GluR2-derived peptide that blocks AMPA receptor endocytosis was shown to inhibit depotentiation, suggesting that AMPA receptor internalization at "mature" synapses may play a pivotal role in extinction. However, activation of presynaptic mGluRII receptors also causes a depotentiation of high-frequency stimulation-induced LTP in BLC projection neurons and blocks the consolidation of fear memory measured with fear-potentiated startle *(232)*. Hence, anything that may disrupt AMPA receptor internalization or presynaptic mGluRII receptor function may retard the extinction of fear memories and facilitate the development of PTSD.

A growing number of studies have examined the role of the medial PFC (mPFC) in modulating amygdala function in relation to extinction of fear memory *(215,233–236)*. However, due to space constraints, this chapter focuses solely on amygdala function.

Fear Conditioning: Unit Oscillations and Synchrony

One of the most interesting sets of findings in recent years with regard to the role of amygdala physiological functioning is the finding of synchronized neuronal oscillations and the role these oscillations play in synchronizing the activity of distant brain regions. Importantly, during the acquisition of fear learning, the firing rate of BLC neurons doubles and becomes highly synchronized *(237–239)*. Hence, single-unit activity in the BLC increases after fear conditioning, peaking 30–50 min postshock and then subsiding to baseline after 2 h. During the period of peak activity, BLC neurons become highly synchronized, suggesting that emotional arousal produces a long-lasting increase in spontaneous firing rates and synchronization of BLC neurons, and the increased synchronization is correlated with consolidation effects on fear learning. Additional studies have revealed a significant increase in synchrony in the theta bandwidth during the retrieval and consolidation of fear memory *(91,240)*.

Projection neurons in the BLC display a continuum of firing patterns, including accommodating, regular, and theta oscillatory activity. Significantly, increases in intracellular cAMP, such as might be expected during stress-induced release of DA or CRF, facilitates regular firing and theta oscillations in BLC neurons *(91)*. Hence, one of the primary functions of these neurotransmitters may be to facilitate rhythmic network activity in the BLC and facilitate the retrieval of long-term fear memory following cued and contextual fear conditioning.

Together, these results suggest that many of the data related to the effects of behavior on firing and modulation of excitability within the BLC may actually occur within the context of unit oscillations and population synchronization. This developing field will surely be an exciting area in the ongoing understanding of how fear is encoded, expressed, and extinguished. Furthermore, it is quite likely that abnormalities in these processes may underlie some of the dysfunction occurring with fear dysregulation in PTSD.

Kindling

Another intriguing model of PTSD that is based on amygdala hyperreactivity is the kindling model of epilepsy. In this model, repeated electrical stimulation (kindling) of the BLC serves as a model of limbic complex partial seizures and produces a variety of intriguing anxiety symptoms. Notably, kindling dramatically increases fearful behavior in rats. Hence, kindled animals show a reduction in exploration on the elevated plus maze and a decrease in social interaction and increase in freezing and immobility *(241–243)*. McIntyre and colleagues examined rats selectively bred for differences in amygdala excitability and found that rats that are faster to kindle, and thus more excitable, exhibit enhanced fear conditioning as measured by the fear-potentiated startle paradigm *(244)*. Moreover, Kalynchuk and Meaney *(245)* also showed that amygdala kindling dramatically increases fearful behavior, and that this may in part occur through the amygdala's interactions with other brain regions *(246)*.

Consistent with the extinction-deficit model of PTSD outlined, it has also been shown that electrical kindling of the amygdala leads to a deficit in extinction and a reinstatement of fear in rats. After classical conditioning, rats were fear extinguished followed by nonepileptogenic amygdala stimulation, which prevented normal extinction. In addition, animals that had already been extinguished were found to have reinstatement of their original fear memory following amygdala stimulation. These results were interpreted to suggest that amygdala stimulation activates "acquired excitatory stimulus-affect neural connections formed during Pavlovian fear conditioning" *(247)*.

The molecular mechanisms of kindling and the effects of seizure-like activity on amygdala are only recently being understood. Tuunanen et al. (1996) demonstrated that status epilepticus causes a selective loss of GABA-ergic neurons in the BLC. In particular, seizure activity was associated with a 67% loss of SST immunoreactive interneurons. As noted, the SST interneurons represent a substantial proportion of feedforward inhibitory interneurons in the BLC, and a loss of this feedforward inhibition can facilitate heterosynaptic LTP and result in generalization of sensory inputs.

At the cellular level, there are numerous changes in the glutamatergic and GABA-ergic circuitry following kindling of the BLC *(61,248–251)*. These results provide evidence that kindling-induced epileptiform activity observed in BLC neurons results from an increase in excitatory NMDA- and non-NMDA-receptor-mediated glutamatergic transmission and a decrease in inhibitory GABA-receptor-mediated transmission. Seizure-dependent decreases in surface $GABA_A$ receptor localization have been shown to occur as a function of active protein kinase C (PKC)-dependent internalization of specific $GABA_A$ receptor subunits during status epilepticus *(252)*. However, the enhanced excitatory transmission cannot be fully accounted for by reduced inhibition. Significantly, kindling results in a reduction in the sensitivity of presynaptic $GABA_B$ receptors on glutamatergic afferents in the BLC *(61)*. As noted, presynaptic $GABA_B$ receptors play a critical role in regulating glutamate release and controlling associative LTP. In addition, kindling of the BLC results in a loss of function of postsynaptic group II mGluRs in BLC projection neurons (253), which would functionally remove the "brake" on BLC hyperactivation induced by excessive glutamate release. Together, a loss of sensitivity of presynaptic $GABA_B$ receptors and loss of postsynaptic group II mGluR function may lead to aberrant sensory generalization and oscillatory activity in the BLC and thus contribute to the etiology of PTSD.

Another intriguing model of kindling involves repeated activation of the DA-containing ventral tegmental area (VTA) neurons. Gelowitz and Kokkinidis found that repeated low-current, high-frequency stimulation of the VTA provoked afterdischarges in the central amygdala and enhanced amygdala kindling rates (254). This study established a fundamental link between VTA activation and neural excitability within the amygdala, suggesting that the proposed alterations in DA function in PTSD could, in part, work through enhancing amygdala excitability.

Together, these behavioral and physiological studies suggest that repeated significant fearful and stressful experiences that strongly activate the amygdala may result in a kindling-like phenomenon in the BLC, which could result in long-lasting alterations in amygdala function. Such changes could produce many of the fear, anxiety, and hyperarousal symptoms that are synonymous with PTSD.

Stress Models of PTSD

Single prolonged stress (SPS) is one of the few animal models specifically proposed for PTSD (see Chapter 6, this volume). SPS has been shown to increase plasma corticosterone and increase contextual fear memory performed 1 week after stress, at a time when LTP was blunted (255). Glucocorticoid antagonists also were found to block this potentiation of fear conditioning. Notably, PTSD is characterized by an inhibition of the HPA axis, and many animal models of PTSD fail to mimic this response, but the SPS model appears to be especially robust in modeling both fear and HPA effects.

Another method of stress-dependent modulation of amygdala responsivity is repeated "priming" injections of a CRF receptor agonist within the BLC (256). When non-anxiety-inducing doses of a potent CRF type 1 and 2 receptor agonist, urocortin (Ucn), were infused locally into the BLC of rats for 5 days, the animals developed increased anxiety-like responses as measured by the social interaction test. In the absence of any additional Ucn treatment, these behavioral and autonomic responses persisted for more than 30 days. Whole-cell patch-clamp recordings from BLC neurons of these hyperreactive animals revealed a pronounced reduction in both spontaneous and stimulation-evoked IPSPs, leading to hyperexcitability of the BLC network. Moreover, this Ucn-induced plasticity appears to be dependent on NMDA receptor activation and subsequent activation of the calcium-calmodulin-dependent protein kinase II (CaMKII) cascade.

Similarly, exposure to restraint stress can facilitate subsequent fear conditioning, an effect that is mimicked by local infusion of GABA$_A$ receptor antagonists. Moreover, restraint stress was shown to facilitate the induction of LTP in non-fear-conditioned animals and reduced GABA inhibition in slices (257). Thus, this behavioral manipulation, which is quite similar to SPS, leads to a similar enhancement in fear conditioning, in part through increasing amygdala excitability through reduced GABA inhibition. Consistent with this observation, acute stress has been shown to increase glutamate efflux in the BLA (258).

Significantly, both stress and epileptogenesis result in a long-lasting depression of α1-adrenoceptor function in the BLC (259,260). As noted, in the BLC α1-adrenoceptors act to facilitate GABA-ergic transmission in the BLC; removal of this facilitatory action would shift the balance of the NA response in BLC neurons toward enhanced excitation due to β-adrenoceptor activation.

Another mechanism of neurochemically inducing stress is withdrawal of chronic neurodepressants, such as benzodiazepine or alcohol withdrawal. Diazepam withdrawal increases freezing in both associative and nonassociative contexts. In anesthetized animals, stimulation of the PFC evoked a population spike (PS) in the BLC of control animals, whereas multiple PSs were observed in animals subjected to diazepam withdrawal. Moreover, in diazepam withdrawal animals, high-frequency stimulation induced a significant potentiation that lasted more than 2 h (LTP); the same stimulation in control rats did not induce LTP (261). The conclusion was that neuronal hyperexcitability leading to facilitated LTP could be due to depressed GABA-ergic activity (disinhibition). Similar to the stress models discussed, it is suggested that the increased synaptic plasticity may be at the root of the increased fear learning observed in withdrawn animals. Notably, prior history of trauma, both adult and childhood, are among the most strong predictors of which people will develop PTSD following trauma (262). Thus, the level of excitability of the amygdala prior to the incident trauma may be a critical factor in the development of PTSD. These data suggest that a stress peptide-induced behavioral syndrome can be correlated with cellular mechanisms of neural plasticity, which may be related to the effects of prior stress and chronic stress in amygdala in patients with PTSD.

In contrast to these results with CRF agonist priming into BLA, repetitive injections of NPY into the BLA appears to lead to a long-term resilience effect on social responses to restraint stress (263). This is particularly interesting given the recent suggestions that NPY may serve as a resilience factor in subjects exposed to trauma and thus may be protective against the development of PTSD (264,265).

SUMMARY

We reviewed a number of electrophysiological mechanisms of amygdala control of fear acquisition, expression, generalization, discrimination, inhibition, and extinction. Many or even all of these processes may be abnormal in the complex syndrome of PTSD, for which a previously experienced trauma is relived and reexperienced through traumatic fear memories. These memories are intrusive, often generalized to nonspecific cues, and are accompanied by a host of physiological reactions consistent with activation of the endogenous fear response.

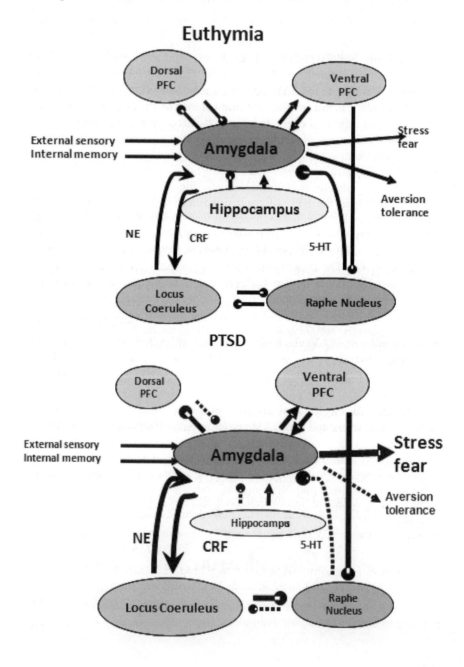

Figure 6 illustrates how amygdala hyperactivity or lack of cue discrimination may in part contribute to some of the symptoms of PTSD. Dysfunction in the amygdala, and in regions that are part of the broader fear circuit, may lead to increased likelihood of activation of hardwired fear output pathways in the presence of neutral CS cues (or only weak CS cues). This dysregulation can occur within the amygdala itself, as outlined in many of the sections here, or may occur in the mPFC, sensory cortical and thalamic areas, brain stem monoamine modulatory regions, and hippocampus, which all serve as part of a broader emotional circuit regulating amygdala excitability and emotional memory and fear response.

By further understanding the physiological mechanisms underlying acquisition, expression, and extinction of fear memories, the dysfunctional neural responses mediating PTSD symptoms will continue to be elucidated. There is reason for much hope as the mammalian fear circuitry is remarkably conserved from mice to humans. Progress to date suggests that PTSD may provide one of the most well-understood neuropathological pathways in the area of psychiatric

---

Fig. 6. Model of altered amygdala function in PTSD. The amygdala, via modulation from the prefrontal cortex, hippocampus, and brain stem areas, regulates affective state and approach/avoidance behavior. These affective states can be modeled by stress and fear response in contrast to aversion tolerance. During the euthymic (healthy) state, stress and fearful stimuli lead to an initial activation of the locus coeruleus (LC)-NE (norepinephrine) system via release of corticotropin-releasing factor (CRF) from the amygdala and from the paraventricular nucleus of the hypothalamus. This release is opposed by the inhibition of these circuits via serotonin (5HT) release that promotes tolerance to aversion and decreases the amygdala and bed nucleus of the stria terminalis (BNST) stress response. Other limbic regions, including the hippocampus, are modulated by these pathways, with NE tending to increase expression of memories of aversive context and 5HT tending to decrease expression of such memories. Both dorsal prefrontal cortex (PFC) and ventral/orbital PFC are thought to be critical in mediating extinction of fearful memories and aversion tolerance. The ventral prefrontal areas, however, may also activate the affective circuitry and may inhibit Raphe Nucleus (RN) activity. NE and 5HT have complex modulatory roles in cortical functioning that are not easily summarized in this diagram. Multiple genetic and environmental determinants lead to alterations in these systems, which lead to a dysregulated state of functioning in post-traumatic stress disorder (PTSD). In this state, the LC-NE system may be hyperresponsive to stress/fear stimuli and aversion responsiveness, and the RN-5HT system may be hyporesponsive, with decreased inhibition of stress reactivity and decreased tolerance to aversion. The cortical modulation of limbic reactivity is dysregulated and likely also contributes to the altered NE/5HT functioning. In addition, dysregulation of the NE/5HT systems contributes to abnormal sleep, attention, concentration, appetite, and libido via other pathways. This altered circuit is hyperresponsive to stress and fearful cues, with an increased tendency to lead to stronger fear and stress (fight-or-flight) responses. Extinction, a principal component to recovery, involved PFC and hippocampal interactions with amygdala and is likely in part dependent on these neurotransmitter systems as well

disorders, providing hope for a new understanding of translationally derived rational approaches to treatment and prevention.

ACKNOWLEDGMENTS

This work was supported by MH069852 and MH074079 to D. G. R.; DA-019624, NARSAD, and Burroughs Wellcome Fund to K. J. R.; and Center for Behavioral Neuroscience STC Center: NSF agreement IBN-9876754, National Primate Research Center base grant RR-00165, Animal Resource Program at the National Institutes of Health.

REFERENCES

1. LeDoux, J. E. (2000) Emotion circuits in the brain. Annu Rev Neurosci 23, 155–84.
2. Davis, M., and Whalen, P. J. (2001) The amygdala: vigilance and emotion. Mol Psychiatry 6, 13–34.
3. Hamann, S. B., Stefanacci, L., Squire, L. R., et al. (1996) Recognizing facial emotion. Nature 379, 497.
4. Whalen, P. J., Rauch, S. L., Etcoff, N. L., McInerney, S. C., Lee, M. B., and Jenike, M. A. (1998) Masked presentations of emotional facial expressions modulate amygdala activity without explicit knowledge. J Neurosci 18, 411–18.
5. Hamann, S. B., Ely, T. D., Grafton, S. T., and Kilts, C. D. (1999) Amygdala activity related to enhanced memory for pleasant and aversive stimuli. Nat Neurosci 2, 289–93.
6. Drevets, W. C. (2000) Functional anatomical abnormalities in limbic and prefrontal cortical structures in major depression. Prog Brain Res 126, 413–31.
7. Drevets, W. C., Price, J. L., Bardgett, M. E., Reich, T., Todd, R. D., and Raichle, M. E. (2002) Glucose metabolism in the amygdala in depression: relationship to diagnostic subtype and plasma cortisol levels. Pharmacol Biochem Behav 71, 431–47.
8. Blumberg, H. P., and Charney, D. S. (2002) The neuroanatomy of mood disorders. Introduction. Semin Clin Neuropsychiatry 7, 221–22.
9. Gorman, J. M., Kent, J. M., Sullivan, G. M., and Coplan, J. D. (2000) Neuroanatomical hypothesis of panic disorder, revised. Am J Psychiatry 157, 493–505.
10. Hull, A. M. (2002) Neuroimaging findings in post-traumatic stress disorder. Systematic review. Br J Psychiatry 181, 102–10.
11. Bremner, J. D. (2006) The relationship between cognitive and brain changes in posttraumatic stress disorder. Ann N Y Acad Sci 1071, 80–86.
12. Rauch, S. L., Shin, L. M., and Phelps, E. A. (2006) Neurocircuitry models of posttraumatic stress disorder and extinction: human neuroimaging research–past, present, and future. Biol Psychiatry 60, 376–82.
13. Millhouse, O. E., and DeOlmos, J. (1983) Neuronal configurations in lateral and basolateral amygdala Neuroscience 10, 1269–1300.
14. McDonald, A. J. (1984) Neuronal organization of the lateral and basolateral amygdaloid nuclei in the rat. J Comp Neurol 222, 589–606.
15. Carlsen, J., and Heimer, L. (1988) The basolateral amygdaloid complex as a cortical-like structure. Brain Res 441, 377–380.
16. Fanselow, M. S., and LeDoux, J. E. (1999) Why we think plasticity underlying Pavlovian fear conditioning occurs in the basolateral amygdala. Neuron 23, 229–32.

17. Blair, H. T., Schafe, G. E., Bauer, E. P., Rodrigues, S. M., and LeDoux, J. E. (2001) Synaptic plasticity in the lateral amygdala: a cellular hypothesis of fear conditioning. Learn Mem 8, 229–42.

18. McDonald, A. J. (1998) Cortical pathways to the mammalian amygdala. Prog Neurobiol 55, 257–332.

19. Savander, V., Miettinen, R., LeDoux, J. E., and Pitkänen, A. (1997) Lateral nucleus of the rat amygdala is reciprocally connected with basal and accessory basal nuclei: a light and electron microscopic study. Neuroscience 77, 767–81.

20. Pitkänen, A., Savander, V., and LeDoux, J. E. (1997) Organization of intra-amygdaloid circuitries in the rat: an emerging framework for understanding functions of the amygdala. Trends Neurosci 20, 517–23.

21. Pitkanen, A., Pikkarainen, M., Nurminen, N., and Ylinen, A. (2000) Reciprocal connections between the amygdala and the hippocampal formation, perirhinal cortex, and postrhinal cortex in rat. A review. Ann N Y Acad Sci 911, 369–91.

22. McDonald, A. J. (1985) Morphology of peptide-containing neurons in the rat basolateral amygdaloid nucleus. Brain Res 338, 186–91.

23. Sorvari, H., Miettinen, R., Soininen, H., and Pitkänen, A. (1996) Parvalbumin-immunoreactive neurons make inhibitory synapses on pyramidal cells in the human amygdala: a light and electron microscopic study. Neurosci Lett 217, 93–96.

24. Smith, Y., Pare, J. F., and Pare, D. (1998) Cat intraamygdaloid inhibitory network: ultrastructural organization of parvalbumin-immunoreactive elements. J Comp Neurol 391, 164–79.

25. McDonald, A. J. (1992) Projection neurons of the basolateral amygdala: a correlative Golgi and retrograde tract tracing study. Brain Res Bull 28, 179–85.

26. Sorvari, H., Soininen, H., Paljärvi, L., Karkola, K., and Pitkänen, A. (1995) Distribution of parvalbumin-immunoreactive cells and fibers in the human amygdaloid complex. J Comp Neurol 360, 185–212.

27. Smith, Y., Pare, J. F., and Pare, D. (1998) Cat intraamygdaloid inhibitory network: ultrastructural organization of parvalbumin-immunoreactive elements. J Comp Neurol 391, 164–79.

28. McDonald, A. J., and Betette, R. L. (2001) Parvalbumin-containing neurons in the rat basolateral amygdala: morphology and co-localization of Calbindin-D(28k). Neuroscience 102, 413–25.

29. McDonald, A. J., Mascagni, F., and Augustine, J. R. (1995) Neuropeptide Y and somatostatin-like immunoreactivity in neurons of the monkey amygdala. Neuroscience 66, 959–82.

30. McDonald, A. J., and Mascagni, F. (2002) Immunohistochemical characterization of somatostatin containing interneurons in the rat basolateral amygdala. Brain Res 943, 237–44.

31. McDonald, A. J., and Mascagni, F. (2001) Localization of the CB1 type cannabinoid receptor in the rat basolateral amygdala: high concentrations in a subpopulation of cholecystokinin-containing interneurons. Neuroscience 107, 641–52.

32. McDonald, A. J. (1994) Calretinin immunoreactive neurons in the basolateral amygdala of the rat and monkey Brain Res 667, 238–42.

33. Sorvari, H., Soininen, H., and Pitkanen, A. (1996) Calretinin-immunoreactive cells and fibers in the human amygdaloid complex. J Comp Neurol 369, 188–208.

34. Kemppainen, S., and Pitkanen, A. (2000) Distribution of parvalbumin, calretinin, and calbindin-D(28k) immunoreactivity in the rat amygdaloid complex and colocalization with gamma-aminobutyric acid. J Comp Neurol 426, 441–67.

35. Woodruff, A. R., and Sah, P. (2007) Networks of parvalbumin-positive interneurons in the basolateral amygdala. J Neurosci 27, 553–63.
36. Rainnie, D. G., Mania, I., Mascagni, F., and McDonald, A. J. (2006) Physiological and morphological characterization of parvalbumin-containing interneurons of the rat basolateral amygdala. J Comp Neurol 498, 142–61.
37. Muller, J. F., Mascagni, F., and McDonald, A. J. (2005) Coupled networks of parvalbumin-immunoreactive interneurons in the rat basolateral amygdala. J Neurosci 25, 7366–76.
38. Woodruff, A. R., and Sah, P. (2007) Networks of parvalbumin-positive interneurons in the basolateral amygdala. J Neurosci 27, 553–63.
39. Cobb, S. R., Halasy, K., Vida, I., et al. (1997) Synaptic effects of identified interneurons innervating both interneurons and pyramidal cells in the rat hippocampus. Neuroscience 79, 629–648.
40. Fricker, D., and Miles, R. (2001) Interneurons, spike timing, and perception. Neuron 32, 771–74.
41. Fricker, D., and Miles, R. (2000) EPSP amplification and the precision of spike timing in hippocampal neurons. Neuron 28, 559–69.
42. Cope, D. W., Maccaferri, G., Marton, L. F., Roberts, J. D., Cobden, P. M., and Somogyi, P. (2002) Cholecystokinin-immunopositive basket and Schaffer collateral-associated interneurones target different domains of pyramidal cells in the CA1 area of the rat hippocampus. Neuroscience 109, 63–80.
43. Cobb, S. R., Buhl, E. H., Halasy, K., Paulsen, O., and Somogyi, P. (1995) Synchronization of neuronal activity in hippocampus by individual GABAergic interneurons. Nature 378, 75–78.
44. Buhl, E. H., Cobb, S. R., Halasy, K., and Somogyi, P. (1995) Properties of unitary IPSPs evoked by anatomically identified basket cells in the rat hippocampus. Eur J Neurosci 7, 1989–2004.
45. Acsady, L., Gorcs, T. J., and Freund, T. F. (1996) Different populations of vasoactive intestinal polypeptide-immunoreactive interneurons are specialized to control pyramidal cells or interneurons in the hippocampus. Neuroscience 73, 317–34.
46. Gulyas, A. I., Hajos, N., and Freund, T. F. (1996) Interneurons containing calretinin are specialized to control other interneurons in the rat hippocampus. J Neurosci 16, 3397–3411.
47. Pouille, F., and Scanziani, M. (2001) Enforcement of temporal fidelity in pyramidal cells by somatic feed-forward inhibition. Science 293, 1159–63.
48. McDonald, A. J. (1998) Cortical pathways to the mammalian amygdala. Prog Neurobiol 55, 257–332.
49. McDonald, A. J., Mascagni, F., Mania, I., and Rainnie, D. G. (2005) Evidence for a perisomatic innervation of parvalbumin-containing interneurons by individual pyramidal cells in the basolateral amygdala. Brain Res 1035, 32–40.
50. Rainnie, D. G., Mania, I., Mascagni, F., and McDonald, A. J. (2006) Physiological and morphological characterization of parvalbumin-containing interneurons of the rat basolateral amygdala. J Comp Neurol 498, 142–61.
51. Rainnie, D. G., Asprodini, E. K., and Shinnick-Gallagher, P. (1991) Excitatory transmission in the basolateral amygdala. J Neurophysiol 66, 986–98.
52. Rainnie, D. G., Asprodini, E. K., and Shinnick-Gallagher, P. (1991) Inhibitory transmission in the basolateral amygdala. J Neurophysiol 66, 999–1009.
53. Gean, P.-W., and Chang, F.-C. (1992) Pharmacological characterization of excitatory synaptic potentials in rat basolateral amygdaloid neurons. Synapse 11, 1–9.
54. Washburn, M. S., and Moises, H. C. (1992) Electrophysiological and morphological properties of rat basolateral amygdaloid neurons in vitro. J Neurosci 12, 4066–79.

55. Sugita, S., Tanaka, E., and North, R. A. (1993) Membrane properties and synaptic potentials of three types of neurone in rat lateral amygdala. J Physiol 460, 705–18.

56. Li, X. F., Phillips, R., and LeDoux, J. E. (1995) NMDA and non-NMDA receptors contribute to synaptic transmission between the medial geniculate body and the lateral nucleus of the amygdala Exp Brain Res 105, 87–100.

57. Smith, B. N., and Dudek, F. E. (1996) Amino acid-mediated regulation of spontaneous synaptic activity patterns in the rat basolateral amygdala. J Neurophysiol 76, 1958–67.

58. Sugita, S., Tanaka, E., and North, R. A. (1993) Membrane properties and synaptic potentials of three types of neurone in rat lateral amygdala. J Physiol 460, 705–18.

59. Pouille, F., and Scanziani, M. (2001) Enforcement of temporal fidelity in pyramidal cells by somatic feed-forward inhibition. Science 293, 1159–63.

60. Lawrence, J. J., and McBain, C. J. (2003) Interneuron diversity series: containing the detonation--feedforward inhibition in the CA3 hippocampus. Trends Neurosci 26, 631–40.

61. Asprodini, E. K., Rainnie, D. G., and Shinnick-Gallagher, P. (1992) Epileptogenesis reduces the sensitivity of presynaptic gamma-aminobutyric acid B receptors on glutamatergic afferents in the amygdala. J Pharmacol Exp Ther 262, 1011–21.

62. Huang, C.-C., and Gean, P.-W. (1994) Paired-pulse depression of the N-methyl-D-aspartate receptor-mediated synaptic potentials in the amygdala. Br J Pharmacol 113, 1029–35.

63. Li, X. F., Armony, J. L., and LeDoux, J. E. (1996) GABAA and GABAB receptors differentially regulate synaptic transmission in the auditory thalamo-amygdala pathway: an in vivo microiontophoretic study and a model. Synapse 24, 115–24.

64. Yamada, J., Saitow, F., Satake, S., Kiyohara, T., and Konishi, S. (1999) GABAB receptor-mediated presynaptic inhibition of glutamatergic and GABAergic transmission in the basolateral amygdala. Neuropharmacology 38, 1743–53.

65. Yamada, J., Saitow, F., Satake, S., Kiyohara, T., and Konishi, S. (1999) GABAB receptor-mediated presynaptic inhibition of glutamatergic and GABAergic transmission in the basolateral amygdala. Neuropharmacology 38, 1743–53.

66. Shaban, H., Humeau, Y., Herry, C., et al. (2006) Generalization of amygdala LTP and conditioned fear in the absence of presynaptic inhibition. Nat Neurosci 9, 1028–35.

67. Shaban, H., Humeau, Y., Herry, C., et al. (2006) Generalization of amygdala LTP and conditioned fear in the absence of presynaptic inhibition. Nat Neurosci 9, 1028–35.

68. Rainnie, D. G., and Shinnick-Gallagher, P. (1992) Trans-ACPD and L-APB presynaptically inhibit excitatory glutamatergic transmission in the basolateral amygdala (BLA). Neurosci Lett 139, 87–91.

69. Neugebauer, V., Keele, N. B., and Shinnick-Gallagher, P. (1997) Epileptogenesis in vivo enhances the sensitivity of inhibitory presynaptic metabotropic glutamate receptors in basolateral amygdala neurons in vitro. J Neurosci 17, 983–95.

70. Muly, E. C., Mania, I., Guo, J. D., and Rainnie, D. G. (2007) Group II metabotropic glutamate receptors in anxiety circuitry: correspondence of physiological response and subcellular distribution J Comp Neurol 505, 682–700.

71. Li, H., Weiss, S. R., Chuang, D. M., Post, R. M., and Rogawski, M. A. (1998) Bidirectional synaptic plasticity in the rat basolateral amygdala: characterization of an activity-dependent switch sensitive to the presynaptic metabotropic glutamate receptor antagonist 2S-α-ethylglutamic acid. J Neurosci 18, 1662–70.

72. Neugebauer, V., Keele, N. B., and Shinnick-Gallagher, P. (1997) Epileptogenesis in vivo enhances the sensitivity of inhibitory presynaptic metabotropic glutamate receptors in basolateral amygdala neurons in vitro. J Neurosci 17, 983–95.

73. Braga, M. F., Aroniadou-Anderjaska, V., Xie, J., and Li, H. (2003) Bidirectional modulation of GABA release by presynaptic glutamate receptor 5 kainate receptors in the basolateral amygdala. J Neurosci 23, 442–52.
74. Gracy, K. N., and Pickel, V. M. (1995) Comparative ultrastructural localization of the NMDAR1 glutamate receptor in the rat basolateral amygdala and bed nucleus of the stria terminalis. J Comp Neurol 362, 71–85.
75. Farb, C. R., Aoki, C., and LeDoux, J. E. (1995) Differential localization of NMDA and AMPA receptor subunits in the lateral and basal nuclei of the amygdala: a light and electron microscopic study. J Comp Neurol 362, 86–108.
76. Pickel, V. M., Colago, E. E., Mania, I., Molosh, A. I., and Rainnie, D. G. (2006) Dopamine D1 receptors co-distribute with N-methyl-d-aspartic acid type-1 subunits and modulate synaptically-evoked N-methyl-d-aspartic acid currents in rat basolateral amygdala. Neuroscience 142, 671–90.
77. Duguid, I., and Sjostrom, P.J. (2006) Novel presynaptic mechanisms for coincidence detection in synaptic plasticity. Curr Opin Neurobiol 16, 312–22.
78. Humeau, Y., Shaban, H., Bissiere, S., and Luthi, A. (2003) Presynaptic induction of heterosynaptic associative plasticity in the mammalian brain. Nature 426, 841–45.
79. Tsvetkov, E., Shin, R. M., and Bolshakov, V. Y. (2004) Glutamate uptake determines pathway specificity of long-term potentiation in the neural circuitry of fear conditioning. Neuron 41, 139–51.
80. Rosenkranz, J. A., and Grace, A. A. (2002) Dopamine-mediated modulation of odour-evoked amygdala potentials during pavlovian conditioning. Nature 417, 282–87.
81. Collins, D. R., Pelletier, J. G., and Pare, D. (2001) Slow and fast (gamma) neuronal oscillations in the perirhinal cortex and lateral amygdala. J Neurophysiol 85, 1661–72.
82. Rainnie, D. G. (1999) Serotonergic modulation of neurotransmission in the rat basolateral amygdala. J Neurophysiol 82, 69–85.
83. McDonald, A. J., Mascagni, F., Mania, I., and Rainnie, D. G. (2005) Evidence for a perisomatic innervation of parvalbumin-containing interneurons by individual pyramidal cells in the basolateral amygdala. Brain Res 1035, 32–40.
84. Rainnie, D. G., Mania, I., Mascagni, F., and McDonald, A. J. (2006) Physiological and morphological characterization of parvalbumin-containing interneurons of the rat basolateral amygdala. J Comp Neurol 498, 142–61.
85. Rainnie, D. G. (1999) Serotonergic modulation of neurotransmission in the rat basolateral amygdala. J Neurophysiol 82, 69–85.
86. Rainnie, D. G., Mania, I., Mascagni, F., and McDonald, A. J. (2006) Physiological and morphological characterization of parvalbumin-containing interneurons of the rat basolateral amygdala. J Comp Neurol 498, 142–61.
87. Woodruff, A. R., and Sah, P. (2007) Networks of parvalbumin-positive interneurons in the basolateral amygdala. J Neurosci 27, 553–563.
88. Sinfield, J. L., and Collins, D. R. (2006) Induction of synchronous oscillatory activity in the rat lateral amygdala in vitro is dependent on gap junction activity. Eur J Neurosci 24, 3091–95.
89. Bauer, E. P., Paz, R., and Pare, D. (2007) Gamma oscillations coordinate amygdalorhinal interactions during learning. J Neurosci 27, 9369–79.
90. Pelletier, J. G., and Pare, D. (2004) Role of amygdala oscillations in the consolidation of emotional memories. Biol Psychiatry 55, 559–62.
91. Pape, H. C., Narayanan, R. T., Smid, J., Stork, O., and Seidenbecher, T. (2005) Theta activity in neurons and networks of the amygdala related to long-term fear memory. Hippocampus 15, 874–80.

92. Seidenbecher, T., Laxmi, T. R., Stork, O., and Pape, H. C. (2003) Amygdalar and hippocampal theta rhythm synchronization during fear memory retrieval. Science 301, 846–50.

93. Woodruff, A. R., and Sah, P. (2007) Networks of parvalbumin-positive interneurons in the basolateral amygdala. J Neurosci 27, 553–63.

94. Pelletier, J. G., and Pare, D. (2004) Role of amygdala oscillations in the consolidation of emotional memories. Biol Psychiatry 55, 559–62.

95. Seidenbecher, T., Laxmi, T. R., Stork, O., and Pape, H. C. (2003) Amygdalar and hippocampal theta rhythm synchronization during fear memory retrieval. Science 301, 846–50.

96. Smith, H. R., and Porrino, L. J. (2008) The comparative distributions of the monoamine transporters in the rodent, monkey, and human amygdala. Brain Struct Funct 213, 73–91.

97. Woolf, N. J., Eckenstein, F., and Butcher, L. L. (1984) Cholinergic systems in the rat brain: I. projections to the limbic telencephalon Brain Res Bull 13, 751–84.

98. Kitt, C. A., Höhmann, C., Coyle, J. T., and Price, D. L. (1994) Cholinergic innervation of mouse forebrain structures. J Comp Neurol 341, 117–29.

99. Haber, S. N., and Fudge, J. L. (1997) The interface between dopamine neurons and the amygdala: implications for schizophrenia. Schizophr Bull 23, 471–82.

100. Brinley-Reed, M., and McDonald, A. J. (1999) Evidence that dopaminergic axons provide a dense innervation of specific neuronal subpopulations in the rat basolateral amygdala. Brain Res 850, 127–35.

101. Asan, E. (1998) The catecholaminergic innervation of the rat amygdala. Adv Anat Embryol Cell Biol 142, 1–118.

102. Kawahara, H., Yoshida, M., Yokoo, H., Nishi, M., and Tanaka, M. (1993) Psychological stress increases serotonin release in the rat amygdala and prefrontal cortex assessed by in vivo microdialysis. Neurosci Lett 162, 81–84.

103. Funada, M., and Hara, C. (2001) Differential effects of psychological stress on activation of the 5-hydroxytryptamine- and dopamine-containing neurons in the brain of freely moving rats. Brain Res 901, 247–51.

104. Rainnie, D. G. (1999) Serotonergic modulation of neurotransmission in the rat basolateral amygdala. J Neurophysiol 82, 69–85.

105. Stutzmann, G. E., and Ledoux, J. E. (1999) GABAergic antagonists block the inhibitory effects of serotonin in the lateral amygdala: a mechanism for modulation of sensory inputs related to fear conditioning. J Neurosci 19, RC8.

106. Stein, C., Davidowa, H., and Albrecht, D. (2000) 5-HT(1A) receptor-mediated inhibition and 5-HT(2) as well as 5-HT(3) receptor-mediated excitation in different subdivisions of the rat amygdala. Synapse 38, 328–37.

107. Rainnie, D. G. (1999) Serotonergic modulation of neurotransmission in the rat basolateral amygdala. J Neurophysiol 82, 69–85.

108. Wang, S. J., Cheng, L. L., and Gean, P. W. (1999) Cross-modulation of synaptic plasticity by beta-adrenergic and 5-HT1A receptors in the rat basolateral amygdala. J Neurosci 19, 570–77.

109. Chen, A., Hough, C. J., and Li, H. (2003) Serotonin type II receptor activation facilitates synaptic plasticity via N-methyl-D-aspartate-mediated mechanism in the rat basolateral amygdala. Neuroscience 119, 53–63.

110. Huang, Y. Y., and Kandel, E. R. (2007) 5-Hydroxytryptamine induces a protein kinase A/mitogen-activated protein kinase-mediated and macromolecular synthesis-dependent late phase of long-term potentiation in the amygdala. J Neurosci 27, 3111–19.

111. Pollandt, S., Drephal, C., and Albrecht, D. (2003) 8-OH-DPAT suppresses the induction of LTP in brain slices of the rat lateral amygdala. NeuroReport 14, 895–97.
112. Huang, Y. Y., and Kandel, E. R. (2007) 5-Hydroxytryptamine induces a protein kinase A/mitogen-activated protein kinase-mediated and macromolecular synthesis-dependent late phase of long-term potentiation in the amygdala. J Neurosci 27, 3111–19.
113. Cheng, L. L., Wang, S. J., and Gean, P. W. (1998) Serotonin depresses excitatory synaptic transmission and depolarization-evoked Ca2+ influx in rat basolateral amygdala via 5-HT1$_A$ receptors. Eur J Neurosci 10, 2163–72.
114. Koyama, S., Matsumoto, N., Murakami, N., Kubo, C., Nabekura, J., and Akaike, N. (2002) Role of presynaptic 5-HT(1A) and 5-HT(3) receptors in modulation of synaptic GABA transmission in dissociated rat basolateral amygdala neurons. Life Sci 72, 375–87.
115. Kishimoto, K., Koyama, S., and Akaike, N. (2000) Presynaptic modulation of synaptic gamma-aminobutyric acid transmission by tandospirone in rat basolateral amygdala. Eur J Pharmacol 407, 257–65.
116. Koyama, S., Matsumoto, N., Murakami, N., Kubo, C., Nabekura, J., and Akaike, N. (2002) Role of presynaptic 5-HT(1A) and 5-HT(3) receptors in modulation of synaptic GABA transmission in dissociated rat basolateral amygdala neurons. Life Sci 72, 375–87.
117. Young, A. M., and Rees, K. R. (1998) Dopamine release in the amygdaloid complex of the rat, studied by brain microdialysis Neurosci Lett 249, 49–52.
118. Guarraci, F. A., Frohardt, R. J., Young, S. L., and Kapp, B. S. (1999) A functional role for dopamine transmission in the amygdala during conditioned fear. Ann N Y Acad Sci 877, 732–36.
119. Inglis, F. M., and Moghaddam, B. (1999) Dopaminergic innervation of the amygdala is highly responsive to stress. J Neurochem 72, 1088–94.
120. Pezze, M. A., and Feldon, J. (2004) Mesolimbic dopaminergic pathways in fear conditioning. Prog Neurobiol 74, 301–20.
121. Lamont, E. W., and Kokkinidis, L. (1998) Infusion of the dopamine D1 receptor antagonist SCH 23390 into the amygdala blocks fear expression in a potentiated startle paradigm. Brain Res 795, 128–36.
122. Guarraci, F. A., Frohardt, R. J., Young, S. L., and Kapp, B. S. (1999) A functional role for dopamine transmission in the amygdala during conditioned fear. Ann N Y Acad Sci 877, 732–36.
123. Macedo, C.E., Martinez, R.C., Brechet-Souza, L., Molina, V.A., and Brandao, M.L. (2007) 5-HT2- and D1-mechanisms of the basolateral nucleus of the amygdala enhance conditioned fear and impair unconditioned fear. Behav Brain Res 177, 100–8.
124. Rosenkranz, J. A., and Grace, A. A. (2001) Dopamine attenuates prefrontal cortical suppression of sensory inputs to the basolateral amygdala of rats. J Neurosci 21, 4090–4103.
125. Rosenkranz, J. A., and Grace, A. A. (2002) Cellular mechanisms of infralimbic and prelimbic prefrontal cortical inhibition and dopaminergic modulation of basolateral amygdala neurons in vivo. J Neurosci 22, 324–37.
126. Rosenkranz, J. A., and Grace, A. A. (2002) Dopamine-mediated modulation of odour-evoked amygdala potentials during pavlovian conditioning. Nature 417, 282–87.
127. Kroner, S., Rosenkranz, J. A., Grace, A. A., and Barrionuevo, G. (2005) Dopamine modulates excitability of basolateral amygdala neurons in vitro. J Neurophysiol 93, 1598–1610.
128. Levita, L., Mania, I., and Rainnie, D. G. Dopamine activates multiple conductances in the basolateral amygdala [abstract]. Society for Neuroscience Abstract Viewer and Itinerary Planner [CD-ROM], Program 336.19. 2003.
129. Kroner, S., Rosenkranz, J. A., Grace, A. A., and Barrionuevo, G. (2005) Dopamine modulates excitability of basolateral amygdala neurons in vitro. J Neurophysiol 93, 1598–1610.

130. Bissiere, S., Humeau, Y., and Luthi, A. (2003) Dopamine gates LTP induction in lateral amygdala by suppressing feedforward inhibition. Nat Neurosci 6, 587–92.
131. Marowsky, A., Yanagawa, Y., Obata, K., and Vogt, K. E. (2005) A specialized subclass of interneurons mediates dopaminergic facilitation of amygdala function. Neuron 48, 1025–37.
132. Dalmaz, C., Introini-Collison, I. B., and McGaugh, J. L. (1993) Noradrenergic and cholinergic interactions in the amygdala and the modulation of memory storage. Behav. Brain Res 58, 167–74.
133. Iimori, K., Tanaka, M., Kohno, Y., et al. (1982) Psychological stress enhances noradrenaline turnover in specific brain regions in rats. Pharmacol Biochem Behav 16, 637–40.
134. McGaugh, J. L., McIntyre, C. K., and Power, A. E. (2002) Amygdala modulation of memory consolidation: interaction with other brain systems. Neurobiol Learn Mem 78, 539–52.
135. Buffalari, D. M., and Grace, A. A. (2007) Noradrenergic modulation of basolateral amygdala neuronal activity: opposing influences of alpha-2 and beta receptor activation. J Neurosci 27, 12358–66.
136. Chen, F. J., and Sara, S. J. (2007) Locus coeruleus activation by foot shock or electrical stimulation inhibits amygdala neurons. Neuroscience 144, 472–81.
137. Braga, M. F., Aroniadou-Anderjaska, V., Manion, S. T., Hough, C. J., and Li, H. (2004) Stress impairs alpha(1A) adrenoceptor-mediated noradrenergic facilitation of GABAergic transmission in the basolateral amygdala. Neuropsychopharmacology 29, 45–58.
138. Ferry, B., Magistretti, P. J., and Pralong, E. (1997) Noradrenaline modulates glutamate-mediated neurotransmission in the rat basolateral amygdala in vitro. Eur J Neurosci 9, 1356–64.
139. DeBock, F., Kurz, J., Azad, S. C., et al. (2003) Alpha2-adrenoreceptor activation inhibits LTP and LTD in the basolateral amygdala: involvement of Gi/o-protein-mediated modulation of Ca2+-channels and inwardly rectifying K+-channels in LTD. Eur J Neurosci 17, 1411–24.
140. Berlau, D. J., and McGaugh, J. L. (2006) Enhancement of extinction memory consolidation: the role of the noradrenergic and GABAergic systems within the basolateral amygdala. Neurobiol Learn Mem 86, 123–32.
141. Myers, K. M., and Davis, M. (2002) Behavioral and neural analysis of extinction. Neuron 36, 567–84.
142. Huang, C. C., Lin, C. H., and Gean, P. W. (1998) Potentiation of N-methyl-D-aspartate currents by isoproterenol in the acutely dissociated rat amygdalar neurons. Neurosci Lett 253, 9–12.
143. Ferry, B., Magistretti, P. J., and Pralong, E. (1997) Noradrenaline modulates glutamate-mediated neurotransmission in the rat basolateral amygdala in vitro. Eur J Neurosci 9, 1356–64.
144. Tully, K., Li, Y., Tsvetkov, E., and Bolshakov, V. Y. (2007) Norepinephrine enables the induction of associative long-term potentiation at thalamo-amygdala synapses. Proc Natl Acad Sci U S A 104, 14146–50.
145. Faber, E. S., and Sah, P. (2002) Physiological role of calcium-activated potassium currents in the rat lateral amygdala. J Neurosci 22, 1618–28.
146. Bremner, J. D., Krystal, J. H., Southwick, S. M., and Charney, D. S. (1996) Noradrenergic mechanisms in stress and anxiety: II. Clinical studies. Synapse 23, 39–51.
147. Bremner, J. D., Krystal, J. H., Southwick, S. M., and Charney, D. S. (1996) Noradrenergic mechanisms in stress and anxiety: I. Preclinical studies. Synapse 23, 28–38.
148. Abelson, J. L., and Nesse, R. M. (1994) Pentagastrin infusions in patients with panic disorder. I. Symptoms and cardiovascular responses. Biol Psychiatry 36, 73–83.

149. Rotzinger, S., Bush, D. E., and Vaccarino, F. J. (2002) Cholecystokinin modulation of mesolimbic dopamine function: regulation of motivated behaviour. Pharmacol Toxicol 91, 404–13.

150. van, Kampen J., Frydryszak, H., and Stoessl, A.J. (1996) Behavioural evidence for chole-cystokinin-dopamine D1 receptor interactions in the rat. Eur J Pharmacol 298, 7–15.

151. Gray, T. S. (1993) Amygdaloid CRF pathways. Role in autonomic, neuroendocrine, and behavioral responses to stress. Ann N Y Acad Sci 697, 53–60.

152. Roozendaal, B., Brunson, K. L., Holloway, B. L., McGaugh, J. L., and Baram, T. Z. (2002) Involvement of stress-released corticotropin-releasing hormone in the basola-teral amygdala in regulating memory consolidation. Proc Natl Acad Sci U S A 99, 13908–13.

153. Hubbard, D. T., Nakashima, B. R., Lee, I., and Takahashi, L. K. (2007) Activation of basolateral amygdala corticotropin-releasing factor 1 receptors modulates the consoli-dation of contextual fear. Neuroscience 150, 818–28.

154. Sajdyk, T. J., Schober, D. A., Gehlert, D. R., and Shekhar, A. (1999) Role of corticotro-pin-releasing factor and urocortin within the basolateral amygdala of rats in anxiety and panic responses. Behav Brain Res 100, 207–15.

155. Shekhar, A., Sajdyk, T. J., Gehlert, D. R., and Rainnie, D. G. (2003) The amygdala, panic disorder, and cardiovascular responses. Ann N Y Acad Sci 985, 308–25.

156. Sajdyk, T. J., and Gehlert, D. R. (2000) Astressin, a corticotropin releasing factor antag-onist, reverses the anxiogenic effects of urocortin when administered into the basola-teral amygdala. Brain Res 877, 226–34.

157. Rainnie, D. G., Fernhout, B.-J. H., and Shinnick-Gallagher, P. (1992) Differential actions of corticotropin releasing factor on basolateral and central amygdaloid neu-rones, in vitro. J Pharmacol Exp Ther 263, 846–58.

158. Bergeron, R., and Rainnie, D. G. (2000) Acute urocortin modulates Ih and neuronal excitability in the rat basolateral amygdala. Soc Neurosci Abstr 26.

159. Spiga, F., Lightman, S. L., Shekhar, A., and Lowry, C. A. (2006) Injections of urocortin 1 into the basolateral amygdala induce anxiety-like behavior and c-Fos expression in brainstem serotonergic neurons. Neuroscience 138, 1265–76.

160. Yehuda, R., Flory, J. D., Southwick, S., and Charney, D. S. (2006) Developing an agenda for translational studies of resilience and vulnerability following trauma exposure. Ann N Y Acad Sci 1071, 379–96.

161. Morgan, C. A., III, Wang, S., Southwick, S. M., et al. (2000) Plasma neuropeptide-Y concentrations in humans exposed to military survival training. Biol Psychiatry 47, 902–9.

162. Rasmusson, A. M., Hauger, R. L., Morgan, C. A., Bremner, J. D., Charney, D. S., and Southwick, S. M. (2000) Low baseline and yohimbine-stimulated plasma neuropeptide Y (NPY) levels in combat-related PTSD. Biol Psychiatry 47, 526–39.

163. Heilig, M. (2004) The NPY system in stress, anxiety and depression. Neuropeptides 38, 213–24.

164. Sajdyk, T. J., Vandergriff, M. G., and Gehlert, D. R. (1999) Amygdalar neuropeptide Y Y_1 receptors mediate the anxiolytic-like actions of neuropeptide Y in the social inter-action test. Eur J Pharmacol 368, 143–47.

165. Sajdyk, T. J., Shekhar, A., and Gehlert, D. R. (2004) Interactions between NPY and CRF in the amygdala to regulate emotionality. Neuropeptides 38, 225–34.

166. Sajdyk, T.J., Johnson, P.L., Leitermann, R.J., et al. (2008) Neuropeptide Y in the amygdala induces long-term resilience to stress-induced reductions in social responses but not hypothalamic-adrenal-pituitary axis activity or hyperthermia. J Neurosci 28, 893–903.

167. Truitt, W. A., Sajdyk, T. J., Dietrich, A. D., Oberlin, B., McDougle, C. J., and Shekhar, A. (2007) From anxiety to autism: spectrum of abnormal social behaviors modeled by progressive disruption of inhibitory neuronal function in the basolateral amygdala in Wistar rats. Psychopharmacology (Berl) 191, 107–18.

168. Meis, S., Sosulina, L., Schulz, S., Hollt, V., and Pape, H. C. (2005) Mechanisms of somato-statin-evoked responses in neurons of the rat lateral amygdala Eur J Neurosci 21, 755–62.

169. Gehlert, D. R., Sajdyk, T. J., Rainnie, D. G., and Shekhar, A. (2003) Neuropeptide Y (NPY) and corticotropin releasing factor (CRF) interactions in models of anxiety and panic disorder. Neuropeptides.

170. Pitkanen, A., Tuunanen, J., Kalviainen, R., Partanen, K., and Salmenpera, T. (1998) Amygdala damage in experimental and human temporal lobe epilepsy. Epilepsy Res 32, 233–53.

171. Azad, S.C., Monory, K., Marsicano, G., et al. (2004) Circuitry for associative plasticity in the amygdala involves endocannabinoid signaling. J Neurosci 24, 9953–61.

172. Pistis, M., Perra, S., Pillolla, G., Melis, M., Gessa, G. L., and Muntoni, A. L. (2004) Cannabinoids modulate neuronal firing in the rat basolateral amygdala: evidence for CB1- and non-CB1-mediated actions Neuropharmacology 46, 115–25.

173. Chhatwal, J. P., Davis, M., Maguschak, K. A., and Ressler, K. J. (2005) Enhancing cannabinoid neurotransmission augments the extinction of conditioned fear. Neuropsy-chopharmacology 30, 516–24.

174. Johnson, L. R., Farb, C., Morrison, J. H., McEwen, B. S., and LeDoux, J. E. (2005) Localization of glucocorticoid receptors at postsynaptic membranes in the lateral amy-gdala. Neuroscience 136, 289–99.

175. Roozendaal, B., Hui, G. K., Hui, I. R., Berlau, D. J., McGaugh, J. L., and Weinberger, N. M. (2006) Basolateral amygdala noradrenergic activity mediates corticosterone-induced enhancement of auditory fear conditioning. Neurobiol Learn Mem 86, 249–55.

176. Roozendaal, B., Okuda, S., Van der Zee, E. A., and McGaugh, J. L. (2006) Glucocorti-coid enhancement of memory requires arousal-induced noradrenergic activation in the basolateral amygdala. Proc Natl Acad Sci U S A 103, 6741–46.

177. Duvarci, S., and Pare, D. (2007) Glucocorticoids enhance the excitability of principal basolateral amygdala neurons. J Neurosci 27, 4482–91.

178. Stout, S. C., Owens, M. J., and Nemeroff, C. B. (2002) Regulation of corticotropin-releasing factor neuronal systems and hypothalamic-pituitary-adrenal axis activity by stress and chronic antidepressant treatment. J Pharmacol Exp Ther 300, 1085–92.

179. Holsboer, F. (2003) Corticotropin-releasing hormone modulators and depression. Curr Opin Investig Drugs 4, 46–50.

180. Yehuda, R., Teicher, M. H., Trestman, R. L., Levengood, R. A., and Siever, L. J. (1996) Cortisol regulation in posttraumatic stress disorder and major depression: a chronobio-logical analysis. Biol Psychiatry 40, 79–88.

181. Heim, C., Newport, D. J., Bonsall, R., Miller, A. H., and Nemeroff, C. B. (2001) Altered pituitary-adrenal axis responses to provocative challenge tests in adult survivors of childhood abuse. Am J Psychiatry 158, 575–81.

182. Heim, C., Owens, M. J., Plotsky, P. M., and Nemeroff, C. B. (1997) The role of early adverse life events in the etiology of depression and posttraumatic stress disorder. Focus on corticotropin-releasing factor. Ann N Y Acad Sci 821, 194–207.

183. Yehuda, R. (2001) Biology of posttraumatic stress disorder. J Clin Psychiatry 62(suppl 17), 41–46.

184. van Rossum, E. F., and Lamberts, S. W. (2004) Polymorphisms in the glucocorticoid receptor gene and their associations with metabolic parameters and body composition. Recent Prog Horm Res 59, 333–57.

185. Huizenga, N. A., de Lange P., Koper, J. W., et al. (1998) Human adrenocorticotropin-secreting pituitary adenomas show frequent loss of heterozygosity at the glucocorticoid receptor gene locus. J Clin Endocrinol Metab 83, 917–21.

186. Di Blasio, A. M., van Rossum, E. F., Maestrini, S., et al. (2003) The relation between two polymorphisms in the glucocorticoid receptor gene and body mass index, blood pressure and cholesterol in obese patients. Clin Endocrinol (Oxf) 59, 68–74.

187. Binder, E. B., Bradley, R. G., Liu, W., et al. (2008) Association of FKBP5 polymorphisms and childhood abuse with risk of posttraumatic stress disorder symptoms in adults. JAMA 299, 1291–1305.

188. McGaugh, J. L., Introini-Collison, I. B., Nagahara, A. H., Cahill, L., Brioni, J. D., and Castellano, C. (1990) Involvement of the amygdaloid complex in neuromodulatory influences on memory storage. Neurosci Biobehav Rev 14, 425–31.

189. LeDoux, J. E. (1993) Emotional memory: in search of systems and synapses. Ann N Y Acad Sci 702, 149–57.

190. Davis, M. (1997) Neurobiology of fear responses: the role of the amygdala. J Neuropsychiatry Clin Neurosci 9, 382–402.

191. Fanselow, M. S., and LeDoux, J. E. (1999) Why we think plasticity underlying pavlovian fear conditioning occurs in the basolateral amygdala. Neuron 23, 229–32.

192. Ressler, K. J., Paschall, G., Zhou, X. L., and Davis, M. (2002) Regulation of synaptic plasticity genes during consolidation of fear conditioning. J Neurosci 22, 7892–7902.

193. McDonald, A. J. (1998) Cortical pathways to the mammalian amygdala. Prog Neurobiol 55, 257–332.

194. Davis, M., Walker, D. L., and Lee, Y. (1997) Amygdala and bed nucleus of the stria terminalis: differential roles in fear and anxiety measured with the acoustic startle reflex. Philos Trans R Soc Lond B Biol Sci 352, 1675–87.

195. McKernan, M. G., and Shinnick-Gallagher, P. (1997) Fear conditioning induces a lasting potentiation of synaptic currents in vitro. Nature 390, 607–11.

196. Rogan, M. T., Staubli, U. V., and LeDoux, J. E. (1997) Fear conditioning induces associative long-term potentiation in the amygdala. Nature 390, 604–5.

197. Tsvetkov, E., Carlezon, W. A., Benes, F. M., Kandel, E. R., and Bolshakov, V. Y. (2002) Fear conditioning occludes LTP-induced presynaptic enhancement of synaptic transmission in the cortical pathway to the lateral amygdala. Neuron 34, 289–300.

198. Sah, P., and Isaacson, J. S. (1995) Channels underlying the slow afterhyperpolarization in hippocampal pyramidal neurons: neurotransmitters modulate the open probability. Neuron 15, 435–41.

199. Liao, D., Hessler, N. A., and Malinow, R. (1995) Activation of postsynaptically silent synapses during pairing- induced LTP in CA1 region of hippocampal slice. Nature 375, 400–4.

200. Zinebi, F., Xie, J., Liu, J., et al. (2003) NMDA currents and receptor protein are downregulated in the amygdala during maintenance of fear memory. J Neurosci 23, 10283–91.

201. Tsvetkov, E., Shin, R. M., and Bolshakov, V. Y. (2004) Glutamate uptake determines pathway specificity of long-term potentiation in the neural circuitry of fear conditioning. Neuron 41, 139–51.

202. Schroeder, B. W., and Shinnick-Gallagher, P. (2004) Fear memories induce a switch in stimulus response and signaling mechanisms for long-term potentiation in the lateral amygdala. Eur J Neurosci 20, 549–56.

203. Schroeder, B. W., and Shinnick-Gallagher, P. (2005) Fear learning induces persistent facilitation of amygdala synaptic transmission. Eur J Neurosci 22, 1775–83.

204. Rumpel, S., LeDoux, J., Zador, A., and Malinow, R. (2005) Postsynaptic receptor trafficking underlying a form of associative learning. Science 308, 83–88.

205. Szinyei, C., Narayanan, R. T., and Pape, H. C. (2007) Plasticity of inhibitory synaptic network interactions in the lateral amygdala upon fear conditioning in mice. Eur J Neurosci 25, 1205–11.
206. Myers, K. M., and Davis, M. (2002) Behavioral and neural analysis of extinction. Neuron 36, 567–84.
207. Rothbaum, B. O., and Davis, M. (2003) Applying learning principles to the treatment of post-trauma reactions. Ann N Y Acad Sci 1008, 112–21.
208. Davis, M., Walker, D. L., and Myers, K. M. (2003) Role of the amygdala in fear extinction measured with potentiated startle. Ann N Y Acad Sci 985, 218–32.
209. Falls, W. A., Miserendino, M. J. D., and Davis, M. (1992) Extinction of fear-potentiated startle: blockade by infusion of an NMDA antagonist into the amygdala. J Neurosci 12, 854–63.
210. Royer, S., and Pare, D. (2002) Bidirectional synaptic plasticity in intercalated amygdala neurons and the extinction of conditioned fear responses. Neuroscience 115, 455–62.
211. Walker, D. L., and Davis, M. (2002) The role of amygdala glutamate receptors in fear learning, fear-potentiated startle, and extinction. Pharmacol Biochem Behav 71, 379–92.
212. Ressler, K. J., Paschall, G., Zhou, X. L., and Davis, M. (2002) Regulation of synaptic plasticity genes during consolidation of fear conditioning. J Neurosci 22, 7892–7902.
213. Quirk, G. J., and Gehlert, D. R. (2003) Inhibition of the amygdala: key to pathological states? Ann N Y Acad Sci 985, 263–72.
214. Herry, C., and Mons, N. (2004) Resistance to extinction is associated with impaired immediate early gene induction in medial prefrontal cortex and amygdala. Eur J Neurosci 20, 781–90.
215. Berretta, S., Pantazopoulos, H., Caldera, M., Pantazopoulos, P., and Pare, D. (2005) Infralimbic cortex activation increases c-Fos expression in intercalated neurons of the amygdala. Neuroscience 132, 943–53.
216. Myers, K. M., Goulet, M., Rusche, J., Boismenu, R., and Davis, M. (2005) Partial reversal of phencyclidine-induced impairment of prepulse inhibition by secretin. Biol Psychiatry 58, 67–73.
217. Yang, Y. L., and Lu, K. T. (2005) Facilitation of conditioned fear extinction by d-cycloserine is mediated by mitogen-activated protein kinase and phosphatidylinositol 3-kinase cascades and requires de novo protein synthesis in basolateral nucleus of amygdala. Neuroscience 134, 247–60.
218. Chhatwal, J. P., Stanek-Rattiner, L., Davis, M., and Ressler, K. J. (2006) Amygdala BDNF signaling is required for consolidation but not encoding of extinction. Nat Neurosci 9, 870–72.
219. Yang, Y. L., Chao, P. K., and Lu, K. T. (2006) Systemic and intra-amygdala administration of glucocorticoid agonist and antagonist modulate extinction of conditioned fear. Neuropsychopharmacology 31, 912–24.
220. Segall, L. A., Perrin, J. S., Walker, C. D., Stewart, J., and Amir, S. (2006) Glucocorticoid rhythms control the rhythm of expression of the clock protein, Period2, in oval nucleus of the bed nucleus of the stria terminalis and central nucleus of the amygdala in rats. Neuroscience 140, 753–57.
221. Richardson, R., Ledgerwood, L., and Cranney, J. (2004) Facilitation of fear extinction by D-cycloserine: theoretical and clinical implications. Learn Mem 11, 510–16.
222. Botreau, F., and Gisquet-Verrier, P. (2006) Memory reactivation, dissociated from behavioural expression, decreases ERK phosphorylation in the rat prefrontal cortex and amygdala. Behav Brain Res 169, 176–80.
223. Lee, J. L., Milton, A. L., and Everitt, B. J. (2006) Reconsolidation and extinction of conditioned fear: inhibition and potentiation. J Neurosci 26, 10051–56.

224. Ressler, K.J., Rothbaum, B.O., Tannenbaum, L., et al. (2004) Cognitive enhancers as adjuncts to psychotherapy: use of D-cycloserine in phobic individuals to facilitate extinction of fear. Arch Gen Psychiatry 61, 1136–44.

225. Hofmann, S.G., Meuret, A.E., Rosenfield, D., et al. (2007) Preliminary evidence for cognitive mediation during cognitive-behavioral therapy of panic disorder. J Consult Clin Psychol 75, 374–79.

226. Kushner, M. G., Kim, S. W., Donahue, C., et al. (2007) D-cycloserine augmented exposure therapy for obsessive-compulsive disorder. Biol Psychiatry 62, 835–38.

227. Rothbaum, B. O., and Davis, M. (2003) Applying learning principles to the treatment of post-trauma reactions. Ann N Y Acad Sci 1008, 112–21.

228. Falls, W. A., Miserendino, M. J., and Davis, M. (1992) Extinction of fear-potentiated startle: blockade by infusion of an NMDA antagonist into the amygdala. J Neurosci 12, 854–63.

229. Goosens, K. A., and Maren, S. (2004) NMDA receptors are essential for the acquisition, but not expression, of conditional fear and associative spike firing in the lateral amygdala. Eur J Neurosci 20, 537–48.

230. Rogan, M.T., Leon, K.S., Perez, D.L., and Kandel, E.R. (2005) Distinct neural signatures for safety and danger in the amygdala and striatum of the mouse. Neuron 46, 309–20.

231. Kim, J., Lee, S., Park, K., et al. (2007) Amygdala depotentiation and fear extinction. Proc Natl Acad Sci U S A 104, 20955–60.

232. Lin, C. H., Lee, C. C., Huang, Y. C., Wang, S. J., and Gean, P. W. (2005) Activation of group II metabotropic glutamate receptors induces depotentiation in amygdala slices and reduces fear-potentiated startle in rats. Learn Mem 12, 130–37.

233. Milad, M. R., Rauch, S. L., Pitman, R. K., and Quirk, G. J. (2006) Fear extinction in rats: implications for human brain imaging and anxiety disorders. Biol Psychol 73, 61–71.

234. Pare, D., Quirk, G. J., and LeDoux, J. E. (2004) New vistas on amygdala networks in conditioned fear. J Neurophysiol 92, 1–9.

235. Milad, M. R., and Quirk, G. J. (2002) Neurons in medial prefrontal cortex signal memory for fear extinction. Nature 420, 70–74.

236. Likhtik, E., Pelletier, J. G., Paz, R., and Pare, D. (2005) Prefrontal control of the amygdala. J Neurosci 25, 7429–37.

237. Pelletier, J. G., Likhtik, E., Filali, M., and Pare, D. (2005) Lasting increases in basolateral amygdala activity after emotional arousal: implications for facilitated consolidation of emotional memories. Learn Mem 12, 96–102.

238. Pare, D., Collins, D. R., and Pelletier, J. G. (2002) Amygdala oscillations and the consolidation of emotional memories. Trends Cogn Sci 6, 306–14.

239. Pare, D., and Collins, D. R. (2000) Neuronal correlates of fear in the lateral amygdala: multiple extracellular recordings in conscious cats. J Neurosci 20, 2701–10.

240. Pare, D., and Collins, D. R. (2000) Neuronal correlates of fear in the lateral amygdala: multiple extracellular recordings in conscious cats. J Neurosci 20, 2701–10.

241. Mohapel, P., and McIntyre, D. C. (1998) Amygdala kindling-resistant (SLOW) or -prone (FAST) rat strains show differential fear responses. Behav Neurosci 112, 1402–13.

242. Mohapel, P., Dufresne, C., Kelly, M. E., and McIntyre, D. C. (1996) Differential sensitivity of various temporal lobe structures in the rat to kindling and status epilepticus induction. Epilepsy Res 23, 179–87.

243. Mohapel, P., and Corcoran, M. E. (1996) Kindling antagonism: Interactions of the amygdala with the piriform, perirhinal, and insular cortices. Brain Res 733, 211–18.

244. Anisman, H., Kelly, O., Hayley, S., Borowski, T., Merali, Z., and McIntyre, D. C. (2000) Acoustic startle and fear-potentiated startle in rats selectively bred for fast and slow kindling rates: relation to monoamine activity. Eur J Neurosci 12, 4405–16.

245. Kalynchuk, L. E., and Meaney, M. J. (2003) Amygdala kindling increases fear responses and decreases glucocorticoid receptor mRNA expression in hippocampal regions. Prog Neuropsychopharmacol Biol Psychiatry 27, 1225–34.

246. Kalynchuk, L. E., Pinel, J. P., and Meaney, M. J. (2006) Serotonin receptor binding and mRNA expression in the hippocampus of fearful amygdala-kindled rats. Neurosci Lett 396, 38–43.

247. Kellett, J., and Kokkinidis, L. (2004) Extinction deficit and fear reinstatement after electrical stimulation of the amygdala: implications for kindling-associated fear and anxiety. Neuroscience 127, 277–87.

248. Rainnie, D. G., Asprodini, E. K., and Shinnick-Gallagher, P. (1992) Kindling-induced long-lasting changes in synaptic transmission in the basolateral amygdala. J Neurophysiol 67, 443–54.

249. Neugebauer, V., Keele, N. B., and Shinnick-Gallagher, P. (1997) Epileptogenesis in vivo enhances the sensitivity of inhibitory presynaptic metabotropic glutamate receptors in basolateral amygdala neurons in vitro. J Neurosci 17, 983–95.

250. Holmes, K. H., Keele, N. B., and Shinnick-Gallagher, P. (1996) Loss of mGluR-mediated hyperpolarizations and increase in mGluR depolarizations in basolateral amygdala neurons in kindling-induced epilepsy. J Neurophysiol 76, 2808–12.

251. Asprodini, E. K., Rainnie, D. G., Anderson, A. C., and Shinnick-Gallagher, P. (1992) In vivo kindling does not alter afterhyperpolarisations (AHPs) following action potential firing in vitro in basolateral amygdala neurons. Brain Res 588, 329–34.

252. Terunuma, M., Xu, J., Vithlani, M., et al. (2008) Deficits in phosphorylation of GABA(A) receptors by intimately associated protein kinase C activity underlie compromised synaptic inhibition during status epilepticus. J Neurosci 28, 376–84.

253. Holmes, K. H., Keele, N. B., and Shinnick-Gallagher, P. (1996) Loss of mGluR-mediated hyperpolarizations and increase in mGluR depolarizations in basolateral amygdala neurons in kindling-induced epilepsy. J Neurophysiol 76, 2808–12.

254. Gelowitz, D. L., and Kokkinidis, L. (1999) Enhanced amygdala kindling after electrical stimulation of the ventral tegmental area: Implications for fear and anxiety. J Neurosci 19, NIL17–NIL21.

255. Kohda, K., Harada, K., Kato, K., et al. (2007) Glucocorticoid receptor activation is involved in producing abnormal phenotypes of single-prolonged stress rats: a putative post-traumatic stress disorder model. Neuroscience 148, 22–33.

256. Rainnie, D. G., Bergeron, R., Sajdyk, T. J., Patil, M., Gehlert, D. R., and Shekhar, A. (2004) Corticotrophin releasing factor-induced synaptic plasticity in the amygdala translates stress into emotional disorders. J Neurosci 24, 3471–79.

257. Rodriguez Manzanares, P. A., Isoardi, N. A., Carrer, H. F., and Molina, V. A. (2005) Previous stress facilitates fear memory, attenuates GABAergic inhibition, and increases synaptic plasticity in the rat basolateral amygdala. J Neurosci 25, 8725–34.

258. Reznikov, L. R., Grillo, C. A., Piroli, G. G., Pasumarthi, R. K., Reagan, L. P., and Fadel, J. (2007) Acute stress-mediated increases in extracellular glutamate levels in the rat amygdala: differential effects of antidepressant treatment. Eur J Neurosci 25, 3109–14.

259. Roniadou-Anderjaska, V., Fritsch, B., Qashu, F., and Braga, M. F. (2008) Pathology and pathophysiology of the amygdala in epileptogenesis and epilepsy. Epilepsy Res 78, 102–16.

260. Braga, M.F., Aroniadou-Anderjaska, V., Manion, S.T., Hough, C.J., and Li, H. (2004) Stress impairs alpha(1A) adrenoceptor-mediated noradrenergic facilitation of GABAergic transmission in the basolateral amygdala. Neuropsychopharmacology 29, 45–58.
261. Isoardi, N. A., Martijena, I. D., Carrer, H. F., and Molina, V. A. (2004) Increased fear learning coincides with neuronal dysinhibition and facilitated LTP in the basolateral amygdala following benzodiazepine withdrawal in rats. Neuropsychopharmacology 29, 1852–64.
262. Delahanty, D. L., and Nugent, N. R. (2006) Predicting PTSD prospectively based on prior trauma history and immediate biological responses. Ann N Y Acad Sci 1071, 27–40.
263. Sajdyk, T. J., Johnson, P. L., Leitermann, R. J., et al. (2008) Neuropeptide Y in the amygdala induces long-term resilience to stress-induced reductions in social responses but not hypothalamic-adrenal-pituitary axis activity or hyperthermia. J Neurosci 28, 893–903.
264. Morgan, C. A., III, Wang, S., Southwick, S. M., et al. (2000) Plasma neuropeptide-Y concentrations in humans exposed to military survival training. Biol Psychiatry 47, 902–9.
265. Yehuda, R., Flory, J. D., Southwick, S., and Charney, D. S. (2006) Developing an agenda for translational studies of resilience and vulnerability following trauma exposure. Ann N Y Acad Sci 1071, 379–96.
266. J. Tuunanen, K. Lukasiuk, T. Halonen, and A. Pitkanen (1999) Status epilepticus-induced neuronal damage in the rat amygdaloid complex: distribution, time-course and mechanisms. Neuroscience 94 (2):473–495.
267. J. Tuunanen, T. Halonen, and A. Pitkänen (1996) Status epilepticus causes selective regional damage and loss of GABAergic neurons in the rat amygdaloid complex. Eur J Neurosci. 8 (12):2711–2725.

4

Counteracting Molecular Pathways Regulating the Reduction of Fear: Implications for the Treatment of Anxiety Diseases

Andre Fischer and Li-Huei Tsai

CONTENTS

INTRODUCTION
LEARNED FEAR: A RODENT MODEL FOR ANXIETY
    DISORDERS
EXTINCTION OF LEARNED FEAR
GENE EXPRESSION
FROM THE MOLECULAR TO THE NETWORK LEVEL
PERSPECTIVE
REFERENCES

Abstract

The pathogenesis of emotional disorders often involves associative learning that links anxiogenic stimuli to certain life experiences. Among these are phobias and post-traumatic stress disorders that severely affect the life of patients and are an increasing burden to our societies. Treatment of such disorders generally involves the promotion of extinction processes, which are defined as the reduction of an aversively motivated behavior. Therefore, understanding the molecular mechanisms underlying extinction may help to develop therapeutic strategies for emotional disorders. Here, we discuss recent advances in the understanding of the molecular machinery that regulates the extinction of learned fear in mice. On this basis, we suggest that extinction is regulated by counteracting signaling pathways that either promote or prevent extinction of

From: *Post-Traumatic Stress Disorder: Basic Science and Clinical Practice*
Edited by: P. J. Shiromani et al., DOI: 10.1007/978-1-60327-329-9_4
© Humana Press, a part of Springer Science+Business Media, LLC 2009

fear. Targeting such pathways should be beneficial for the treatment of patients suffering from anxiety disorders.

Key Words: Anxiety diseases, Cdk5, cycline-dependent kinase 5, cytoskeleton, extinction, fear conditioning, hippocampus, MAP kinases, reduction of learned fear

INTRODUCTION

Emotional disorders are often characterized by excessive fear and anxiety. Such mental diseases are disabling and devastating for patients and caretakers and represent a huge economic burden to health care systems. Therapeutic approaches to treat such diseases often involve inhibition of fear through cognitive-behavioral therapy. For example, patients who suffer from phobia such as fear of heights would, guided by a therapist, be repeatedly exposing themselves to the frightening stimuli and thereby experiencing habituation (1,2).

Similar therapeutic strategies are employed to treat patients with post-traumatic stress disorder (PTSD). PTSD can develop in some individuals as a result of a terrifying and traumatic event, which could involve physical harm or be experienced as extremely threatening. Patients suffering from PTSD display extreme traumatic stress to the extent that normal psychological defense mechanisms fail. Symptoms may involve persistent reexperience of the traumatic event, impairment of social interaction, and aversive behaviors such as self-injury. In the framework of cognitive-behavioral therapy, patients are repeatedly confronted with the feared memories while the therapist aims to create a feeling of safety. Ideally, over time this procedure leads to reduced anxiety and aversive behavior associated with the fear memory (3, 4).

While throughout the last decade substantial progress has been made regarding the pharmacological and psychological treatment of anxiety disorder (5–7), the underlying molecular mechanisms of both the pathogenesis of such diseases as well as the reduction of fear through therapy are only poorly understood. In this chapter, we review recent progress that has been made toward understanding the molecular pathways underlying the reduction of learned fear in mice. We discuss the role of counteracting molecular machineries, with a strong emphasis on intracellular signaling, that either prevent or promote the reduction of learned fear. In conclusion, we suggest that a better understanding of the molecular mechanisms underlying the reduction of fear will help to develop suitable therapeutic approaches to treat anxiety diseases.

LEARNED FEAR: A RODENT MODEL
FOR ANXIETY DISORDERS

In the laboratory, the inhibition of fear is mostly studied in the fear-conditioning paradigm. The basic principle consists of exposing the animal, such as a mouse or a rat, to an initially harmless stimulus (the conditioned stimulus, CS), which is paired with a naturally aversive stimulus (the unconditioned stimulus, US).

Subsequently, the animal will display a conditioned fear response (CR) when reexposed to the initially harmless CS. In classical Pavlovian fear conditioning, the CS consists of a novel context, normally an observation chamber with defined lighting, odor, and background noise. After exploring this chamber for a certain time period (e.g., 3 min), the animal receives an electric foot shock (US). On the basis of associative learning, the animal displays aversive freezing behavior (CR) on reexposure to the conditioning context. Freezing is an inborn behavior rodents show in response to a frightening stimulus and is widely used as an index of learned fear *(8)* (Fig. 1A).

Many variations of the fear-conditioning paradigm exist. For example, the electric foot shock can be paired with a tone (Fig. 1B). Fear conditioning is also routinely investigated in the fear-potentiated startle paradigm, by which animals associate a light with electric foot shock *(9)*. Interestingly, distinct brain regions, the hippocampus and the amygdala, were shown to regulate the acquisition of contextual and cued (e.g., tone, light) fear, respectively. The significance of the fear-conditioning paradigm in light of anxiety diseases is explained by the fact that, after the initial acquisition of fear memories, the animals display an aversive behavior on reexposure to the threatening situation (reexposure to the CS). In Pavlovian fear conditioning, this could be a reexposure to the observation chamber. Notably, the animals do not receive the electric foot shock again during this reexposure, and when repeated for several times, the aversive freezing behavior gradually declines, a process termed *extinction* (Fig. 1C). Importantly, a single fear-conditioning training also induces other symptoms seen in PTSD patients, such as depressive-like behaviors and impaired social interaction *(10, 11)*. Therefore, certain aspects of anxiety diseases and cognitive-behavioral therapy are recapitulated in the rather simple fear-conditioning paradigm.

It is, however, important to note that in the literature the term *extinction* is often used in multiple senses. Myers and Davis therefore suggested to distinguish among (1) *extinction training,* which refers to the experimental procedure that is employed to reduce the fear response; (2) *within-session extinction,* which is used to describe the reduction of fear that occurs during the extinction training interval; and (3) the *extinction retention,* which is measured as the reduction of fear sometime after the extinction training (usually 24 h) (for further details, see Ref. *12).*

Obviously, care has to be taken when translating data obtained from animal experiments to humans. This is particularly important for novel therapeutic approaches and their translation into clinical trials. Nevertheless, the fear-conditioning paradigm has proven to be very fruitful with respect to anxiety disorders. For example, it was demonstrated that in rodents NMDA (*N*-methyl D-aspartate) receptor antagonists in the hippocampus and amygdala impair extinction of fear *(13–15)*. Consistently, the partial NMDA receptor agonist D-cycloserine (DCS) was shown to facilitate extinction in multiple experimental settings *(16,17)*. Based on these data, clinical pilot studies have been carried out testing the therapeutic potential of DCS to facilitate exposure therapy. Ressler and colleagues were able to show that, in conjunction with exposure therapy, oral administration

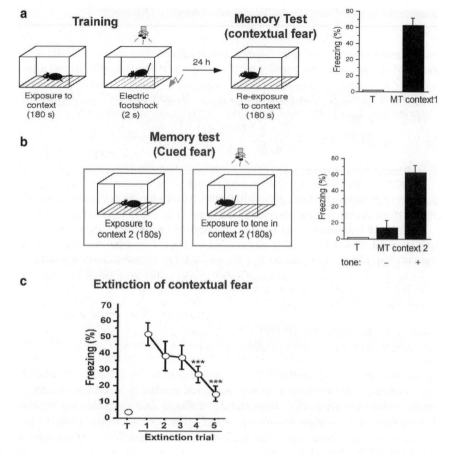

Fig. 1. Acquisition and extinction fear in the fear-conditioning paradigm. **a** In the Pavlovian fear-conditioning paradigm, the training procedure consists of mice that are exposed to a novel context (context 1), consisting of an observation chamber with defined lightning, odor, background noise, and geometry. After exploring this novel environment for 180 s, a mild electric foot shock is delivered for 2 s. In addition, the mice can be exposed to a tone for 30 s. On the basis of associative learning, mice display aversive freezing behavior during a memory test consisting of reexposure to the conditioning context 24 h after the training. Freezing is an inborn behavior that rodents express in threatening situations. It is defined as the complete absence of movement, except respiration and heartbeat. Whereas mice display no freezing behavior during training, a significant increase of freezing behavior is observed on reexposure to the conditioned context only. Therefore, freezing behavior is commonly used to quantify the amount of learning. **b** To test cued learning (e.g., freezing to a tone), 24 h after training mice are exposed to a novel context (context 2) that differs significantly from context 1. The animals show no freezing behavior in this novel context, demonstrating the specificity of the associated fear memory. On presentation of the tone, mice will show freezing, indicating cued fear. **c** Mice were trained in the contextual fear-conditioning paradigm. Subsequently, all mice were subjected to a daily extinction trial (E) on five consecutive days (E1–E5). Each extinction trial consists of a 3-min reexposure to the conditioned context without presenting the foot shock again. In this extinction paradigm, mice display a significant reduction of freezing behavior, indicating the reduction of learned fear on four or five extinction trials ***$P < .0001$ freezing on E1 versus E4/5. *T* training, *MT* memory test

of DCS to patients suffering from acrophobia (fear of heights) significantly improved the reduction of fear when compared to a placebo group (2). Similar findings were obtained in patients suffering from arachnophobia (18).

The data raise hope that a better understanding of the molecular pathways underlying the extinction of fear will lead to powerful therapeutic approaches that will eventually help people with anxiety disorders.

EXTINCTION OF LEARNED FEAR

Extinction of a CS-US association was first described by Pavlov (19) and is a complex process. Many behavioral and theoretical essays discuss this issue. For further reading, we suggest more specialized reviews (20–23). It is, however, important to note that extinction of fear does not equal the erasure or forgetting of the fear memory trace itself. This has been demonstrated in multiple experiments by the fact that even after substantial extinction training the aversive behavior (e.g., freezing in the fear-conditioning paradigm) is subjected to reinstatement, renewal, and spontaneous recovery (12). Interestingly, such phenomena were also observed in human patients who suffered from anxiety diseases and underwent therapy.

The most prominent theories of extinction propose an associative process in which the initial CS-US association is assumed to be excitatory, whereas extinction initiates new learning of an inhibitory CS-US association. The inhibitory association eventually dominates and inhibits the fear memory trace, leading to a reduction of aversive behavior (24,25). In addition, nonassociative processes have been suggested in which modulation of the excitatory fear memory trace would modify the degree to which the CS will trigger the CR (26–28) (Fig. 2).

The most recent data suggest that extinction likely involves associative and nonassociative mechanisms (for review, see Ref. 12). In the following, we discuss molecular pathways that may underlie the extinction of fear.

Molecular Players in the Extinction of Fear

Neurotransmitter Systems

Multiple brain structures, such as the lateral septum (29), striatum (30,31), and several cortical areas (32), have been implicated in the extinction of fear. The majority of the data, however, point toward an important role of the amygdala, prefrontal cortex, and hippocampus (33–35). The amygdala not only is required for the acquisition and storage of cued fear memories but also is essential to produce fear-associated behaviors such as the freezing response in rodents (36,37). The medial prefrontal cortex (mPFC) has been implicated in the retention and expression of fear extinction, and recent data indicate that the mPFC may regulate the amygdala (34,38,39).

In general, the hippocampus is believed to process spatial information, and a number of studies demonstrated a role for the hippocampus in the extinction of contextual fear (35,40). For example, lesions to the hippocampus after

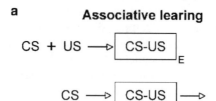

a   **Associative learing**

CS + US ⟶ CS-US ᴇ

CS ⟶ CS-US ᴇ ⟶

b   **Extinction:Associatve mechanisms**

CS no US ⟶ CS-US ɪ

CS ⟶ CS-US ᴇ ⟶ CR

c   **Extinction: Non-associative mechanisms**

CS ⟶ CS-US ⟶ CR

CS ⟶ CS-US ⟶ CR

CS ⟶ CS-US ⟶ CR

CS ⟶ CS-US ⟶ CR

Fig. 2. Associative and nonassociative mechanisms of fear extinction. **a** During the acquisition of fear, a neutral stimulus (the conditioned stimulus, CS) such as a context or a tone is paired with an unconditioned stimulus (US) such as an electric foot shock. As a result, an excitatory association between the CS and the US (CS-US$_E$) develops. The subsequent presentation of the CS alone results in a conditioned response (CR), such as aversive freezing behavior observed in the Pavlovian fear-conditioning paradigm. **b** If the CS is repeatedly presented without the US, the CR declines, a phenomenon termed *extinction*. It is postulated that associative mechanisms of extinction involve new learning of an inhibitory CS-US association (CS-US$_I$) that inhibits the original excitatory CS-US association, leading to a decreased CR. **c** Nonassociative mechanisms of extinction argue that extinction involves a modulation CS-US association that regulates the degree to which a CS can activate a CR. In such a scenario, the sensory input of the CS, such as a conditioned tone or context, is no longer able to activate the CS-US association. It can also be speculated that the CS-US association is not able to cause a CR. In any case, the CS is no longer able to elicit the CR, such as a fear response. It is likely that extinction involved a combination of associative and nonassociative mechanisms

extinction prevented reinstatement of the extinguished fear *(41,42)*, and pharmacological and genetic modification of hippocampal signaling pathways were shown to affect extinction *(23,43–46)*.

As for the neurotransmitter systems, γ-aminobutyric acid-ergic (GABA-ergic) neurotransmission seems to be essential for extinction. Since GABA serves as the major inhibitory neurotransmitter, it is a straightforward assumption that extinction involves GABA signaling. Indeed, the administration of FG7142, an inverse agonist of GABA receptors, impaired extinction in rats (47) . Moreover, it was shown that intrahippocampal injection of GABA receptor agonists like muscimol impairs extinction of fear (48). In line with this, GABA antagonists such as picrotoxin or muscimol facilitate extinction (49,50). A role for GABA signaling during extinction is supported by findings that extinction training upregulates the expression of gephryin in the amygdala, a protein that mediates clustering of GABA$_A$ receptors at synapses (51). Notably, during the acquisition of fear, gephrin is downregulated (52). Whether GABA signaling would affect associative or nonassociative mechanisms remains to be elucidated.

Interestingly, the major excitatory neurotransmitter in the brain, glutamate, has also been implicated in extinction of fear. It was shown that pharmacological inhibition of amygdala and hippocampal NMDA receptors inhibits extinction (13–15,53). Consistently, the partial NMDA receptor agonist DCS facilitates extinction of fear (17). The role of metabotropic glutamate receptors during extinction, however, is less studied, and conclusive data are not yet available. The signaling mechanisms by which GABA and NMDA receptors affect extinction training are not well understood.

Other neurotransmitter systems have also been implicated in extinction of fear (for review, see Ref. 12). Of particular interest is dopamine signaling because multiple studies showed that learning is facilitated by dopamine receptor agonists and impaired by antagonists (54–56). Unlike GABA and glutamate signaling, the involvement of dopamine in extinction seems opposite to that during memory acquisition. For example, systemic application of dopamine receptor 1 or 2 agonists as well as cocaine-impaired extinction (55,57,58). In line with this, it was shown that systemic administration of D2 receptor antagonists facilitates extinction (59). The picture is, however, complicated by findings that mice deficient for dopamine receptor 1 display impaired extinction (60). Since deletion of dopamine receptor 1 was not region restricted, those data are difficult to interpret. It will be interesting to elucidate which brain regions are involved in the dopamine effect on extinction.

In addition, great interest has been paid to the endogenous cannabinoid system. It was shown that region- and temporal-restricted deletion of the cannabinoid receptor 1 (CB1) in the forebrain of mice resulted in a robust impairment of extinction, while memory acquisition was unaffected (61). Consistent with this finding, administration of CB1 antagonists impaired extinction in wild-type mice. This effect was only observed when the antagonist was injected before, but not after, the extinction training, suggesting that CB1 signaling is not required for the consolidation of extinction memory (61–63). CB1 is highly enriched in GABA-ergic interneurons in the basolateral amygdala (61,64), which is in line with findings showing that cannabinoids regulate GABA-ergic neurotransmission (65–67). Indeed, CB1-deficient mice display impaired long-term depression of GABA$_A$ receptor-mediated inhibitory postsynaptic currents *(61)*. In addition, extinction training induces the levels of two endogenous cannabinoids, anandemide and 2-arachidonolyglycerol, in the basolateral amygdala *(61)* .

These data suggest that activation of the cannabinoid system should facilitate extinction. While administration of CB1 agonist WIN 55,212-2 had no effect on extinction, the cannabinoid reuptake inhibitor AM404 indeed facilitated extinction *(63)*. The molecular mechanisms by which cannabinoid signaling regulates extinction remain to be elucidated. In a first attempt, it has been shown that CB1-deficient mice display altered regulation of several protein kinases/phosphatases implicated in extinction *(68)*. Whether cannabinoid signaling affects associative or nonassociative mechanisms of extinction is still debated in the literature. A study, however, suggested that the impaired extinction in CB1-deficient mice is mainly due to a deficit in habituation processes, which would argue for the latter *(69)*.

In conclusion, it is interesting to note that several of the neurotransmitter systems discussed are required for both the acquisition of fear memories and the regulation of extinction. Notably, the effect of some transmitter systems during learning is opposite to that on extinction. As such, in contrast to glutamate and GABA-ergic transmission, dopaminergic signaling facilitates learning but impairs extinction, whereas endogenous cannabinoids exclusively affect extinction.

Similar findings were obtained for intracellular signaling pathways. For example, it was demonstrated that cyclic adenosine monophosphate (cAMP) is required for the acquisition of fear memory *(70)*, but mice overexpressing the type I adenylyl cyclase Adcy1 in the forebrain and displaying elevated hippocampal cAMP levels show slower extinction of fear *(70)*. In addition to those data, it is interesting to mention that brain-derived neurotrophic factor (BDNF) has been implicated in hippocampal long-term potentiation (LTP) and acquisition of fear memories by multiple studies *(71,72)*. More recently, it was shown that BDNF also regulates extinction. To this end, extinction training in the fear-potentiated startle paradigm specifically upregulated BDNF exon V-containing messenger ribonucleic acid (mRNA) in the baslolateral amygdala. Inhibition of BDNF signaling by lentiviral-mediated expression of a TrkB.t1 dominant negative form of the BDNF receptor caused impaired extinction *(73)*. Similar findings were obtained for the hippocampus-dependent extinction of contextual fear *(74)* .

Kinase Signaling During Extinction of Fear

A number of pharmacological and genetic studies demonstrated the importance of the mitogen-activated protein (MAP) kinase signaling pathway for the acquisition of fear memories *(75)*. It was, for example, shown that hippocampal Erk1/2 activity is transiently increased after fear conditioning *(76)*. Moreover, intrahippocampal injection of MEK inhibitors impairs memory formation *(77)*. In line with these data, mice that express a dominant negative form of MEK in the forebrain display impaired learning *(78)*. The exact molecular mechanisms by which the MAP kinase signaling pathway regulates learning are not entirely understood, but it was demonstrated that after fear conditioning, Erk1/2 activates multiple pathways, such as p90RSK-1 and the Elk-1 transcription factor, suggesting that Erk1/2 eventually regulates gene transcription. Moreover, recent studies showed that activation of the Erk1/2 pathways during fear conditioning induces chromatin changes, such as increased acetylation of histone 3 *(79)*. Importantly, it has been reported that epigenetic regulation of chromatin is an essential mechanism during memory formation *(80)*, and that pharmacological approaches that increase histone acetylation, such as application of histone-deacetylase inhibitors, facilitate learning *(81, 82)*. Activation of Erk1/2 during learning has also been implicated in the regulation of the cytoskeleton *(83)*. Consistently, actin dynamics were shown to be required for hippocampal LTP and fear learning *(44,84)*. Interestingly, Erk1/2 signaling was also found to regulate extinction of fear. To this end, intrahippocampal injection of MEK inhibitor was shown to impair extinction retention in the passive avoidance and Pavlovian fear-conditioning paradigm *(45,46)*.

The fact that the MAP kinase pathway is essential for the acquisition of fear memories and for the subsequent extinction suggests that, at least in this case, the molecular machinery that regulates learning also regulates extinction. As a consequence, it could be speculated that Erk1/2 signaling during the initial learning process is the same as during the extinction learning. Such a view would be in line with an associative mechanism of extinction by which a newly formed memory trace inhibits the original CS-US association. It must be reiterated that such a view cannot be generalized since, as discussed, a number of studies indicating that, although extinction may involve new learning, the molecular mechanisms that regulate learning cannot be exactly the same as extinction learning. Therefore, it would be important to know whether molecules such as Erk1/2 that are required for learning and extinction affect the same downstream targets under both conditions.

It is important to note that Pavlovian fear conditioning is a suitable approach to investigate the molecular mechanisms underlying extinction. This is because extinction normally occurs only after repeated presentation of the CS alone. As such, mice still display robust fear responses during the initial extinction trials, and the aversive freezing behavior declines only after multiple nonsignaled CS presentations. It is therefore possible to compare the molecular mechanism activated in distinct brain regions after an extinction trial that will or will not result in significant reduction of learned fear during the next test (Fig. 3). Using such an approach, it was shown that the levels of active phospho-Erk1/2 increase after extinction training. Here, mice were trained in Pavlovian fear conditioning and subsequently subjected to daily extinction trials that consisted of reexposing the mice to the conditioned context. Notably, cytoplasmic levels of phospho-Erk-1/2 transiently increased 1 h after fear conditioning and 1 h after extinction training on days 1 and 2 but not after extinction training on day 4. In contrast, the levels of nuclear pErk1 but not pErk2 increased only after extinction training on days 3 and 4. It has to be reiterated that, in this paradigm, mice

Fig. 3. Using the Pavlovian fear-conditioning paradigm to analyze the molecular mechanisms of fear extinction. The Pavlovian fear-conditioning paradigm allows investigation of the molecular mechanisms of fear extinction in a top-down approach. To gain further insight into the mechanisms of extinction, it is possible to compare molecular processes after E1 versus E5. This is due to the fact that the molecular mechanisms activated after E1 (mice show no extinction) versus E4/E5 (mice show significant extinction) might be different. This approach was successfully used in multiple reports (Sananbenesi, 2007) (Fischer, 2006)

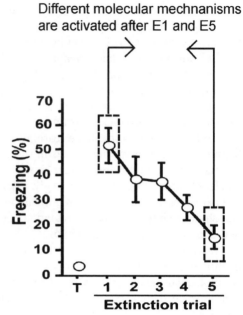

Different molecular mechnanisms are activated after E1 and E5

showed robust fear during extinction training on days 1 and 2 but significantly less during the extinction training performed on day 4 *(45)*. These data indicate a distinct regulation of the MAP kinase pathway during fear memory formation and extinction.

On the basis of these data, it can be speculated that the cytoplasmic action of pErk1/2 is required during learning and extinction, whereas pErk1 distinctly affects nuclear signaling pathways required for extinction. In line with this observation, it was shown that during learning a distinct fraction of cytoskeleton-associated Erk1/2 is activated via N-cadherin signaling *(83)*. Inhibition of N-cadherin dimerization consistently impaired learning. Notably, extinction was not affected by such treatment. In summary, the data suggest that activation of cytoskeletally associated Erk1/2 could be specific to the initial CS-US learning, whereas nuclear action of pErk2 is required for extinction.

Another study linked Erk1/2 activity during learning to the Arc/ARG3.1 pathway. It was reported that LTP-inducing high-frequency stimulation causes actin polymerization via the Rho/Rock pathway. In conjunction with activation of Erk1/2 signaling, this pathway was found to be required for targeting Arc/ARG3.1 mRNA to active synapses *(85)*. Mice deficient for Arc/ARG3.1 displayed impaired learning and memory and altered hippocampal LTP and LTD *(86)*. Whether Arc/ARG3.1 also affects extinction remains to be elucidated. Future research will help to identify and delineate the downstream targets of Erk1/2 signaling during learning and extinction.

In summary, a scenario can be envisioned in which inhibition of Erk1/2 activity could impair learning and extinction, although different downstream mechanisms would be involved. To this end, it would also be important to elucidate the upstream mechanisms that lead to Erk1/2 activation during learning and extinction.

Analogous to the role of Erk1/2 during learning and extinction, calcium/calmodulin-dependent protein kinase II (CaMKII) was shown to be an essential regulator of memory formation (87) and has also been implicated in extinction. As such, it was shown that injection of the CaMKII inhibitor KN-62 into the hippocampus or entorhinal cortex impaired extinction in the step-down avoidance paradigm (15,88). Similar to those findings, there are data indicating that the src families of nonreceptor tyrosine kinases are required for the acquisition of fear memories and its extinction (88) .

Another kinase implicated in learning and extinction is protein kinase A (PKA). Multiple studies demonstrated the involvement of PKA signaling with the formation of fear memories (8). To this end, pharmacological and genetic inactivation of PKA causes severe learning deficits. While PKA was also shown to activate Erk1/2 kinase under certain conditions (89), the major downstream target during memory formation seems to be activation of the transcription factor cyclic adenosine monophosphate response element-binding (CREB) (8).

Protein kinase A has also been implicated in extinction, although the present data are somewhat controversial. As such, Szapiro et al. reported that administration of PKA inhibitor into the CA1 region of the hippocampus impaired extinction in the step-down avoidance paradigm (15). Another study employing the Pavlovian fear-conditioning paradigm, however, found no effect of intrahippocampal injection of PKA inhibitors on extinction (10). The inconsistency among those data might be due to the different behavior paradigms in which extinction was tested. One striking difference among the Pavlovian fear-conditioning and step-down avoidance paradigms is that in the latter extinction occurs only after a single nonreinforced reexposure to the conditioned context. The picture is further complicated by a study reporting that genetic inhibition of PKA, by expressing the PKA inhibitory domain using the tet-OFF system, facilitated extinction of fear in the Pavlovian fear-conditioning paradigm (43). Obviously, more work is needed to understand the role of PKA during extinction, but the data at least suggest that under some circumstances PKA could be a molecule that is required for learning but subsequently prevents extinction of the fear memory.

Notably, similar findings were obtained for two other protein kinases, PKC and cycline-dependent kinase 5 (Cdk5). It was shown that inhibition of PKC impairs learning (90) but facilitates extinction (10). Similar to the data available for PKA, much is known about the molecular mechanisms activated by PKC during learning (90), whereas its effect on extinction is less well understood. Although initially discovered as an important regulator of neurodevelopmental processes, Cdk5 has emerged as a key player in synaptic plasticity, learning, and memory (91–93). Cdk5 is only active on binding to its activator proteins p35 or p39. The activity of Cdk5 is mainly restricted to postmitotic neurons because p35 and p39 expression is highly enriched in central nervous system tissue (94). It was shown that the levels of Cdk5 and p35 are dynamically regulated during associative learning in mice, and pharmacological inhibition of septal or hippocampal Cdk5 activity significantly impaired learning and memory (95,96). Consistently, mice deficient for p35 (97) or mice that express a dominant negative Cdk5 mutant (dnCdk5) in the forebrain display altered plasticity and impaired learning and memory (97–99). On the molecular level, Cdk5 function has been implicated in synaptic plasticity, synaptic remodeling, and synaptogenesis. For example, it was shown that Cdk5 phosphorylates the NR2A subunit of NMDA receptors on serine 1232 (100, 101), which results in increased channel conductivity of the NMDA receptor (102) . In line with this observation, pharmacological inhibition of Cdk5 impaired LTP in hippocampal slices (100). Moreover, increased phosphorylation of $NR2A_{S1232}$ in transgenic mice that display elevated hippocampal Cdk5 activity correlates with facilitated NMDA receptor currents and LTP (97). Furthermore, increased Cdk5 activity in the hippocampus significantly elevated the density of dendritic spines and synapses on CA1 pyramidal neurons (97), whereas mice deficient in the p35 protein had reduced baseline density of dendritic spines on hippocampal CA1 neurons. Thus, Cdk5 plays a crucial role in maintaining the density of dendritic spines and synapses in the hippocampus. It is interesting to note that a report found that Cdk5-mediated phosphorylation of WAVE1, a protein that regulates actin dynamics via the Arp2/3 complex, contributed to the retraction of dendritic spines in a Cdk5-dependent manner (103).

In summary, the data suggest that Cdk5 critically regulates the refining of the synaptic network of the adult brain. Whether Cdk5 activity promotes the formation or strengthening of new synapses or the retraction of existing dendritic spines seems to depend on the cellular context and is likely tightly regulated in vivo. This is particularly interesting because it was demonstrated that inhibition of hippocampal Cdk5 activity facilitated extinction. In line with these data, targeted deletion of Cdk5 in the forebrain of mice also facilitated extinction (104). Notably, when mice were trained in the Pavlovian fear-conditioning paradigm and subsequently exposed to daily extinction trials, Cdk5 activity was critical for extinction only within a time window of 3 h after the extinction training (105). Consistently, upregulation of hippocampal Cdk5 activity after fear memories had formed completely abolished extinction (105). It should be emphasized that upregulation of hippocampal Cdk5 activity ultimately leads to an increased number of dendritic spines on CA1 neurons (97). Therefore, it could be speculated that extinction requires synaptic remodeling of existing synapses. In support of this notion, it was shown that inhibition of actin dynamics by intrahippocampal injection of cytocalasin D or lactruculin A, drugs that inhibit actin dynamics, completely prevented extinction of contextual fear (44). Notably, a dynamic actin cytoskeleton is a prerequisite for synaptic plasticity and intimately involved in the synapse formation and remodeling (106).

On the molecular level, extinction correlated with a depletion of p35 from the membrane and resulted in reduced membrane-associated Cdk5 activity. Membrane depletion of p35 during extinction was mediated via the small guanosine triphosphatase (GTPase) Rac-1. Rac-1 has been implicated in synaptic plasticity *(107)* and is known to bind p35. Interestingly, similar to Cdk5, membrane-associated Rac-1 activity declines during extinction, and pharmacological inhibition of hippocampal Rac-1 activity facilitates extinction of contextual fear *(82)* . Taken together, these data suggest that Rac-1 and p35/Cdk5 are part of a distinctive signaling pathway that prevents extinction under physiological conditions.

Interestingly, it was shown that Cdk5/p35 directly phosphorylates p21-activated kinase 1 (PAK-1) in a Rac-1-dependent manner on threonine 212, which affects PAK-1 localization and could impair PAK-1 activity. PAK-1 is implicated in the dynamics of actin cytoskeleton, learning, and synaptic remodeling in the adult brain *(108)*. Notably, it was shown that PAK-1$_{T212}$ levels decrease during extinction, suggesting that PAK-1 activity might be upregulated. In line with this assumption, it was demonstrated that phosphorylation of membrane-associated PAK-1 at the non-Cdk5 site threonine 423 was increased during extinction. The autophosphorylation of threonine 423 of PAK-1 liberates the PAK-1 inhibitory domain and is a marker for active PAK-1 *(108,109)*. These findings suggest that the reduction of aversive freezing behavior correlates with increased PAK-1 activity. Importantly, Sananbenesi and colleagues further showed that the increase of PAK-1 activity, as measured by phosphorylation on T212 and T423, was dependent on Rac-1 and Cdk5 activity, suggesting that Cdk5 activity regulates PAK-1 during extinction in a Rac-1-dependent manner. Consistently, inhibition of PAK-1 by viral-mediated hippocampal expression of a dominant negative PAK-1 mutant significantly impaired extinction.

In summary, these data indicate that, during extinction, membrane depletion of Cdk5 activity and dissociation of p35 from PAK-1 in the cytosol remove the inhibitory tone on PAK-1 activity. This eventually results in an increase of mainly cytosolic PAK-1 activity. It is likely that in addition to the removal of Cdk5-dependent inhibitory tone, PAK-1 is activated directly by other mechanisms. Interestingly, it has been shown that PAK-1 phosphorylation on T423 can also be catalyzed by phosphoinositide-dependent kinase 1 (PDK1). PDK1 is activated by phosphatidyl-inositol 3-kinase (PI3K) and in turn activates the protein kinase Akt. Importantly, the PI3K-PDK1-Akt pathway has also been implicated in learning and extinction. To this end, extinction training was shown to affect phospho-Akt levels in the basolateral amygdala, and administration of PI3K inhibitors impaired extinction *(68,110)*.

Notably, the effect of PAK-1 inhibition on extinction is opposite that of Rac-1 and Cdk5 inhibition. This finding supports the idea that Rac-1/Cdk5 and PAK-1 are counteracting components of a hippocampal-signaling pathway that regulates extinction of contextual fear. When taken together, the data delineate an interlinked molecular pathway by which extinction requires downregulation of Rac/Cdk5 and upregulation of PAK-1 activity (Fig. 4).

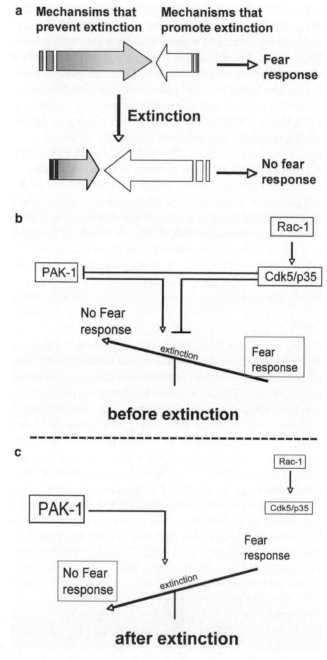

Fig. 4. Counteracting molecular pathways regulate the extinction of fear. **a** We suggest that extinction of learned fear involves two counteracting molecular processes. Initially, mechanisms that prevent extinction dominate over processes that promote extinction. It is likely that both associative and nonassociative mechanisms contribute to those

In addition to the role of protein kinases, several protein phosphatases were implicated in extinction of fear. As such, it was shown that extinction training causes upregulation of calcineurin, a phosphatase implicated in multiple synaptic pathways, including synaptic vesicle endocytosis and synaptic depotentiation. Consistently, pharmacological inhibition of calcineurin impaired extinction *(111)*. Interestingly, calcineurin is the counterplayer of many kinases that have been implicated in learning. The fact that calcineurin, for example, dephosphorylates Erk1/2 or CaMKII was taken as an argument that extinction involves unlearning, which is not in agreement with the phenomena of renewal, reinstatement, and spontaneous recovery. Moreover, the fact that inhibition of CaMKII or Erk1/2 as well as calcineurin impairs extinction does not support the notion that those pathways are interlinked. It is, however, possible that calcineurin affects distinct subcellular populations of Erk1/2 or that calcineurin-mediated extinction is linked to a different population of neurons than Erk1/2 signaling. Another phosphatase that might be involved in extinction is protein-phosphatase 1 (PP1). It was shown that genetic inhibition of PP1 facilitates learning in mice, suggesting that PP1 is a constraint of memory formation *(112)*. Although it has not been addressed experimentally so far, these data suggest that PP1 might also affect extinction.

GENE EXPRESSION

Among other targets, the action of intracellular signaling pathways often leads to altered gene expression. For example, Erk1/2 signaling is known to affect transcription factors *(76,78)*. More recently, it was shown that Erk1/2 activity affects chromatin remodeling, such as histone acetylation *(79)*. The DNA is wrapped around a complex of eight histones (dimers of H2A, H2B, H3, H4) to form the basic unit/level of chromatin structure. The basic amino terminal tails of histones carry diverse posttranslational modifications, like acetylation, methylation, and ubiquitination, which build up a discrete pattern of chemical marks recognized and bound by other proteins. This idea is often referred to as *histone code (113)*. Lysine acetylation of H3 and most H4 sites leads to the relaxation of chromatin, thereby making the DNA accessible for DNA binding proteins such

---

Fig. 4. (continued) counteracting activities. Throughout extinction training, the preventing pathways are downregulated so that the mechanisms promoting extinction will eventually dominate and might be actively induced. As a result, extinction of fear manifests in the reduction of aversive behavior. **b** Mechanisms that promote and prevent extinction do not have to be part of the same signaling pathway. The Rac/Cdk5/PAK-1 pathway, however, serves as an example in which counteracting components of the same signaling pathway either promote or prevent extinction. Rac-1/Cdk5 activity prevents extinction and inhibits PAK-1 activity, which in turn promotes extinction. During extinction, Rac-1 and Cdk5 activity is downregulated, thereby releasing the inhibitory tone on PAK-1, which now contributes to the extinction of fear

as transcription factors. Histone acetylation is therefore generally considered to promote gene expression.

The acetylation of histones is regulated by histone-acetyl transferases (HATs) and histone deacetylases (HDACs), which transfer or remove acetyl groups on specific lysine residues on histone tails, respectively. The HDACs in particular have gained considerable attention since the pattern of histone acetylation is altered in cancer cells, and HDACs have become a very promising drug target for various types of cancers. Interestingly, changes in the chromatin structure have been implicated in neurodegenerative and psychiatric diseases *(114)*. Moreover, systemic or intrahippocampal administration of HDAC inhibitors facilitates synaptic plasticity and learning in rodents and attenuates learning deficits in animal models for neurodegenerative diseases *(82, 115)*.

The mechanisms by which HDACs affect learning and memory are poorly understood, but it seems obvious to assume that distinct changes in the chromatin structure would affect the expression of certain genes. Interestingly, it was shown that intrahippocampal or systemic administration of the unselective HDAC inhibitor TSA facilitates extinction of contextual fear in mice *(116)*. Another study reported that the levels of histone 3 acetylation increased during within-extinction training sessions, and that this correlated with increased acetylation of the BDNF promoter *(117)*. Furthermore, valporate, another unselective HDAC inhibitor that is often used to treat epilepsy in humans, was shown to facilitate extinction of fear *(117,118)*. Although not conclusive, those data suggest that HDAC inhibitors may serve as a suitable therapeutic tool to treat anxiety diseases. It would be important to follow up on those initial findings since HDAC inhibitors are well studied, and numerous compounds are already approved or in clinical trials for other indications. As such, HDAC inhibitors could become available quickly for patients.

FROM THE MOLECULAR TO THE NETWORK LEVEL

The data discussed so far suggest that intracellular signaling molecules could be essential for both memory acquisition and extinction. In addition, the involvement of protein kinases, such as Cdk5, is essential for the consolidation of the fear memory trace but subsequently impairs its extinction. As elaborated, it is possible that the same molecules affect different downstream pathways during learning and extinction. It is important to consider that it is not clear whether the activation of molecular players such as Erk1/2 or Cdk5 during learning and extinction occurs in the same neuronal population. Due to novel technical advances in the field, it should soon be possible to address such questions.

To this end, Reijmers, Perkins, Matsuo, and Mayford described an animal model in which neurons activated during learning, as measured by expression of the immediately early gene cFOS, could be labeled by lacZ expression *(119)*. Interestingly, the majority of the neurons activated in the basolateral amygdala during fear conditioning were also reactivated during memory retrieval. Reactivation was measured by induction of another immediate early gene,zif/EGR.

When mice were exposed to extinction training on three subsequent days, the number of reactivated neurons in the lateral and basolateral amygdala correlated with the amount of aversive freezing behavior, which indicates fear. In sum, it was shown that fewer reactivated neurons correlated with less freezing, hence a reduction of fear *(119)*. On the basis of these data, it can be speculated that extinction is accompanied by a reduced number of neurons reactivated during extinction training. In line with this, it was shown that expression of cFOS gradually declines with the number of extinction trainings (unpublished observation). One interesting question would be to see whether the neuronal population initially activated by cFOS during learning and to a lesser extent during extinction would show increased nuclear pErk2 levels or PAK-1 activity.

In summary, the data suggest multiple cellular and molecular explanations for extinction to occur. (1) A neuronal population is tagged during learning (e.g., by cFOS expression) and reactivated during memory retrieval. Reactivation of the same neurons declines during extinction. Such a process would be in line with nonassociative mechanisms, for which, because of modulation of the network, the CS no longer triggers the CR. (2) In addition, the same neuronal population could activate associative mechanisms required for a new "inhibitory" memory trace. Here, nonassociative and associative mechanisms would be activated in the same cell. (3) It can also be envisioned that although associative and nonassociative mechanisms are initiated simultaneously, this occurs in different neuronal populations. With the development of new molecular tools, future work will be able to address those questions.

PERSPECTIVE

One major conclusion from the data discussed is that, in addition to mechanisms that promote extinction, strategies that impair extinction have evolved as molecular counterplayers. In particular, the Rac-1/Cdk5/PAK-1 signaling pathway provides an example by which pathways that impair and promote extinction are mechanistically linked (Fig. 4). From an evolutionary point of view, mechanisms that impair extinction seem reasonable since rapid extinction of fear after exposure to threatening situations, such as places where a predator attacked, could be disadvantageous for survival. In fact, at least in the Pavlovian fear-conditioning paradigm in mice, extinction of the aversive freezing behavior occurs only after multiple extinction trials. This is in line with the fact that patients suffering from emotional disorders such as phobias usually require multiple exposure sessions before the aversively motivated behavior is extinguished *(32)*.

From a therapeutic perspective, this conclusion is of utmost importance because two different therapeutic strategies can be envisioned. To facilitate extinction in the context of cognitive-behavioral therapy, it should be possible to target (1) mechanisms that promote extinction and (2) mechanisms that prevent extinction. Promising drugs regarding the first approach would be partial NMDA agonists such as DCS or inhibitors of MAP kinase signaling. In addition, drugs that facilitate learning such as HDAC inhibitors may prove suitable strategies, whereas Cdk5 inhibitors may represent a promising tool to inhibit mechanisms that prevent extinction.

Regarding the translation of basic research or preclinical data into therapeutic approaches, it is important to note that so far all strategies discussed are designed to facilitate extinction of fear. To this end, it is likely that drugs may only work in conjunction with therapeutic treatments such as cognitive-behavioral therapy. The general idea is that during therapy the aversive memory trace is reactivated. During this phase, pharmacological intervention may be able to facilitate extinction processes, thereby leading to the reduction of fear. The advantage of such an approach would be that drugs only need to be given during or shortly after a therapeutic session and would only need to remain in the patients for a short time; hence, Cdk5 activity was only essential for extinction within a time window of 3 h after the extinction training. Possible side effects of drug treatment should therefore be minimal. It is also possible that some treatments might be able to reduce learned fear in the absence of exposure therapy.

Another important issue for future research would be to address which mechanisms are affected during the pathogenesis of anxiety diseases and why some people are more prone to develop phobias or PTSD than others. Little is known about the molecular changes that occur in patients who develop trauma, phobia, or PTSD. Although in this chapter we discuss the molecular pathways involved with fear extinction and argue that targeting such pathways may help to treat anxiety disorder, it is not clear whether such therapeutic approaches would simply be disease modifying or counteract pathogenic mechanisms.

In conclusion, a better understanding of molecular changes during the pathogenesis of anxiety diseases and further elucidation of the mechanisms underlying the reduction of learned fear in rodents will certainly help to develop powerful therapeutic strategies to treat such illnesses.

ACKNOWLEDGMENTS

We thank J. Wittman for reading the manuscript and critical discussion. This work was supported by an EURYI award and partially by funds from the ENI Goettingen to A. F. The ENI is jointly funded by the Medical School University Goettingen and the Max Planck Society. L.-H. T. is an investigator for Howard Hughes Medical Institute.

REFERENCES

1. Deacon, B. J., and Abramowitz, J. S. (2004) Cognitive and behavioral treatments for anxiety disorders: a review of meta-analytic findings. J Clin Psychol 60, 429–41.
2. Ressler, K. J., Rothbaum, B. O., Tannenbaum, L., et al. (2004) Cognitive enhancers as adjuncts to psychotherapy: use of D-cycloserine in phobic individuals to facilitate extinction of fear Arch Gen Psychiatry 61, 1136–44.
3. Adshead, G. (2000) Psychological therapies for post-traumatic stress disorder. Br J Psychiatry 177, 144–48.

97

4. Bisson, J., and Andrew, M. (2007) Psychological treatment of post-traumatic stress disorder (PTSD). Cochrane Database Syst Rev 18, CD003388.
5. Ballenger, J. C. (1999) Current treatments of the anxiety disorders in adults. Biol Psychiatry 46, 1579–94.
6. Schoenfeld, F. B., Marmar, C. R., and Neylan, T. C. (2004) Current concepts in pharmacotherapy for posttraumatic stress disorder. Psychiatr Serv 55, 19–31.
7. Keane, T. M., Marshall, A. D., and Taft, C. T. (2006) Posttraumatic stress disorder: etiology, epidemiology, and treatment outcome. Annu Rev Clin Psychol 2, 161–97.
8. Kandel, E. R. (2001) The molecular biology of memory storage: a dialogue between genes and synapses. Science 294, 1030–38.
9. Davis, M., Falls W. A., Campeau, S., and Kim, M. (1993) Fear-potentiated startle: a neural and pharmacological analysis. Behav Brain Res 58, 175–98.
10. Tronson, N. C., Schrick, C., Fischer, A., et al. (2008) Regulatory mechanisms of fear extinction and depression-like behavior. Neuropsychopharmacology 33, 1570–83.
11. Siegmund, A., and Wotjak, C. T. (2007) A mouse model of posttraumatic stress disorder that distinguishes between conditioned and sensitised fear. J Psychiatr Res 41, 848–60.
12. Myers, K. M., and Davis, M. (2007) Mechanisms of fear extinction. Mol Psychiatry 12, 120–50.
13. Falls, W. A., Miserendino, M. J., and Davis, M. (1992) Extinction of fear-potentiated startle: blockade by infusion of an NMDA antagonist into the amygdala. J Neurosci 12, 854–63.
14. Baker, J. D., and Azorlosa, J. L. (1996) The NMDA antagonist MK-801 blocks the extinction of Pavlovian fear conditioning. Behav Neurosci 10, 618–20.
15. Szapiro, G., Vianna, M. R., McGaugh, J. L., Medina, J. H., and I., I (2003) The role of NMDA glutamate receptors, PKA, MAPK, and CAMKII in the hippocampus in extinction of conditioned fear. Hippocampus 13, 53–58.
16. Walker, D. L., Ressler, K. J., Lu, K. T., and Davis, M. (2002) Facilitation of conditioned fear extinction by systemic administration or intra-amygdala infusions of D-cycloserine as assessed with fear-potentiated startle in rats. J Neurosci 22, 2343.
17. Davis, M., Ressler, K., Rothbaum, B. O., and Richardson, R. (2006) Effects of D-cycloserine on extinction: translation from preclinical to clinical work. Biol Psychiatry 60, 369–75.
18. Guastella, A. J., Dadds, M. R., Lovibond, P. F., Mitchell, P., and Richardson, R. (2007) A randomized controlled trial of the effect of D-cycloserine on exposure therapy for spider fear. J Psychiatr Res 41, 466–71.
19. Pavlov, I. P. (1927) Conditioned Reflexes. New York: Oxford University Press.
20. Bouton, M. E. (2004) Context and behavioral processes in extinction. Learn Mem 11, 485–95.
21. Delamater, A. R. (2004) Experimental extinction in Pavlovian conditioning: behavioural and neuroscience perspectives. Q J Exp Psychol B 57, 97–132.
22. Rescorla, R. A. (2001) Experimental extinction in Pavlovian conditioning: behavioural neuroscience perspective. Q J Exp Psychol B 57, 97–132.
23. Lattal, K. M., Radulovic, J., and Lukowiak, K. (2006) Extinction: does it or doesn't it? The requirement of altered gene activity and new protein synthesis. Biol Psychiatry 60, 344–51.
24. Bouton, M. E. (1993) Context, time, and memory retrieval in the interference paradigms of Pavlovian learning. Psychol Bull 114, 80–99.
25. Konorski, J. (1946) Conditioned Reflexes and Neuronal Organisation. London: Cambridge University Press.

26. Wagner, A.R. (1981) SPO: a model of automatic memory processing in animal behavior. In: Spear, N. E., M. R. R., eds., Information Processing in Animals: Memory Mechanisms.
27. Kamprath, K., and Wotjak, C. T. (2004) Nonassociative learning processes determine expression and extinction of conditioned fear in mice. Learn Mem 11, 770–86.
28. McSweeney, F. K., and Swindell, S. (2002) Common processes may contribute to extinction and habituation. J Gen Psychol 129, 364–400.
29. Thomas, E., and Yadin, E. (1980) Multiple-unit activity in the septum during Pavlovian aversive conditioning: evidence for an inhibitory role of the septum. Exp Neurol 69, 50–60.
30. Waddell, J., Morris, R. W., and Bouton, M. E. (2006) Effects of bed nucleus of the stria terminalis lesions on conditioned anxiety: aversive conditioning with long-duration conditional stimuli and reinstatement of extinguished fear. Behav Neurosci 120, 324–36.
31. Rogan, M. T., Leon, K. S., Perez, D. L., and Kandel, E. R. (2005) Distinct neural signatures for safety and danger in the amygdala and striatum of the mouse. Neuron 46, 309–20.
32. Sotres-Bayon, F., Cain, C. K., and LeDoux, J. E. (2006) Brain mechanisms of fear extinction: historical perspectives on the contribution of prefrontal cortex. Biol Psychiatry 60, 329–36.
33. Barad, M., Gean, P. W., and Lutz, B. (2006) The role of the amygdala in the extinction of conditioned fear. Biol Psychiatry 15, 322–28.
34. Quirk, G. J., and Mueller, D. (2008) Neural mechanisms of extinction learning and retrieval. Neuropsychopharmacology 33, 56–72.
35. Ji, J., and Maren, S. (2007) Hippocampal involvement in contextual modulation of fear extinction. Hippocampus 17, 749–58.
36. Fanselow, M. S., and LeDoux, J. E. (1999) Why we think plasticity underlying Pavlovian fear conditioning occurs in the basolateral amygdala. Neuron 23, 229–32.
37. Sanders, M. J., Wiltgen, B. J., and Fanselow, M. S. (2003) The place of the hippocampus in fear conditioning. Eur J Pharmacol 463, 217–23.
38. Hugues, S., and Garcia, R. (2007) Reorganization of learning-associated prefrontal synaptic plasticity between the recall of recent and remote fear extinction memory. Learn Mem 14, 520–24.
39. Milad, M. R., and Quirk, G. J. (2002) Neurons in medial prefrontal cortex signal memory for fear extinction. Nature 420, 70–74.
40. Kim, J. J., and Fanselow, M. S. (1992) Modality-specific retrograde amnesia of fear. Science 256, 675–77.
41. Wilson, A., Brooks, D. C., and Bouton, M. E. (1995) The role of the rat hippocampal system in several effects of context in extinction. Behav Neurosci 109, 255–60.
42. Frohardt, R. J., Guarraci, F. A., and Bouton, M. E. The effects of neurotoxic hippocampal lesions on two effects of context after fear extinction. Behav Neurosci 114, 227–40.
43. Isiegas, C., Park, A., Kandel, E. R., Abel, T., and Lattal, K. M. (2006) Transgenic inhibition of neuronal protein kinase A activity facilitates fear extinction. J Neurosci 26, 12700–7.
44. Fischer, A., Sananbenesi, F., Schrick, C., Spiess, J., and Radulovic, J. (2004) Distinct roles of hippocampal de novo protein synthesis and actin rearrangement in extinction of contextual fear. J Neurosci 24, 1962–66.
45. Fischer, A., Radulovic, M., Schrick, C., Sananbenesi, F., Godovac-Zimmermann, J., and Radulovic, J. (2006) Hippocampal Mek/Erk signaling mediates extinction of contextual freezing behavior. Neurobiol Learn Mem 87, 149–58.

46. Cammarota, M., Bevilaqua, L. R., Kerr, D., Medina, J. H., and Izquierdo, I. (2003) Inhibition of mRNA and protein synthesis in the CA1 region of the dorsal hippocampus blocks reinstallment of an extinguished conditioned fear response. J Neurosci 23, 737–41.
47. Harris, J. A., and Westbrook, R. F. (2001) Evidence that GABA transmission mediates context-specific extinction of learned fear. Psychopharmacology 140, 105–15.
48. Corcoran, K. A., Desmond, T. J., K.A., F., and Maren, S. (2005) Hippocampal inactivation disrupts the acquisition and contextual encoding of fear extinction. J Neurosci 25, 9821–25.
49. McGaugh, J. L., Castellano, C., and Brioni, J. (1990) Picrotoxin enhances latent extinction of conditioned fear. Behav Neurosci 104, 264–67.
50. Berlau, D. J., and McGaugh, J. L. (2006) Enhancement of extinction memory consolidation: the role of the noradrenergic and GABAergic systems within the basolateral amygdala. Neurobiol Learn Mem 86, 123–32.
51. Chhatwal, J. P., Myers, K. M., Ressler, K. J., and Davis, M. (2005) Regulation of gephyrin and GABAA receptor binding within the amygdala after fear acquisition and extinction. J Neurosci 25, 502–6.
52. Ressler, K. J., Paschall, G., Zhou, X. L., and Davis, M. (2002) Regulation of synaptic plasticity genes during consolidation of fear conditioning J Neurosci 15, 7892–7902 .
53. Cammarota, M., Bevilaqua, L. R., Rossato, J. I., Ramirez, M., Medina, J. H., and Izquierdo, I. (2005) Relationship between short- and long-term memory and short- and long-term extinction. Neurobiol Learn Mem 84, 25–32.
54. Borowski, T. B., and Kokkinidis, L. (1996) Contribution of ventral tegmental area dopamine neurons to expression of conditional fear: effects of electrical stimulation, excitotoxin lesions, and quinpirole infusion on potentiated startle in rats. Behav Neurosci 110, 1349–64.
55. Borowski, T. B., and Kokkinidis, L. (1998) The effects of cocaine, amphetamine, and the dopamine D1 receptor agonist SKF 38393 on fear extinction as measured with potentiated startle: implications for psychomotor stimulant psychosis. Behav Neurosci 112, 952–65.
56. Pezze, M. A., and Feldon, J. (2004) Mesolimbic dopaminergic pathways in fear conditioning. Prog Neurobiol 74, 301–20.
57. Willick, M. L., and Kokkinidis, L. (1995) Cocaine enhances the expression of fear-potentiated startle: evaluation of state-dependent extinction and the shock-sensitization of acoustic startle. Behav Neurosci 109, 929–38.
58. Nader, K., and LeDoux, J. (1999) The dopaminergic modulation of fear: quinpirole impairs the recall of emotional memories in rats. Behav Neurosci 113, 152–65.
59. Ponnusamy, R., Nissim, H. A., and Barad, M. (2005) Systemic blockade of D2-like dopamine receptors facilitates extinction of conditioned fear in mice. Learn Mem 12, 399–406.
60. El-Ghundi, M., O'Dowd, B. F., and George, S. R. (2001) Prolonged fear responses in mice lacking dopamine D1 receptor. Brain Res 892, 86–93.
61. Marsicano, G., Wotjak, C. T., Azad, S. C., et al. (2002) The endogenous cannabinoid system controls extinction of aversive memories. Nature 418, 530–34.
62. Suzuki, A., Josselyn, S. A., Frankland, P. W., Masushige, S., Silva, A. J., and Kida, S. (2004) Memory reconsolidation and extinction have distinct temporal and biochemical signatures. J Neurosci 24, 4787–95.
63. Chhatwal, J. P., Davis, M., Maguschak, K. A., and Ressler, K. J. (2005) Enhancing cannabinoid neurotransmission augments the extinction of conditioned fear. Neuropsychopharmacology 30, 516–24.

64. McDonald, A. J., and Mascagni, F. (2001) Localization of the CB1 type cannabinoid receptor in the rat basolateral amygdala: high concentrations in a subpopulation of cholecystokinin-containing interneurons. Neuroscience 107, 641–52.

65. Azad, S. C., Eder, M., Marsicano, G., Lutz, B., Zieglgä;nsberger, W., and Rammes, G. (2003) Activation of the cannabinoid receptor type 1 decreases glutamatergic and GABAergic synaptic transmission in the lateral amygdala of the mouse. Learn Mem 10, 116–28.

66. Domenici, M. R., Azad, S. C., Marsicano, G., et al. (2006) Cannabinoid receptor type 1 located on presynaptic terminals of principal neurons in the forebrain controls glutamatergic synaptic transmission. J Neurosci 26, 5794–99.

67. Katona, I., Sperlágh, B., Maglóczky, Z., et al. (2000) GABAergic interneurons are the targets of cannabinoid actions in the human hippocampus. Neuroscience 100, 797–804.

68. Cannich, A., Wotjak, C. T., Kamprath, K., Hermann, H., Lutz, B., and Marsicano, G. (2004) CB1 cannabinoid receptors modulate kinase and phosphatase activity during extinction of conditioned fear in mice. Learn Mem 11, 625–32.

69. Kamprath, K., Marsicano, G., Tang, J., et al. (2006) Cannabinoid CB1 receptor mediates fear extinction via habituation-like processes. J Neurosci 26, 6677–86.

70. Wang, H., Ferguson, G. D., Pineda, V. V., Cundiff, P. E., and Storm, D. R. (2004) Overexpression of type-1 adenylyl cyclase in mouse forebrain enhances recognition memory and LTP. Nat Neurosci 7, 635–42.

71. Korte, M., Minichiello, L., Klein, R., and Bonhoeffer, T. (1995) Hippocampal long-term potentiation is impaired in mice lacking brain-derived neurotrophic factor. Proc Natl Acad Sci U S A 92, 8856–60.

72. Alonso, M., Vianna, M. R., Depino, A. M., et al. (2002) BDNF-triggered events in the rat hippocampus are required for both short- and long-term memory formation. Hippocampus 12, 551–60.

73. Chhatwal, J. P., Stanek-Rattiner, L., Davis, M., and Ressler, K. J. (2006) Amygdala BDNF signaling is required for consolidation but not encoding of extinction. Nat Neurosci 9, 870–72.

74. Heldt, S. A., Stanek, L., Chhatwal, J. P., and Ressler, K. J. (2007) Hippocampus-specific deletion of BDNF in adult mice impairs spatial memory and extinction of aversive memories. Mol Psychiatry 12, 656–70.

75. Sweatt, J. D. (2001) The neuronal MAP kinase cascade: a biochemical signal integration system subserving synaptic plasticity and memory. J Neurochem 76, 1–10.

76. Sananbenesi, F., Fischer, A., Schrick, C., Spiess, J., and Radulovic, J. (2002) Phosphorylation of hippocampal Erk-1/2, Elk-1, and p90-Rsk-1 during contextual fear conditioning: interactions between Erk-1/2 and Elk-1 Mol Cell Neurosci 21, 463–76.

77. Atkins, C. M., Selcher, J. C., Petraitis, J. J., Trzaskos, J. M., and Sweatt, J. D. (1998) The MAPK cascade is required for mammalian associative learning. Nat Neurosci 1, 602–9.

78. Kelleher, R. J., 3rd, Govindarajan, A., Jung, H. Y., Kang, H., and Tonegawa, S. (2004) Translational control by MAPK signaling in long-term synaptic plasticity and memory. Cell 116, 467–79.

79. Chwang, W. B., O'Riordan, K. J., Levenson, J. M., and Sweatt, J. D. (2006) ERK/MAPK regulates hippocampal histone phosphorylation following contextual fear conditioning. Learn Mem 13, 322–28.

80. Levenson, J. M., and Sweatt, J. D. (2005) Epigenetic mechanisms in memory formation. Nat Rev 6, 108–19.

81. Levenson, J. M., O'Riordan, K. J., Brown, K. D., Trinh, M. A., Molfese, D. L., and Sweatt, J.D. (2004) Regulation of histone acetylation during memory formation in the hippocampus. J Biol Chem 279, 40545–59.

82. Fischer, A., Sananbenesi, F., Wang, X., Dobbin, M., and Tsai, L. H. (2007) Recovery of learning and memory after neuronal loss is associated with chromatin remodeling. Nature 447, 178–82.

83. Schrick, C., Fischer, A., Srivastava, D., Tronson, N. C., Penzes, P., and Radulovic, J. (2007) N-cadherin regulates cytoskeletally associated IQGAP1/ERK signaling and memory formation. Neuron 55, 786–98.

84. Fukazawa, Y., Saitoh, Y., Ozawa, F., Ohta, Y., Mizuno, K., and Inokuchi, K. (2003) Hippocampal LTP is accompanied by enhanced F-actin content within the dendritic spine that is essential for late LTP maintenance in vivo. Neuron 38, 447–60.

85. Huang, F., Chotiner, J. K., and Steward, O. (2007) Actin polymerization and ERK phosphorylation are required for Arc/Arg3.1 mRNA targeting to activated synaptic sites on dendrites. J Neurosci 27, 9054–67.

86. Plath, N., Ohana, O., Dammermann, B., et al. (2006) Arc/Arg3.1 is essential for the consolidation of synaptic plasticity and memories. Neuron 52, 437–44.

87. Silva, A. (2003) Molecular and cellular cognitive studies of the role of synpatic plasticity in memory. J Neurobiol 54, 224–37.

88. Bevilaqua, L. R., Medina, J. H., Izquierdo, I., and Cammarota, M. (2005) Memory consolidation induces N-methyl-D-aspartic acid-receptor- and Ca2+/calmodulin-dependent protein kinase II-dependent modifications in alpha-amino-3-hydroxy-5-methylisoxazole-4-propionic acid receptor properties. Neuroscience 136, 397–403.

89. Sananbenesi, F., Fischer, A., Schrick, C., Spiess, J., and Radulovic, J. (2003) Mitogen-activated protein kinase signaling in the hippocampus and its modulation by corticotropin-releasing factor receptor 2: a possible link between stress and fear memory. J Neurosci 23, 11436–43.

90. Amadio, M., Battaini, F., and Pascale, A. (2006) The different facets of protein kinases C: old and new players in neuronal signal transduction pathways. Pharmacol Res 54, 317–25.

91. Fischer, A., Sananbenesi, F., Spiess, J., and Radulovic, J. (2003) Cdk5 in the adult non-demented brain. Curr Drug Targets CNS Neurol Disord 6, 375–81.

92. Angelo, M., Plattner, F., and Giese, K. P. (2006) Cyclin-dependent kinase 5 in synaptic plasticity, learning and memory. J Neurochem 99, 353–70.

93. Samuels, B. A., Hsueh, Y. P., Shu, T., et al. (2007) Cdk5 promotes synaptogenesis by regulating the subcellular distribution of the MAGUK family member CASK. Neuron 56, 823–37.

94. Dhavan, R., and Tsai, L. H. (2001) A decade of CDK5. Nat Rev Mol Cell Biol 2, 749–59.

95. Fischer, A., Sananbenesi, F., Schrick, C., Spiess, J., and Radulovic, J. (2002) Cyclin-dependent kinase 5 is required for associative learning. J Neurosci 22, 3700–7.

96. Fischer, A., Sananbenesi, F., Schrick, C., Spiess, J., and Radulovic, J. (2003) Regulation of contextual fear conditioning by baseline and inducible septo-hippocampal cyclin-dependent kinase 5. Neuropharmacology 44, 1089–99.

97. Fischer, A., Sananbenesi, F., Pang, P. T., Lu, B., and Tsai, L. H. (2005) Opposing roles of transient and prolonged expression of p25 in synaptic plasticity and hippocampus-dependent memory. Neuron 48, 825–38.

98. Fu, W. Y., Chen, Y., Sahin, M., et al. (2007) Cdk5 regulates EphA4-mediated dendritic spine retraction through an ephexin1-dependent mechanism. Nat Neurosci 10, 67–76.

99. Ohshima, T., Ogura, H., Tomizawa, K., et al. (2005) Impairment of hippocampal long-term depression and defective spatial learning and memory in p35-/- mice. J Neurochem 10, 4159–68.

100. Patel, L. S., Wenzel, H. J., and Schwartkroin, P. A. (2004) Physiological and morphological characterization of dentate granule cells in the p35 knock-out mouse hippocampus: evidence for an epileptic circuit. J Neurosci 24, 9005–14.

101. Li, B. S., Sun, M. K., Zhang, L., et al. (2001) Regulation of NMDA receptors by cyclin-dependent kinase-5. Proc Natl Acad Sci U S A 98, 12742–47.

102. Wang, J., Liu, S., Fu, Y., Wang, J. H., and Lu, Y. (2003) Cdk5 activation induces hippocampal CA1 cell death by directly phosphorylating NMDA receptors. Nat Neurosci 6, 1039–47.

103. Gong, X., Tang, X., Wiedmann, M., et al. (2003) Cdk5-mediated inhibition of the protective effects of transcription factor MEF2 in neurotoxicity-induced apoptosis. Neuron 38, 33–46.

104. Kim, Y., Sung, J. Y., Ceglia., I, et al. (2006) Phosphorylation of WAVE1 regulates actin polymerization and dendritic spine morphology. Nature 442, 814–17.

105. Hawasli, A. H., Benavides, D. R., Nguyen, C., et al. (2007) Cyclin-dependent kinase 5 governs learning and synaptic plasticity via control of NMDAR degradation. Nat Neurosci 10, 880–86.

106. Sananbenesi, F., Fischer, A., Wang, X., et al. (2007) A hippocampal Cdk5 pathway regulates extinction of contextual fear. Nat Neurosci 10, 1012–19.

107. Matus, A. (2000) Actin-based plasticity in dendritic spines. Science 290, 754–58.

108. Nakayama, A. Y., Harms, M. B., and Luo, L. (2000) Small GTPases Rac and Rho in the maintenance of dendritic spines and branches in hippocampal pyramidal neurons. J Neurosci 20, 5329–38.

109. Hayashi, M. L., Choi, S. Y., Rao, B. S., et al. (2004) Altered cortical synaptic morphology and impaired memory consolidation in forebrain- specific dominant-negative PAK transgenic mice. Neuron 42, 773–87.

110. Lei, M., Lu, W., Meng, W., et al. (2000) Structure of PAK1 in an autoinhibited conformation reveals a multistage activation switch. Cell 102, 387–97.

111. Yang, Y. L., and Lu, K. T. (2005) Facilitation of conditioned fear extinction by d-cycloserine is mediated by mitogen-activated protein kinase and phosphatidylinositol 3-kinase cascades and requires de novo protein synthesis in basolateral nucleus of amygdala. Neuroscience 134, 247–60.

112. Lin, W. L., Lewis, J., Yen, S. H., Hutton, M., and Dickson, D. W. (2003) Filamentous tau in oligodendrocytes and astrocytes of transgenic mice expressing the human tau isoform with the P301L mutation. Am J Pathol 162, 213–18.

113. Genoux, D., Haditsch, U., Knobloch, M., Michalon, A., Storm, D., and Mansuy, I. M. (2002) Protein phosphatase 1 is a molecular constraint on learning and memory. Nature 418, 970–75.

114. Strahl, B. D., and Allis, C. D. (2000) The language of covalent histone modifications. Nature 403, 41–45.

115. Tsankova, N., Renthal, W., Kumar, A., and Nestler, E. J. (2007) Epigenetic regulation in psychiatric disorders. Nat Rev Neurosci 8, 355–67.

116. Lattal, K. M., Barrett, R. M., and Wood, M. A. (2007) Systemic or intrahippocampal delivery of histone deacetylase inhibitors facilitates fear extinction. Behav Brain Res 121, 1125–31.

117. Bredy, T. W., Wu, H., Crego, C., Zellhoefer, J., Sun, Y. E., and Barad, M. (2007) Histone modifications around individual BDNF gene promoters in prefrontal cortex are associated with extinction of conditioned fear. Learn Mem 14, 268–76.

118. Bredy, T. W., and Barad, M. (2008) The histone deacetylase inhibitor valproic acid enhances acquisition, extinction, and reconsolidation of conditioned fear. Learn Mem 15, 39–45.

119. Reijmers, L. G., Perkins, B. L., Matsuo, N., and Mayford, M.(2007) Localization of a stable neural correlate of associative memory. Science317, 1230–3.

5 Memory in PTSD: A Neurocognitive Approach

Mieke Verfaellie and Jennifer J. Vasterling

CONTENTS

INTRODUCTION
AUTOBIOGRAPHICAL MEMORY
NEW LEARNING
CONCLUSION
REFERENCES

Abstract

Memory changes associated with post-traumatic stress disorder (PTSD) are pervasive. How the traumatic event is encoded and retrieved is central to the experience of the disorder; however, more general abnormalities in auto-biographical recollection and in new learning are also commonly observed. These memory abnormalities are likely due at least in part to the impact of the traumatic event and the neurobiological alterations associated with PTSD, but memory factors that exist prior to trauma also play a role in the development and maintenance of PTSD. Thus, we consider memory as both a symptom and a risk factor for PTSD. In the domain of autobiographical memory, we examine recollection of personally experienced general and trauma-related events. In the domain of new learning, we characterize everyday memory for emotionally neutral information and consider distinct changes in PTSD in the encoding and retrieval of information that has strong emotional valence and trauma relevance. We highlight specifically the contribution of neuropsychological and cognitive neuroscience studies, with the goal of elucidating the neurocognitive mechanisms underlying memory changes associated with PTSD.

Key Words: Amygdala, autobiographical memory, frontal lobes, hippocampus, new learning, trauma memory.

From: *Post-Traumatic Stress Disorder: Basic Science and Clinical Practice*
Edited by: P. J. Shiromani et al., DOI: 10.1007/978-1-60327-329-9_5
© Humana Press, a part of Springer Science+Business Media, LLC 2009

INTRODUCTION

Over the last few years, the centrality of memory to a comprehensive understanding of post-traumatic stress disorder (PTSD) has become abundantly clear. First, memory alterations are a core feature of PTSD. PTSD reexperiencing symptoms include unwanted, distressing, and seemingly poorly controlled recollections of a personally experienced traumatic event. Further, an inability to recall important aspects of the trauma event is considered a diagnostic symptom of PTSD (1), albeit one that appears to occur in only a smaller subset of trauma victims (2). More generally, impairments in declarative memory are commonly observed in trauma survivors with PTSD, and these encompass disturbances in the retrieval of autobiographical memories as well as inefficiencies in the encoding and retrieval of new information. Consequently, many theories of PTSD involve memory as a central component, providing explanations for different facets of the memory impairment in terms of psychosocial, cognitive, or neurobiological factors.

Second, and no less important, memory factors play a critical role in the development and maintenance of PTSD. Individual differences in memory and processing style prior to trauma exposure influence susceptibility to PTSD, and how victims process, encode, and subsequently relive traumatic events has a direct impact on the development and maintenance of PTSD symptoms. In the most radical expression of this view, Rubin, Berntsen, and Johansen (2) suggested that a pathogenic memory rather than a pathogenic event is the critical causal event in PTSD.

In this chapter, we consider memory both as a symptom and as a risk factor for PTSD, focusing separately on autobiographical memory (i.e., the retrieval of personally experienced past events) and on new learning (i.e., the encoding and retrieval of current information). In the domain of autobiographical memory, we review recent work on personal memories generally as well as on trauma memory specifically. In the domain of new learning, we consider everyday memory for emotionally neutral information and then examine whether there are distinct alterations in PTSD in the encoding and retrieval of information that has strong emotional valence. We focus specifically on the cognitive and neural mechanisms underlying memory changes associated with PTSD, and in so doing, highlight the contribution of neuropsychological and cognitive neuroscience approaches to the study of memory in PTSD.

AUTOBIOGRAPHICAL MEMORY

As is true for all memory, the recollection of personal past events reflects a construction of the past in light of current goals and attitudes rather than the retrieval of an actual record of past events. This is particularly important to keep in mind when examining autobiographical memory in PTSD because, as noted, the formation and recall of autobiographical memories, especially those involving the trauma event, are thought to be central to the experience of PTSD. Paradoxically, alterations in memory for the trauma event take the form both of intrusive recollections and of inability to recall aspects of the trauma. Adding further to the complexity, autobiographical abnormalities associated with PTSD are not limited to recall of trauma-specific memories but extend to events unrelated to the trauma, suggesting a larger, overarching autobiographical memory impairment.

In the following sections, we focus on general abnormalities in autobiographical memory in individuals with PTSD and on the cognitive processes underlying them. We next examine PTSD-associated abnormalities in memory for the trauma specifically. A comprehensive discussion of the formation and recall of trauma memories is beyond the scope of the chapter (for reviews, *see* Refs. *2–6)*. Instead, we summarize here the central themes that are directly relevant to understanding memory in PTSD from a neurocognitive perspective.

Overgeneral Nature of Autobiographical Memory

One of the most common methods of assessing autobiographical memory is by means of a cued recall task known as the Autobiographical Memory Test (AMT) *(7)*. The AMT requires the respondent to generate specific autobiographical episodes in response to cue words that vary in their emotional valence (e.g., positive, negative, neutral). These narratives are then rated for their specificity. *Specific recall* refers to a description of unique events that occurred at a specific time and place. In contrast, *overgeneral memory recall* is vague and refers to entire classes of events rather than to discrete events.

Among studies using the AMT paradigm in trauma-exposed samples, a fairly consistent pattern has emerged. Trauma survivors with acute stress disorder *(8,9)* or a PTSD diagnosis *(10–12)* tend to produce fewer specific and more overgeneral autobiographical memories relative to trauma survivors without psychiatric diagnoses. Although most studies have used word cues, a similar pattern was reported in a study that used concrete, imageable pictorial cues *(13)*, suggesting that overgeneral autobiographical memory is not simply a consequence of the abstract processing elicited by verbal cues but also occurs in response to stimuli that more closely approximate sensory cues encountered in the environment.

Although overgeneral recall has been observed when memories are generated in response to both negative and positive cues, individuals with PTSD appear to have particular difficulty recalling positive memories with specificity *(10,14)*. In one study, priming with a trauma-related video led to more general recall of events *(11)*. In another study, the difficulty in retrieving specific memories among war veterans with PTSD was particularly pronounced in those individuals wearing military regalia *(10)*; these individuals also retrieved a disproportionate number of war-related memories, a finding that was interpreted as reflecting the centrality of their war experience to their sense of self. One explanation of these findings is that impoverished recall of positive memories reflects a problem among PTSD-diagnosed trauma survivors in accessing the emotionally positive aspects of their histories and identities *(10,11,14)*. In keeping with this formulation, when asked to produce self-defining memories, PTSD-diagnosed trauma survivors, as compared to non-PTSD-diagnosed trauma survivors and nonexposed controls, reported more self-defining memories that were trauma related and of negative valence *(15)*. Similarly suggesting a link between self-identity and autobiographical recall, trauma survivors with PTSD were more likely to provide trauma-focused memories in response to positive cue words when their perception of actual self fell short of their perception of ideal self than when actual and ideal perceptions were more closely aligned *(16)*.

Mechanisms of Overgeneral Memory in PTSD

Attempts to understand the mechanisms responsible for overgeneral memory draw heavily on a cognitive model of autobiographical memory proposed by Conway and Pleydell-Pearce *(17,18)*. According to this model, autobiographical memory is part of a larger self-memory system that maintains an integrated representation of one's sense of self as well as a record of ongoing experiences as they contribute to one's goals and sense of self. Autobiographical memory depends on the retrieval of information from an autobiographical knowledge base by an executive system, called the *working self*. The autobiographical memory base is organized hierarchically, with representations of life time periods at the highest level, general event descriptions at an intermediate level, and unique, event-specific representations that contain sensory-perceptual information at the lowest level. According to this model, retrieval of an autobiographical memory in response to a verbal cue requires top-down search processes to access specific event representations as well as executive control processes to evaluate whether the retrieved memory fits the search criteria. Overgeneral memory occurs because the search during top-down retrieval is aborted too early, at the level of general event descriptions.

Building on this model, Williams et al. *(19)* proposed three mechanisms that may contribute to truncation of the retrieval search in emotional disorders: (1) capture and rumination, (2) functional avoidance, and (3) executive deficits. The capture/rumination component involves difficulty disengaging from the level of categorical retrieval when the retrieval cue activates abstract, conceptual self-representations. Such capture may occur in individuals in whom negative self-representations are already highly activated and elaborated. The retrieval cue primes other negative categories, thereby facilitating rumination and perpetuating a negative-feedback loop by which activation is maintained at an abstract conceptual level rather than propagating to a more specific level. The role of self-focused abstract thinking in decreased memory specificity has been studied in detail in depressed patients *(20,21)*. Although it has not been tested directly in PTSD, it has been speculated that PTSD-related ruminative tendencies may operate in a similar manner *(22)*.

The second mechanism of truncated memory search is based on the "affect regulation" hypothesis *(23)*, which proposes that trauma-exposed individuals fail to retrieve specific trauma memories as a means of avoiding the distress associated with remembering details of the trauma. The impact of avoidance, however, is not limited to the trauma memories but instead extends to the whole domain of autobiographical memory. Generalization to non-trauma-related autobiographical memories purportedly occurs because the avoidance truncates effortful, hierarchical search of the entire autobiographical knowledge base at the level of general event descriptors.

Several studies provided support for this hypothesis. Schonfeld, Ehlers, Bollinghaus, and Reif *(12)* examined the conditions under which overgeneral memory was most likely to occur in assault-related PTSD by manipulating the instructions to either suppress or not suppress assault memories during the AMT task. PTSD-diagnosed survivors retrieved fewer, and more general, memories when asked to suppress assault memories than when instructed not to suppress assault memories. The authors interpreted these results in relation to cognitive avoidance associated with PTSD; specifically, attempts to suppress negative trauma-related intrusions that are highly specific may have led to difficulty with recall of specific non-trauma-related life events. Also consistent with the affect regulation model, Wessel, Merckelbach, and Dekkers *(24)* found that overgeneral memory production among patients previously exposed to war atrocities was associated with more frequent intrusions and greater avoidance of trauma reminders.

Interestingly, although linked mechanistically to avoidance, reduced memory specificity may not effectively regulate affect. Golden, Dalgleish, and Mackintosh *(25)* compared the memories of bereaved individuals with complicated grief to those without complicated grief; they used an autobiographical memory test and two biographical tests, one cueing memories from the deceased's life and one cueing memories from a living significant other's life. They found that participants with complicated grief, as compared to those without complicated grief, showed reduced specificity in response to negative cue words when retrieving both autobiographical memories and memories about living others. In contrast, when retrieving memories about deceased others in response to negative cues, those with complicated grief retrieved more specific memories than those without complicated grief. Although this study did not examine trauma and PTSD specifically, the finding that distress-related memories seem to be resistant to affect regulation may also apply to trauma memories in individuals with PTSD.

The third mechanism of truncated memory search is a reduction in executive resources, thought to be associated with prefrontal dysfunction *(19)*. This represents the most well-developed neurocognitive hypothesis of overgeneral autobiographical memory in PTSD. In the autobiographical memory model of Conway and Pleydell-Pearce *(17,18)*, executive resources, including working memory and inhibitory functions, are critical at several stages in the process of memory retrieval. For instance, working memory is critical for holding a retrieval template in mind both during generation of retrieval cues and in a final search and comparison stage. Cognitive inhibition is important during the search process as a mechanism to sort through relevant and irrelevant autobiographical memories. The reduced executive capacity hypothesis is compelling in relation to PTSD given (1) the documented association between PTSD and working memory and inhibition deficits *(26–28)*, (2) the observable difficulties individuals with PTSD have in inhibiting unwanted trauma-related memories (i.e., reexperiencing symptoms), and (3) neuroimaging (e.g., *29,30–34)* and electrophysiological (e.g., *35,36)* findings suggestive of attenuated prefrontal functioning in PTSD. However, the strongest empirical support that executive resources are mechanistically related to autobiographical memory comes from non-PTSD psychiatric samples *(19)*.

Only a few studies have directly examined the relationship between cognitive resources more broadly and overgeneral memory in trauma-exposed samples. For example, Schonfeld et al. *(12)* found that in assault survivors with PTSD, verbal intelligence was negatively associated with overgeneral memory production, whereas working memory measures (digit span forward and backward) were not significantly associated with AMT performance. De Decker, Hermans, Raes, and Eelen *(37)* observed nonsignificant, albeit moderate, associations between immediate and delayed recall of standardized narratives and autobiographical specificity in trauma-exposed adolescents, but the specificity of autobiographical memories was only very weakly related to performance on a working memory task. Wessel et al. *(24)* did not find any significant relationships between anterograde memory performance on tasks of immediate recall, total memory capacity, and strategic retrieval from semantic memory. Thus, although a neurocognitive basis of overgeneral retrieval in PTSD is compelling theoretically, the few available studies have not revealed strong evidence for such an association.

Overgeneral recall characterizes autobiographical memory not only in PTSD but also in clinically significant depressive disorders (e.g., major depressive disorder) and in subclinical presentations of dysphoric mood *(19,38)*. Because of the dysphoric characteristics of some PTSD symptoms (e.g., diminished interest in normal activities) and the high comorbidity of depression with PTSD *(5,39,40)*, it could be hypothesized that the overgeneral memory observed in PTSD is due primarily to associated depression symptoms. However, when depressive symptoms are controlled statistically, overgeneral memory remains associated with symptoms of PTSD *(13)* and acute stress disorder *(9)*, suggesting that depression is not the sole cause of overgeneral memory in trauma survivors with PTSD. In contrast, overgeneral autobiographical recall is rarely observed in non-PTSD anxiety disorders unless the anxiety is accompanied by comorbid depression *(41,42)*. In fact, although trauma history has been linked to overgeneral memory *(43–45)*, the vast majority of studies examining the relationship of trauma exposure to overgeneral memory recall suggest that either PTSD or depressed mood must be present for overgeneral memory to occur in trauma survivors *(19)*.

Alterations in Autobiographical Memory: Predisposition or Consequence?

To help determine the causal direction of the relationship between overgeneral autobiographical recall and PTSD, several studies have used longitudinal methodology. In general, findings indicate that preexposure tendencies for overgeneral memory are associated with increased risk of PTSD. For example, Bryant, Sutherland, and Guthrie *(14)* found that impaired retrieval of specific memories in response to positive cues prior to trauma exposure among trainee firefighters predicted post-traumatic stress symptom severity after trauma exposure, a finding consistent with the cross-sectional literature. Harvey and Bryant *(46)* likewise found that overgeneral retrieval of autobiographical memories shortly after motor vehicle accident exposure predicted subsequent PTSD. In contrast, Kangas, Henry, and Bryant *(9)* found that early deficits in recalling specific memories among cancer patients with acute stress disorder did not predict subsequent PTSD 6 months later, raising the possibility that trauma characteristics may influence the relationship between overgeneral memory and PTSD. In the only treatment study that assessed autobiographical memory in participants exposed to assault or motor vehicle accident before and after cognitive-behavioral therapy, it was found that improvement in PTSD symptoms was related to improved retrieval of specific memories and decreased overgeneral recall in response to positive cues *(47)*.

Although the mechanism by which overgeneral memory contributes to the development or maintenance of PTSD is unknown, it is of note that several studies have demonstrated a link between overgeneral memory on the one hand and decreased ability to imagine future events *(48)* and solve social problems *(49,50)* on the other. Such a link is intriguing as recent cognitive neuroscience findings suggest that the ability to retrieve past events has a direct impact on the ability to coherently simulate future events because future thought requires the flexible recombination of details from the past *(51)*.

Trauma Memory

One of the most debated conceptual issues surrounding the study of memory in PTSD concerns the uniqueness of trauma memories in comparison to other autobiographical memories. Central in this discussion is the question of whether trauma memories differ solely in quantity (e.g., frequency and intensity of occurrence) or also in quality (i.e., underlying memory processes or representations).

One consideration concerns the accuracy of trauma memories in comparison to other memories. The literature on flashbulb memories *(52)* has been invoked as potentially relevant to this question as it is often assumed that events that are extremely surprising, infrequent, and relevant to the individual are remembered in a more durable and fixed form. However, the available evidence suggests that trauma memories, like other autobiographical memories with high emotional intensity *(53)*, are prone to errors and distortions. A recent review of studies that assessed on two separate occasions memories of assault or of wartime exposure indicated that inconsistencies in report of the index event over time are common *(54)*. Of note, in several studies, there was a slight tendency for changes in report, including amplification of the memory, to be associated with severity of PTSD symptoms *(55–58)*.

With regard to qualitative characteristics of trauma memories, we noted that there is some evidence to suggest that the overgeneral recall of autobiographical events may not extend to trauma-related memories (*see also 9,25*). One interpretation of these findings is that trauma-related memories, because of their vividness and potency, do not require a hierarchical search of the autobiographical memory base but rather are accessed directly through activation of event-specific information *(17)*.

A number of studies have used self-reported memory ratings to evaluate the characteristics of trauma memories. These studies indicate that, in comparison to trauma-exposed control subjects, trauma survivors with PTSD have more vivid recollection, experience their trauma memories as richer in feelings and sensory details, and find the memories to be of greater personal significance *(59–61)*. One study that directly compared traumatic and positive memories found that these differences were specific to traumatic memories *(59)*. However, another study limited to individuals with PTSD found no differences in trauma and nontrauma memories with regard to their sensory qualities or stability *(62)*. Findings from these studies are somewhat difficult to interpret, however, because ratings may be subject to mood-related biases due to their subjective and retrospective nature and because studies differ in terms of the specific memory attributes rated.

Arguments for the uniqueness of trauma memories center on the issue of "memory fragmentation." *Memory fragmentation* refers to the lack of coherence within a memory and reflects a failure to integrate different aspects of a memory into an internally consistent whole. Such fragmentation is thought to result from disorganized initial encoding of the traumatic event, which leads to inconsistent consolidation and poorly regulated retrieval. Van der Kolk *(63,64)*, for example, proposed that the lack of narrative coherence of trauma memories is a reflection of emotionally induced dissociative states at the time of trauma, which result in routing of the memories through distinct neurochemical pathways. According to this model, trauma memories are preserved in an implicit memory system as vivid sensory and perceptual experiences but are not accessible as explicit verbal narratives. Ehlers and Clark *(65)* likewise purported that some trauma memories remain inaccessible because they are poorly integrated during encoding but believed that the initial encoding is dependent on the amount of "conceptual" (i.e., relating to the meaning of the event and its integration into a larger autobiographical context) versus "data-driven" (i.e., sensory) processing.

Brewin *(66,67)* proposed a dual-representation model according to which trauma memories are based on two separate representations: (1) a hippocampally mediated narrative representation that supports verbally accessible memories that are integrated with the rest of the autobiographical memory base and can be retrieved either automatically or strategically, and (2) an image-based representation mediated by the amygdala that does not interact with the autobiographical memory base and can only be retrieved automatically by trauma cues (i.e., is situationally accessible). According to this model, the two systems may be differentially impacted by neurohormonal responses to stress, leading to enhanced encoding of situationally accessible trauma memories and reduced encoding of verbally accessible trauma memories. Further, it is suggested that as part of the process of healthy adaptation to trauma, such imbalance is corrected through a process of reencoding image-based memories into verbally accessible memories; in PTSD, by contrast, such reencoding does not take place, with the result that verbal memories cannot inhibit maladaptive amygdala responses *(68)*.

Most memory fragmentation theories of trauma memory assert that some combination of heightened arousal, emotional distress, and dissociation at the time of the event lead to disorganized encoding of trauma memories. Consistent with the view that extreme distress during trauma affects the manner in which an event is encoded, studies of emotional memory encoding in nonclinical samples suggest that intensely negative and arousing memories lead to enhanced memory for the information central to the event but impoverished memory of peripheral details (for a review, *see 69*), a phenomenon referred to as *tunnel memory (70)*. However, tunnel memory is a common source of memory distortion for emotionally significant events and can equally be explained with reference to general principles of autobiographical memory *(71)*. Further, as noted by Rubin et al. *(2)*, the phenomenon of tunnel memory is inconsistent with one of the symptoms of PTSD *(1)* (criterion C3: difficulty remembering an important aspect of the event), although as noted, this symptom may occur relatively infrequently. More important, perhaps, the phenomenon of tunnel memory fails to explain the enhanced clarity of peripheral trauma details thought to be associated with intense reliving phenomena *(72)*.

The empirical basis for memory fragmentation models has largely been based on narrative recall paradigms and metamemory studies. In narrative recall paradigms, participants are asked to describe the trauma event, and the narratives are then coded for their cohesiveness and semantic structure. In metamemory studies, participants are asked to make a subjective appraisal of the coherence of their own memory. Some studies have found that traumatic memories are more fragmented in individuals with acute stress disorder (e.g., *46*) or PTSD *(73)* than in trauma-exposed control groups, but other studies have failed to find group differences *(59,60)*. In a recent comprehensive review of this literature, Zoellner and Bittenger *(6)* concluded that the lack of clarity can be attributed in large part to methodological limitations of the current literature, including the frequent failure to control for PTSD diagnosis and trauma characteristics and the failure to consider non-PTSD psychopathology.

Of special note in the literature on trauma memory is the subgroup of studies that have attempted to link other symptoms to autobiographical memories of the trauma. These studies are particularly interesting because they address a seeming paradox in PTSD: the prominence of unwanted intrusions of the trauma memory as reexperiencing symptoms in the context of difficulties with deliberate retrieval of certain aspects of the trauma event. This has led some theorists to maintain that those memories manifested in the form of reexperiencing symptoms, in particular, may differ qualitatively from other trauma and nontrauma autobiographical memories *(17,66,74)*. Brewin *(75)*, for example, has suggested that flashbacks are clearer than other trauma memories, albeit more fragmented and less easy to retrieve in a well-regulated manner. Supporting this notion, Hellawell and Brewin *(72,76)* found that "flashback" reexperiencing episodes, as compared to "normal" trauma memories, were associated with more autonomic and motor behaviors and greater sensory detail; they were experienced more often in the present tense and were characterized more often by primary emotions such as horror, fear, and helplessness. In examining non-flashback intrusions, Rubin, Feldman, and Beckham *(61)*, however, found no evidence that trauma memories differed from nontrauma memories in coherence, although reliving phenomena increased as memories were more related to the trauma. Indeed, recurrent involuntary trauma memories appear to share many of the same characteristics (e.g., proportion of positive to negative memories, associated emotional intensity, dominance for recent events) as ordinary autobiographical memories *(77)*. However, even different symptoms within the reexperiencing class (e.g., recurrent thoughts vs. nightmares) are poorly correlated *(77)* and therefore may differ in their associated features.

NEW LEARNING

Although alterations in autobiographical memory in PTSD are well documented, clinical complaints of memory problems in individuals with PTSD typically concern the ability to remember day-to-day information and events experienced after the trauma. In this section, we characterize the nature of these difficulties; consider how they can best be understood in terms of underlying cognitive and neural mechanisms; and evaluate how they are causally related to the development of PTSD. We also examine the impact of emotional valence on new learning and consider factors that may be responsible for the enhanced learning of trauma-related as compared to trauma-neutral information in PTSD.

Characterizing the New Learning Impairments

The results of neuropsychological studies examining the presence and nature of difficulties in new learning remain unclear. On the one hand, there are now a considerable number of studies that have documented impairments in new learning and memory in PTSD *(78,79)*. Several of these observed that memory impairments tend to be selective to the verbal domain *(80)*, but others have documented impairments in visual memory as well *(28,81–83)*. Different conclusions also have been drawn with regard to the nature of the impairment, with studies variably highlighting problems with the initial registration of information *(28,84,85)*, with both immediate and delayed memory *(86–88)*, and with sensitivity to interference *(28,89,90)*.

On the other hand, a number of studies have failed to find evidence for memory impairment specific to PTSD *(91–94)*. These studies raise the question of whether impaired memory, when observed, may be due to comorbid conditions such as substance abuse or depression *(95)*. Examining specifically the contribution of comorbid alcohol use, Samuelson and colleagues *(84)* found that alcohol history was associated with visual memory impairments, but that PTSD was associated with problems in verbal memory, even controlling for alcohol use. Similarly, although depression can lead to memory impairment in its own right, PTSD-associated memory impairments cannot fully be accounted for in terms of depression *(96,97)*. Other potentially important variables in explaining discrepant findings concern the nature of the control group to which PTSD patients are compared (individuals with trauma exposure without PTSD or individuals who did not experience trauma), the inclusion of individuals with head injury in the PTSD group, the chronicity of PTSD, and the nature of the trauma itself.

A meta-analysis by Brewin, Kleiner, Vasterling, and Field *(78)* helps to clarify the role of several of these variables. These authors concluded that there is a robust and selective association between PTSD and verbal memory problems that exists in both civilian and military samples and that cannot be explained by concurrent head injury. Although the magnitude of memory impairment is greater when the comparison group consists of individuals without trauma exposure, a significant impairment remains when a trauma-matched control group is used, which is on the order of one-third of a standard deviation. Perhaps less clear at this point is the role of time since trauma. In a majority of studies, participants have been combat veterans who are more likely to have a chronic, and possibly intractable, form of PTSD. To the extent that continued stress exposure may lead to a progressive course of the disorder, cognitive deficits might be more obvious over time; indeed, in at least one study, memory impairment was absent on most measures of memory in recent adult trauma survivors with post-traumatic stress symptoms *(98)*. However, memory impairments have been documented in children and adolescents with PTSD following a recent trauma *(99)*, as well as in veterans with PTSD tested within 5 years of return from the Gulf War *(28)*. These findings suggest that memory problems are not limited to individuals with chronic PTSD. Aside from chronicity, age per se may also need to be taken into account as there is some evidence for greater memory decline associated with PTSD in elderly than in younger individuals *(100)* and a steeper longitudinal decline in elderly individuals with PTSD than without PTSD *(101)*. Both of these findings suggest an interaction between PTSD-related memory loss and aging, the exact nature of which remains to be further elucidated.

Neural and Cognitive Bases of New Learning Impairments

Successful memory depends on both the medial temporal lobes (MTLs) and the frontal lobes, and thus a natural question arises regarding relative contributions of compromised MTL versus frontal lobe functioning to PTSD-associated memory impairments. The MTL system is the core memory system that binds together different aspects of an episode into a single memory trace and allows reactivation of that trace in the context of an appropriate cue. The frontal lobes, by contrast, are critical for strategic aspects of encoding and retrieval. They organize the input to the MTL and allow its output to be monitored and used deliberately, in the function of task goals and requirements.

Against the backdrop of diminished attention and executive function in PTSD *(26–28)*, several aspects of memory performance have been attributed to impaired frontal function. Specifically, it has been suggested that a disruption of strategic encoding processes, leading to impoverished encoding, may underlie enhanced susceptibility to interference *(79)*. A similar sensitivity to interference is often seen in patients with structural lesions to the frontal lobes *(102,103)*. Further, since strategic encoding processes are more critical for encoding of unrelated compared to related word lists, the fact that memory impairment is seen more consistently on the Rey Auditory Verbal Learning test (which is composed of unrelated words) than on the California Verbal Learning Test (which is composed of categorized words) is consistent with this interpretation *(79)*. It should be noted that such frontal encoding deficits are not simply a consequence of poor attention as memory impairments persist even when attention is controlled for *(84,87)*.

Frontal functions are also critical for monitoring the appropriateness of a retrieved memory. Memory errors such as intrusions in free recall and false alarms in recognition, which are thought to reflect impoverished monitoring, provide further evidence for a frontal contribution to the memory impairment seen in PTSD. Examining the relationship between monitoring errors and aspects of psychopathology, we found that intrusions and false alarms were positively correlated with reexperiencing symptoms and negatively correlated with avoidance and emotional numbing symptoms *(28)*. One explanation of these findings is in terms of a failure to inhibit task-irrelevant processes, reflecting a faulty gating mechanism for the controlled processing of task-relevant information *(28)*. Another explanation is that hyperarousal and associated frontal system disruption may interfere with the controlled aspects of memory. The relationship between symptom severity and memory performance, however, is likely multidetermined as another study found that memory performance correlated not with current symptoms but rather with reported worst-episode symptoms *(104)*.

Interest in the role of MTL impairment in the day-to-day memory problems seen in PTSD stems from the established effects of severe stress on hippocampal structure and function in animals, which are thought to be mediated at least in part through elevated levels of glucocorticoids *(105,106)*. Analogously, it has been suggested that in individuals with PTSD, excessive release of cortisol during the acute stress or throughout the course of illness might lead to hippocampal abnormalities *(107)*, although it is now apparent that stress also has a direct impact on frontal lobe functioning *(108)*. The well-established link between stress and the hippocampus, coupled with reports starting in the mid-1990's of reduced hippocampal volume in individuals with PTSD *(80,109–111)* initially appeared to provide a ready explanation for the memory deficits seen in PTSD.

Subsequent studies, however, have questioned whether there is a direct link between MTL dysfunction and the observed memory deficits. First, although a majority of studies have documented hippocampal volume reductions in PTSD (for review, *see 112,113)*, there are a number of exceptions to this pattern, both in patients with recent-onset *(98,114,115)* and those with chronic PTSD *(116,117)*. Second, despite initial evidence of a direct relationship between hippocampal volume and memory performance *(80)*, a number of more recent studies have failed to find such a correlation *(89,118,119)*. One caveat, however, is that most of these studies have used clinical neuropsychological tests that rely to a varying extent on both MTL and frontal functions rather than tests that are selectively sensitive to MTL function. For example, several studies have examined memory retention over a delay, but findings concerning the rate of forgetting in PTSD have been inconsistent. Further, although an abnormally fast rate of forgetting is often seen in patients with MTL lesions, it is also seen in association with severe memory loss that results from some frontal lesions *(120)* and thus does not in itself help to specify the neural basis of the impairment.

Of note, in a recent study that specifically targeted the role of the hippocampus in configural processing, the ability to perform a configural task was significantly correlated with hippocampal volume *(119)*. It has been suggested that the ability of the hippocampus to process and encode the configural relationships among multiple elements is critical for the contextual regulation of emotional responses *(121)*. It also forms the hallmark of episodic memory.

In light of the mounting evidence for both frontal and MTL abnormalities in PTSD (see Chapter 15, this volume), it seems increasingly unlikely that PTSD-related memory impairments are exclusively frontal or MTL based, but rather dysfunction in each of these regions may contribute in distinct ways to the observed memory impairment. To elucidate which aspects of memory or memory processes are linked to MTL or frontal dysfunction in PTSD, memory probes that are uniquely sensitive to the contribution of each these regions will be necessary. Perhaps more important, given the intricate link among these regions, functional imaging studies that examine not only distinct patterns of activation in each of these regions but also the functional connectivity among these regions will be critical.

New Learning Impairments: Predisposition or Consequence?

The findings reviewed leave unanswered the question of whether PTSD causes memory impairment, whether poorer memory is a risk factor for PTSD, or whether the observed association between memory and PTSD is bidirectional. Until recently, the notion that PTSD leads to memory impairment was largely based on evidence from animal studies documenting that stress leads to neurobiological changes in the hippocampus that have a direct impact on learning and memory *(122–124)*. In the last few years, several prospective studies in humans have documented similar adverse effects on memory of acute stress associated with military exercises *(125)* or special operations *(126)*. In the first prospective study of Army soldiers deployed to Iraq, significant pre- to post-deployment declines were observed in both verbal and visuospatial memory *(127)*. Of note, these studies all documented memory decline immediately following stress exposure, but whether such changes are transient or chronic, and how they relate to PTSD, is currently unknown. In the Iraq deployment study, memory decline was more pronounced in individuals who had symptoms of PTSD, but PTSD in itself did not fully account for the deployment-associated memory loss *(127)*. Thus, the cognitive effects of stress and PTSD may be partially dissociable.

Initial recognition of the possibility that lower cognitive function might serve as a risk factor for PTSD came from studies demonstrating that lower intelligence is associated with more severe PTSD symptoms *(128,129)*, and importantly, that the development of PTSD was not associated with a deterioration in IQ *(129)*. Specifically with respect to memory, Bustamante, Mellman, Davide, and Fins *(130)* found that less-proficient verbal memory shortly after trauma exposure was related to subsequent development of PTSD. Studies comparing the performance of twin pairs, in which one twin is a combat veteran and the other twin is not, provide further compelling evidence for the notion that memory and hippocampal functioning may be predictive of the development of PTSD following trauma *(96,119,131)*. Comparing the performance of pairs in which the combat-exposed twin developed PTSD (PTSD pairs) to that of pairs in which the combat-exposed twin did not develop PTSD (non-PTSD pairs), it was found that both the combat-exposed twin and the nonexposed sibling from the PTSD pairs performed similarly on tests of verbal memory and performed more poorly than the combat-exposed twin and nonexposed sibling of non-PTSD pairs *(96)*. Both siblings of the PTSD pairs also had reduced hippocampal volumes in comparison to the siblings of the non-PTSD pairs, and the hippocampal volumes of the combat-exposed twin and nonexposed sibling of the PTSD pair were equally predictive of the severity of PTSD of the combat-exposed twin *(131)*. Finally, the configural processing deficit mentioned earlier, which appears to be a sensitive measure of hippocampal functioning, was present in both the combat-exposed twin and nonexposed sibling of the PTSD pairs, suggesting that these specifically hippocampal impairments may predispose individuals to PTSD.

The evidence reviewed suggests that the link between memory impairment and PTSD is likely bidirectional. In particular, we suggest that premorbid differences in cognitive ability, including memory, may act as a preexisting risk factor for PTSD, but that independent of risk for PTSD, stress itself also affects cognitive functioning. Preliminary evidence for this bidirectional relationship is emerging *(132)*, but further studies examining the combined effects of risk factors for PTSD and actual stress exposure are needed to uncover the exact bases of the memory impairments associated with PTSD.

New Learning of Emotional Information

Against the backdrop of a general impairment in new learning, a question of considerable interest is whether there are differences in the way individuals with and without PTSD process and learn emotional, and especially trauma-related, information in comparison to nonemotional information. To address this question, a number of studies have compared memory for neutral and trauma-related words in the context of list-learning tasks. Several studies have done so following conditions of incidental learning, when participants processed the information without a subsequent memory task in mind. Individuals with PTSD recalled more trauma-related words than did individuals without PTSD, whereas the groups did not differ in their recall of neutral words *(133–135)*. When memory was assessed by means of recognition rather than recall, groups did not differ in their memory for trauma-related words, but one study found that PTSD patients had a more liberal response bias for trauma-related information regardless of whether that information had in fact been presented *(136)*. These findings suggest a processing bias that may favor both attending and responding to trauma-related information and that may have an impact on memory, especially under conditions that require self-initiated retrieval.

It is unlikely, however, that the trauma-related memory advantage seen in PTSD can be accounted for completely in terms of a processing bias. In one of the recall studies mentioned *(133)*, an independent probe indicated that trauma-related words did not receive preferential attention, and yet they were better recalled. Moreover, in intentional memory studies, in which attention is focused directly on each stimulus that is to be memorized, individuals with PTSD also show relatively better memory for trauma-related information. In two studies, recall of neutral words was impaired in individuals with PTSD, whereas recall of trauma-related words was not *(129,137)*. In a third study, recall was generally impaired, but the PTSD group showed an advantage in memory for trauma-related information that was not present in the group without PTSD *(138)*.

On a cognitive level, this "memory bias" may be due to the fact that trauma-related information is encoded more richly and, to the extent that it evokes memories of the traumatic event, is assimilated within an already existing emotional memory network, thus making it easier to retrieve later. Emotion enhances the subjective characteristics associated with memory, such as its vividness and recollective quality *(139,140)*, and interestingly, preliminary evidence suggests that in individuals with PTSD memory for trauma-related information may be associated with enhanced feelings of recollection *(141)*. On a neurobiological level, emotional arousal activates b-adrenergic receptors in the amygdala, and amygdala activation in turn modulates hippocampally mediated consolidation *(142)*. Functional imaging studies have demonstrated that individuals with PTSD show greater enhancement in amygdala activation than individuals without PTSD in association with the recall or imagination of traumatic events *(143,144)*. It is possible that increased amygdala responsivity plays a similar role in the enhanced encoding of trauma-related information.

Laboratory studies of emotional memory have also tried to shed light on the autobiographical memory abnormalities described in the beginning of this chapter. As discussed, some have suggested that the repeated intrusion of highly detailed traumatic memories triggered by situations that reinstate some characteristic of the traumatic event reflects the operation of involuntary, implicit memory processes that automatically activate information related to the traumatic event. If this view is correct, one might expect implicit memory for emotional information to be enhanced in individuals with PTSD. The evidence does not strongly support this view: Some studies have found enhanced implicit memory for threat- *(145,146)* or trauma-related *(147)* information in PTSD, but several other studies have not

(134,138,148). It is important to keep in mind, however, that the presentation of threat-related words in the laboratory in no manner mimics the richness of information—physiological, emotional, and cognitive—that may act as cues to activate intrusive memories in the real world.

CONCLUSION

For the sake of conceptual organization, we have discussed separately the status of autobiographical memory and new learning in PTSD, but of course, in the development and maintenance of PTSD, these two forms of memory are intrinsically linked. Less-proficient new learning prior to trauma will necessarily have an impact on the encoding of the trauma event and, consequently, its subsequent retrieval. For instance, a configural deficit as postulated by Gilbertson et al. *(119)* could lead to a failure to encode relevant contextual information during the traumatic event, with the result that later retrieval of the trauma memory will be more fragmented or lacking in important details. Conversely, intrusive memories (or attempts to suppress their occurrence) expend limited attentional and executive resources. As a result, the elaboration and organization of new incoming information may suffer, and retrieved information may not be adequately monitored. Longitudinal studies that evaluate new learning as well as autobiographical memory prior to and after trauma, or prior to and after treatment, will be critical to fully elucidate these interactions.

Just as there is a dynamic interplay between the encoding of new information and the revival of established memories, it is important to emphasize that memories themselves are not fixed but rather are continually susceptible to change. Upon retrieval of a memory, the memory trace may be updated with new information obtained during the retrieval situation, or new memories may be formed that become interlinked with the already existing one. Further, ample evidence now suggests that by virtue of retrieval, some forms of memory can be returned to a labile state in which the memory trace is modifiable and subject to reconsolidation *(149,150)*.

The malleability of memories has important consequences for PTSD. On the one hand, ongoing modification of memories can potentially provide a mechanism for the maintenance or exacerbation of PTSD symptoms. Reactivation of intrusive memories, accompanied by emotional and physiological changes experienced during the trauma, can lead to the incorporation of new contextual elements that are part of the current retrieval situation but not the original trauma event. As such, intrusive memories may strengthen memory of the traumatic event, not only through reactivation, but also by virtue of the fact that additional contextual elements may now in themselves act as cues to activate the traumatic memory.

On the other hand, the dynamic nature of memory may also offer the potential for altering traumatic memories in adaptive ways. Several successful cognitive-behavioral interventions for PTSD center on the trauma memory. The impetus for exposure interventions, for example, relies strongly on emotional processing theory, which suggests that PTSD emerges and is maintained via a fear network in memory that leads to avoidance behaviors and emotional numbing. According to this theory, fear is reduced through activation of the fear structure and the introduction of new information inconsistent with the maladaptive components within the fear network. Thus, exposure interventions require not only activation of the trauma memory but also its modification *(151,152)*. Likewise, recent evidence indicates that it may be equally important to alter the meaning of the traumatic event, suggesting that access to cognitions associated with the trauma memories may be as essential to positive outcomes, if not more so, than reexposure per se *(153)*. To the degree that access to trauma memories can be improved, as shown by Sutherland and Bryant *(47)*, it could be reasoned that incorporation of new information in memory in ways that reduce fear, sadness, anger, and other trauma-related emotions could be facilitated.

Pharmacological interventions may also provide a mechanism by which traumatic memories can be altered. Preliminary evidence suggests that administration of a b-adrenergic blocker in association with retrieval of a traumatic memory may reduce physiological responding to imagery of that traumatic event a week later *(154)*, but much further work is needed to explore the boundary conditions and mechanisms of this effect.

Finally, in considering the clinical significance of memory to PTSD, it is critical to keep in mind that memory does not work in isolation but operates in the service of a person's current goals and concerns, serving an important functional role in maintaining a coherent sense of self. In Conway and Pleydell-Pearce's *(17,18)* model, the encoding and retrieval of autobiographical memories reflect a constant interplay between the working self and the autobiographical memory knowledge base. Thus, the need to maintain a coherent sense of self will bias which memory contents are retrieved as well as the particular features or aspects of a memory that are emphasized; the dominance of particular memories will in turn influence one's sense of self. Illustrating the former, the amplification of trauma memories over time in PTSD may reflect at least in part an attempt to make sense of developing psychopathology and the accompanying change in the sense of self *(56,58,155–157)*. Consistent with the latter, a positive relation has been found between the extent to which trauma-focused memories become a central reference point for organizing other memories and the presence and severity of symptoms of PTSD *(158)*. The intimate relationship between memory and self has important implications for treatment. Changing the memory bias, by virtue of altering or better integrating trauma memories or by introducing nontraumatic memories in situations that are perceived to be threatening, may dampen the impact of a traumatic experience on one's sense of self. Likewise, changes in the sense of self and its associated goals may have an impact on the accessibility of memories, favoring those that are consistent with a more positive self-appraisal.

In closing, the study of memory in PTSD is a rich and fruitful area of research. At a theoretical level, a number of debates remain—the nature of trauma memory and the underlying neuroanatomical basis of memory abnormalities in PTSD, to name but two. Future work will undoubtedly lead to a better understanding of the basic mechanisms underlying memory alterations in PTSD; it likely also will have important ramifications for cognitive and neural theories that aim to elucidate the complex interactions between emotion and memory in normal functioning. At a clinical level, recognition of the centrality of memory in PTSD now opens the way to the development and refinement of treatment options, whether behavioral or pharmaceutical, that are informed by our understanding of the nature of memory processes and representations. This convergence of basic and applied interests and the potential for the study of each to inform the other provide a particularly exciting juncture in the study of memory in PTSD.

ACKNOWLEDGMENT

Preparation of this chapter was supported by the Office of Research and Development, Medical Research Service, Department of Veterans Affairs.

REFERENCES

1. American Psychological Association. (2000) Diagnostic and Statistical Manual of Mental Disorders. 4th ed., text rev. Washington, DC: American Psychological Association.
2. Rubin, D. C., Berntsen, D., and Bohni, M. K. (2008) A memory based model of post-traumatic stress disorder: evaluating basic assumptions underlying the PTSD diagnosis. Psychol Rev 115, 985–1011.
3. Brewin, C. R. (2007) Autobiographical memory for trauma: update on four controversies. Memory 15, 227–48.
4. McNally, R. J. (2003) Remembering Trauma. Cambridge, MA: Harvard University Press.
5. Shobe, K. K., and Kihlstrom, J. F. (2007) Is traumatic memory special? Curr Dir Psychol Sci 3, 70–74.
6. Zoellner, L. A., and Bittenger, J. N. (2004) On the uniqueness of trauma memories in PTSD. In: Rosen, G. M., ed., Posttraumatic Stress Disorder: Issues and Controversies. New York: Wiley, 2004.
7. Williams, J. M. G., and Broadbent, K. (1986) Autobiographical memory in suicide attempts. J Abnorm Psychol 95, 144–49.
8. Harvey, A. G., Bryant, R. A., and Dang, S. T. (1998) Autobiographical memory in acute stress disorder. J Consult Clin Psychol 66, 500–6.
9. Kangas, M., Henry, J. L., and Bryant, R. A. (2005) A prospective study of autobiographical memory and posttraumatic stress disorder following cancer. J Consult Clin Psychol 73, 293–99.
10. McNally, R. J., Lasko, N. B., Macklin, M. L., and Pitman, R. K. (1995) Autobiographical memory disturbance in combat-related posttraumatic stress disorder. Behav Res Ther 6, 619–30.
11. McNally, R. J., Litz, B. T., Prassas, A., Shin, L. M., and Weather, F. W. (1994) Emotional priming of autobiographical memory in post-traumatic stress disorder. Cogn Emot 8, 351–57.
12. Schonfeld, S., Ehlers, A., Bollinghaus, I., and Reif, W. (2007) Overgeneral memory and suppression of trauma memories in post-traumatic stress disorder. Memory 15, 339–52.

13. Schonfeld, S., and Ehlers, A. (2006) Overgeneral memory extends to pictorial retrieval cues and correlates with cognitive features in posttraumatic stress disorder. Emotion 6, 611–21.
14. Bryant, R. A., Sutherland, K., and Guthrie, R. M. (2007) Impaired specific autobiographical memory as a risk factor for posttraumatic stress after trauma. J Abnorm Psychol 116, 837–41.
15. Sutherland, K., and Bryant, R. A. (2005) Self-defining memories in post-traumatic stress disorder. Br J Clin Psychol 44, 591–98.
16. Sutherland, K., and Bryant, R. A. (2008) Autobiographical memory and the self-memory system in posttraumatic stress disorder. J Anxiety Disord 22, 555–60.
17. Conway, M. A., and Pleydell-Pearce, C. W. (2000) The construction of autobiographical memories in the self-memory system. Psychol Rev 107, 261–88.
18. Conway, M. A. (2005) Memory and the self. J Mem Lang 53, 594–628.
19. Williams, J. M. G., Barnhofer, T., Crane, C., et al. (2007) Autobiographical memory specificity and emotional disorder. Psychol Bull 133, 122–48.
20. Crane, C., Barnhofer, T., Visser, C., Nightingale, H., and Williams, J. M. G. (2007) The effects of analytical and experiential rumination on autobiographical memory specificity in individuals with a history of major depresssion. Behav Res Ther 45, 3077–87.
21. Watkins, E., and Teasdale, J. D. (2001) Rumination and over-general memory in depression: effects of self-focus and analytic thinking. J Abnorm Psychol 110, 353–57.
22. Guthrie, R., and Bryant, R. A. (2000) Attempting suppression of traumatic memories over extended periods in acute stress disorder. Behav Res Ther 38, 899–907.
23. Williams, J. M. G., Stiles, W. B., and Shapiro, D. A. (1999) Cognitive mechanisms in the avoidance of painful and dangerous thoughts: elaborating the assimilation model. Cogn Ther Res 23, 285–306.
24. Wessel, I., Merckelbach, H., and Dekkers, T. (2002) Autobiographical memory specificity, intrusive memory, and general memory skills in Dutch-Indonesian survivors of the World War II era. J Trauma Stress 15, 227–34.
25. Golden, A. M., Dalgleish, T., and Mackintosh, B. (2007) Levels of specificity of autobiographical memories and of biographical memories of the deceased in bereaved individuals with and without complicated grief. J Abnorm Psychol 116, 786–95.
26. Jenkins, M. A., Langlais, P. J., Delis, D., and Cohen, R. A. (2000) Attentional dysfunction associated with posttraumatic stress disorder among rape survivors. Clin Neuropsychol 14, 7–12.
27. Leskin, L. P., and White, P. M. (2007) Attentional networks reveal executive function deficits in posttraumatic stress disorder. Neuropsychology 21, 275–84.
28. Vasterling, J. J. (1998) Attention and memory dysfunction in posttraumatic stress disorder. Neuropsychology 12, 125–33.
29. Bremner, J. D., Vythilingam, M., Vermetten, E., et al. (2003) Neural correlates of declarative memory for emotionally valenced words in women with posttraumatic stress disorder related to early childhood sexual abuse. Biol Psychiatry 53, 879–89.
30. Hou, C., Liu, J., Wang, K., et al. (2007) Brain responses to symptom provocation and trauma-related short-term memory recall in coal mining accident survivors with acute severe PTSD. Brain Res 1144, 165–74.
31. Lanius, R. A., Williamson, P. C., Densmore, M., et al. (2001) Neural correlates of traumatic memories in posttraumatic stress disorder: a functional MRI investigation. Am J Psychiatry 158, 1920–22.
32. Shin, L. M., Orr, S. P., Carson, M. A., et al. (2004) Regional cerebral blood flow in the amygdala and medial prefrontal cortex during traumatic imagery in male and female Vietnam veterans with PTSD. Arch Gen Psychiatry 61, 168–76.

33. Shin, L. M., Wright, C. I., Cannistraro, P. A., et al. (2005) A functional magnetic reso-
    nance imaging study of amygdala and medial prefrontal cortex responses to overtly pre-
    sented fearful faces in posttraumatic stress disorder. Arch Gen Psychiatry 62, 273–81.
34. Williams, L. M., Kemp, A. H., Felmingham, K., et al. (2006) Trauma modulates amy-
    gdala and medial prefrontal responses to consciously attended fear. Neuro Image 29,
    347–57.
35. Weber, D. L., Clark, C. R., McFarlane, A. C., Moores, K. A., Morris, P., and Egan, G.
    F. (2005) Abnormal frontal and parietal activity during working memory updating in
    post-traumatic stress disorder. Psychiatry Res 140, 27–44.
36. Wessa, M., Jatzko, A., and Flor, H. (2006) Retrieval and emotional processing of trau-
    matic memories in posttraumatic stress disorder: peripheral and central correlates. Neu-
    ropsychologia 44, 1683–96.
37. de Decker, A., Hermans, D., Raes, F., and Eelen, P. (2003) Autobiographical memory
    specificity and trauma in inpatient adolescents. J Clin Child Adolesc Psychol 32, 22–31.
38. Van Vreeswijk, M. F., and de Wilde, E. J. (2004) Autobiographical memory specificity,
    psychopathology, depressed mood and the use of the Autobiographical Memory Test: a
    meta-analysis. Behav Res Ther 42, 731–43.
39. Breslau, N., Davis, G. C., Peterson, E. L., and Schultz, L. R. (2000) A second look at
    comorbidity in victims of trauma: the posttraumatic stress disorder-major depression
    connection. Biol Psychiatry 48, 902–9.
40. Shalev, A. (2001) What is posttraumatic stress disorder? J Clin Psychiatry 61, 85–95.
41. Burke, M., and Mathews, A. (1992) Autobiographical memory and clinical anxiety.
    Cogn Emot 6, 23–25.
42. Wilhelm, S., McNally, R. J., Baer, L., and Florin, I. (1997) Autobiographical memory
    in obsessive-compulsive disorder. Br J Clin Psychol 36, 21–31.
43. Dalgleish, T., Tchanturia, K., Seerpell, L., et al. (2003) Self-reported parental abuse
    relates to autobiographical memory style in patients with eating disorders. Emotion 3,
    211–22.
44. Hermans, D., Van den Broeck, K., Belis, G., Raes, F., Pieters, G., and Eelen, P. (2004)
    Trauma and autobiographical memory specificity in depressed inpatients. Behav Res
    Ther 42, 775–89.
45. Kuyken, W., and Brewin, C. R. (1995) Autobiographical memory functioning in depres-
    sion and reports of early abuse. J Abnorm Psychol 104, 585–91.
46. Harvey, A. G., and Bryant, R. A. (1999) A qualitative investigation of the organization
    of traumatic memories. Br J Clin Psychol 38, 401–5.
47. Sutherland, K., and Bryant, R. A. (2007) Autobiographical memory in posttraumatic
    stress disorder before and after treatment. Behav Res Ther 445, 2915–23.
48. Williams, J. M. G., Ellis, N. C., Tyers, C., Healy, H., Rose, G., and MacLeod, A. K.
    (1996) The specificity of autobiographical memory and imageability of the future. Mem
    Cogn 24, 116–25.
49. Raes, F., Hermans, D., Willimas, J. M. G., et al. (2005) Reduced specificity of autobio-
    graphical memories: a mediator between rumination and ineffective problem solving in
    major depression? J Affect Disord 87, 331–35.
50. Sutherland, K., and Bryant, R. A. (2008) Social problem solving and autobiographical
    memory in posttraumatic stress disorder. Behav Res Ther 46, 154–61.
51. Schacter, D. L., and Addis, D. R. (2007) The cognitive neuroscience of constructive
    memory: remembering the past and imagining the future. Philos Trans R Soc London B
    Biol Sci 362, 773–86.
52. Brown, R., and Kulik, J. (1977) Flashbulb memories. Cognition 5, 73–99.

53. Talarico, J. M., and Rubin, D. (2003) Confidence, not consistency, characterizes flash-bulb memories. Psychol Sci 14, 455–61.

54. Van Giezen, A. E., Arensman, E., Spinhoven, P., and Wolters, G. (2005) Consistency of memory for emotionally arousing events. Clin Psychol Rev 25, 935–53.

55. Schwartz, E. D., Kowalski, J. M., and McNally, R. J. (1993) Malignant memories: post-traumatic changes in memory in adults after a school shooting. J Trauma Stress 6, 545–53.

56. Southwick, S. M., Morgan, A., Nicolaou, A. L., and Charney, D. S. (1997) Consistency of memory for combat-related traumatic events in veterans of Operation Desert Storm. Am J Psychiatry 154, 173–77.

57. Qin, J., Mitchell, K. J., Johnson, M. K., et al. (2003) Reactions to and memories for the September 11, 2001 terrorist attacks in adults with posttraumatic stress disorder. Appl Cogn Psychol 17, 1081–97.

58. Engelhard, I. M., van den Hout, M. A., and McNally, R. J. (2008) Memory consistency for traumatic events in Dutch soldiers deployed to Iraq. Memory 16, 3–9.

59. Megias, J. L., Ryan, E., Vaquero, J. M. M., and Frese, B. (2007) Comparisons of trau-matic and positive memories in people with and without PTSD profile. Appl Cogn Psychol 21, 117–30.

60. Berntsen, D., Willert, M., and Rubin, D. C. (2003) Splintered memories or vivid land-marks? Reliving and coherence of traumatic memories in PTSD. Appl Cogn Psychol 17, 675–93.

61. Rubin, D. C., Feldman, M. E., and Beckham, J. C. (2004) Reliving, emotions, and frag-mentation in the autobiographical memories of veterans diagnosed with PTSD. Appl Cogn Psychol 18, 17–35.

62. Geraerts, E., Kozaric-Kovacic, D., Merckelbach, H., Peraica, T., Jelicic, M., and Candel, I. (2007) Traumatic memories of war events: not so special after all. Conscious Cogn 16, 170–77.

63. Van der Kolk, B. A. (1997) The psychobiology of posttraumatic stress disorder. J Clin Psychiatry 58, 16–24.

64. Van der Kolk, B. A. (1998) Trauma and memory. Psychiatry Clin Neurosci 52, S97–S109.

65. Ehlers, A., and Clark, D. M. (2000) A cognitive model of posttraumatic stress disorder. Behav Res Ther 38, 319–45.

66. Brewin, C. R. (2001) A cognitive neuroscience account of posttraumatic stress disorder and its treatment. Behav Res Ther 39, 373–93.

67. Brewin, C. R. (2005) Encoding and retrieval of traumatic memories. In: Vasterling, J. J., and Brewin, C. R., eds., Neuropsychology of PTSD: Biological, Cognitive, and Clinical Perspectives. New York: Guilford Press: 131–50.

68. Brewin, C. R. (2007) What is it that a neurobiological model of PTSD must explain? Prog Brain Res 167, 217–26.

69. Christianson, S. A. (1992) Emotional stress and eyewitness memory: a critical review. Psychol Bull 112, 284–309.

70. Safer, M. A., Christianson, S. A., Autry, M. W., and Osterlund, K. (1998) Tunnel mem-ory for traumatic events. Appl Cogn Psychol 12, 99–117.

71. Bernsten, D., and Rubin, D. C. (2007) When a trauma becomes a key to identity: enhanced integration of trauma memories predicts posttraumatic stress disorder symp-toms. Appl Cogn Psychol 21, 417–31.

72. Hellawell, S. J., and Brewin, C. R. (2002) A comparison of flashbacks and ordinary autobiographical memories of trauma: cognitive resources and behavioural observa-tions. Behav Res Ther 40, 1143–56.

73. Amir, N., Stafford, J., Freshman, M. S., and Foa, E. B. (1998) Relationship between trauma narratives and trauma pathology. J Trauma Stress 11, 385–92.
74. Foa, E. B., and Riggs, D. S. (1993) Posttraumatic stress disorder and rape. In: Oldham, J., Riba, M. B., and Tasman, A., eds, Review of Psychiatry. Washington, DC: American Psychiatric Press:273–303.
75. Brewin, C. R. (1998) Intrusive autobiographical memories in depression and post-traumatic stress disorder. Appl Cogn Psychol 12, 359–70.
76. Hellawell, S. J., and Brewin, C. R. (2004) A comparison of flashbacks and ordinary autobiographical memories of trauma: content and language Behav Res Ther 42, 1–12.
77. Berntsen, D., and Rubin, D. C. (2008) The reappearance hypothesis revisited: recurrent involuntary memories after traumatic events and in everyday life. Mem Cogn 36, 449–60.
78. Brewin, C. R., Kleiner, J. S., Vasterling, J. J., and Field, A. P. (2006) Memory for emotionally neutral information in posttraumatic stress disorder: a meta-analytic investigation. J Abnorm Psychol 116, 448–63.
79. Isaac, C. L., Cushway, D., and Jones, G. V. (2006) Is posttraumatic stress disorder associated with specific deficits in episodic memory? Clin Psychol Rev 26, 939–955.
80. Bremner, J. D., Randall, P., Scott, T. M., et al. (1995) MRI-based measurement of hippocampal volume in patients with combat-related posttraumatic stress disorder. Am J Psychiatry 41, 23–32.
81. Jelinek, L., Jacobsen, D., Kellner, M., et al. (2006) Verbal and nonverbal memory functioning in posttraumatic stress disorder (PTSD). J Clin Exp Neuropsychol 28, 940–48.
82. Uddo, M., Vasterling, J. J., Brailey, K., and Sutker, P. B. (1993) Memory and attention in combat-related post-traumatic stress disorder (PTSD). J Consult Clin Psychol 3, 520–30.
83. Vasterling, J. J., Duke, L. M., Brailey, K., Constans, J. I., Allain, A. N., and Sutker, P. B. (2002) Attention, learning, and memory performances and intellectual resources in Vietnam veterans: PTSD and no disorder comparisons. Neuropsychology 16, 5–14.
84. Samuelson, K. W., Neylan, T., Metzler, T. J., et al. (2006) Neuropsychological functioning in posttraumatic stress disorder and alcohol abuse. Neuropsychology 20, 716–26.
85. Yehuda, R., Golier, J. A., Halligan, S. L., and Harvey, P. D. (2004) Learning and memory in Holocaust survivors with PTSD. Biol Psychiatry 55, 291–95.
86. Bremner, J. D., Scott, T. M., Delaney, S. M., et al. (1993) Deficits in short-term memory in post-traumatic stress disorder. Am J Psychiatry 150, 1015–19.
87. Gilbertson, M. W., Gurvits, T. V., Lasko, N. B., Orr, S. P., and Pitman, R. K. (2001) Multivariate assessment of explicit memory function in combat veterans with posttraumatic stress disorder. J Trauma Stress 14, 413–32.
88. Jenkins, M. A., Langlais, P. J., Delis, D., and Cohen, R. (1998) Learning and memory in rape victims with posttraumatic stress disorder. Am J Psychiatry 155, 278–79.
89. Lindauer, R. J. L., Olff, M., van Meijel, E. P. M., Carlier, I. V. E., and Gersons, B. P. R. (2006) Cortisol, learning, memory, and attention in relation to smaller hippocampal volume in police officers with posttraumatic stress disorder. Biol Psychiatry 59, 171–77.
90. Yehuda, R., Keefe, R. S., Harvey, P. D., et al. (1995) Learning and memory in combat veterans with posttraumatic stress disorder. Am J Psychiatry 152, 137–39.
91. Crowell, T., Kieffer, K., Siders, C., and Vanderploeg, R. (2002) Neuropsychological findings in combat-related posttraumatic stress disorder. Clin Neuropsychol 16, 310–21.

92. Neylan, T. C., Lenoci, M., Rothlind, J., et al. (2004) Attention, learning, and memory in posttraumatic stress disorder. J Trauma Stress 17, 41–46.
93. Stein, M. B., Hanna, C., Vaerum, V., and Koverola, C. (1999) Memory functioning in adult women traumatized by childhood sexual abuse. J Trauma Stress 12, 527–34.
94. Stein, M. B., Kennedy, C. M., and Twamley, E. W. (2002) Neuropsychological function in female victims of intimate partner violence with and without posttraumatic stress disorder. Biol Psychiatry 52, 1079–88.
95. Dankwerts, A., and Leathem, J. (2003) Questioning the link between PTSD and cognitive dysfunction. Neuropsychol Rev 13, 221–35.
96. Gilbertson, M. W., Paulus, L. A., Williston, S. K., et al. (2006) Neurocognitive function in monozygotic twins discordant for combat exposure: relationship to posttraumatic stress disorder. J Abnorm Psychol 115, 484–95.
97. Vasterling, J. J., and Brailey, K. (2005) Neuropsychological findings in adults with PTSD. In: Vasterling, J. J., and Brewin, C. R., eds., Neuropsychology of PTSD: Biological, Cognitive, and Clinical Perspectives. New York: Guilford Press:178–207.
98. Brandes, D., Ben-Schachar, G., Gilboa, A., Bonne, O., Freedman, S., and Shalev, A. (2002) PTSD symptoms and cognitive performance in recent trauma survivors. Psychiatry Res 110, 231–38.
99. Moradi, A. R., Neshat Doost, H. T., Taghavi, M. R., Yule, W., and Dalgleish, T. (1999) Everyday memory deficits in children and adolescents with PTSD: performance on the Rivermead Behavioural Memory Test. J Child Psychol Psychiatry 40, 357–61.
100. Golier, J. A., Harvey, P. D., Legge, J., and Yehuda, R. (2006) Memory performance in older trauma survivors. Ann N Y Acad Sci 1071, 54–66.
101. Yehuda, R., Tischler, L., Golier, J. A., et al. (2006) Longitudinal assessment of cognitive performance in Holocaust survivors with and without PTSD. Biol Psychiatry 60, 714–21.
102. Freedman, M., and Cermak, L. S. (1996) Semantic encoding deficits in frontal lobe disease and amnesia. Brain Cogn 5, 108–14.
103. Moscovitch, M. (1982) Multiple dissociations of function in amnesia. In: Cermak, L. S., ed., Human Memory and Amnesia. Hillsdale, NJ: Erlbaum:337–370.
104. Tischler, L., Brand, S. R., Stavitsky, K., et al. (2006) The relationship between hippocampal volume and declarative memory in a population of combat veterans with and without PTSD. Ann N Y Acad Sci 1071, 405–9.
105. McEwen, B. S., and Margarinos, A. M. (1997) Stress effects on morphology and function of the hippocampus. Ann N Y Acad Sci 821, 271–84.
106. Sapolsky, R. M. (1996) Why stress is bad for your brain. Science 273, 749–50.
107. Bremner, J. D. (2001) Hypotheses and controversies related to effects of stress on the hippocampus: an argument for stress-induced damage to the hippocampus in patients with posttraumatic stress disorder. Hippocampus 11, 75–81.
108. Lupien, S. J., Maheu, F., Tu, M., Fiocco, A., and Schramek, T. E. (2007) The effects of stress and stress hormones on human cognition: implications for the field of brain and cognition. Brain Cogn 65, 209–37.
109. Bremner, J. D., Randall, P., Vermetten, E., et al. (1997) Magnetic resonance imaging-based measurement of hippocampal volume in posttraumatic stress disorder related to childhood physical and sexual abuse—a preliminary report. Biol Psychiatry 41, 23–32.
110. Gurvits, T. V., Shenton, M. E., Hokama, H., et al. (1996) Magnetic resonance imaging study of hippocampal volume in chronic, combat-related posttraumatic stress disorder. Biol Psychiatry 40, 1091–99.

111. Stein, M. B., Koverola, C., Hanna, C., Torchia, M., and McClarty, B. (1997) Hippocampal volume in women victimized by childhood sexual abuse. Psychol Med 27, 951–59.
112. Hedges, D. W., and Woon, F. L. M. (2007) Structural magnetic resonance imaging findings in posttraumatic stress disorder and their response to treatment: a systematic review. Curr Psychiatry Rev 4, 85–93.
113. Nemeroff, C. B., Bremner, J. D., Foa, E. B., Mayberg, H. S., North, C. S., and Murray, S. B. (2006) Posttraumatic stress disorder: a state-of-the science review. J Psychiatr Res 40, 1–21.
114. Bonne, O., Brandes, D., Gilboa, A., et al. (2001) Longitudinal MRI study of hippocampal volume in trauma survivors with PTSD. Am J Psychiatry 158, 1248–51.
115. Fennema-Notestine, C., Stein, M. B., Kennedy, C. M., Archibald, S. L., and Jernigan, T. L. (2002) Brain morphometry in female victims of intimate partner violence with and without posttraumatic stress disorder. Biol Psychiatry 52, 1089–1101.
116. Jatzko, A., Rothenhofer, S., Schmitt, A., et al. (2006) Hippocampal volume in chronic posttraumatic stress disorder (PTSD): MRI study using two different evaluation methods. J Affect Disord 94, 121–26.
117. Golier, J. A., Yehuda, R., De Santi, S., Segal, S., Dolan, S., and de Leon, M. J. (2005) Absence of hippocampal volume differences in survivors of the Nazi Holocaust with and without posttraumatic stress disorder. Psychiatry Res 139, 53–64.
118. Emdad, R., Bonekamp, D., Sondergaard, H. P., et al. (2006) Morphometric and psychometric comparisons between non-substance-abusing patients with posttraumatic stress disorder and normal controls. Acta Psychother 75, 122–32.
119. Gilbertson, M. W., Williston, S. K., Paulus, L. A., et al. (2007) Configural cue performance in identical twins discordant for posttraumatic stress disorder: theoretical implications for the role of hippocampal function. Biol Psychiatry 62, 513–20.
120. Isaac, C. L., and Mayes, A. R. (1999) Rate of forgetting in amnesia: I. Recall and recognition of prose. J Exp Psychol Learn Mem Cogn 25, 942–62.
121. Davidson, R. J., Jackson, D. C., and Kalin, N. H. (2000) Emotion, plasticity, context, and regulation: perspectives from affective neuroscience. Psychol Bull 126, 890–909.
122. Pavlides, C., Kimura, A., Magarinos, A. M., and McEwen, B. S. (1995) Hippocampal homosynaptic long-term depression depotentiation induced by adrenal steroids. Neuroscience 68, 379–85.
123. Arbel, I., Kadar, T., Silberman, M., and Levy, A. (1994) The effects of long-term corticosterone administration on hippocampal morphology and cognitive performance of middle-aged rats. Brain Res 657, 227–35.
124. McEwen, B. S. (2007) Physiology and neurobiology of stress and adaptation: central role of the brain. Physiol Rev 87, 873–904.
125. Lieberman, H. R., Bathalon, G. P., Falco, C. M., Kramer, M., Morgan, C. A., and Niro, P. (2005) Severe decrements in cognition function and mood induced by sleep loss, heat, dehydration, and undernutrition during simulated combat. Biol Psychiatry 57, 422–29.
126. Morgan, C. A., Doran, A., Steffian, G., Hazlett, G., and Southwick, S. M. (2006) Stress-induced deficits in working memory and visuo-constructive abilities in special operations soldiers. Biol Psychiatry 60, 722–9.
127. Vasterling, J. J., Proctor, S. P., Amoros, P., Kane, R., Heeren, T., and White, R. F. (2006) Neuropsychological outcomes of Army personnel following deployment to the Iraq war. JAMA 296, 519–29.
128. McNally, R. J., and Shin, L. M. (1995) Association of intelligence with severity of posttraumatic stress disorder symptoms in Vietnam combat veterans. Am J Psychiatry 152, 936–38.

129. Macklin, M. L., Metzger, L. J., Litz, B. T., et al. (1998) Lower precombat intelligence is a risk factor for posttraumatic stress disorder. J Consult Clin Psychol 66, 323–26.
130. Bustamante, V., Mellman, T. A., Davide, D., and Fins, A. I. (2001) Cognitive functioning and the early development of PTSD. J Trauma Stress 14, 791–97.
131. Gilbertson, M. W., Shenton, M. E., Ciszewski, A., et al. (2002) Smaller hippocampal volume predicts pathologic vulnerability to psychological trauma. Nat Neurosci 5, 1242–47.
132. Parslow, R. A., and Jorm, A. F. (2007) Pretrauma and posttrauma neurocognitive functioning and PTSD symptoms in a community sample of young adults. Am J Psychiatry 164, 509–15.
133. Chemtob, C. M., Roitblat, H. L., Hamada, R. S., Muraoka, M. Y., Carlson, J. G., and Bauer, G. B. (1999) Compelled attention: the effects of viewing trauma-related stimuli on concurrent task performance in posttraumatic stress disorder. J Trauma Stress 12, 309–26.
134. Paunovic, N., Lundh, L.-G., and Ost, L.-G. (2002) Attentional and memory bias for emotional information in crime victims with acute posttraumatic stress disorder. J Anxiety Disord 16, 675–92.
135. Vrana, S., Roodman, A., and Beckham, J. (1995) Selective processing of trauma-relevant words in post-traumatic stress disorder. J Anxiety Disord 9, 515–30.
136. Litz, B. T., Weathers, F. W., Monaco, V., et al. (1996) Attention, arousal, and memory in posttraumatic stress disorder. J Trauma Stress 9, 497–519.
137. Moradi, A. R., Taghavi, R., Neshat-Doost, H. T., Yule, W., and Dalgleish, T. (2000) Memory bias for emotional information in children and adolescents with posttraumatic stress disorder: a preliminary study. J Anxiety Disord 14, 521–34.
138. Golier, J. A., Yehuda, R., Lupien, S. J., and Harvey, P. D. (2003) Memory for trauma-related information in Holocaust survivors with PTSD. Psychiatry Res 121, 133–43.
139. Ochsner, K. N. (2000) Are affective events richly recollected or simply familiar? The experience and process of recognizing feelings past. J Exp Psychol Gen 129, 242–61.
140. Sharot, T., Delgado, M. R., and Phelps, E. A. (2004) How emotion enhances the feeling of remembering. Nat Neurosci 7, 1376–80.
141. Tapia, G., Clarys, D., Isingrini, M., and El-Hage, W. (2007) Memoire et emotion dans le trouble de stress post-traumatique (TSPT). Can Psychol 48, 106–19.
142. Cahill, L., and McGaugh, J. L. (1998) Mechanisms of emotional arousal and lasting declarative memory. Trends Neurosci 21, 294–99.
143. Shin, L. M., Kosslyn, S. M., McNally, R. J., et al. (1997) Visual imagery and perception in posttraumatic stress disorder. A positron emission tomographic investigation. Arch Gen Psychiatry 54, 233–41.
144. Shin, L. M., Kosslyn, S. M., McNally, R. J., et al. (1999) Regional cerebral blood flow during script-driven imagery in childhood sexual abuse-related PTSD: a PET investigation. Am J Psychiatry 156, 575–84.
145. Amir, N., McNally, R. J., and Wiegartz, P. S. (1996) Implicit memory bias for threat in posttraumatic stress disorder. Cogn Ther Res 26, 645–55.
146. Zeitlin, S. B., and McNally, R. J. (1991) Implicit and explicit memory bias for threat in post-traumatic stress disorder. Behav Res Ther 29, 451–57.
147. Michael, T., Ehlers, A., and Halligan, S. L. (2005) Enhanced priming for trauma-related material in posttraumatic stress disorder. Emotion 5, 103–12.
148. McNally, R. J., and Amir, N. (1996) Perceptual implicit memory for trauma-related information in post-traumatic stress disorder. Cogn Emot 10, 551–56.
149. Sara, S. J. (2000) Retrieval and reconsolidation: toward a neurobiology of remembering. Learn Mem 7, 73–84.

150. Dudai, Y. (2006) Reconsolidation: the advantage of being refocused. Curr Opin Neurobiol 16, 174–78.
151. Foa, E., and Kozak, M. J. (1986) Emotional processing of fear: exposure to corrective information. Psychol Bull 99, 20–35.
152. Rothbaum, B. O., and Schwartz, A. C. (2002) Exposure therapy for posttraumatic stress disorder. Am J Psychother 56, 59–75.
153. Resick, P. A., Galovski, T. A., Uhlmansiek, M. O., Scher, C. D., Clum, G. A., and Young-Xu, Y. (2008) A randomized clinical trial to dismantle components of cognitive processing therapy for posttraumatic stress disorder in female victims of interpersonal violence. J Consult Clin Psychol 76, 243–58.
154. Brunet, A., Orr, S. P., Tremblay, J., Robertson, K., Nader, K., and Pitman, R. K. (2008) Effect of post-retrieval propranolol on psychophysiologic responding during subsequent script-driven traumatic imagery in post-traumatic stress disorder. J Psychiatr Res 42, 503–6.
155. King, D. W., King, L. A., Erickson, D. J., Huang, M. T., Sharkansky, E. J., and Wolfe, J. (2000) Post-traumatic stress disorder and retrospectively reported stressor exposure: a longitudinal prediction model. J Abnorm Psychol 109, 624–33.
156. Roemer, L., Litz, B. T., Orsillo, S. M., Ehlich, P. J., and Friedman, M. J. (1998) Increases in retrospective accounts of war-zone exposure over time: the role of PTSD symptom severity. J Trauma Stress 11, 597–605.
157. Wesseley, S., Unwin, C., Hotopf, M., et al. (2003) Stability of recall of military hazards over time. Br J Psychiatry 183, 314–22.
158. Berntsen, D., and Rubin, D.C. (2006) The centrality of event scale: a measure of integrating a trauma into one's identity and its relation to post-traumatic stress disorder symptoms. Behav Res Ther 44, 219–231.

Animal Models of Post-Traumatic Stress Disorder

6 | Toward Animal Models of Post-Traumatic Stress Disorder

Hagit Cohen and Gal Richter-Levin

CONTENTS

INTRODUCTION
TRAUMA-STRESS-BASED MODELS
MECHANISM-BASED MODELS
ANIMAL MODELS BASED ON CHANGES IN
    NEUROBIOLOGICAL SYSTEMS
MODELING ADDITIONAL FACTORS
CONCLUSION
REFERENCES

Abstract

The development of animal models for PTSD and other traumatic stress related brain changes is an important part of advancing our neurobiological understanding of the disease process as well as recovery, resilience, and possible therapeutic targets.

Although animal models for PTSD are limited to the assessment of measurable and observable behavioral parameters and cannot assess complex psychological symptoms such as intrusive thoughts, meaning and dreams, valid and reliable animal models offer a means for researching biomolecular, pathophysiological, and pharmacological features of the disorder in ways that are not feasible in human studies.

Trauma/stress-based Models were developed in an attempt to induce in the animal a state similar to PTSD by exposing animals to an equivalent of a traumatic experience.

Mechanism-based models were developed considering potential brain mechanisms that may underlay the disorder. The most studied are enhanced fear conditioning, impaired extinction and more recently, impaired contextualization.

From: *Post-Traumatic Stress Disorder: Basic Science and Clinical Practice*
Edited by: P. J. Shiromani et al., DOI: 10.1007/978-1-60327-329-9_6
© Humana Press, a part of Springer Science+Business Media, LLC 2009

133

Another important line of research addresses the question of additional factors that contribute to the susceptibility to develop PTSD. Genetic background and environmental factors have been studied and have led to the recognition of the importance of individual differences in susceptibility to develop the disorder.

This chapter presents and discusses findings from various animal models, with the understanding that no single model encompasses in full the complexity of the disorder but that each of these models contributes to our understanding of PTSD.

Key Words: Amygdala, animal models, corticotrophin-releasing hormone, HPA axis.

INTRODUCTION

Animal models of psychiatric disorders offer a complementary research modality that supports clinical research. To achieve a satisfactory degree of validity and reliability, animal models of complex and intricate psychiatric disorders must fulfill certain criteria. For example, the behavioral responses must be observable and measurable and must reliably reflect clinical symptomatology; pharmacological agents that are known to affect symptoms in human subjects should correct measurable parameters that model symptoms of the disorder with equal efficacy.

Developing an animal model for post-traumatic stress disorder (PTSD) is not a trivial issue. Diagnosis in human patients relies heavily on personal reports of thoughts, dreams, and images, which cannot be studied in rats. Furthermore, several of the typical symptoms of PTSD may be unique to humans and thus not be found in rats. Likewise, an important factor of the trauma in humans is the perception of the life-threatening potential of the situation. It is not clear whether rats can make this judgment or which stressors will be most effective for rats. In addition, there is as yet no clearly effective pharmacological treatment for PTSD. It is thus difficult to test a potential rodent model for its pharmacological predictability in relation to PTSD or other traumatic stress-related disorders.

Nevertheless, using animals to study PTSD holds advantages for several reasons. First, unlike many other mental disorders, the diagnostic criteria for PTSD specify an etiological factor, which is an exposure to a life-threatening, traumatic event (6). In a model for PTSD, variables such as the quality and intensity of the stressor and the degree of exposure to it can be carefully controlled, and the behavioral and concomitant physiological responses to a (valid) threatening stimulus could be studied. Second, little is known about pretrauma etiological aspects of the disorder since, naturally, the studies so far have focused on retrospective assessments of the patients after the onset of PTSD. An animal model will enable a prospective follow-up design, in which the disorder is triggered at a specified time and in a uniform manner, in controllable and statistically sound population samples, and enable the assessment of behavioral and gross physiological parameters. Moreover, unlike studies in human subjects, animal model studies enable the assessment of concomitant biomolecular changes in dissected brain areas and the experimentation with pharmacological agents with potential therapeutic effects.

This chapter presents and discusses findings from various animal models of PTSD, which differ from one another in the rationale for their development. These models use different paradigms but show a range of behavioral and physiological manifestations seen in PTSD patients.

TRAUMA-/STRESS-BASED MODELS

Stress paradigms in animals studies aim to model criterion A of the DSM diagnostic criteria (2). They consist of extremely stressful experiences aimed to engender a sense of threat and helplessness in the animal. Some of these have focused more on the intensity of the experience, whereas others have combined this with an attempt to design an ethologically valid experience, one that an animal might encounter in its natural environment.

Exposure of rodents to predator stimuli (cat, cat odor, fox odor or trimethyl-thiazoline, a synthetic compound isolated from fox feces) is fear provoking and stressful and produces long-lasting behavioral and physiological responses. Blanchard et al. (3–8), Adamec et al. (9–14), and others (15–20) have established the validity of this paradigm, in which adult rodents are exposed to feline predators for 5–10 min in a closed environment (i.e., inescapable exposure). The resultant freezing response mode is ethologically adaptive for animals when both "fight" and "flight" options are ineffective. Predator stress has ecological validity in that it mimics brief, intense threatening experiences with lasting affective consequences (12–13). The predator stress paradigm has proven to be effective in inducing the expected range of behavioral and physiological responses (1,9–14). These include freezing, avoidance, increased secretion of stress hormones, and changes in transmission from hippocampus via the ventral angular bundle to the basolateral amygdala and from central amygdala to lateral column of the periaqueductal gray (3,4,10,11,13,15–19,21–29). These pathways are of interest because neuroplastic changes within them are associated with aversive learning. Predator stimuli potency is comparable to that of a variety of paradigms in which the threat is more tangible and immediate, such as paradigms based on inescapable pain or electric shock, swimming and near-drowning, a small raised platform, and even direct proximity to a kitten or a car (separated by a mesh divide or a solid divide with an opening large enough for the rodent to slip through).

Richter-Levin (30) developed an interesting stress model, the underwater trauma. Although rats naturally swim well and are able to dive and to cope with exposure to water, brief (30–45 s) uncontrollable restraint under water establishes an ethologically relevant traumatic experience. Exposure of rats to underwater trauma resulted in long-lasting heightened anxiety and context-specific spatial memory deficits (30–32). Underwater trauma in a different (out-of-context) water container had no effects on the ability of rats to perform a spatial memory task in the water maze (30). These results may explain the lack of effect of inescapable tail shock procedure on spatial performance reported by others (*33*) because in their study the stressor was not associated with the context of the maze. Moreover, underwater trauma resulted in both behavioral and electrophysiological aversive effects. At 20 min after the trauma, the traumatized rats performed poorly in the spatial memory task in the water maze, and 40 min after the tetanic stimulation (100 min after the underwater trauma) they showed a reduced level of long-term potentiation (LTP). Thus, the underwater trauma induced electrophysiological alterations that resembled those observed in other models of stress (*34–37*). In addition, the impaired performance in the water maze was significantly correlated with the reduced ability to induce LTP. These findings of a strong correlation between LTP and spatial learning suggest that these two phenomena are related. However, it is possible that the trauma impairs performance not by affecting memory but by affecting memory-related processes such as attention. It was suggested that the underwater trauma could provide an important and potentially powerful model for understanding the mechanisms underlying the relationship among stress, cognition, and learning.

MECHANISM-BASED MODELS

Another approach in developing animal models of PTSD was to consider potential brain mechanisms that could underlay the disorder and to develop behavioral protocols that would mimic the activation of such mechanisms.

Enhanced Fear Conditioning

The persistence of the psychological and biological fear responses could not be satisfactorily explained by the stress theory, leading some to suggest that fear conditioning might underlay the phenomenon (*38*). In certain respects, fear conditioning resembles PTSD (*39*). During Pavlovian fear conditioning, a neutral conditioned stimulus (CS; usually a tone or light) is repeatedly paired with a stressful unconditioned stimulus (US; usually a foot shock). Once the CS-US association has been formed, the CS produces a conditioned fear response (CR; such as freezing [or movement arrest], enhancement of musculature [startle] reflexes, autonomic changes, analgesia and behavioral response suppression) in anticipation of the US (*40,41*). A CR is also evoked when the animal is placed in the environment in which the experiment took place. Translating to PTSD, the traumatic event (US) triggers an Unconditioned Response (UR) which is characterized by strong arousal and intense fear. This UR becomes associated with cues, such as smells, voices, or sights (CSs), that were present during the traumatic event. As a result of this pairing, these cues can trigger similar responses (CRs) even in the absence of the US (*38,42*). Thus, given theassociation between traumatic recall and seemingly unrelated stimuli and the ensuing fearful response, the mechanism of enhanced fear conditioning has often been suggested as a model for the reexperiencing phenomena in PTSD (*43–47*).

Impaired Extinction

Conditioned fear responses can be extinguished by repeatedly presenting the CS without the US (*39*). Pavlov, in his classic investigation of appetitive conditioning in dogs, observed that extinguished responses spontaneously recovered with the passage of time (*39*). This suggested that extinction suppresses, rather than erases, the original CS-US association. Thus, extinction is an important behavioral phenomenon that allows the organism to adapt its behavior to a changing environment (*48*). Moreover, experimental extinction is a behavioral technique that leads to suppression of the acquired fear, that is, a decrease in the amplitude and frequency of a CR as a function of nonreinforced CS presentations (*49*). More recently, impaired extinction learning has been proposed as an alternative mechanism for the formation of PTSD symptoms (*42,50–52*).

Part of the attraction of fear conditioning was that much was concurrently being learned about the neurobiology of this animal paradigm. A large body of evidence from lesion, pharmacological, and neurophysiological studies indicate that the amygdala (corpus amygdaloideum) is involved in the acquisition and extinction of fear memory (*53*) and seems to have a pivotal role in the extinction of learned conditioning fear (*54*). The hypothesis that lateral amygdala (LA) neurons encode fear memories, and conditional stimulus-elicited LA firing is contextually modulated after extinction has been demonstrated to require a functional hippocampus (*55*). Based on this assertion, it has been proposed that contextual modulation of CS-evoked spike firing could be implemented by hippocampal modulation of medial prefrontal cortex (mPFC) control over the amygdala (*56*). Alternatively, direct projections from the hippocampus to the amygdala may regulate fear expression after extinction (*57*). Because the hippocampus is connected with many brain areas (including the mPFC and the amygdala), it is yet unclear which of these connections is important for the contextual modulation of extinction. This model proposes that the hippocampus performs an executive role in the balance of excitation and inhibition in fear circuits, in which the mPFC may come to inhibit LA neuronal activity during fear extinction that would otherwise excite the fear response (*56*). Furthermore, the regulation of this fear is dependent on the context in which fear stimuli are encountered (*56*). When animals are tested in contexts associated with extinction, the hippocampus drives mPFC inhibition of the LA (*56*). However, if animals are presented with an extinguished CS outside the extinction context, the hippocampus may inhibit mPFC activation and thus promote excitation in the LA to renew the previously extinguished fear under these conditions (*56*). In support of this, lesions of rat infralimbic (IL) cortex (analogous to the mPFC in humans) enhance renewal of extinguished appetitive Pavlovian responding when tested in the acquisition context following extinction in an alternative context (*58*). These results parallel previous observations of increased spontaneous recovery and reinstatement in animals with damage to the IL region (*59*). Moreover, they are consistent with previous structural and functional neuroimaging studies in PTSD patients, indicating a hyperresponsive amygdala accompanied by hypoactivation of the PFC (*39,60–72*).

However, PTSD is a complex disorder that involves far more than a fear response and cannot be explained by a simple conditioning model.

Impaired Contextualization

A different mechanism that may contribute to the development of PTSD symptoms is the inability to appropriately "contextualize" the traumatic events in autobiographic memory. Clinically, PTSD patients relive their traumatic experiences repeatedly, unable to assimilate them as time- and context-limited events without negative implications for their future. For example, for a combat veteran, the sound of a passing helicopter in the current, objectively safe environment can evoke the traumatic experience of combat that took place years earlier. Deficient embedding or contextualization of the traumatic events in autobiographic memory is thought to be one of the main problems in PTSD (*73*). Indeed, suggestion of contextual memory deficits has been reported in the single prolonged stress (SPS) animal model of PTSD (*74–76*). However, direct testing of contextual cue processing is required to reliably demonstrate inability to contextualize memory in PTSD animal models.

We recently tested the hypothesis that exposure to a traumatic/stressful experience could impair contextual odor discrimination, and that this impairment is associated with PTSD-like behavioral responses. To support this study, a novel experimental paradigm, differential contextual-odor conditioning (DCOC), was devised to examine the animals' abilities to discriminate between the significance of an odor cue acquired in either safe or dangerous contextual environments when encountered in a novel, neutral environment. The odor cue consists of a cinnamon smell that could signal either reward or punishment (safety or threat signal) depending on the contextual cues that are present. Each of the conditions was learned in a different chamber. Animals were tested in a third, new chamber, so all other contextual cues were controlled for, and the only previously encountered cue that was present was the cinnamon odor (*77*).

Our findings demonstrated that, in this novel experimental paradigm, animals trained in the DCOC paradigm acquired the ability to discriminate between contextual cues signaling safe versus dangerous contextual environments, validating the DCOC paradigm for the assessment of contextualization. Exposure to severe traumatic stress (predator scent stress, PSS) interfered with processes related to subsequent adequate and flexible application of contextualization. Traumatized animals were unable to acquire the ability to accurately evaluate the contextual relevance of an odor stimulus or lost this ability after having effectively acquired it (Fig. 1). Thus, the DCOC paradigm is suggested as an effective animal model that would enable the study of the neurobiology of contextualization and of related pathology (*77*).

Other animal models focus on modeling specific neurobiological sequelae or specific behavior findings reported in PTSD.

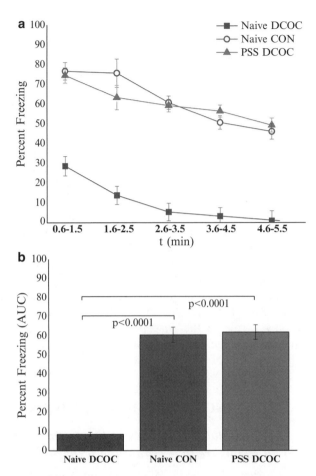

Fig. 1. Percent freezing in the neutral arenas for control and DCOC animals and the effects of pretraining stress-exposure: **a** Percent free zingin five blocks of 1 min each. **b** The area under the curve (AUC) during all training. The DCOC (differential contextual odor conditioning) rats displayed significantly less immobility than control (CON) or stress-exposed DCOC animals in the neutral arena. *PSS* predator scent stress

ANIMAL MODELS BASED ON
CHANGES IN NEUROBIOLOGICAL SYSTEMS

Hypothalamic-Pituitary-Adrenal Axis Response

The SPS model introduced by Liberzon et al (*75,76*), was developed to mimic specific hypothalamic-pituitary-adrenal (HPA) abnormalities and enhanced acoustic startle (*74–6*). In the SPS paradigm, rats are exposed sequentially to 2 h of restraint, 20 min of swimming, and ether exposure until loss of consciousness. One week after the experience, rats show increased startle responses to 50-ms, 108-dB tones, both when compared to a nonstressed control group and compared to their own startle responses before the SPS session (74). Most important, the SPS model has been found to induce long-term alteration of the expression of glucocorticoid receptors in the hippocampal formation (6). Whereas a long-term decrease was observed in type I (mineralocorticoid) receptor, the type II (glucocorticoid) receptors showed a transient decrease (24 h), followed by enhanced expression at 7 days post-SPS.

Another study assessed aspects of the HPA axis response in strains with deficient and excessive HPA axis responsiveness compared to normal rats (78). Stress responses were also examined in populations of inbred Lewis and Fischer rats and compared to outbred Sprague-Dawley rats. Lewis rats exhibit a reduced synthesis and secretion of corticotropin-releasing factor (CRF), leading to reduced plasma adrenocorticotropic hormone (ACTH) and reduced Corticosterone (CORT) release from the adrenal cortex, whereas Fischer rats possess a hyperresponsive HPA axis. Prevalence rates of extreme behavioral response (EBR) individuals were significantly higher in Lewis (50%) than in Fischer rats (10%) or controls (25%) (78). However, exogenous administration of cortisol to Lewis rats before applying the stressor decreased the prevalence of EBR significantly (8%). These results suggest that blunted HPA axis response to stress may play a role in the susceptibility to experimentally induced PTSD-like behavioral changes, especially as these effects may be reversed by preexposure administration of corticosterone (78).

MODELING ADDITIONAL FACTORS

Individual Differences in Response to an Exposure to a Traumatic Experience

It is important to note that, while PTSD requires exposure to a traumatic experience, the trauma alone is not sufficient for PTSD to develop since most individuals exposed to a traumatic event will not develop PTSD.

Identifying the Affected Ones: The Cutoff Behavioral Criteria Approach

The clinical diagnosis of PTSD, one of the most severe outcomes, is made only if an individual exhibits a certain number of symptoms from each of three quite well-defined symptom clusters over a certain period of time (2). Irrespective of the study design or of the stress paradigm, animal studies have generally included the entire stress-exposed population as the study population, and the results discussed and conceptualized as involving this population versus "others," although in practice, just as with humans, the exposed animals display heterogeneous responses. To more closely approximate the approach to understanding animal behavioral models to contemporary understanding of the clinical condition, Cohen and Zohar (79) conceived an approach to understanding the consequences of exposure to a variety of stress paradigms (exposure to a predator or its scent on soiled cat litter, underwater trauma, and elevated platform) in a manner that would enable us to segregate the study animals into groups according to the degree of their response to the stressor, that is, the degree to which their behavior is altered or disrupted. To achieve this, behavioral criteria that would reflect something akin to clinical symptoms needed to be defined and then complemented by the definition of a series of cutoff behavioral criteria (CBC) reflecting severity of response, paralleling clinical inclusion and exclusion criteria applied to clinical research. The idea was to set apart the most clearly affected, that is, the EBR group from their minimal behavioral response (MBR) counterparts (*26–28,32,78–88*).

The CBC method has been applied in a series of studies and has repeatedly enabled a greater degree of resolution in viewing data, a means to reflect them in starker contrast. First, there was highly significant overlap between animals showing EBRs and those with extreme biophysiological measures (i.e., HPA axis assays and heart rate variability [reflecting autonomic nervous system activity]), much more clearly so than when the exposed group was analyzed as a whole (*26–28*),(*79,87*). Different types of traumatic stress paradigm could be seen to cause different proportions of EBR versus MBR animals, not unlike the "dose-response" phenomenon in the human condition, by which different forms of stressor are known to be associated with different incidence rates of PTSD. Serial assessments in the period after exposure to the stressor elicited a curve reflecting the incidence of EBR that parallels that seen in studies of acute stress reaction and subsequent development of chronic disorders: Initially, almost all animals responded "extremely" severely, and over the next 30 days the incidence dropped to an unvarying 25%. This rate of incidence has recurred in all the studies and parallels rates of incidence of PTSD in the general population exposed to trauma (estimated to be between 15% and 35% for most types of trauma throughout the Western Hemisphere).

Modeling Early Life Stress as a
Risk Factor for Developing PTSD

Separating out the more clearly affected animals also elicited significantly different effects on the incidence of chronically disordered behavior when recurrent exposure to trauma occurred in early childhood or later life, both compared to single exposure: In both cases earlier exposure had a greater effect, as is seen in many studies of human subjects exposed to trauma in childhood and youth (*81*).

An important characteristic of stress paradigms is the age at which the animals are exposed to the stressor (*89*). There are many indications that across the life span there are specific windows of vulnerability when high levels of stress have an increased impact on further development (*89–94*). Recent years have witnessed growing interest in effectively modeling in animals the long-term effects of childhood emotional trauma on stress responses in adulthood. Most studies concerned with the impact of early life stress on subsequent stress responses in adulthood in rodents have focused on the postnatal preweaning period (i.e., 3–14 days) and involve some form of maternal deprivation or maternal separation producing acute and long-term effects that vary with the pups' age at exposure to stress (95–97). However, marked differences exist between neonate rats and infants' stress response mechanisms (98). For example, rat pups' HPA axis is characterized by a silent hyporesponsive period (99), while in humans there is no conclusive evidence of a hyporesponsive period in the HPA axis course of development (100). Indeed, it has been suggested that the ages of 3 to 14 days in the rat roughly correspond to the 23rd week of gestation in humans. Furthermore, psychiatric studies often refer to human childhood rather than infancy when investigating the traumatic history of stress-related psychopathologies in patients (101,102). Thus, Richter-Levin and colleagues (81,103–107) have started to examine the consequences of stress exposure at a later early life period: the juvenile or the early adolescent period. The authors reported that the combination of juvenile and adulthood exposures to stress increased anxiety levels, in comparison not only with control unstressed rats but also with rats exposed to stress twice in adulthood. Tsoory and Richter-Levin (107) showed that exposure to stress during juvenility (27–29 days) has a stronger long-term deleterious effect on learning under stressful conditions in adulthood than exposure to the same stressor during "adolescence" (33–35 days). The physiological changes associated with juvenile stress have also been reported and include increases of Dehydroepiandrosterone-sulphate (DHEA-S) concentrations in both the hypothalamus and the entorhinal cortex (103), reduced levels of corticosterone (108), altered autonomic nervous system responses (heart rate and heart rate variability) (81), and downregulation of brain-derived neurotrophic factor (BDNF) messenger ribonucleic acid (mRNA) in the hippocampal CA1 subregion (108). These physiologic changes presumably mediate clinical manifestations of PTSD.

The Contribution of Genetic Background

Twin and family studies of PTSD patients raised questions regarding a possible genetic predisposition to PTSD, although the relative contributions of genotype and environment to endophenotypic expression are unclear (109).

Post-Traumatic Stress Behavioral
Responses in Inbred Mouse Strains

To examine the importance of the genetic background, six inbred strains of mice frequently employed in transgenic research were assessed at baseline and 7 days after PSS exposure (84). Inbred strains are expected to demonstrate about 97.5% homozygosity of loci as the result of at least 20 generations of sibling matings. The results, however, revealed an unexpectedly high degree of within-strain individual heterogeneity at baseline and in the degree of response to stress. This within-strain phenotypic heterogeneity most likely implies that environmental factors play a significant role in characterizing individual responses in spite of the significant strain-related (i.e., genetic) underpinnings. The authors thus suggested that heritable factors may be involved only in part of the endophenotypes associated with the PTSD-like phenotype and may be influenced through a highly indirect route with considerable potential for interaction with environmental variables (*110,111*).

These data imply that the attempt to identify "genetic" versus "environmental" causality as independent main effects is probably logically and procedurally flawed. The evaluation of genetic effects on behavioral phenotypes should consider interactions among genes as well as interactions between genes and environment (*84*).

CONCLUSION

The development of animal models for PTSD and other traumatic stress-related brain changes is an important part of advancing our neurobiological understanding of the disease process as well as recovery, resilience, and possible therapeutic targets. Ultimately, the "optimal" animal model should incorporate trauma-like exposure, will mimic pathophysiological and behavioral findings present in PTSD, and will presumably involve neurobiological mechanisms that participate in PTSD pathophysiology. However, no single widely accepted animal model of PTSD has been established to date, and there is an ongoing debate over what constitutes a valid animal model for this disorder.

Although animal models for PTSD are limited to the assessment of measurable and observable behavioral parameters and cannot assess complex psychological symptoms such as thought, meaning and dreams, valid and reliable animal models offer a means for researching biomolecular, pathophysiological, and pharmacological features of the disorder in ways that are not feasible in human studies.

REFERENCES

1. Nutt D, Davidson J . Post-Traumatic Stress Disorder Diagnosis, Management and Treatment. London: Taylor and Francis; 2000.
2. American Psychiatric Association. Diagnostic and Statistical Manual of Mental Disorders. 4th ed. Washington, DC: American Psychiatric Association; 1994.
3. Blanchard DC, Griebel G, Blanchard RJ. Conditioning and residual emotionality effects of predator stimuli: some reflections on stress and emotion. Prog Neuropsychopharmacol Biol Psychiatry 2003;27(8):1177–85.
4. Blanchard RJ, Blanchard DC. Anti-predator defense as models of fear and anxiety.In: RJBlanchard and SParmigiani, ed. Brain. London: Harwood Academic; 1990.
5. Blanchard RJ, Blanchard DC, Rodgers J, Weiss SM. The characterization and modelling of antipredator defensive behavior. Neurosci Biobehav Rev 1990;14(4):463–72.
6. Blanchard RJ, Griebel G, Henrie JA, Blanchard DC. Differentiation of anxiolytic and panicolytic drugs by effects on rat and mouse defense test batteries. Neurosci Biobehav Rev 1997;21(6):783–89.
7. Blanchard RJ, Nikulina JN, Sakai RR, McKittrick C, McEwen B, Blanchard DC. Behavioral and endocrine change following chronic predatory stress. Physiol Behav 1998;63(4):561–69.
8. Blanchard RJ, Yang M, Li CI, Gervacio A, Blanchard DC. Cue and context conditioning of defensive behaviors to cat odor stimuli. Neurosci Biobehav Rev 2001;25(7–8):587–95.

9. Adamec R. Transmitter systems involved in neural plasticity underlying increased anxiety and defense—implications for understanding anxiety following traumatic stress. Neurosci Biobehav Rev 1997;21(6):755–65.

10. Adamec R, Head D, Blundell J, Burton P, Berton O. Lasting anxiogenic effects of feline predator stress in mice: sex differences in vulnerability to stress and predicting severity of anxiogenic response from the stress experience. Physiol Behav 2006;88(1–2):12–29. Epub 2006 Apr 19.

11. Adamec R, Muir C, Grimes M, Pearcey K. Involvement of noradrenergic and corticoid receptors in the consolidation of the lasting anxiogenic effects of predator stress. Behav Brain Res 2007;179(2):192–207. Epub 2007 Feb 6.

12. Adamec R, Strasser K, Blundell J, Burton P, McKay DW. Protein synthesis and the mechanisms of lasting change in anxiety induced by severe stress. Behav Brain Res 2006;167(2):270–86.

13. Adamec RE, Blundell J, Burton P. Relationship of the predatory attack experience to neural plasticity, pCREB expression and neuroendocrine response. Neurosci Biobehav Rev 2006;30(3):356–75. Epub 2005 Aug 22.

14. Adamec RE, Shallow T. Lasting effects on rodent anxiety of a single exposure to a cat. Physiol Behav 1993;54(1):101–9.

15. Cohen H, Benjamin J, Kaplan Z, Kotler M. Administration of high-dose ketoconazole, an inhibitor of steroid synthesis, prevents posttraumatic anxiety in an animal model. Eur Neuropsychopharmacol 2000;10:429–35.

16. Cohen H, Friedberg S, Michael M, Kotler M, Zeev K. Interaction of CCK-4 induced anxiety and post-cat exposure anxiety in rats. Depress Anxiety 1996;4(3):144–45.

17. Cohen H, Kaplan Z, Kotler M. CCK-antagonists in a rat exposed to acute stress: implication for anxiety associated with post-traumatic stress disorder. Depress Anxiety 1999;10(1):8–17.

18. Diamond DM, Campbell AM, Park CR, et al. Influence of predator stress on the consolidation versus retrieval of long-term spatial memory and hippocampal spinogenesis. Hippocampus 2006;16(7):571–76.

19. File SE, Zangrossi H Jr, Sanders FL, Mabbutt PS. Dissociation between behavioral and corticosterone responses on repeated exposures to cat odor. Physiol Behav 1993;54:1109–11.

20. Griebel G, Blanchard DC, Jung A, Lee JC, Masuda CK, Blanchard RJ. Further evidence that the mouse defense test battery is useful for screening anxiolytic and panicolytic drugs: effects of acute and chronic treatment with alprazolam. Neuropharmacology 1995;34(12):1625–33.

21. Sullivan M, Gratton A. Relationships between stress-induced increases in medial prefrontal cortical dopamine and plasma corticosterone levels in rats: role of cerebral laterality. Neuroscience 1998;83:81–91.

22. Apfelbach R, Blanchard CD, Blanchard RJ, Hayes RA, McGregor IS. The effects of predator odors in mammalian prey species: a review of field and laboratory studies. Neurosci Biobehav Rev 2005;29(8):1123–44. Epub 2005 Aug 8.

23. Blundell J, Adamec R, Burton P. Role of NMDA receptors in the syndrome of behavioral changes produced by predator stress. Physiol Behav 2005;86(1–2):233–43.

24. Endres T, Apfelbach R, Fendt M. Behavioral changes induced in rats by exposure to trimethylthiazoline, a component of fox odor. Behav Neurosci 2005;119(4):1004–10.

25. Takahashi LK, Nakashima BR, Hong H, Watanabe K. The smell of danger: a behavioral and neural analysis of predator odor-induced fear. Neurosci Biobehav Rev 2005;29(8):1157–67. Epub 2005 Aug 10.

26. Cohen H, Maayan R, Touati-Werner D, et al. Decreased circulatory levels of neuroactive steroids in behaviorally more extremely affected rats subsequent to exposure to a potentially traumatic experience. Int J Neuropsychopharmacol 2007;10(2):203–9.
27. Kozlovsky N, Matar MA, Kaplan Z, Kotler M, Zohar J, Cohen H. The immediate early gene Arc is associated with behavioral resilience to stress exposure in an animal model of posttraumatic stress disorder. Eur Neuropsychopharmacol 2007;2:2.
28. Mazor A, Matar M, Kozlovsky N, Zohar J, Kaplan Z, Cohen H. Gender-related qualitative differences in baseline and post stress anxiety responses are not reflected in the incidence of criterion-based PTSD-like behavior patterns. World J Biol Psychiatry 2007;13:1–14.
29. Roseboom PH, Nanda SA, Bakshi VP, Trentani A, Newman SM, Kalin NH. Predator threat induces behavioral inhibition, pituitary-adrenal activation and changes in amygdala CRF-binding protein gene expression. Psychoneuroendocrinology 2007;32(1):44–55. Epub 2006 Nov 20.
30. Richter-Levin G. Acute and long-term behavioral correlates of underwater trauma—potential relevance to stress and post-stress syndromes. Psychiatry Res 1998;79(1):73–83.
31. Wang J, Akirav I, Richter-Levin G. Short-term behavioral and electrophysiological consequences of underwater trauma. Physiol Behav 2000;70(3–4):327–32.
32. Cohen H, Zohar J. Animal models of post traumatic stress disorder: the use of cut off behavioral criteria.Ann N Y Acad Sci 2004;1032:167–78.
33. Warren DA, Castro CA, Rudy JW, Maier SF. No spatial learning impairment following exposure to inescapable shock. Psychobiology 1991;19:127–34.
34. Diamond DM, Rose GM. Stress impairs LTP and hippocampal-dependent memory. Ann N Y Acad Sci 1994;746:411–14.
35. Foy MR, Stanton ME, Levine S, Thompson RF. Behavioral stress impairs long-term potentiation in rodent hippocampus. Behav Neural Biol 1987;48(1):138–49.
36. Shors TJ, Seib TB, Levine S, Thompson RF. Inescapable versus escapable shock modulates long-term potentiation in the rat hippocampus. Science 1989;244(4901):224–26.
37. Xu L, Holscher C, Anwyl R, Rowan MJ. Glucocorticoid receptor and protein/RNA synthesis-dependent mechanisms underlie the control of synaptic plasticity by stress. Proc Natl Acad Sci U S A 1998;95(6):3204–8.
38. Yehuda R, LeDoux J. Response variation following trauma: a translational neuroscience approach to understanding PTSD. Neuron 2007;56(1):19–32.
39. Milad MR, Rauch SL, Pitman RK, Quirk GJ. Fear extinction in rats: implications for human brain imaging and anxiety disorders. Biol Psychol 2006;73(1):61–71. Epub 2006 Feb 13.
40. Dunsmoor JE, Bandettini PA, Knight DC. Neural correlates of unconditioned response diminution during Pavlovian conditioning. Neuroimage 2008;40:811–17.
41. LeDoux J. Emotional networks and motor control: a fearful view. Prog Brain Res 1996;107:437–46.
42. Blechert J, Michael T, Vriends N, Margraf J, Wilhelm FH. Fear conditioning in posttraumatic stress disorder: evidence for delayed extinction of autonomic, experiential, and behavioural responses. Behav Res Ther 2007;45(9):2019–33.
43. Bonne O, Grillon C, Vythilingam M, Neumeister A, Charney DS. Adaptive and maladaptive psychobiological responses to severe psychological stress: implications for the discovery of novel pharmacotherapy. Neurosci Biobehav Rev 2004;28(1):65–94.
44. Foa EB, Kozak MJ. Emotional processing of fear: exposure to corrective information. Psychol Bull 1986;99(1):20–35.

45. Kolb LC. A neuropsychological hypothesis explaining posttraumatic stress disorders. Am J Psychiatry 1987;144(8):989–95.
46. LeDoux JE. Emotion circuits in the brain. Annu Rev Neurosci 2000;23:155–84.
47. Maren S. Neurobiology of Pavlovian fear conditioning. Annu Rev Neurosci 2001;24, 897–931.
48. Bouton ME. Context and behavioral processes in extinction. Learn Mem 2004;11(5):485–94.
49. Akirav I, Maroun M. The role of the medial prefrontal cortex-amygdala circuit in stress effects on the extinction of fear. Neural Plast 2007;2007:30873.
50. Guthrie RM, Bryant RA. Extinction learning before trauma and subsequent posttraumatic stress. Psychosom Med 2006;68(2):307–11.
51. Maren S, Chang CH. Recent fear is resistant to extinction. Proc Natl Acad Sci U S A 2006;103(47):18020–25. Epub 2006 Nov 7.
52. Myers KM, Davis M. Behavioral and neural analysis of extinction. Neuron 2002;36:567–84.
53. Maren S, Aharonov G, Stote DL, Fanselow MS. N-Methyl-Daspartate receptors in the basolateral amygdala are required for both acquisition and expression of conditional fear in rats. Behav Neurosci Biobehav Rev 1996;110:1365–74.
54. Walker DL, Davis M. The role of amygdala glutamate receptors in fear learning, fear-potentiated startle, and extinction. Pharmacol Biochem Behav 2002;71:379–92.
55. Maren S. Auditory fear conditioning increases CS-elicited spike firing in lateral amygdala neurons even after extensive overtraining. Eur J Neurosci 2000;12:4047–54.
56. Goosens KA, Hobin JA, Maren S. Auditory-evoked spike firing in the lateral amygdala and Pavlovian fear conditioning: mnemonic code or fear bias? Neuron 2003;40:1013–22.
57. Maren S, Quirk GJ. Neuronal signalling of fear memory. Nat Rev Neurosci 2004;5:844–52.
58. Rhodes SE, Killcross AS. Lesions of rat infralimbic cortex enhance renewal of extinguished appetitive Pavlovian responding. Eur J Neurosci 2007;25(8):2498–503.
59. Quirk GJ, Russo GK, Barron JL, Lebron K. The role of ventromedial prefrontal cortex in the recovery of extinguished fear. J Neurosci 2000;20:6225–31.
60. Bremner JD, Innis RB, Ng CK, et al. Positron emission tomography measurement of cerebral metabolic correlates of yohimbine administration in combat-related posttraumatic stress disorder. Arch Gen Psychiatry 1997;54(3):246–54.
61. Semple WE, Goyer PF, McCormick R, et al. Higher brain blood flow at amygdala and lower frontal cortex blood flow in PTSD patients with comorbid cocaine and alcohol abuse compared with normals. Psychiatry 2000;63(1):65–74.
62. Semple WE, Goyer PF, McCormick R, et al. Attention and regional cerebral blood flow in posttraumatic stress disorder patients with substance abuse histories. Psychiatry Res 1996;67(1):17–28.
63. Rauch SL, Shin LM. Functional neuroimaging studies in posttraumatic stress disorder. Ann N Y Acad Sci 1997;821:83–98.
64. Shin LM, McNally RJ, Kosslyn SM, et al. Regional cerebral blood flow during script-driven imagery in childhood sexual abuse-related PTSD: a PET investigation. Am J Psychiatry 1999;156(4):575–84.
65. Rauch SL, van der Kolk BA, Fisler RE, et al. A symptom provocation study of posttraumatic stress disorder using positron emission tomography and script-driven imagery. Arch Gen Psychiatry 1996;53(5):380–87.
66. Rauch SL, Whalen PJ, Shin LM, et al. Exaggerated amygdala response to masked facial stimuli in posttraumatic stress disorder: a functional MRI study. Biol Psychiatry 2000;47(9):769–76.
67. Bremner JD. Alterations in brain structure and function associated with post-traumatic stress disorder. Semin Clin Neuropsychiatry 1999;4(4):249–55.

68. Bremner JD, Randall P, Scott TM, et al. MRI-based measurement of hippocampal volume in patients with combat-related posttraumatic stress disorder. Am J Psychiatry 1995; 152(7):973–81.

69. Freeman TW, Cardwell D, Karson CN, Komoroski RA. In vivo proton magnetic resonance spectroscopy of the medial temporal lobes of subjects with combat-related posttraumatic stress disorder. Magn Reson Med 1998;40(1):66–71.

70. De Bellis MD, Keshavan MS, Spencer S, Hall J. N-Acetylaspartate concentration in the anterior cingulate of maltreated children and adolescents with PTSD. Am J Psychiatry 2000;157(7):1175–77.

71. Lanius RA, Williamson PC, Densmore M, et al. Neural correlates of traumatic memories in posttraumatic stress disorder: a functional MRI investigation. Am J Psychiatry 2001;158(11):1920–22.

72. Etkin A, Wager TD. Functional neuroimaging of anxiety: a meta-analysis of emotional processing in PTSD, social anxiety disorder, and specific phobia. Am J Psychiatry 2007;164(10):1476–88.

73. Ehlers A, Clark DM. A cognitive model of posttraumatic stress disorder. Behav Res Ther 2000;38(4):319–45.

74. Khan S, Liberzon I. Topiramate attenuates exaggerated acoustic startle in an animal model of PTSD. Psychopharmacology (Berl) 2004;172(2):225–29. Epub 2003 Oct 30.

75. Liberzon I, Lopez JF, Flagel SB, Vazquez DM, Young EA. Differential regulation of hippocampal glucocorticoid receptors mRNA and fast feedback: relevance to post-traumatic stress disorder. J Neuroendocrinol 1999;11(1):11–17.

76. Liberzon I, Krstov M, Young EA. Stress-restress: effects on ACTH and fast feedback. Psychoneuroendocrinology 1997;22(6):443–53.

77. Cohen H, Liberzon I, Richter-Levin G. Exposure to extreme stress impairs contextual odor discrimination in an animal model of PTSD. In J Neuropsychopharmacol 2008;Aug 13:1–13 [Epub ahead of print].

78. Cohen H, Zohar J, Gidron Y, et al. Blunted HPA axis response to stress influences susceptibility to posttraumatic stress response in rats. Biol Psychiatry 2006;59(12):1208–18.

79. Cohen H, Zohar J, Matar M. The relevance of differential response to trauma in ananimal model of post-traumatic stress disorder. Biol Psychiatry 2003;53(6):463–73.

80. Cohen H, Kaplan Z, Matar M, Loewenthal U, Kozlovsky N, Zohar J. Anisomycin, a protein synthesis inhibitor, disrupts traumatic memory consolidation and attenuates post traumatic stress response in rats. Biol Psychiatry 2006;60(7):767–76.

81. Cohen H, Kaplan Z, Matar MA, Loewenthal U, Zohar J, Richter-Levin G. Long-lasting behavioral effects of juvenile trauma in an animal model of PTSD associated with a failure of the autonomic nervous system to recover. Eur Neuropsychopharmacol 2007;17(6–7):464–77.

82. Cohen H, Matar MA, Richter-Levin G, Zohar J. The contribution of an animal model toward uncovering biological risk factors for PTSD. Ann N Y Acad Sci 2006;1071:335–50.

83. Cohen H, Ziv Y, Cardon M, et al. Maladaptation to mental stress mitigated by the adaptive immune system via depletion of naturally occurring regulatory CD4+CD25+cells. J Neurobiol 2006;66(6):552–63.

84. Cohen H, Zohar J, Matar M, Loewenthal U, Kaplan Z. The impact of environment factors in determining post-exposure responses in isogenic strains of mice:Can genetic predisposition explain phenotypic vulnerability? Int J Neuropsychopharmacol 2008;11:331–49.

85. Cohen H, Zohar J, Matar MA, Kaplan Z, Geva AB. Unsupervised fuzzy clustering analysis supports behavioral cutoff criteria in an animal model of posttraumatic stress disorder. Biol Psychiatry 2005;58(8):640–50.

86. Cohen H, Zohar J, Matar MA, Zeev K, Loewenthal U, Richter-Levin G.Setting apart the affected:the use of behavioral criteria in animal models of post traumatic stress disorder. Neuropsychopharmacology 2004;29(11):1962–70.

87. Kozlovsky N, Matar MA, Kaplan Z, Kotler M, Zohar J, Cohen H. Long-term down-regulation of BDNF mRNA in rat hippocampal CA1 subregion correlates with PTSD-like behavioural stress response. Int J Neuropsychopharmacol 2007, 1–18.

88. Matar MA, Cohen H, Kaplan Z, Zohar J. The effect of early poststressor intervention with sertraline on behavioral responses in an animal model of post-traumatic stress disorder. Neuropsychopharmacology 2006;31(12):2610–18.

89. Schmidt MV, Sterlemann V, Ganea K, et al. Persistent neuroendocrine and behavioral effects of a novel, etiologically relevant mouse paradigm for chronic social stress during adolescence. Psychoneuroendocrinology 2007;32(5):417–29.

90. Ford JD, Kidd P. Early childhood trauma and disorders of extreme stress as predictors of treatment outcome with chronic posttraumatic stress disorder. J Trauma Stress 1998; 11(4):743–61.

91. Heim C, Nemeroff CB. The role of childhood trauma in the neurobiology of mood and anxiety disorders:preclinical and clinical studies. Biol Psychiatry 2001;49(12): 1023–39.

92. Heim C, Newport DJ, Wagner D, Wilcox MM, Miller AH, Nemeroff CB. The role of early adverse experience and adulthood stress in the prediction of neuroendocrine stress reactivity in women:amultiple regression analysis. Depress Anxiety 2002;15(3):117–25.

93. Breslau N. Psychiatric morbidity in adult survivors of childhood trauma. Semin Clin Neuropsychiatry 2002;7(2):80–88.

94. Shea A, Walsh C, Macmillan H, Steiner M. Child maltreatment and HPA axis dysregulation: relationship to major depressive disorder and post traumatic stress disorder in females. Psychoneuroendocrinology 2005;30(2):162–78.

95. Andersen SL, Teicher MH. Delayed effects of early stress on hippocampal development. Neuropsychopharmacology 2004;29(11):1988–93.

96. Schmidt MV, Enthoven L, vander Mark M, Levine S, deKloet ER, Oitzl MS. The postnatal development of the hypothalamic-pituitary-adrenal axis in the mouse. Int J Dev Neurosci 2003;21(3):125–32.

97. Vazquez DM, Bailey C, Dent GW, et al. Brain corticotropin-releasing hormone(CRH) circuits in the developing rat:effect of maternal deprivation.Brain Res 2006;1121(1): 83–94.

98. Vazquez DM. Stress and the developing limbic-hypothalamic-pituitary-adrenal axis. Psychoneuroendocrinology 1998;23(7):663–700.

99. Vazquez DM, VanOers H, Levine S, Akil H. Regulation of glucocorticoid and mineralocorticoid receptor mRNAs in the hippocampus of the maternally deprived infant rat. Brain Res 1996;731(1–2):79–90.

100. Gunnar MR, Donzella B. Social regulation of the cortisol levels in early human development. Psychoneuroendocrinology 2002;27(1–2):199–220.

101. DeBellis MD, Keshavan MS, Shifflett H, etal.Brain structures in pediatric maltreatment-related posttraumatic stress disorder: a sociodemographically matched study. Biol Psychiatry 2002;52(11):1066–78.

102. Nemeroff CB. Neurobiological consequences of childhood trauma. J Clin Psychiatry 2004;65(suppl1):18–28.

103. Avital A, Ram E, Maayan R, Weizman A, Richter-Levin G. Effects of early-life stress on behavior and neurosteroid levels in the rat hypothalamus and entorhinal cortex. Brain Res Bull 2006;68(6):419–24.

104. Avital A, Richter-Levin G. Exposure to juvenile stress exacerbates the behavioural consequences of exposure to stress in the adult rat. Int J Neuropsychopharmacol 2005;8(2):163–73.
105. Tsoory M, Cohen H, Richter-Levin G. Juvenile stress induces a predisposition to either anxiety or depressive-like symptoms following stress in adulthood. Eur Neuropsychopharmacol 2007;17(4):245–56.
106. Tsoory M, Guterman A, Richter-Levin G. Exposure to stressors during juvenility disrupts development-related alterations in thePSA-NCAM to NCAM expression ratio:potential relevance for mood and anxiety disorders. Neuropsychopharmacology 2008;33(2):378–93.
107. Tsoory M, Richter-Levin G. Learning under stress in the adult rat is differentially affected by"juvenile"or"adolescent"stress. Int J Neuropsychopharmacol 2006;9(6):713–28.
108. Bazak N, Kozlovsky N, Kaplan Z, et al. Pre-pubertal stress-exposure affects adult stress-response in correlation with changes in circulating corticosterone and brain-derived neurotrophic factor. In press (Phychoneuroendocrinology).
109. Stein MB, Jang KL, Taylor S, Vernon PA, Livesley WJ. Genetic and environmental influences on trauma exposure and posttraumatic stress disorder symptoms:a twin study. Am J Psychiatry 2002;159(10):1675–81.
110. Caspi A, Moffitt T. Gene-environment interactions in psychiatry: joining forces with neuroscience. Nat Rev Neurosci 2006;7:583–90.
111. Moffitt T, Caspi A, Rutter M. Measured gene-environment interactions in psychopathology. Perspect Psychol Sci 2006;1:5–27.

7

PTSD: From Neurons to Networks

Rajnish P. Rao, Aparna Suvrathan,
Melinda M. Miller, Bruce S. McEwen,
and Sumantra Chattarji

CONTENTS

INTRODUCTION
BRAIN REGIONS IMPLICATED IN PTSD
NEURAL SUBSTRATES OF PTSD: INSIGHTS GAINED
    FROM ANIMAL MODELS OF STRESS
BEYOND CHRONIC STRESS MODELS: BRIEF STRESSORS
    AND THEIR DELAYED IMPACT
SYNAPTIC AND MOLECULAR CORRELATES OF STRESS
    EFFECTS ON KEY BRAIN REGIONS
SYNTHESIS AND FUTURE DIRECTIONS
REFERENCES

Abstract

Animal models of post-traumatic stress disorder (PTSD) must not only capture salient features of the disorder at the behavioral level but also provide insights into the underlying neuronal, physiological, and endocrine mechanisms. The fact that exposure to severe stress leads to the development of PTSD in humans provides the basic rationale for all rodent models of the disorder. The early focus of many of these models was on studying the debilitating effects of chronic or repeated stress on the hippocampus, a key component of the stress-inhibitory circuit that is reduced in volume in PTSD. Neuroimaging and clinical studies, however, also implicate two other brain areas, the amygdala and the prefrontal cortex, in PTSD. Moreover, structural and functional changes in all three brain structures appear to differ from each other in PTSD. These findings

From: *Post-Traumatic Stress Disorder: Basic Science and Clinical Practice*
Edited by: P. J. Shiromani et al., DOI: 10.1007/978-1-60327-329-9_7
© Humana Press, a part of Springer Science + Business Media, LLC 2009

from human studies pose a challenge for animal models of PTSD: can the same stressful experience elicit contrasting cellular effects in the hippocampus, amygdala, and prefrontal cortex? Another striking characteristic of PTSD, which is not fully reflected in commonly used animal models of chronic stress, lies in the temporal domain. While PTSD is triggered by a single intensely traumatic event, some symptoms persist well beyond the original event. Can animal studies on the delayed, long-term impact of brief, but severe, stressors shed any light on these temporal features of human PTSD? Finally, while the hippocampus, amygdala, and prefrontal cortex are distinct in their associations with the severity of PTSD symptoms, there are significant neuroanatomical interconnections between the three areas. Can stress-induced modulation of structure and function in one of these brain areas affect changes in another? If so, can we construct new animal models that expand the scope of their analyses by studying stress-induced changes distributed across a wider network encompassing all three brain areas implicated in PTSD? In this review, we address these key questions by summarizing findings from various rodent models of stress. We focus on the morphological, electrophysiological, endocrine and molecular effects of stress in the hippocampus, amygdala, and prefrontal cortex. We end by discussing some of the gaps in our current understanding and explore experimental strategies that may lead to more powerful animal models in the future.

Key Words: Amygdala, anxiety, dendritic remodeling, glucocorticoids, hippocampus, post-traumatic stress disorder, prefrontal cortex, stress, synaptic plasticity.

INTRODUCTION

Study of the neurobiological mechanisms of post-traumatic stress disorder (PTSD) has been driven by two complementary lines of investigation. On the one hand, the advent of functional and structural imaging of the human brain, along with careful and detailed clinical assessments of PTSD etiology and psychopathology, have provided valuable information on candidate brain regions and behavioral dysfunction in PTSD. Top-down information gathered from the human clinical realm in turn has aided a second line of inquiry that relies on animal models to study basic mechanisms underlying the development of the disorder. This bottom-up strategy combines a range of neurobiological tools and models to analyze the effects of stress at multiple levels of neural organization—from molecular and cellular correlates at one end to network and behavioral-level analysis at the other. Increasingly, these two approaches are converging to give rise to a comprehensive intellectual framework that bridges the gap between clinical and basic research. This review focuses on the interplay between top-down information gleaned from studies of PTSD subjects and mechanistic insights gained from bottom-up studies using animal models. To this end, we first summarize clinical findings that have helped identify key brain structures implicated in PTSD. This is followed by a detailed description of a range of observations, made from animal models, on the effects of chronic and acute stress on these brain areas. Other sections attempt to synthesize these findings into cellular models of stress-induced modulation of synaptic structure and function that may mediate the short- and long-terms effects of stress in brain structures affected by PTSD. We conclude by discussing areas of neuroscience research that are likely to play an influential role in shaping the next generation of more powerful and sophisticated animal models of PTSD.

BRAIN REGIONS IMPLICATED IN PTSD

Clinical studies based on structural and functional neuroimaging studies implicate three brain areas in the pathophysiology of PTSD: the hippocampus, amygdala, and medial prefrontal cortex (mPFC). Reduced hippocampal volumes, compared to either trauma-exposed control subjects or trauma-unexposed healthy subjects, have been reported in PTSD patients (1). Importantly, hippocampal volumes have been inversely associated with combat exposure (2) and PTSD symptom severity (Fig. 1) (3,4). Taken together, these findings support the view that not only is decreased hippocampal volume linked to cognitive deficits associated with PTSD but also it may act as a risk factor for the development of the disorder (5). These findings on abnormalities in hippocampal structure and

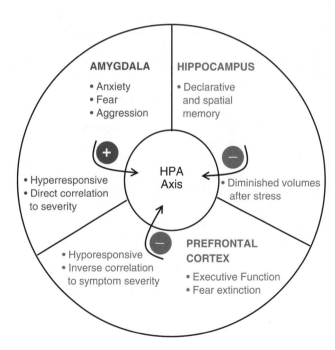

Fig. 1. Brain areas implicated in post-traumatic stress disorder (PTSD). The amygdala, prefrontal cortex, and hippocampus, which are altered structurally and functionally in PTSD, respond differentially to stress-induced adrenal steroids and in turn differentially regulate hypothalamic-pituitary-adrenal (HPA) activity (both positively and negatively). The schematic shows the role of each area in cognitive/emotional function and why it is implicated in PTSD (*See Color Plates*)

function are particularly relevant in light of the central role played by this structure in both the neuroendocrine stress response (Fig. 1) and memory deficits, similar to what has been seen in individuals suffering from PTSD *(6,7)*.

Although neuroimaging studies have not yielded conclusive evidence for structural or volume changes in the amygdala, amygdalar hyperresponsivity has been reported in PTSD patients during the presentation of not only trauma-related visual and auditory cues *(8–15)* but also trauma-unrelated affective cues such as fearful facial expressions *(16–18)*. Strikingly, unlike the hippocampus, amygdala activation is reported to be positively correlated with the severity of PTSD symptoms (Fig. 1) *(8,9,15,19)*. Reports that in PTSD patients the amygdala is more responsive to both traumatic reminders and more general affective stimuli are noteworthy in view of the large body of evidence from animal research demonstrating a pivotal role for the amygdala in Pavlovian fear conditioning *(20)*.

Fear conditioning is a robust learning paradigm in which subjects rapidly learn to associate a previously neutral tone (the conditioned stimulus, CS) with a coincident aversive stimulus (unconditioned stimulus, US), such as electric shock, which invariably evokes an unconditioned response (UCR). Reexposure to the CS alone elicits a conditioned response (CR) that provides a measure for the learned association between CS and US. It is now well established that the amygdala plays an essential role in the acquisition of the tone-shock association, the initial stages of which involve strengthening of thalamic afferent synapses to the lateral amygdala (LA) *(21,22)*.

This form of associative learning paradigm is attractive because it provides a convenient framework for viewing PTSD as fear conditioning gone wrong. Individuals naturally exhibit an initial reaction to a traumatic or severely stressful event (which can be viewed as an US) with arousal and fear (UCR). However, those who eventually develop PTSD continue to show heightened vigilance and avoidance (CR) long after the trauma when they are exposed to cues related to the triggering event (CS). A compelling link between this animal model of fear learning and the affective symptoms of PTSD comes from reports that patients exhibit an increased acquisition of aversive conditioning in the laboratory *(23,24)*. Further, functional imaging studies on abuse survivors demonstrated enhanced responses in the amygdala during the acquisition of fear conditioning *(25)*.

The third brain region implicated in PTSD is the mPFC. In contrast to amygdalar hyperresponsivity, structural neuroimaging studies have reported decreased volumes of frontal cortex in PTSD. Studies that have specifically focused on the mPFC have shown anterior cingulate (ACg) volumes to be smaller in PTSD compared to trauma-exposed control groups *(26,27)*. Similar to findings on hippocampal volumes, the severity of PTSD symptoms is inversely correlated with ACg volume (Fig. 1) *(26,27)*. Several functional neuroimaging studies have also demonstrated an inverse correlation between PTSD symptom severity and mPFC activation (Fig. 1) *(9,17,18,28)*.

These imaging studies involving the mPFC are particularly relevant in light of another form of learning and memory called *extinction*. Extinction is an inhibitory learning process by which the conditioned fear response (CR) can be attenuated or extinguished when the CS no longer predicts the US. Importantly, while the fear response (CR) subsides after extinction, the fear memory itself is not erased; it is merely suppressed by the inhibitory memory that is formed during extinction *(22)*. Pharmacological, lesion, and electrophysiological studies in rodents, as well as imaging studies in humans, have established a role for both the amygdala and mPFC in fear extinction *(29–32)*. These studies, taken together with reports that PTSD patients have a diminished extinction of conditioned fear responses in laboratory experiments *(23,33)*, have led to the suggestion that malfunction of the mPFC also contributes to the pathophysiology of PTSD.

NEURAL SUBSTRATES OF PTSD: INSIGHTS GAINED FROM ANIMAL MODELS OF STRESS

Investigations into the neural substrates underlying the cognitive and affective symptoms of PTSD have been driven by the fact that exposure to severe stress triggers the development of PTSD *(34)*. To this end, a variety of animal models of stress have been used to analyze specific cellular and molecular changes in brain areas that are known, especially from imaging studies, to be affected in PTSD. First, as mentioned, reduction in hippocampal and PFC volumes have been reported by many neuroimaging studies *(35,36)*, and these are believed to underlie functional deficits associated with PTSD (Fig. 1). Second, both structures play a pivotal role in negative-feedback regulation of the stress response via the hypothalamic-pituitary-adrenal (HPA) axis (Fig. 1) *(37–40)*. Third, a dominant hypothesis, which looks beyond the genesis of the disorder, suggests that PTSD represents an eventual failure in reinstating physiological homeostasis that was disrupted by traumatic stress *(41,42)*. Thus, as key components of the stress-inhibitory circuit, the hippocampus and PFC have attracted considerable attention in studies using rodent models of stress. Therefore, we first summarize some of the key findings from animal models of chronic stress and their effects on cells and synapses of the hippocampus and PFC and follow with a discussion of stress effects on another brain area that has an opposing influence on the HPA axis: the amygdala.

Effects of Repeated Stress on the Hippocampus and PFC

Earlier investigations into cellular mechanisms underlying stress-induced impairment of hippocampal function have focused on two common metrics of hippocampal plasticity—one structural and the other electrophysiological (reviewed in subsequent sections). Morphological analyses of how stress and stress hormones affect the rat hippocampus revealed that 21 days (6 h per day) of repeated restraint stress produces significant dendritic remodeling in CA3 pyramidal neurons (Fig. 2) *(43–47)*. This dendritic remodeling is characterized by a shortening and debranching of apical dendrites *(48)* and is mediated by mechanisms involving high levels of glucocorticoid secretion, glutamate, and serotonin *(44)*. More recently, it has been shown that even shorter durations of immobilization stress (2 h per day for 10 days) are capable of causing significant atrophy of both apical and basal dendrites

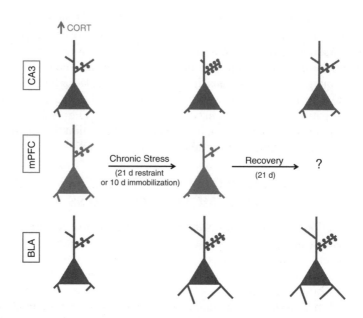

Fig. 2. Chronic stress leads to contrasting patterns of structural plasticity in excitatory pyramidal neurons in the basolateral amygdala (BLA), hippocampal area CA3, and layer II/III of medial prefrontal cortex (mPFC). Repeated exposure to restraint (6 h/day, 21 days) or immobilization (2 h/day, 10 days) stress triggers dendritic atrophy in pyramidal cells in hippocampal area CA3 (*top*) and layer II/III of mPFC (*middle*), which is opposite to the dendritic hypertrophy seen in BLA projection neurons (*bottom*). Chronic stress-induced morphological changes also differ in terms of their temporal longevity—BLA hypertrophy, unlike CA3 atrophy, persists even after 21 days of stress-free recovery. A third point of difference lies at the level of dendritic spine density, which is enhanced in BLA and CA3 neurons but is reduced in mPFC cells (*See Color Plates*)

on CA3 pyramidal cells (Fig. 2) *(49)*. These findings have contributed to rodent models of stress-induced neuronal atrophy that may provide one potential explanation for the hippocampal volume loss associated with PTSD *(2,3)*.

The PFC, which (like the hippocampus) exerts negative-feedback regulation of the stress response *(50,51)*, appears to be affected by chronic stress in a similar fashion. The mPFC and prelimbic cortex exhibit a shortening of dendritic length and a simplification of dendritic branching in layer II/III neurons in response to repeated stress and repeated corticosterone treatment (Fig. 2) *(52–55)*. It is not yet known if the infralimbic cortex (IL) of the mPFC also shows remodeling after 21 days of chronic restraint stress (Fig. 2). This would be important because of the involvement of this region in extinction of fear conditioning *(56)*. These structural changes predict that prefrontal cortical functions in working memory, executive function, and fear memory extinction would be impaired by chronic stress (Fig. 1). Indeed, this has been demonstrated for a form of cognitive flexibility *(55,57)*. Glucocorticoid treatment and adrenalectomy (ADX) have both been reported to alter the morphology of PFC neurons as well as the cognitive flexibility that is associated with PFC function. Dexamethasone treatment resulted in a pronounced impairment in working memory and behavioral flexibility, effects that correlated with atrophy of layer II of the infralimbic, prelimbic, and cingulate cortices. Exposure to corticosterone produced milder impairments in behavioral flexibility, but not in working memory, and reduced the volume of layer II of all prefrontal areas. These volume reductions were accompanied by atrophy of distal apical dendrites, but also by increased branching of middle dendrites. Interestingly, ADX-induced effects were apparent on reversal of learning and were associated with reduction of length of middle dendrites. None of the experimental procedures influenced the morphology of retrosplenial or motor cortices *(57–59)*.

Dendritic remodeling, through its modulation of postsynaptic dendritic surface, will have a profound impact on the availability of synaptic inputs and thereby synaptic plasticity. Indeed, it has long been hypothesized that morphological and numerical alterations in dendritic spines, the site of excitatory synaptic transmission in the brain, underlie long-term structural encoding of behavioral experiences. In this context, plasticity at the level of dendritic spines can be viewed from two different perspectives. First, spine synapses may act as the primary site of plasticity elicited by stressful experiences. This possibility, a very likely one, is discussed in detail in sections subsequent.

A second scenario is based on the consideration that repeated application of the same stressor can lead to habituation in the stress response *(60)*. This raises the possibility that although chronic stress triggers dendritic remodeling, it may eventually set in motion adaptive changes that counter the initial effects of stress on dendritic morphology. Such homeostatic mechanisms, triggered by prolonged stress, could be mediated by changing the number of spines, thereby regulating the overall synaptic connectivity in the affected area. This possibility finds support in the observation that dendritic atrophy in hippocampal CA3 pyramidal neurons, caused by repeated restrained stress, is accompanied by a numerical increase in spines (Fig. 2) *(61)*. This is indicative of an adaptive mechanism that may compensate for the loss of dendritic area for synaptic inputs to terminate. If similar adaptive plasticity mechanisms are activated in the mPFC by repeated application of stress, then one would also predict an increase in the number of spines along atrophied dendrites in the mPFC. However, contrary to this scenario, following 21 days of chronic restraint stress, there is a *reduction* in spine density on the apical dendrites of layer II/III neurons (Fig. 2) *(54)*. The net result of these changes is estimated to be a 40% reduction in synaptic inputs to the mPFC (Fig. 2). Thus, while chronic stress elicits similar forms of structural plasticity at the level of dendrites, its impact at the levels of spines may differ between the hippocampus and PFC. These results also raise interesting questions about the relationship between dendritic remodeling and modulation of spine density: for example, is one always accompanied by the other? Does dendritic remodeling follow or precede spine plasticity? Do the rules governing these forms of structural plasticity vary in different brain regions?

Impact of Repeated Stress on the Amygdala

The impetus for the search for cellular correlates of stress in the amygdala came from findings that highlight the contrasting manner in which the hippocampus and amygdala affect the stress response and how their behavioral outputs in turn are modulated by stress. First, there are anatomical data showing that limbic inputs impinging on the paraventricular nucleus (PVN) of the hypothalamus and hypothalamic γ-aminobutyric acid-ergic (GABA-ergic) neurons can be either excitatory from the hippocampus and thereby enhance GABA-ergic tone or inhibitory from the amygdala and thereby reduce GABA-ergic tone *(37–40,62)*. This implies that whereas enhanced hippocampal input would suppress the HPA axis, enhanced amygdalar input could have the opposite effect on HPA activity (Fig. 1). Second, stress facilitates aversive learning but impairs spatial learning in rodents *(63,64)*. Although repeated stress that produces dendritic atrophy in the CA3 region impairs hippocampal-dependent learning *(65)*, the basolateral amygdala (BLA) has been shown to be essential for stress-induced facilitation of aversive learning *(66,67)*. Taken together, these observations highlighted the need to examine the cellular effects of stress in the amygdala.

Applying the same tools of morphometric analysis of Golgi-stained neurons that were earlier used in the hippocampus, the first cellular evidence for contrasting patterns of stress-induced structural plasticity was found in the BLA *(49)*. In this study, chronic immobilization stress (2 h per day for 10 days) induced dendritic atrophy and debranching in CA3 pyramidal neurons of the hippocampus, which is consistent with earlier reports using other forms of repeated stress (Fig. 2). By contrast, principal neurons in the BLA exhibited *enhanced* dendritic arborization in response to the same chronic stress (Fig. 2). This stress-induced enhancement in dendritic arborization was restricted only to pyramidal and stellate neurons of the BLA, which are presumably excitatory projection neurons *(68,69)*. The efficacy of chronic immobilization stress in eliciting dendritic hypertrophy in BLA was also shown to be relevant in terms of its anxiogenic properties.

Chronic immobilization stress also caused a significant increase in anxiety-like behavior *(70)*. On the other hand, chronic unpredictable stress, which failed to enhance anxiety, did not cause any dendritic remodeling of BLA principal neurons *(49)*. Importantly, the positive correlation between stress-induced BLA dendritic hypertrophy and greater anxiety was further strengthened in a subsequent study that also brought into focus the temporal dimension, a key feature of PTSD. Even after 21 days of stress-free recovery following exposure to chronic immobilization stress, animals continued to exhibit enhanced anxiety *(70,71)*. At the cellular level, stress-induced dendritic growth of spiny BLA pyramidal neurons was also as persistent as enhanced anxiety after 21 days of recovery (Fig. 2). Interestingly, BLA hypertrophy is distinct from hippocampal CA3 atrophy, which is reversible within the same period of stress-free recovery (Fig. 2) *(71)*. Further, following 10-day exposure to immobilization stress, dendritic hypertrophy is accompanied by an equally robust increase in spine density that spreads across both primary and secondary dendrites of BLA pyramidal neurons *(73)*. Thus, chronic stress leads to a significant increase in the structural basis of synaptic connectivity in the BLA, which is opposite to the significant loss of synaptic connectivity in the mPFC (Fig. 2) *(54)*.

In summary, findings on structural plasticity induced by chronic stress highlight important differences between the hippocampus, amygdala, and PFC. Principal neurons in specific subregions of the hippocampus and PFC, both part of the stress-inhibitory circuitry, undergo dendritic atrophy (Fig. 2). But, spine density increases in the hippocampus while it reduces in the mPFC (Fig. 2). In contrast, dendrites grow bigger in the BLA following chronic stress, and these elongated dendrites also possess higher spine densities (Fig. 2). These results from animal models of chronic stress are quite striking because they are consistent with neuroimaging findings from humans with PTSD that also point to a negative correlation between the amygdala on the one hand and the mPFC and hippocampus on the other (Fig. 1). Taken together, these changes in the structural basis of synaptic connectivity will affect information processing by these three brain areas and might contribute significantly to the varied cognitive and affective symptoms in PTSD.

BEYOND CHRONIC STRESS MODELS: BRIEF STRESSORS AND THEIR DELAYED IMPACT

Despite the convergence of findings from animal models and human neuroimaging in identifying key brain areas implicated in PTSD, animal models of PTSD based on chronic stress paradigms have two specific limitations. Two of the defining features of PTSD are not fully reflected in these animal models. First, the most commonly held view of PTSD is that it is triggered by a *single* overwhelmingly traumatic, often life-threatening, event. Second, this disorder is defined as one in which some components of the fear response persist well beyond the original traumatic event. Indeed, symptoms must persist more than 1 month after the trauma for acute PTSD and 3 months after the trauma for chronic PTSD *(34)*. However, the animal models discussed so far have not used brief stressors that better reflect features of traumatic stress, and almost all measurements were carried out soon after the termination of the chronic stress protocol. An acute, but severe, stressor would replicate more accurately the initial triggering event and enable studies on the further cascade of endocrine, cellular, and behavioral changes, especially those manifested well after the initial triggering event. This section focuses on some of these issues in greater detail.

Adding a Temporal Axis

Allostatic overload in an animal or person is normally caused by chronic elevation and dysregulation of stress responses *(74,75)*. Although milder forms of acute stress result in increase in levels of cortisol and other neurochemicals such as epinephrine, norepinephrine, and serotonin, these often serve only to increase available energy and help the animal to escape or respond suitably to the stressor *(76–78)*. Acute stress can also increase memory and attention, which is of adaptive benefit. However, when the stressor is of extreme severity, a cascade of events is triggered that can lead to PTSD in humans. Such an acute stressor would therefore need to be severe enough to result in delayed ill effects.

Several animal models have been developed that allow investigations into the impact of an acute, but severe, stressor over time—especially at time points that are removed from the period of stress itself *(72,79)*. One study, using a single 2-h episode of immobilization stress, has reported a delayed increase in anxiety-like behavior that is paralleled by an increase in spine density in principal neurons of the BLA. These findings are particularly striking because the increase in anxiety and BLA spine density is evident only 10 days after the acute stress and not the day after *(72)*. Further, the newly formed spines are localized proximal to the cell soma, also in the absence of any dendritic remodeling. This study also suggests that BLA spinogenesis in itself may be adequate to increase behavioral anxiety, a correlation that has also emerged from another study in which BLA spinogenesis, caused by transgenic overexpression of brain-derived neurotrophic factor (BDNF), leads to enhanced anxiety *(80)*.

Taken together, these findings raise the possibility that an acute episode of severe stress initiates plasticity mechanisms culminating in delayed and restricted spinogenesis, and this in itself may be sufficient to modulate anxiety-like behavior. But, repeated exposure to the same stressor pushes the same cellular machinery to scale up to a greater magnitude of spinogenesis along with enlargement of the dendritic tree *(49)*. Although hippocampal volume loss has been the traditional focus of human studies on PTSD *(1)*, these findings on the delayed manifestation of enhanced anxiety and BLA spinogenesis, triggered by a single temporally restricted episode of stress, may provide a new framework for studying cellular mechanisms of PTSD in the amygdala. The delayed buildup of spines and anxiety after exposure to acute stress also highlights the unique temporal characteristics of stress-induced structural plasticity in the amygdala. An earlier report using 10-day chronic immobilization stress showed that BLA hypertrophy and anxiety endure for a number of weeks after termination of the stressor (Fig. 2) *(71)*. Thus, the amygdala appears to have special features, especially with respect to its temporal manifestation and persistence, which fit well with the delayed and prolonged enhancing effects on fear and anxiety observed in PTSD *(81)*.

A single prolonged stress, consisting of 2-h restraint stress followed by 20-min forced swimming and ether anesthesia, is another animal model that has been proposed for PTSD *(82)*. In this model, rats showed enhanced inhibition of the HPA axis and potentiated acoustic startle response 1 week, but not 1 day, after single prolonged stress *(79)*. This form of stress also impaired spatial memory, which paralleled the deficits in hippocampal long-term potentiation (LTP), a candidate synaptic plasticity mechanism for learning and memory. This study also reported enhanced contextual fear memory and impaired LTP in the amygdala in the rats 1 week after stress exposure. Consistent with the acute stress findings mentioned, many of the behavioral and synaptic changes were not evident a day after single prolonged stress, but a week later when plasma corticosterone had recovered from an initial increase caused by the stress *(79)*.

In contrast to the acute stress models discussed, an alternative approach has employed more ethologically relevant paradigms in which rodents are subjected to their natural predators to examine long-term behavioral and neurochemical changes. Adamec et al. *(83)* reported a long-lasting increase in anxiety-like behavior and a decrease in risk assessment in the elevated plus maze following a single 5-min direct exposure of a rat to a cat. These effects could be seen 30 min to 1 h after predator exposure and persisted for at least 3 weeks. Likewise, acute predator stress increased acoustic startle response and decreased entries into the light box of the light-dark box paradigm *(84)* and potentiated neural transmission both to and from the amygdala 10 days poststress *(83)*. Acute predator exposure has also been shown to impair long-term memory in rats exposed to a cat immediately prior to water maze training when tested 24 h later. Further, the learning-induced increase in basal dendritic spines on CA1 pyramidal neurons, typically seen 24 h after water maze training, was inhibited in the stressed animals *(85)*. Rodents, even those bred and raised in a laboratory, show an innate and immediate stress response to odors produced in the urine, hair, and scent glands of their predators. Cat odors alone, using odorants coming from a used collar worn by a cat *(86)*, a ball of cat fur *(87)*, or used cat litter *(88)*, have also been shown to cause both immediate and long-term changes to behavior commensurate with those seen after actual predator exposure.

Finally, there is an important methodological issue that is often overlooked in the process of designing animal models of PTSD; this has to do with the animals themselves. While some studies have chosen to focus on the entire group of stressed animals, others have used behavioral measures to differentiate animals displaying the most extreme behavioral changes. Some rat strains are known to have higher baseline anxiety than others. For example, the Lewis rat strain, an inbred strain developed from the Sprague-Dawley (SD) rats, has been proposed as a model for PTSD because a higher percentage of these develop severe stress-induced anxiety-like behaviors *(88)*. Furthermore, Lewis rats have been characterized by their abnormal HPA stress response. Lewis rats have normal basal blood corticosterone levels, as compared to their SD cousins, but have a hypoactive response to stress. This is relevant in light of clinical evidence that individuals who produce lower-than-average levels of cortisol after a traumatic event may have a higher probability of later developing PTSD *(42,89)*. In comparison with other strains of rats, Lewis rats exhibited greater baseline anxiety behaviors and greater stress-induced increases in anxiety. According to studies by Cohen and colleagues *(88,90)*, 1 week after a cat odor exposure paradigm, the majority of animals demonstrated "extreme behavioral responses," such as never entering the open arms of the plus maze, and heightened acoustic startle that did not habituate. An increase in acoustic startle response has also been seen in patients with PTSD *(91)*.

In summary, animal studies using chronic or repeated stress have led to models of acute stress that can capture salient features of PTSD, especially symptoms that become evident with a time delay. Importantly, these models enable more detailed examination of the cellular and molecular changes that gradually develop after the initial endocrine and physiological response triggered during, and immediately after, the severe stress. The study of such cellular changes, however, also poses a challenge in that it becomes hard to distinguish changes underlying the development of a disease state from those that are adaptive (i.e., help the organism reestablish homeostasis). This fundamental challenge in turn highlights the need for careful sequential analysis of how key markers of neural change—molecular, cellular, or behavioral—evolve over time. Moreover, analysis of this progression of the initial stress response into a psychiatric condition would also provide valuable insights into possible time points for therapeutic interventions after the initial traumatic event.

SYNAPTIC AND MOLECULAR CORRELATES OF STRESS EFFECTS ON KEY BRAIN REGIONS

Animal models of PTSD of the kind discussed so far are aimed at uncovering important cellular and molecular mechanisms underlying the disorder that can also be targeted for pharmacological interventions. Indeed, these models have given rise to a wide range of findings that not only implicate endocrinological and physiological factors directly linked to the immediate response to stress, but also changes in excitatory and inhibitory synaptic transmission that eventually give rise to a variety of plasticity mechanisms that may underlie a range of PTSD symptoms at the behavioral level. Since a comprehensive review of all these changes is beyond the scope of the present discussion, we focus on the actions of stress hormones and how these influence synaptic transmission and plasticity in brain circuits that play a major role in the stress models discussed.

Mechanisms of Adrenal Steroid Actions

Exposure to stressful events leads to glucocorticoid release by the activation of the HPA axis. The action of these stress hormones in conjunction with other stress mediators (epinephrine/norepinephrine, parasympathetic nervous system, cytokines) is key in facilitating an adaptation to the stressor, thereby restoring homeostasis (92). However, prolonged exposure to these hormones is damaging to several brain areas, especially the hippocampus under conditions of ischemia and seizures, and this is thought to underlie some of the adverse behavioral and physiological effects of chronic stress (92).

A shared feature of the mediators of stress and adaptation is that they operate as a nonlinear network, with each mediator having regulatory actions on the production and activity of the other (92). Some mediators, such as adrenal steroids, act in a dose-dependent manner along an inverted U-shaped curve (85,93) involving the mineralocorticoid receptors (MRs) (94) and the glucocorticoid receptors (GRs) (95). Using overexpression (96–98) or knockout mouse models (99–100), MRs have been shown to be actively involved in the stability of neuronal networks and hippocampal cell survival *(6,101,102)*. As a consequence of stress, when glucocorticoid levels rise, the MRs begin to saturate, and the GRs take over as the chief mediators of glucocorticoid action and thus are key to the feedback inhibition of the HPA axis *(93)*.

There are other factors that add to the subtlety of adrenal steroid actions. The first is the diversity of transcriptional regulation. On binding of the hormone, the corticosteroid receptors are translocated to the nucleus, where they bind as homodimers to the DNA *(103)* or interact with a whole host of transcription factors (AP-1, nuclear factor kappa B [NFκB], cyclic adenosine monophosphate response element-binding [CREB], STATs) *(104)* as monomers. Different brain regions, which not only have different MR/GR ratios and expression of splice variants of the receptors but also express various combinations of these transcriptional coactivators and corepressors, can thus contribute to differential gene expression. This in turn may produce a diverse array of receptor-mediated actions. Second, local intracellular concentrations of glucocorticoids can be regulated by the expression of modifying enzymes such as 11-β-steroid dehydrogenase 1 and 2 *(105–107)*, 3-α- and 5-α reductases *(105)*. Also, by the action of the multidrug resistance (MDR) pump, cortisol, but not corticosterone, has been shown to be extruded from cells *(108)*. Finally, MRs have an unusual role: as determined by genetic deletion of the MR, they are essential for a rapid nongenomic effect of corticosterone in the mouse hippocampus that increases excitatory postsynaptic potentials (EPSPs) *(109)*. A similar rapid corticosterone effect on glutamate levels has been reported for the rat hippocampus, and this action is not blocked by RU486 and hence does not appear to be mediated by the glucocorticoid (GR or type II) receptors *(110)*.

Given this array of factors, it may be more understandable that adrenal steroids appear to play contradictory roles in the actions of stress on hippocampus, PFC, and amygdala. In the hippocampus, low levels of adrenal steroids have trophic effects in maintaining dendritic branch patterns in the dentate gyrus and may do so via MRs *(111)*. Similar effects have been reported in the PFC *(57,58)*. Yet, in both hippocampus and PFC, repeated stress and high-dose corticosteroid treatment promotes dendritic remodeling *(46,52,54,112)*, and we know for the hippocampus that these actions require excitatory amino acids and N-methyl D-aspartate (NMDA) receptors *(44,123–125)*. In the amygdala, adrenal steroids are implicated in dendritic lengthening in neurons of the basolateral nucleus as well as increased anxiety *(113)*. Yet, at the same time adrenal steroids are also implicated in the ability of an acute stress prior to acute immobilization to reduce the immobilization-induced anxiety and induction of excitatory spine synapses *(114)*. Thus, it appears that the actions of adrenal steroids are very much dependent on their concentration, as well as on time and the activities of other mediators such as excitatory amino acids and serotonin. For example, adrenal steroids are required for serotonin to exert gating effects on synaptic transmission in the BLA *(115)*, while, as described in another section, acute corticosteroid treatment enhances excitability of BLA neurons and reduces inhibitory tone *(116)*.

Effects on Excitatory Synaptic Transmission

Stress has a profound impact on transmission and plasticity at excitatory glutamatergic synapses in two ways. First, stress leads to significant increase in the extracellular levels of glutamate in the hippocampus, amygdala, and PFC (Fig. 3) *(117,118)*. This suggests that at least one of the immediate consequences of stress is similar in all three brain areas that subsequently exhibit contrasting patterns of structural plasticity of dendrites and spines. In other words, two key factors—glucocorticoids and glutamate—are both elevated following exposure to stress (Fig. 3). This implies that cellular mechanisms more downstream of these short-term changes may hold the key to the differential response of the

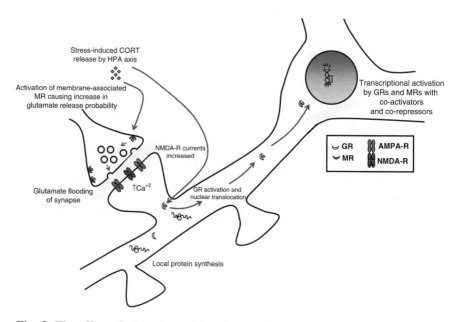

Fig. 3. The effect of adrenal steroids (via glucocorticoid receptors [GRs] and mineralocorticoid receptors [MRs]) on excitatory amino acid neurotransmission through *N*-methyl-D-aspartate (NMDA) and α-amino-3-hydroxy-5-methyl-4-isoxazolepropionic acid (AMPA) receptors (NMDA-R and AMPA-R, respectively). Stress-induced elevation of corticosterone *(44)* leads to the rapid activation of the presynaptic membrane-associated MR, which results in an increase in the glutamate release probability *(109)* and subsequent abundance of glutamate in and around synapses *(117,118)*. This surge of glutamate in turn leads to activation of postsynaptic AMPA and NMDA receptors. Calcium influx through NMDA receptors *(120,121)*, in addition to triggering intracellular signaling cascades related to synaptic plasticity, causes protein synthesis at the synaptic level that is essential for dendritic remodeling *(193)*. Corticosterone (CORT) also binds to the GRs, which then translocate to the nucleus and trigger gene expression *(95)* in coordination with a host of cell-specific transcriptional coactivators and corepressors *(93)* (*See Color Plates*)

three brain areas to stress. This in turn points to the second major effect of glucocorticoids: their impact on glutamate receptor subtypes and synaptic plasticity mechanisms mediated by them.

Both stress and glucocorticoid treatment cause enhanced expression of NMDA receptors in the hippocampus (Fig. 3) *(119,120)*, and this is another potential mechanism by which adrenal steroids are involved in the dendritic remodeling described. Chronic stress also increases the deactivation time constant and the amplitude of NMDA receptor-mediated excitatory postsynaptic currents (EPSCs) in the CA3, further supporting increased NMDA receptor signaling in response to stress *(121)*. It is puzzling, however, that NMDA receptors are not expressed in the stratum lucidum, where mossy fibers terminate on hippocampal CA3 pyramidal cells *(122)*, given the evidence cited for the importance of this innervation for dendritic atrophy. The presence of NMDA receptors on the more distal aspects of CA3 dendrites suggests that the mossy fiber activation of glutamate release triggers a much more widespread activity of excitatory amino acids affecting the entire dendritic tree of the CA3 pyramidal neurons. Following up on the widespread activation of NMDA receptors, the increased levels of intracellular calcium (Fig. 3) may make the dendritic cytoskeleton become depolymerized or undergo proteolysis *(46)*.

The effects of stress on the hippocampus are dependent on the NMDA subtype of glutamate receptors as NMDA antagonism blocks the stress-induced hippocampal plasticity *(44,123–125)*, including impairment of neurogenesis in the dentate gyrus. Conversely, direct in vitro application of corticosterone enhances NMDA currents (Fig. 3) *(126)*, and glucocorticoids increase NR2A and NR2B subunit expression in the hippocampus after chronic administration *(120)*. The enhancement of amygdala-dependent aversive learning is also blocked if the NMDA channel is blocked transiently during the stress episode *(67)*. Therefore, NMDA conductance serves as a gating mechanism for the cascade of stress responses that eventually result in both impaired hippocampal and amygdalar plasticity and memory tasks.

Besides regulating NMDA receptors, stress and glucocorticoids also regulate excitatory amino acid transporters in the hippocampus *(127,128)*. Whereas chronic stress that causes dendritic remodeling in the CA3 region increases glutamate transporter Glt1a and Glt1b expression, adrenal steroids appear to suppress the expression of Glt1a, as evidenced by studies with ADX and adrenal steroid replacement *(128)*. This counterregulation by adrenal steroids is similar to what happens with inflammatory responses, which are suppressed by adrenal steroids *(92)*.

Effects on Plasticity at Excitatory Synapses

Adrenal steroids acutely modulate synaptic plasticity in hippocampal neurons, commonly assayed by the measurement of LTP *(129)*. In the hippocampal CA1 field and the dentate gyrus, acute stress and acute glucocorticoid elevation impairs LTP or its close relative, primed-burst potentiation (PBP). Further, there is a U-shaped dose-response curve, with low levels of corticosterone facilitating PBP and high levels inhibiting PBP in the CA1 region (for review, see Refs. *92* and *130)*.Glucocorticoids also lower the NMDA-dependent long-term depression (LTD) of the synapses *(125)* and increases voltage-gated calcium currents *(131)* in the hippocampus. Glucocorticoids act on neurons in both the hippocampus and the BLA to increase the amplitude of high-voltage activated calcium currents without changing any of their passive properties *(132)*. However, glucocorticoids have also been shown to cause an increase in the excitability of LA neurons *(116)*. Unlike the hippocampus, the amplitude of the low afterhyperpolarization potentials are not changed in the BLA, possibly due to differences in subunit expression of calcium channels *(133)*.

In a manner similar to chronic stress, a single stress episode affects synaptic plasticity in the hippocampus: LTP is impaired, and LTD is enhanced *(134–137)*. This defect in synaptic plasticity correlates with the stress-induced impairment of hippocampus-dependent memory *(124)*. It is well documented that stress interferes with performance of hippocampus-dependent tasks but facilitates tasks such as eyeblink conditioning in both rats *(63)* and humans *(138)*. Hippocampus-dependent spatial learning tasks are impaired by chronic stress, and these changes endure well beyond the duration of the stressor *(139)*. Unlike chronic stress, however, the changes in plasticity caused by at least certain types of acute stress do not last long *(136)*.

If the effects of acute stress in animal models show any parallel with the human disorder of PTSD, behavioral impairments should be expressed long after an acute stress episode. Although there is no evidence of a delayed onset of aberrant hippocampus-dependent memory tasks, there are experiments showing that anxiety-like behavior can have a delayed onset after a single stressful experience *(72,79)*. In this context, the interaction between the amygdala, where the effects of chronic stress can be persistent *(71)*, and the hippocampus may explain the temporal evolution of the behavioral changes *(140)*.

Mechanistically, the effects on the hippocampus are known to be dependent, at least in part, on glucocorticoids *(141,142)*. Although both the hippocampus and the amygdala have high levels of MRs and GRs, agonists of the GRs are known to enhance retention memory for learning tasks by acting on the BLA *(103,143–145)*. While the stress effects are dependent on glucocorticoids, there is evidence that this is not sufficient to explain the behavioral enhancement of memory seen after stress, and that this enhancement may be selective for certain forms of memory *(146,147)*.

In the amygdala, as in the hippocampus, mechanisms of plasticity are impaired by stress in a glucocorticoid-dependent manner *(148)*, even though amygdala-dependent fear conditioning learning is enhanced *(63)*. Yet, the populations of cells recruited by acute versus chronic stress may be different *(149)*. Acute stress causes a suppression of unit activity in the BLA, and reexposure to the stressful context also causes a decrease in activity in an NMDA-dependent manner. This is similar to the recall and reactivation hypothesis in PTSD *(150)*.

Effects on Inhibitory Synaptic Transmission

As for inhibitory neurotransmission, the link between stress-induced anxiety disorders and the GABA-ergic system in the amygdala is a well-established one *(151,152)*. Stress and glucocorticoids reduce inhibitory currents in the BLA (Fig. 4) *(116,153)* and in the PVN of the hypothalamus *(154)* and reduce extracellular GABA in the hippocampus *(155)*. A study by Duvarci and Pare provided valuable insights into the direct synaptic impact of glucocorticoid action on intrinsic excitability and inhibitory synaptic transmission in the LA (Fig. 4). Direct wash in of glucocorticoids onto a brain slice resulted in an increase in excitability in amygdalar neurons and a reduction in evoked inhibitory postsynaptic potentials (IPSPs) *(116)*.

Acute stress results in an immediate, short-lived decrease in spontaneous miniature inhibitory postsynaptic currents (mIPSCs) (Fig. 4) *(156)*. It has also

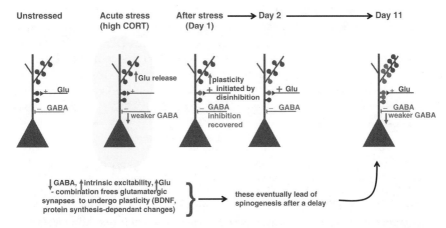

Fig. 4. Effects of acute stress on basolateral amygdala (BLA) principal neurons. Brief but severe stress, such as 2 h of immobilization, triggers a surge of high corticosterone (CORT) and glutamate release (*yellow cloud*) *(117,118)*. High CORT in turn causes a reduction in γ-aminobutyric acid-ergic (GABA-ergic) inhibitory synaptic inputs to BLA cells, which also exhibit enhanced intrinsic excitability by way of enhanced action potential firing *(116)*. Stress-induced disinhibition frees up the excitatory glutamatergic synapses to undergo plasticity, which eventually leads to a delayed strengthening of these inputs through biochemical signaling mechanisms. These plasticity mechanisms, once triggered, continue despite restoration of normal levels of inhibition, glutamate, and CORT after the termination of acute stress. Eventually, this leads to strengthening of the structural basis of synaptic connectivity that is manifested as newly formed spines in the BLA *(72)*, which are restricted to dendritic segments that are closer to the soma. However, as noted in the text, CORT elevation prior to the time of the severe stress has the ability to prevent the increased anxiety and increased synaptogenesis *(114)* via mechanisms still to be elucidated (*See Color Plates*)

been found that acute stress results in a delayed structural change in the form of increase in spine density in the LA 10 days later *(72)*. This change in excitatory synaptic connections is similar to that caused by 10 days of chronic stress and is similarly accompanied by a decrease in mIPSCs (Fig. 5). Although the delayed structural effects of acute stress are less widespread than those of chronic stress *(49)*, they are similar in terms of modified amygdalar output. The original period

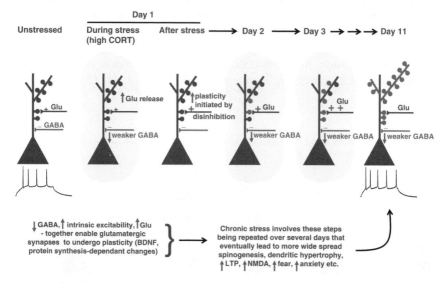

Fig. 5. Effects of chronic stress on basolateral amygdala (BLA) principal neurons. The first episode of stress (on day 1) elicits a reduction in γ-aminobutyric acid-ergic (GABA-ergic) inhibition as well as an increase in excitability *(116)*. Although this inhibition is reduced *(153,156)* only during and short periods after stress-induced increases in corticosterone (CORT) and glutamate release (*yellow cloud*), this brief window of disinhibition sets in motion plasticity mechanisms in the excitatory synapses that persist beyond the duration of the first stress episode (see Fig. 4). Exposure to repeated stress on subsequent days has a cumulative effect *(157)* in that the same single stress episode-induced changes in synaptic inhibition and excitation now act on a cellular substrate that is already undergoing plasticity as a result of earlier exposure to stress. Thus, chronic exposure to stress acts on a sliding, and continuously strengthening, baseline of plastic inputs that quickly add up to give rise to more robust and widespread structural changes (*new spines in red*). These plastic changes are eventually manifested as extensive spinogenesis across both primary and secondary dendrites (as opposed to more localized spinogenesis that is triggered by a single episode, as depicted in Fig. 4). This enhanced structural connectivity also supports enhanced long-term potentiation (LTP) *(157)*, possibly mediated by larger N-methyl-D-aspartate (NMDA) receptor-mediated currents *(157)*. Finally, chronic stress-induced strengthening of the physiological and structural basis of synaptic connectivity may also lead to dendritic elongation. As noted in the text, CORT has the ability to mimic, and therefore possibly to mediate, the dendritic elongation *(113)* (*See Color Plates*)

of low inhibition may therefore set off a cascade of synaptic and molecular events that result, 10 days later, in the changes in both excitatory and inhibitory synapses in the LA (Fig. 4).

The link between enhanced excitability and decreased inhibition in the amygdala after stress is of relevance in the action of anxiolytics such as benzodiazepines, which act by enhancing inhibition *(151,152,157)*. Stress-induced anxiety may therefore be tightly coupled to levels of inhibition in the amygdala and possibly in other brain areas. In parallel with the increase in NMDA currents *(120,121)*, α-amino-3-hydroxy-5-methyl-4-isoxazolepropionic acid (AMPA) binding *(158)*, and extracellular glutamate *(117,118)* caused by stress or glucocorticoid application, this reduction in inhibition may be shifting the balance away from homeostasis into a disease state (Figs. 4 and 5). Both from the point of view of therapeutic drugs and from a possible role in gating the cascade of stress-induced changes seen in PTSD, the inhibitory GABA-ergic system is very likely to be a key player.

Besides excitation, inhibitory mechanisms are also modulated by adrenal steroids. For example, low levels of corticosterone alter messenger ribonucleic acid (mRNA) levels for specific subunits of $GABA_A$ receptors in hippocampal area CA3 and the dentate gyrus of ADX rats *(159)*, whereas stress levels of corticosterone have produced different effects on $GABA_A$ receptor subunit mRNA levels and receptor binding in hippocampal subregions, including CA3 *(160)*. Therefore, it appears that corticosterone may alter the excitability of hippocampal neurons through regulation of $GABA_A$ receptor expression as well as excitatory amino acid expression, but it remains to be seen if the corticosteroid effects on neuronal morphology involve changes in the number or pharmacological properties of $GABA_A$ receptors.

SYNTHESIS AND FUTURE DIRECTIONS

Animal models of stress, aimed at explaining many of the symptoms of PTSD, have relied on a wide range of analyses spanning multiple levels of neural organization—from behavior, through cells and synapses, down to molecules. These studies have yielded a rich collection of findings in three brain structures that have also been implicated in clinical and neuroimaging analyses of PTSD in humans. As discussed, two broad themes have emerged from these findings in the hippocampus, amygdala, and PFC. First, although many of the mechanistic details are yet to be fully elucidated, there is growing evidence pointing to a common set of endocrinological and physiological changes that are triggered in all three brain areas during and immediately after stress (Fig. 3). Second, despite sharing common features in their genesis, the plasticity mechanisms that eventually take shape in cells and synapses across these three areas exhibit strikingly different patterns (Fig. 2), which in turn may explain the diversity of symptoms of PTSD. A major challenge for future research will be to unravel the precise mechanisms and spatiotemporal features of how these diverse patterns emerge over time. Three issues, discussed next, are particularly important in this regard.

Differential Modulation of Synaptic Signaling During and Immediately After Stress

While elevation in the levels of glucocorticoids and glutamate appears to be one of the earliest changes induced by stress, there may be subtle differences in how such an increase affects excitatory and inhibitory synaptic transmission in the hippocampus, amygdala, and PFC. For example, evidence from the hippocampus suggests that there is an inverted U-shaped curve (for an example of "hormesis," see Ref. *161*), in which low physiological levels of adrenal steroids enhance excitability and memory processes and exert trophic and protective effects on hippocampal neurons. It is not clear if a similar profile of glucocorticoid dependence is in play in the amygdala as well. However, clinical studies on PTSD treatment are strongly suggestive of a protective role for cortisol in alleviating symptoms of PTSD. Adrenal glucocorticoids have a powerful effect on the human brain. In Cushing's disease, there is hippocampal atrophy, depressed mood, and impaired cognitive function that can be at least partially reversed by reducing the hypercortisolemia *(162,163)*.

In contrast, there are reports that individuals having lower levels of salivary or urinary cortisol are more susceptible to developing PTSD *(89)*. This has been studied therapeutically in a clinical research setting so that patients who receive stress levels of cortisol as part of their treatment in medical intensive care units (ICUs) have a lower probability of developing ICU-related PTSD symptoms *(164–168)*. These data suggest that glucocorticoids may protect against the development of stress-related disorders. Work with abuse victims has shown that there is an exaggerated adrenocorticotropic hormone (ACTH) response to stress or corticotropin-releasing hormone (CRH), suggesting that hypocortisolism in these people is an adaptation of the adrenal gland to the exaggerated response to stress at the level of the hypothalamus/pituitary. In response to this decreased production of cortisol, there is an increased responsiveness of GRs in PTSD patients *(169)*. An interesting theory put forward to give an evolutionary basis for this phenomenon posits that glucocorticoid insufficiency might be adaptive in that it allows inflammatory healing to occur by favoring innate immunity mechanisms. Also, reduced glucocorticoid signaling would favor an enhancement of noradrenergic function, which is key to the consolidation of emotionally laden experiences *(170)*, and might increase arousal and facilitate emotional memory formation.

Preliminary studies using animal models of acute stress suggest a similar protective role for corticosterone in the amygdala. As described, rats exposed to acute immobilization stress exhibit a delayed increase in anxiety-like behavior *(72)*. Using this same acute stress model, it has been reported that oral administration of corticosterone prior to acute stress prevents the delayed increase in anxiety *(114)*. Furthermore, whereas either corticosterone administration or repeated restraint stress will cause dendrites to be shortened in the CA3 region, the combination of the two treatments nullifies the dendritic remodeling in CA3 *(171)*. And, as noted, adrenal steroids are implicated in the ability of chronic stress to cause dendritic lengthening in BLA neurons as well as increased anxiety *(113)*. Yet, at the same time, adrenal steroids are also implicated in the ability of an acute stress prior to acute immobilization to reduce the immobilization-induced anxiety and spinogenesis in the BLA *(114)*.There are also paradoxes in the role of adrenal steroids in inhibition in amygdala. On the one hand, an electrophysiological study has demonstrated that in vitro application of stress levels of corticosterone leads to a reduction in GABA-ergic inhibitory synaptic transmission, along with an increase in intrinsic excitability of excitatory principal neurons, in brain slices of the LA (Fig. 4) *(116)*. There is also evidence for an inverse relationship between GABA-ergic inhibitory tone in the BLA and behavioral anxiety *(151,152)*. On the other hand, in vivo recordings and immunocytochemical labeling have also shown that the ability of serotonin to inhibit glutamatergic activity in the LA is dependent on the presence of corticosterone and possibly glucocorticoid activation. While serotonin inhibited both synaptically and glutamate-evoked action potentials in LA neurons, it failed to do so in ADX rats. Strikingly, high, but not low, corticosterone doses given to ADX animals reinstated the inhibition of excitatory transmission of serotonin *(115)*. These findings raise the intriguing possibility that varying levels of corticosterone may have different effects on amygdalar function and its behavioral consequences, possibly following a U-shaped dose-response curve. In other words, very high levels of corticosterone (e.g., triggered by severe and chronic stress in rats), as well as very low levels (e.g., insufficient cortisol in ICU patients), may cause an imbalance between excitation and inhibition in the amygdala, thereby eliciting affective symptoms (Figs. 4 and 5). Taken together, these findings highlight the need for future studies to examine the precise dose dependence of how glucocorticoids modulate excitatory and inhibitory synaptic transmission in the amygdala and PFC and how these compare with the hippocampus.

Similarly, the availability of large amounts of extracellular glutamate after stress could have a profound impact on glutamate receptor activation and consequent plasticity (Fig. 3). For example, the dominant form of Hebbian LTP that is impaired by stress depends on the activation of postsynaptic NMDA receptors in the hippocampus *(172)*. Strikingly, the LA also supports a form of associative Hebbian LTP that requires the activation of presynaptic, and not postsynaptic, NMDA receptors. Would the surge in extracellular glutamate triggered by stress affect these two forms of Hebbian NMDA receptor-dependent LTP differently? Indeed, LTP itself appears to be quite different in terms of its ease of induction in the hippocampus versus the amygdala. In the amygdala, GABA-ergic inhibition exerts a potent regulatory influence on LTP induction, which is not the case in the hippocampus *(173)*. In other words, the differential modulation of GABA-ergic modulation by stress and stress hormones could serve as an early point of divergence between the hippocampus and amygdala. These early differences in turn could trigger biochemical signaling cascades that eventually set the plasticity mechanisms in excitatory glutamatergic synapses on a different course in the different brain areas.

Differences in Network Architectures

It is quite possible that the contrasting patterns of plasticity in the three brain areas (Fig. 2) are not all caused by intrinsic differences in the early steps of synaptic signaling triggered by stress. It is also possible that the common set of early changes triggered by stress elicits plasticity mechanisms that do not differ between the three areas—and that the difference lies in their drastically different neuronal circuitry. Indeed, there is evidence for very different forms of stress-induced structural plasticity even within the amygdala. For example, while repeated restraint stress for 21 days leads to the formation of spine synapses in the BLA, it causes the opposite effect—a loss of spines—in the medial amygdala (MeA). Furthermore, stress-induced spine loss in the MeA depends on the extracellular matrix protease tPA, which plays no role in spine formation in the BLA *(174,175)*. Further, stress-induced upregulation of tPA is restricted to the MeA and central nucleus of the amygdala (CeA), the two major noncortical output nuclei of the amygdala. While these observations highlight differences between input and output nuclei of the amygdala, there may also be important differences between the output nuclei themselves. For example, studies using the startle reflex indicated that the bed nucleus of stria terminalis (BNST) in the so-called extended amygdala may be involved in processing signals more akin to cue-nonspecific fear or anxiety, whereas the CeA is more involved in cue-specific fear *(176,177)*. Therefore, rules governing neuronal plasticity that vary even between microcircuits located in the same brain structure could also contribute to the divergent effects of stress.

Interconnectivity and Interdependence

In earlier reports of the specific findings described, stress-induced plasticity in different brain regions was treated as stand-alone effects manifested as properties intrinsic to individual structures. However, a large body of neuroanatomical data also points to extensive interconnections among the hippocampus, amygdala, and PFC *(130,178,179)*. This raises the intriguing possibility that some of the structural and physiological changes triggered by stress in one brain area may, at least in part, influence changes in other areas.

In a series of influential studies, McGaugh and colleagues reported that pharmacological perturbations in the amygdala, affecting synaptic transmission mediated by GABA, opioid, norepinephrine, and acetylcholine, can facilitate or impair the formation of hippocampal memory *(180–182)*. Lesions and drug infusions targeting the amygdala, as well as stimulation of the amygdala, have also been shown to modulate the magnitude of LTP in the dentate gyrus *(183)*. These findings raise the possibility that the amygdala is in a position to play a significant role in mediating the effects of stress on hippocampal function.

Consistent with this view, Kim and colleagues reported that electrolytic lesions of the amygdala before exposure to uncontrollable restraint-tail shock stress prevent impairment of hippocampal LTP and spatial memory in rats *(184)*. More recent experiments by the same group, using microinfusions of the GABA$_A$ receptor agonist muscimol into the amygdala before stress, prevented stress-induced impairment of LTP in hippocampal slices *(185)*. Consistent with these physiological effects, at the behavioral level, stress failed to impair spatial memory in the Morris water maze task in animals receiving muscimol infusions in the amygdala. Importantly, muscimol infusions into the amygdala immediately after stress did not rescue stress-induced deficits in LTP and spatial memory *(184)*.

These studies, which provide compelling evidence for a role of the amygdala in mediating the effects of stress on hippocampal LTP and memory, have also been extended to one of the earliest reported cellular correlates of stress-induced plasticity in the hippocampus—dendritic atrophy of CA3 pyramidal neurons. A report suggested that 21-day restraint stress failed to elicit dendritic atrophy in hippocampal CA3 cells in rats with lesions of the BLA *(186)*. Taken together, these physiological and behavioral findings highlight the role of amygdalar neuronal activity in the impairment of hippocampal synaptic plasticity and memory caused by stress. Similar studies will be needed to examine if stress-induced changes in the PFC contribute to, or are influenced by, changes in the amygdala and hippocampus.

Future Directions: Investigating the Spatiotemporal Dynamics of Stress Effects Across Distributed Networks

As informative as the studies reviewed here have been in constructing a powerful framework for animal models of PTSD, our current understanding is limited by the fact that function is inferred from analysis at the cellular and behavioral levels without any online readout of dynamic changes in neuronal activity in the intact animal. In other words, although a large body of evidence has been gleaned from snapshots at fixed time points in various brain regions, much less is known about stress effects on neuronal activity in the hippocampus, amygdala, or PFC while animals perform behavioral tasks that are known to be affected by stress. The next generation of animal studies aimed at investigating neural mechanisms of PTSD will have to bridge this crucial gap in knowledge. Rapid advances in powerful multichannel single-unit recording tools for behaving animals, first in the hippocampus *(187)* and more recently in the amygdala and PFC *(188,189)*, provide an ideal foundation to extend the scope of current animal models of PTSD in this direction. Indeed, one recent study *(190)* did this by analyzing the effects of audiogenic stress on hippocampal "place cells," the firing of which indicates a specific location in the environment of the rat and has been shown to encode memories of familiar spatial locations *(187,191,192)*. This study reported for the first time that, in addition to impairing the consolidation of spatial memory and hippocampal LTP in vitro, audiogenic stress impairs the stability of firing rates of place cells recorded from area CA1 in rats foraging freely on a novel open-field platform. These observations raise the possibility that stress-induced impairment in synaptic plasticity may block the storage of stable "rate maps" by hippocampal place cells, and this may underlie spatial memory deficits triggered by stress *(190)*.

In vivo electrophysiological recording techniques in awake, behaving rodents that enabled detailed studies linking spatial memory and place cells in the hippocampus have also been very valuable in establishing that neurons in the LA encode aversive memories during the acquisition and extinction of Pavlovian fear conditioning (reviewed by Maren and Quirk in Ref. *22*). Further, in vivo unit recordings in behaving animals, combined with lesions and pharmacological inactivation, have shown that extinction of fear memory reduces associative plasticity in the LA and involves the hippocampus and PFC. In addition to the inherent power of these in vivo multielectrode recording studies in providing valuable insights into the encoding of information in neuronal networks implicated in PTSD, they also bring us back to the dominant theme emerging from human neuroimaging studies: interactions between activity in the hippocampus, amygdala, and PFC.

We began this chapter by summarizing results from neuroimaging research that revealed enhanced responsivity of the amygdala and diminished responsivity of the mPFC. Further, while amygdala responsivity is positively associated with symptom severity in PTSD, mPFC responsivity has the opposite association *(35,36)*, which points to a functional relationship between these two regions. There is also evidence for reduced hippocampal volumes and function in PTSD. In this context, several recent in vivo recording studies are particularly relevant. For example, simultaneous recordings of electrical activity have provided evidence for an increase in rhythmically synchronized activity at theta frequencies between the LA and hippocampal area CA1 in freely behaving mice during fear memory retrieval *(188)*. Further evidence highlighting the importance of synchronization of neuronal activities between networks comes from another study that used simultaneous tetrode recordings from the CA1 area and mPFC in rats *(189)*. This study showed that correlated firing in the two brain areas is selectively enhanced during behavior that recruits spatial working memory, allowing the integration of hippocampal spatial information into a broader, decision-making network. Importantly, the increased correlations are paralleled by enhanced coupling of the mPFC and CA1 area in the theta frequency range, the same range earlier shown to play a role in synchronization of activities in the amygdalo-hippocampal network in fear-conditioned mice *(188)*. These studies suggest that neural synchrony may represent a more general mechanism through which brain structures that are differentially affected in PTSD encode information independently and interact selectively according to specific needs imposed by any given behavioral task (e.g., decision making based on efficient recall of a particular cue or context related to a fearful experience).

The power of these in vivo electrophysiological recording methods opens up new avenues to investigate how the hippocampus, PFC, and amygdala interact dynamically during and after stress. Such studies will also help us understand the precise role for the amygdala in plasticity mechanisms triggered in other brain regions, possibly revealing a common target for clinical interventions for PTSD. Furthermore, future studies will have to analyze how stress-induced modulation of cellular and synaptic mechanisms in these three brain areas affects neural synchrony both within and across these structures. Finally, it will be particularly interesting to examine if and how such network effects manifest themselves as disruption of cognitive and emotional function at the behavioral level.

REFERENCES

1. Bremner JD, Randall P, Vermetten E, et al. Magnetic resonance imaging-based measurement of hippocampal volume in posttraumatic stress disorder related to childhood physical and sexual abuse-a preliminary report. Biol Psychiatry 1997;41:23–32.
2. Gurvits TV, Shenton ME, Hokama H, et al. Magnetic resonance imaging study of hippocampal volume in chronic, combat-related posttraumatic stress disorder. Biol Psychiatry 1996;40:1091–99.
3. Bremner JD, Vythilingam M, Vermetten E, et al. MRI and PET study of deficits in hippocampal structure and function in women with childhood sexual abuse and posttraumatic stress disorder. Am J Psychiatry 2003;160:924–32.
4. Gilbertson MW, Shenton ME, Ciszewski A, et al. Smaller hippocampal volume predicts pathologic vulnerability to psychological trauma. Nat Neurosci 2002;5:1242–47.
5. Vasterling JJ, Duke LM, Brailey K, Constans JI, Allain AN Jr, Sutker PB. Attention, learning, and memory performances and intellectual resources in Vietnam veterans: PTSD and no disorder comparisons. Neuropsychology 2002;16:5–14.
6. McEwen BS, Gould EA, Sakai RR. The vulnerability of the hippocampus to protective and destructive effects of glucocorticoids in relation to stress. Br J Psychiatry Suppl 1992;160:18–24.
7. Golier JA, Harvey PD, Legge J, Yehuda R. Memory performance in older trauma survivors: implications for the longitudinal course of PTSD. Ann N Y Acad Sci 2006;1071:54–66.
8. Rauch SL, van der Kolk BA, Fisler RE, et al. A symptom provocation study of posttraumatic stress disorder using positron emission tomography and script-driven imagery. Arch Gen Psychiatry 1996;53:380–87.
9. Shin LM, Orr SP, Carson MA, et al. Regional cerebral blood flow in the amygdala and medial prefrontal cortex during traumatic imagery in male and female Vietnam veterans with PTSD. Arch Gen Psychiatry 2004;61:168–76.
10. Driessen M, Beblo T, Mertens M, et al. Posttraumatic stress disorder and fMRI activation patterns of traumatic memory in patients with borderline personality disorder. Biol Psychiatry 2004;55:603–11.
11. Liberzon I, Taylor SF, Amdur R, et al. Brain activation in PTSD in response to trauma-related stimuli. Biol Psychiatry 1999;45:817–26.
12. Pissiota A, Frans O, Fernandez M, von Knorring L, Fischer H, Fredrikson M. Neurofunctional correlates of posttraumatic stress disorder: a PET symptom provocation study. Eur Arch Psychiatry Clin Neurosci 2002;252:68–75.
13. Hendler T, Rotshtein P, Yeshurun Y, et al. Sensing the invisible: differential sensitivity of visual cortex and amygdala to traumatic context. Neuroimage 2003;19:587–600.
14. Shin LM, McNally RJ, Kosslyn SM, et al. A positron emission tomographic study of symptom provocation in PTSD. Ann N Y Acad Sci 1997;821:521–23.
15. Protopopescu X, Pan H, Tuescher O, et al. Differential time courses and specificity of amygdala activity in posttraumatic stress disorder subjects and normal control subjects. Biol Psychiatry 2005;57:464–73.
16. Rauch SL, Whalen PJ, Shin LM, et al. Exaggerated amygdala response to masked facial stimuli in posttraumatic stress disorder: a functional MRI study. Biol Psychiatry 2000;47:769–76.
17. Shin LM, Wright CI, Cannistraro PA, et al. A functional magnetic resonance imaging study of amygdala and medial prefrontal cortex responses to overtly presented fearful faces in posttraumatic stress disorder. Arch Gen Psychiatry 2005;62:273–81.

18. Williams LM, Kemp AH, Felmingham K, et al. Trauma modulates amygdala and medial prefrontal responses to consciously attended fear. Neuroimage 2006;29:347–57.
19. Armony JL, Corbo V, Clement MH, Brunet A. Amygdala response in patients with acute PTSD to masked and unmasked emotional facial expressions. Am J Psychiatry 2005;162:1961–63.
20. LeDoux JE. Emotion circuits in the brain. Annu Rev Neurosci 2000;23:155–84.
21. Lamprecht R, LeDoux J. Structural plasticity and memory. Nat Rev Neurosci 2004; 5:45–54.
22. Maren S, Quirk GJ. Neuronal signalling of fear memory. Nat Rev Neurosci 2004; 5:844–52.
23. Orr SP, Metzger LJ, Lasko NB, Macklin ML, Peri T, Pitman RK. De novo conditioning in trauma-exposed individuals with and without posttraumatic stress disorder. J Abnorm Psychol 2000;109:290–98.
24. Peri T, Ben-Shakhar G, Orr SP, Shalev AY. Psychophysiologic assessment of aversive conditioning in posttraumatic stress disorder. Biol Psychiatry 2000;47:512–19.
25. Bremner JD, Vermetten E, Schmahl C, et al. Positron emission tomographic imaging of neural correlates of a fear acquisition and extinction paradigm in women with childhood sexual-abuse-related post-traumatic stress disorder. Psychol Med 2005; 35:791–806.
26. Yamasue H, Kasai K, Iwanami A, et al. Voxel-based analysis of MRI reveals anterior cingulate gray-matter volume reduction in posttraumatic stress disorder due to terrorism. Proc Natl Acad Sci U S A 2003;100:9039–43.
27. Woodward SH, Kaloupek DG, Streeter CC, Martinez C, Schaer M, Eliez S. Decreased anterior cingulate volume in combat-related PTSD. Biol Psychiatry 2006;59:582–87.
28. Britton JC, Phan KL, Taylor SF, Fig LM, Liberzon I. Corticolimbic blood flow in posttraumatic stress disorder during script-driven imagery. Biol Psychiatry 2005;57:832–40.
29. Phelps EA, LeDoux JE. Contributions of the amygdala to emotion processing: from animal models to human behavior. Neuron 2005;48:175–87.
30. Quirk GJ, Beer JS. Prefrontal involvement in the regulation of emotion: convergence of rat and human studies. Curr Opin Neurobiol 2006;16:723–27.
31. Sotres-Bayon F, Bush DE, LeDoux JE. Acquisition of fear extinction requires activation of NR2B-containing NMDA receptors in the lateral amygdala. Neuropsychopharmacology 2007;32:1929–40.
32. Myers KM, Davis M. Mechanisms of fear extinction. Mol Psychiatry 2007;12:120–50.
33. Rothbaum BO, Kozak MJ, Foa EB, Whitaker DJ. Posttraumatic stress disorder in rape victims: autonomic habituation to auditory stimuli. J Trauma Stress 2001;14:283–93.
34. American Psychiatric Association. Diagnostic and Statistical Manual of Mental Disorders. 3rd ed. Washington, DC: American Psychiatric Association; 1980.
35. Rauch SL, Shin LM, Phelps EA. Neurocircuitry models of posttraumatic stress disorder and extinction: human neuroimaging research-past, present, and future. Biol Psychiatry 2006;60:376–82.
36. Bremner JD. Functional neuroimaging in post-traumatic stress disorder. Expert Rev Neurother 2007;7:393–405.
37. Herman JP, Schafer MK, Young EA, et al. Evidence for hippocampal regulation of neuroendocrine neurons of the hypothalamo-pituitary-adrenocortical axis. J Neurosci 1989;9:3072–82.
38. Jacobson L, Sapolsky R. The role of the hippocampus in feedback regulation of the hypothalamic-pituitary-adrenocortical axis. Endocr Rev 1991;12:118–34.

39. Sapolsky RM, Zola-Morgan S, Squire LR. Inhibition of glucocorticoid secretion by the hippocampal formation in the primate. J Neurosci 1991;11:3695–704.

40. Herman JP, Cullinan WE. Neurocircuitry of stress: central control of the hypothalamo-pituitary-adrenocortical axis. Trends Neurosci 1997;20:78–84.

41. Yehuda R, McFarlane AC. Conflict between current knowledge about posttraumatic stress disorder and its original conceptual basis. Am J Psychiatry 1995;152:1705–13.

42. Schelling G. Post-traumatic stress disorder in somatic disease: lessons from critically ill patients. Prog Brain Res 2008;167:229–37.

43. Watanabe Y, Gould E, Cameron HA, Daniels DC, McEwen BS. Phenytoin prevents stress- and corticosterone-induced atrophy of CA3 pyramidal neurons. Hippocampus 1992;2:431–35.

44. Magarinos AM, McEwen BS. Stress-induced atrophy of apical dendrites of hippocampal CA3c neurons: involvement of glucocorticoid secretion and excitatory amino acid receptors. Neuroscience 1995;69:89–98.

45. Magarinos AM, McEwen BS. Stress-induced atrophy of apical dendrites of hippocampal CA3c neurons: comparison of stressors. Neuroscience 1995;69:83–88.

46. McEwen BS. Stress and hippocampal plasticity. Annu Rev Neurosci 1999;22:105–22.

47. Sousa N, Lukoyanov NV, Madeira MD, Almeida OF, Paula-Barbosa MM. Reorganization of the morphology of hippocampal neurites and synapses after stress-induced damage correlates with behavioral improvement. Neuroscience 2000;97:253–66.

48. Conrad CD, LeDoux JE, Magarinos AM, McEwen BS. Repeated restraint stress facilitates fear conditioning independently of causing hippocampal CA3 dendritic atrophy. Behav Neurosci 1999;113:902–13.

49. Vyas A, Mitra R, Shankaranarayana Rao BS, Chattarji S. Chronic stress induces contrasting patterns of dendritic remodeling in hippocampal and amygdaloid neurons. J Neurosci 2002;22:6810–18.

50. Diorio D, Viau V, Meaney MJ. The role of the medial prefrontal cortex (cingulate gyrus) in the regulation of hypothalamic-pituitary-adrenal responses to stress. J Neurosci 1993;13:3839–47.

51. Radley JJ, Arias CM, Sawchenko PE. Regional differentiation of the medial prefrontal cortex in regulating adaptive responses to acute emotional stress. J Neurosci 2006;26:12967–76.

52. Wellman CL. Dendritic reorganization in pyramidal neurons in medial prefrontal cortex after chronic corticosterone administration. J Neurobiol 2001;49:245–53.

53. Cook SC, Wellman CL. Chronic stress alters dendritic morphology in rat medial prefrontal cortex. J Neurobiol 2004;60:236–48.

54. Radley JJ, Sisti HM, Hao J, et al. Chronic behavioral stress induces apical dendritic reorganization in pyramidal neurons of the medial prefrontal cortex. Neuroscience 2004;125:1–6.

55. Liston C, Miller MM, Goldwater DS, et al. Stress-induced alterations in prefrontal cortical dendritic morphology predict selective impairments in perceptual attentional set-shifting. J Neurosci 2006;26:7870–74.

56. Santini E, Ge H, Ren K, Pena de Ortiz S, Quirk GJ. Consolidation of fear extinction requires protein synthesis in the medial prefrontal cortex. J Neurosci 2004;24:5704–10.

57. Cerqueira JJ, Pego JM, Taipa R, Bessa JM, Almeida OF, Sousa N. Morphological correlates of corticosteroid-induced changes in prefrontal cortex-dependent behaviors. J Neurosci 2005;25:7792–800.

58. Cerqueira JJ, Taipa R, Uylings HB, Almeida OF, Sousa N. Specific configuration of dendritic degeneration in pyramidal neurons of the medial prefrontal cortex induced by differing corticosteroid regimens. Cereb Cortex 2007;17:1998–2006.

59. Cerqueira JJ, Mailliet F, Almeida OF, Jay TM, Sousa N. The prefrontal cortex as a key target of the maladaptive response to stress. J Neurosci 2007;27:2781–87.

60. Melia KR, Ryabinin AE, Schroeder R, Bloom FE, Wilson MC. Induction and habituation of immediate early gene expression in rat brain by acute and repeated restraint stress. J Neurosci 1994;14:5929–38.

61. Sunanda, Rao MS, Raju TR. Effect of chronic restraint stress on dendritic spines and excrescences of hippocampal CA3 pyramidal neurons--a quantitative study. Brain Res 1995;694:312–17.

62. Pitkanen A, Amaral DG. The distribution of GABAergic cells, fibers, and terminals in the monkey amygdaloid complex: an immunohistochemical and in situ hybridization study. J Neurosci 1994;14:2200–24.

63. Shors TJ, Weiss C, Thompson RF. Stress-induced facilitation of classical conditioning. Science 1992;257:537–39.

64. Luine V, Villegas M, Martinez C, McEwen BS. Repeated stress causes reversible impairments of spatial memory performance. Brain Res 1994;639:167–70.

65. Conrad CD, Galea LA, Kuroda Y, McEwen BS. Chronic stress impairs rat spatial memory on the Y maze, and this effect is blocked by tianeptine pretreatment. Behav Neurosci 1996;110:1321–34.

66. Liang KC, Hon W, Davis M. Pre- and posttraining infusion of N-methyl-D-aspartate receptor antagonists into the amygdala impair memory in an inhibitory avoidance task. Behav Neurosci 1994;108:241–53.

67. Shors TJ, Mathew PR. NMDA receptor antagonism in the lateral/basolateral but not central nucleus of the amygdala prevents the induction of facilitated learning in response to stress. Learn Mem 1998;5:220–30.

68. McDonald AJ. Neurons of the lateral and basolateral amygdaloid nuclei: a Golgi study in the rat. J Comp Neurol 1982;212:293–312.

69. McDonald AJ. Cell Types and Intrinsic Connections of the Amygdala. New York: Wiley-Liss; 1992.

70. Vyas A, Chattarji S. Modulation of different states of anxiety-like behavior by chronic stress. Behav Neurosci 2004;118:1450–54.

71. Vyas A, Pillai AG, Chattarji S. Recovery after chronic stress fails to reverse amygdaloid neuronal hypertrophy and enhanced anxiety-like behavior. Neuroscience 2004;128:667–73.

72. Mitra R, Jadhav S, McEwen BS, Vyas A, Chattarji S. Stress duration modulates the spatiotemporal patterns of spine formation in the basolateral amygdala. Proc Natl Acad Sci U S A 2005;102:9371–76.

73. Vyas A, Jadhav S, Chattarji S. Prolonged behavioral stress enhances synaptic connectivity in the basolateral amygdala. Neuroscience 2006;143:387–93.

74. McEwen BS, Wingfield JC. The concept of allostasis in biology and biomedicine. Horm Behav 2003;43:2–15.

75. Miller MM, McEwen BS. Establishing an agenda for translational research on PTSD. Ann N Y Acad Sci 2006;1071:294–312.

76. Bonne O, Grillon C, Vythilingam M, Neumeister A, Charney DS. Adaptive and maladaptive psychobiological responses to severe psychological stress: implications for the discovery of novel pharmacotherapy. Neurosci Biobehav Rev 2004;28:65–94.

77. Adamec R, Kent P, Anisman H, Shallow T, Merali Z. Neural plasticity, neuropeptides and anxiety in animals-implications for understanding and treating affective disorder following traumatic stress in humans. Neurosci Biobehav Rev 1998;23:301–18.

78. McEwen BS. Protection and damage from acute and chronic stress: allostasis and allostatic overload and relevance to the pathophysiology of psychiatric disorders. Ann N Y Acad Sci 2004;1032:1–7.

79. Kohda K, Harada K, Kato K, et al. Glucocorticoid receptor activation is involved in producing abnormal phenotypes of single-prolonged stress rats: a putative post-traumatic stress disorder model. Neuroscience 2007;148:22–33.
80. Govindarajan A, Rao BS, Nair D, et al. Transgenic brain-derived neurotrophic factor expression causes both anxiogenic and antidepressant effects. Proc Natl Acad Sci U S A 2006;103:13208–13.
81. Yehuda R. Post-traumatic stress disorder. N Engl J Med 2002;346:108–14.
82. Liberzon I, Young EA. Effects of stress and glucocorticoids on CNS oxytocin receptor binding. Psychoneuroendocrinology 1997;22:411–22.
83. Adamec RE, Burton P, Shallow T, Budgell J. Unilateral block of NMDA receptors in the amygdala prevents predator stress-induced lasting increases in anxiety-like behavior and unconditioned startle-effective hemisphere depends on the behavior. Physiol Behav 1999;65:739–51.
84. Blundell J, Adamec R, Burton P. Role of NMDA receptors in the syndrome of behavioral changes produced by predator stress. Physiol Behav 2005;86:233–43.
85. Diamond DM, Bennett MC, Fleshner M, Rose GM. Inverted-U relationship between the level of peripheral corticosterone and the magnitude of hippocampal primed burst potentiation. Hippocampus 1992;2:421–30.
86. Dielenberg RA, McGregor IS. Habituation of the hiding response to cat odor in rats (Rattus norvegicus). J Comp Psychol 1999;113:376–87.
87. Vazdarjanova A, Cahill L, McGaugh JL. Disrupting basolateral amygdala function impairs unconditioned freezing and avoidance in rats. Eur J Neurosci 2001;14:709–18.
88. Cohen H, Zohar J. An animal model of posttraumatic stress disorder: the use of cut-off behavioral criteria. Ann N Y Acad Sci 2004;1032:167–78.
89. Yehuda R, McFarlane AC, Shalev AY. Predicting the development of posttraumatic stress disorder from the acute response to a traumatic event. Biol Psychiatry 1998;44:1305–13.
90. Cohen H, Kaplan Z, Matar MA, Loewenthal U, Zohar J, Richter-Levin G. Long-lasting behavioral effects of juvenile trauma in an animal model of PTSD associated with a failure of the autonomic nervous system to recover. Eur Neuropsychopharmacol 2007;17:464–77.
91. Morgan CA 3rd, Grillon C, Southwick SM, Davis M, Charney DS. Fear-potentiated startle in posttraumatic stress disorder. Biol Psychiatry 1995;38:378–85.
92. McEwen BS. Physiology and neurobiology of stress and adaptation: central role of the brain. Physiol Rev 2007;87:873–904.
93. Joels M. Corticosteroid effects in the brain: U-shape it. Trends Pharmacol Sci 2006;27:244–50.
94. Pascual-Le Tallec L, Lombes M. The mineralocorticoid receptor: a journey exploring its diversity and specificity of action. Mol Endocrinol 2005;19:2211–21.
95. Zhou J, Cidlowski JA. The human glucocorticoid receptor: one gene, multiple proteins and diverse responses. Steroids 2005;70:407–17.
96. Ferguson D, Sapolsky R. Mineralocorticoid receptor overexpression differentially modulates specific phases of spatial and nonspatial memory. J Neurosci 2007;27:8046–52.
97. Lai M, Horsburgh K, Bae SE, et al. Forebrain mineralocorticoid receptor overexpression enhances memory, reduces anxiety and attenuates neuronal loss in cerebral ischaemia. Eur J Neurosci 2007;25:1832–42.
98. Rozeboom AM, Akil H, Seasholtz AF. Mineralocorticoid receptor overexpression in forebrain decreases anxiety-like behavior and alters the stress response in mice. Proc Natl Acad Sci U S A 2007;104:4688–93.
99. Berger S, Wolfer DP, Selbach O, et al. Loss of the limbic mineralocorticoid receptor impairs behavioral plasticity. Proc Natl Acad Sci U S A 2006;103:195–200.

100. Gass P, Kretz O, Wolfer DP, et al. Genetic disruption of mineralocorticoid receptor leads to impaired neurogenesis and granule cell degeneration in the hippocampus of adult mice. EMBO Rep 2000;1:447–51.
101. Macleod MR, Johansson IM, Soderstrom I, et al. Mineralocorticoid receptor expression and increased survival following neuronal injury. Eur J Neurosci 2003;17:1549–55.
102. Sloviter RS, Valiquette G, Abrams GM, et al. Selective loss of hippocampal granule cells in the mature rat brain after adrenalectomy. Science 1989;243:535–38.
103. Karst H, Karten YJ, Reichardt HM, de Kloet ER, Schutz G, Joels M. Corticosteroid actions in hippocampus require DNA binding of glucocorticoid receptor homodimers. Nat Neurosci 2000;3:977–78.
104. De Bosscher K, Vanden Berghe W, Haegeman G. The interplay between the glucocorticoid receptor and nuclear factor-kappaB or activator protein-1: molecular mechanisms for gene repression. Endocr Rev 2003;24:488–522.
105. Seckl JR, Walker BR. Minireview: 11beta-hydroxysteroid dehydrogenase type 1–a tissue-specific amplifier of glucocorticoid action. Endocrinology 2001;142:1371–76.
106. Edwards CR, Stewart PM, Burt D, et al. Localisation of 11 beta-hydroxysteroid dehydrogenase–tissue specific protector of the mineralocorticoid receptor. Lancet 1988;2:986–89.
107. Funder JW, Pearce PT, Smith R, Smith AI. Mineralocorticoid action: target tissue specificity is enzyme, not receptor, mediated. Science 1988;242:583–85.
108. Karssen AM, Meijer OC, van der Sandt IC, et al. Multidrug resistance P-glycoprotein hampers the access of cortisol but not of corticosterone to mouse and human brain. Endocrinology 2001;142:2686–94.
109. Karst H, Berger S, Turiault M, Tronche F, Schutz G, Joels M. Mineralocorticoid receptors are indispensable for nongenomic modulation of hippocampal glutamate transmission by corticosterone. Proc Natl Acad Sci U S A 2005;102:19204–7.
110. Venero C, Borrell J. Rapid glucocorticoid effects on excitatory amino acid levels in the hippocampus: a microdialysis study in freely moving rats. Eur J Neurosci 1999;11:2465–73.
111. Gould E, Woolley CS, McEwen BS. Short-term glucocorticoid manipulations affect neuronal morphology and survival in the adult dentate gyrus. Neuroscience 1990;37:367–75.
112. Radley JJ, Rocher AB, Miller M, et al. Repeated stress induces dendritic spine loss in the rat medial prefrontal cortex. Cereb Cortex 2006;16:313–20.
113. Mitra R, Sapolsky RM. Acute corticosterone treatment is sufficient to induce anxiety and amygdaloid dendritic hypertrophy. Proc Natl Acad Sci U S A 2008;105:5573–78.
114. Rao RP, Tomar A, McEwen BS, Chattarji S. Multiple roles for corticosterone in the modulation of stress-induced anxiety. In: Annual Meeting of the Society for Neuroscience; November 3–7, 2007; San Diego; p. 840.21.
115. Stutzmann GE, McEwen BS, LeDoux JE. Serotonin modulation of sensory inputs to the lateral amygdala: dependency on corticosterone. J Neurosci 1998;18:9529–38.
116. Duvarci S, Pare D. Glucocorticoids enhance the excitability of principal basolateral amygdala neurons. J Neurosci 2007;27:4482–91.
117. Lowy MT, Gault L, Yamamoto BK. Adrenalectomy attenuates stress-induced elevations in extracellular glutamate concentrations in the hippocampus. J Neurochem 1993;61:1957–60.
118. Reznikov LR, Grillo CA, Piroli GG, Pasumarthi RK, Reagan LP, Fadel J. Acute stress-mediated increases in extracellular glutamate levels in the rat amygdala: differential effects of antidepressant treatment. Eur J Neurosci 2007;25:3109–14.
119. Bartanusz V, Aubry JM, Pagliusi S, Jezova D, Baffi J, Kiss JZ. Stress-induced changes in messenger RNA levels of N-methyl-D-aspartate and AMPA receptor sub-

units in selected regions of the rat hippocampus and hypothalamus. Neuroscience 1995;66:247–52.

120. Weiland NG, Orchinik M, Tanapat P. Chronic corticosterone treatment induces parallel changes in N-methyl-D-aspartate receptor subunit messenger RNA levels and antagonist binding sites in the hippocampus. Neuroscience 1997;78:653–62.

121. Kole MH, Swan L, Fuchs E. The antidepressant tianeptine persistently modulates glutamate receptor currents of the hippocampal CA3 commissural associational synapse in chronically stressed rats. Eur J Neurosci 2002;16:807–16.

122. Monaghan DT, Holets VR, Toy DW, Cotman CW. Anatomical distributions of four pharmacologically distinct 3H-L-glutamate binding sites. Nature 1983;306:176–79.

123. Gould E, McEwen BS, Tanapat P, Galea LA, Fuchs E. Neurogenesis in the dentate gyrus of the adult tree shrew is regulated by psychosocial stress and NMDA receptor activation. J Neurosci 1997;17:2492–98.

124. Baker KB, Kim JJ. Effects of stress and hippocampal NMDA receptor antagonism on recognition memory in rats. Learn Mem 2002;9:58–65.

125. Kim JJ, Foy MR, Thompson RF. Behavioral stress modifies hippocampal plasticity through N-methyl-D-aspartate receptor activation. Proc Natl Acad Sci U S A 1996;93:4750–53.

126. Takahashi T, Kimoto T, Tanabe N, Hattori TA, Yasumatsu N, Kawato S. Corticosterone acutely prolonged N-methyl-d-aspartate receptor-mediated Ca2+ elevation in cultured rat hippocampal neurons. J Neurochem 2002;83:1441–51.

127. Reagan LP, Rosell DR, Wood GE, et al. Chronic restraint stress up-regulates GLT-1 mRNA and protein expression in the rat hippocampus: reversal by tianeptine. Proc Natl Acad Sci U S A 2004;101:2179–84.

128. Autry AE, Grillo CA, Piroli GG, Rothstein JD, McEwen BS, Reagan LP. Glucocorticoid regulation of GLT-1 glutamate transporter isoform expression in the rat hippocampus. Neuroendocrinology 2006;83:371–79.

129. Bliss TV, Lomo T. Long-lasting potentiation of synaptic transmission in the dentate area of the anaesthetized rabbit following stimulation of the perforant path. J Physiol 1973;232:331–56.

130. McEwen BS, Chattarji S. Neuroendocrinology of Stress. Berlin: Springer-Verlag; 2006.

131. Kerr DS, Campbell LW, Thibault O, Landfield PW. Hippocampal glucocorticoid receptor activation enhances voltage-dependent Ca2+ conductances: relevance to brain aging. Proc Natl Acad Sci U S A 1992;89:8527–31.

132. Karst H, Nair S, Velzing E, et al. Glucocorticoids alter calcium conductances and calcium channel subunit expression in basolateral amygdala neurons. Eur J Neurosci 2002;16:1083–89.

133. Liebmann L, Karst H, Sidiropoulou K, et al. Differential effects of corticosterone on the slow afterhyperpolarization in the basolateral amygdala and CA1 region: possible role of calcium channel subunits. J Neurophysiol 2008;99:958–68.

134. Shors TJ, Gallegos RA, Breindl A. Transient and persistent consequences of acute stress on long-term potentiation (LTP), synaptic efficacy, theta rhythms and bursts in area CA1 of the hippocampus. Synapse 1997;26:209–17.

135. Shors TJ, Thompson RF. Acute stress impairs (or induces) synaptic long-term potentiation (LTP) but does not affect paired-pulse facilitation in the stratum radiatum of rat hippocampus. Synapse 1992;11:262–65.

136. Garcia R, Musleh W, Tocco G, Thompson RF, Baudry M. Time-dependent blockade of STP and LTP in hippocampal slices following acute stress in mice. Neurosci Lett 1997;233:41–44.

137. Chaouloff F, Hemar A, Manzoni O. Acute stress facilitates hippocampal CA1 metabotropic glutamate receptor-dependent long-term depression. J Neurosci 2007;27:7130–35.
138. Spence KW, Taylor J. Anxiety and strength of the UCS as determiners of the amount of eyelid conditioning. J Exp Psychol 1951;42:183–88.
139. Bodnoff SR, Humphreys AG, Lehman JC, Diamond DM, Rose GM, Meaney MJ. Enduring effects of chronic corticosterone treatment on spatial learning, synaptic plasticity, and hippocampal neuropathology in young and mid-aged rats. J Neurosci 1995;15:61–69.
140. Akirav I, Richter-Levin G. Biphasic modulation of hippocampal plasticity by behavioral stress and basolateral amygdala stimulation in the rat. J Neurosci 1999;19:10530–35.
141. Xu L, Holscher C, Anwyl R, Rowan MJ. Glucocorticoid receptor and protein/RNA synthesis-dependent mechanisms underlie the control of synaptic plasticity by stress. Proc Natl Acad Sci U S A 1998;95:3204–8.
142. Blank T, Nijholt I, Eckart K, Spiess J. Priming of long-term potentiation in mouse hippocampus by corticotropin-releasing factor and acute stress: implications for hippocampus-dependent learning. J Neurosci 2002;22:3788–94.
143. Roozendaal B, McGaugh JL. Glucocorticoid receptor agonist and antagonist administration into the basolateral but not central amygdala modulates memory storage. Neurobiol Learn Mem 1997;67:176–79.
144. McGaugh JL, Roozendaal B. Role of adrenal stress hormones in forming lasting memories in the brain. Curr Opin Neurobiol 2002;12:205–10.
145. Vouimba RM, Yaniv D, Richter-Levin G. Glucocorticoid receptors and beta-adrenoceptors in basolateral amygdala modulate synaptic plasticity in hippocampal dentate gyrus, but not in area CA1. Neuropharmacology 2007;52:244–52.
146. Shors TJ. Acute stress rapidly and persistently enhances memory formation in the male rat. Neurobiol Learn Mem 2001;75:10–29.
147. Beylin AV, Shors TJ. Glucocorticoids are necessary for enhancing the acquisition of associative memories after acute stressful experience. Horm Behav 2003;43:124–31.
148. Maroun M, Richter-Levin G. Exposure to acute stress blocks the induction of long-term potentiation of the amygdala-prefrontal cortex pathway in vivo. J Neurosci 2003;23:4406–9.
149. Reznikov LR, Reagan LP, Fadel JR. Activation of phenotypically distinct neuronal subpopulations in the anterior subdivision of the rat basolateral amygdala following acute and repeated stress. J Comp Neurol 2008;508:458–72.
150. Shors TJ. Acute stress and re-exposure to the stressful context suppress spontaneous unit activity in the basolateral amygdala via NMDA receptor activation. Neuroreport 1999;10:2811–15.
151. Shekhar A, Truitt W, Rainnie D, Sajdyk T. Role of stress, corticotrophin releasing factor (CRF) and amygdala plasticity in chronic anxiety. Stress 2005;8:209–19.
152. Rainnie DG, Bergeron R, Sajdyk TJ, Patil M, Gehlert DR, Shekhar A. Corticotrophin releasing factor-induced synaptic plasticity in the amygdala translates stress into emotional disorders. J Neurosci 2004;24:3471–79.
153. Suvrathan A, Tomar A, Chattarji S. Whats synaptic transmission in the amygdala got to do with PTSD? In: Annual Meeting of Society for Neuroscience; November 3–7, 2007; San Diego; p.841.12.
154. Verkuyl JM, Karst H, Joels M. GABAergic transmission in the rat paraventricular nucleus of the hypothalamus is suppressed by corticosterone and stress. Eur J Neurosci 2005;21: p.841.12.

155. Gronli J, Fiske E, Murison R, et al. Extracellular levels of serotonin and GABA in the hippocampus after chronic mild stress in rats. A microdialysis study in an animal model of depression. Behav Brain Res 2007;181:42–51.

156. Chattarji S, Suvrathan A, Tomar A, et al. Delayed impact of stress on amygdalar synapses: implications for an animal model of PTSD. In: Annual Meeting of Society for Neuroscience; 2008; Washington, D.C.; p. 193.5.

157. Suvrathan A, Bennur S, Chattarji S. Silent synapses speak up in the amygdala. In: Annual Meeting of Society for Neuroscience; 2006; Atlanta; p. 370.14.

158. Tocco G, Shors TJ, Baudry M, Thompson RF. Selective increase of AMPA binding to the AMPA/quisqualate receptor in the hippocampus in response to acute stress. Brain Res 1991;559:168–71.

159. Orchinik M, Weiland NG, McEwen BS. Adrenalectomy selectively regulates GABAA receptor subunit expression in the hippocampus. Mol Cell Neurosci 1994;5:451–58.

160. Orchinik M, Carroll SS, Li YH, McEwen BS, Weiland NG. Heterogeneity of hippocampal GABA(A) receptors: regulation by corticosterone. J Neurosci 2001;21:330–39.

161. Calabrese EJ. Neuroscience and hormesis: overview and general findings. Crit Rev Toxicol 2008;38:249–52.

162. Starkman MN, Giordani B, Gebarski SS, Berent S, Schork MA, Schteingart DE. Decrease in cortisol reverses human hippocampal atrophy following treatment of Cushing's disease. Biol Psychiatry 1999;46:1595–602.

163. Starkman MN, Giordani B, Gebarski SS, Schteingart DE. Improvement in learning associated with increase in hippocampal formation volume. Biol Psychiatry 2003;53:233–38.

164. Schelling G, Stoll C, Kapfhammer HP, et al. The effect of stress doses of hydrocortisone during septic shock on posttraumatic stress disorder and health-related quality of life in survivors. Crit Care Med 1999;27:2678–83.

165. Briegel J, Forst H, Haller M, et al. Stress doses of hydrocortisone reverse hyperdynamic septic shock: a prospective, randomized, double-blind, single-center study. Crit Care Med 1999;27:723–32.

166. Schelling G, Briegel J, Roozendaal B, Stoll C, Rothenhausler HB, Kapfhammer HP. The effect of stress doses of hydrocortisone during septic shock on posttraumatic stress disorder in survivors. Biol Psychiatry 2001;50:978–85.

167. Schelling G, Kilger E, Roozendaal B, et al. Stress doses of hydrocortisone, traumatic memories, and symptoms of posttraumatic stress disorder in patients after cardiac surgery: a randomized study. Biol Psychiatry 2004;55:627–33.

168. Schelling G, Roozendaal B, De Quervain DJ. Can posttraumatic stress disorder be prevented with glucocorticoids? Ann N Y Acad Sci 2004;1032:158–66.

169. Yehuda R. Current status of cortisol findings in post-traumatic stress disorder. Psychiatr Clin North Am 2002;25:341–68, vii.

170. Roozendaal B, Okuda S, Van der Zee EA, McGaugh JL. Glucocorticoid enhancement of memory requires arousal-induced noradrenergic activation in the basolateral amygdala. Proc Natl Acad Sci U S A 2006;103:6741–46.

171. Magarinos AM, Orchinik M, McEwen BS. Morphological changes in the hippocampal CA3 region induced by non-invasive glucocorticoid administration: a paradox. Brain Res 1998;809:314–18.

172. Bliss TV, Collingridge GL. A synaptic model of memory: long-term potentiation in the hippocampus. Nature 1993;361:31–39.

173. Chapman PF, Chattarji S. Synaptic Plasticity in the Amygdala. 2nd ed. New York: Oxford University Press; 2000.

174. Pawlak R, Magarinos AM, Melchor J, McEwen B, Strickland S. Tissue plasminogen activator in the amygdala is critical for stress-induced anxiety-like behavior. Nat Neurosci 2003;6:168–74.

175. Bennur S, Shankaranarayana Rao BS, Pawlak R, Strickland S, McEwen BS, Chattarji S. Stress-induced spine loss in the medial amygdala is mediated by tissue-plasminogen activator. Neuroscience 2007;144:8–16.

176. Davis M, Shi C. The extended amygdala: are the central nucleus of the amygdala and the bed nucleus of the stria terminalis differentially involved in fear versus anxiety? Ann N Y Acad Sci 1999;877:281–91.

177. Davis M, Shi C. The amygdala. Curr Biol 2000;10:R131.

178. Pikkarainen M, Ronkko S, Savander V, Insausti R, Pitkanen A. Projections from the lateral, basal, and accessory basal nuclei of the amygdala to the hippocampal formation in rat. J Comp Neurol 1999;403:229–60.

179. Petrovich GD, Canteras NS, Swanson LW. Combinatorial amygdalar inputs to hippocampal domains and hypothalamic behavior systems. Brain Res Brain Res Rev 2001;38:247–89.

180. Packard MG, Cahill L, McGaugh JL. Amygdala modulation of hippocampal-dependent and caudate nucleus-dependent memory processes. Proc Natl Acad Sci U S A 1994; 91:8477–81.

181. McGaugh JL. Memory-a century of consolidation. Science 2000;287:248–51.

182. Roozendaal B, Griffith QK, Buranday J, De Quervain DJ, McGaugh JL. The hippocampus mediates glucocorticoid-induced impairment of spatial memory retrieval: dependence on the basolateral amygdala. Proc Natl Acad Sci U S A 2003;100:1328–33.

183. Abe K. Modulation of hippocampal long-term potentiation by the amygdala: a synaptic mechanism linking emotion and memory. Jpn J Pharmacol 2001;86:18–22.

184. Kim JJ, Lee HJ, Han JS, Packard MG. Amygdala is critical for stress-induced modulation of hippocampal long-term potentiation and learning. J Neurosci 2001;21:5222–28.

185. Kim JJ, Koo JW, Lee HJ, Han JS. Amygdalar inactivation blocks stress-induced impairments in hippocampal long-term potentiation and spatial memory. J Neurosci 2005;25:1532–39.

186. Nair DV, Chattarji S, Raju TR, Rao BSS. Permanent inactivation of basolateral amygdala prevents chronic stress induced cognitive deficits and associated morphological and biochemical changes in the hippocampus. In: Annual Meeting of the Society for Neuroscience; November 3–7, 2007; San Diego; p. 628.10.

187. Wilson MA, McNaughton BL. Dynamics of the hippocampal ensemble code for space. Science 1993;261:1055–58.

188. Seidenbecher T, Laxmi TR, Stork O, Pape HC. Amygdalar and hippocampal theta rhythm synchronization during fear memory retrieval. Science 2003;301:846–50.

189. Jones MW, Wilson MA. Theta rhythms coordinate hippocampal-prefrontal interactions in a spatial memory task. PLoS Biol 2005;3:e402.

190. Kim JJ, Lee HJ, Welday AC, et al. Stress-induced alterations in hippocampal plasticity, place cells, and spatial memory. Proc Natl Acad Sci U S A 2007;104:18297–302.

191. O'Keefe J, Nadel L. The Hippocampus as a Cognitive Map. Oxford, U.K.: Oxford University Press; 1978.

192. McHugh TJ, Blum KI, Tsien JZ, Tonegawa S, Wilson MA. Impaired hippocampal representation of space in CA1-specific NMDAR1 knockout mice. Cell 1996;87:1339–49.

193. Kandel ER. The molecular biology of memory storage: a dialogue between genes and synapses. Science 2001;294:1030–38.

Post-Traumatic Stress Disorder and Arousal

Color Plates

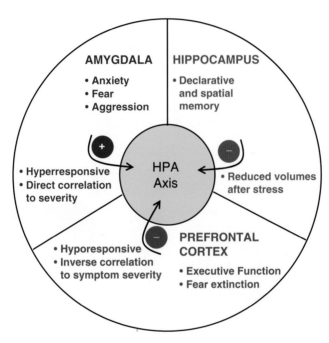

Chapter 7, Fig. 1. Brain areas implicated in post-traumatic stress disorder (PTSD). (*For complete caption refer page 153*)

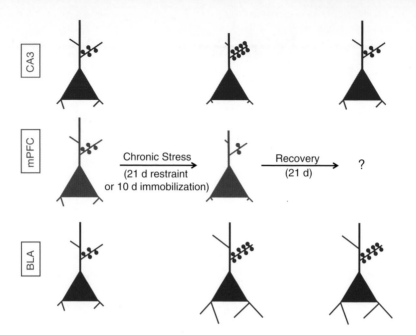

Chapter 7, Fig. 2. Chronic stress leads to contrasting patterns of structural plasticity in excitatory pyramidal neurons in the basolateral amygdala (BLA), hippocampal area CA3, and layer II/III of medial prefrontal cortex (mPFC). (*For complete caption refer page 156*)

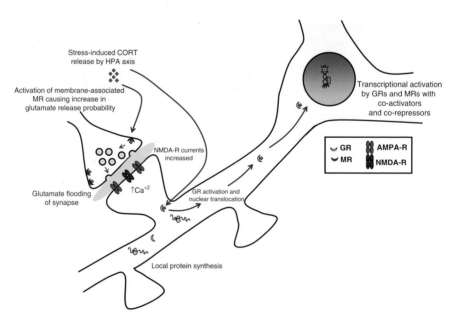

Chapter 7, Fig. 3. The effect of adrenal steroids (via glucocorticoid receptors [GRs] and mineralocorticoid receptors [MRs]) on excitatory amino acid neurotransmission through *N*-methyl-D-aspartate (NMDA) and α-amino-3-hydroxy-5-methyl-4-isoxazolepropionic acid (AMPA) receptors (NMDA-R and AMPA-R, respectively). (*For complete caption refer page 164*)

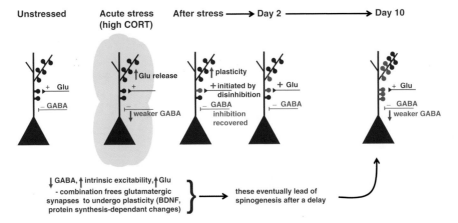

Chapter 7, Fig. 4. Effects of acute stress on basolateral amygdala (BLA) principal neurons. (*For complete caption refer page 167*)

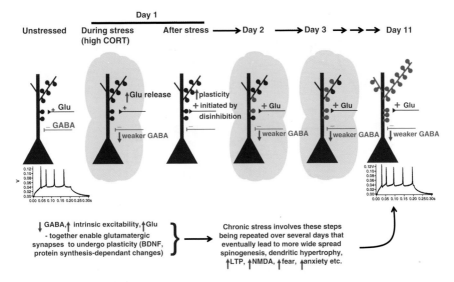

Chapter 7, Fig. 5. Effects of chronic stress on basolateral amygdala (BLA) principal neurons. (*For complete caption refer page 168*)

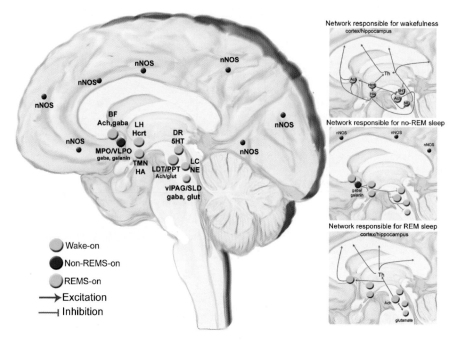

Chapter 8, Fig. 1. Neuronal circuitry underlying wake, non-REM (rapid eye movement) sleep, and REM sleep. (*For complete caption refer page 189*)

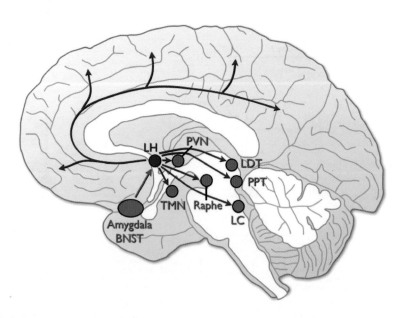

Chapter 9, Fig. 1. A model for the role of hypocretins in post-traumatic stress disorder (PTSD). (*For complete caption refer page 206*)

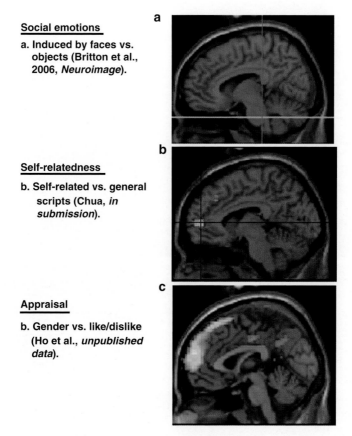

Social emotions

a. Induced by faces vs. objects (Britton et al., 2006, *Neuroimage*).

Self-relatedness

b. Self-related vs. general scripts (Chua, *in submission*).

Appraisal

b. Gender vs. like/dislike (Ho et al., *unpublished data*).

Chapter 14, Fig. 2. Activation of the medial prefrontal cortex (mPFC) resulting from social emotions, self-relatedness, and emotional appraisal. **a**. Reference number 68, **b**. Reference number 69, and **c**. No reference number

Chapter 18, Fig. 1-4. Virtual Iraq city and desert HUMVEE scenario scenes

Chapter 18, Fig. 1-4. (continued)

Fig. 5. User Centered feedback on the Virtual Iraq application being collected by a U.S. Army Combat Stress Control team member (Reger), while in "real" Iraq

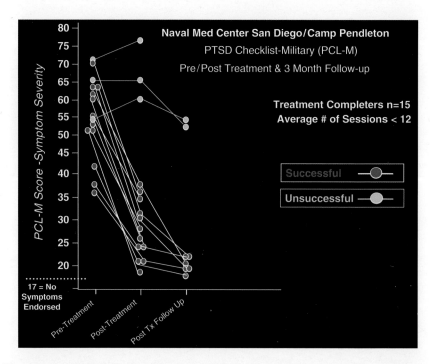

Fig. 6. Individual PTSD Checklist-military (PCL-M) from first 15 virtual reality exposure therapy (VRET) treatment completers. The average score pre- and posttreatment indicates a decline in scores. The scores remained low at 3-month follow-up. Three were unsuccessful

8   Arousal Neurons in the Brain

Priyattam J. Shiromani and Carlos Blanco-Centurion

CONTENTS

INTRODUCTION
NEURONS RESPONSIBLE FOR SLEEP: THE VENTRAL
    LATERAL PREOPTIC AREA
NEURONAL NETWORK REGULATING WAKEFULNESS
NEURONS REGULATING REM SLEEP
BF, TMN, AND LC: AROUSAL TRIGGERS DURING SLEEP
REFERENCES

Abstract

A distributed network of neurons is hypothesized to be responsible for wake, non-REM (rapid eye movement) and REM sleep. First-order circuit models have emerged, and in the last few years these models have been empirically tested. We review the evidence and advance the hypothesis that cholinergic, histamine, and noradrenergic neurons trigger arousal in the event of an alarm (either internal or external) and maintain vigilance. In post-traumatic stress disorder (PTSD), the hyperarousal and frequent awakenings during sleep might be related to overactivation of these neurons.

Key Words: Histamine, hypocretin, locus coeruleus, rapid eye movement sleep.

INTRODUCTION

Sleep disturbance is a frequent and common complaint among our veterans and within the general population. There are 70 million Americans who suffer from some sort of sleep disorder. Patients with post-traumatic stress disorder (PTSD) are hyperaroused, have trouble falling asleep, and when they do fall

From: *Post-Traumatic Stress Disorder: Basic Science and Clinical Practice*
Edited by: P. J. Shiromani et al., DOI: 10.1007/978-1-60327-329-9_8
© Humana Press, a part of Springer Science+Business Media, LLC 2009

asleep they have distressing dreams or nightmares, often of the traumatic event that led to their illness. When they are awake they are startled easily.

How the brain switches between wake and sleep is an intriguing question. Even within sleep, the brain is periodically activated, at times surpassing the activity seen during waking. These periods of activity during sleep are called rapid eye movement (REM) sleep or paradoxical sleep. The other portion of sleep is called non-REM sleep. We review the evidence that wake, non-REM, and REM sleep are generated by specific neuronal populations and advance the hypothesis that some of the arousal populations function to rapidly awaken the brain from sleep and to keep the brain awake during a stressful event. We hypothesize that these neuronal populations rapidly terminate a sleep bout in the event of danger, and they maintain vigilance in a stressful condition. If these arousal neurons are overactivated, then it may lead to the hyperarousal, including the frequent arousals during sleep, evident in PTSD.

NEURONS RESPONSIBLE FOR SLEEP: THE VENTRAL LATERAL PREOPTIC AREA

At the start of the 20th century, it was believed that sleep occurred because people simply closed their eyes, which then shut out the arousing sensory stimuli from reaching the nervous system. A young Viennese physician, Baron Constantin von Economo, provided the first evidence that wake and sleep are generated from specific brain regions. During the influenza pandemic of 1918, he noticed that many of his patients with encephalitis were excessively sleepy and lethargic, and he called the illness *encephalitis lethargica*. He performed autopsies on some of the patients who had succumbed to the disease and concluded that a region in the posterior hypothalamus was responsible for wake, whereas a region more rostrally in the hypothalamus was responsible for sleep (*1*).

Von Economo's observations intrigued many researchers at the time. Among them was a young neuroanatomist, Walle Nauta, who in his formative years as a scientist was puzzled by sleep and wanted to understand how it was generated. His experiments in rats supported von Economo's concept of a sleep center because discrete lesions in the rostral portions of the hypothalamus, in an area now referred to as the preoptic area, produced insomnia (*2*). It is now known that stimulation of this region (see Fig. 1) by small electrical currents, warming, or pharmacological means will produce sleep. Electrophysiology studies have now identified sleep-active neurons in this region and the adjacent basal forebrain (BF) in rats, cats, and rabbits (for review, *see* Ref. *3*). These neurons begin to fire during drowsiness, and peak activity is seen during non-REM sleep. The sleep-active cells comprise about 25% of the recorded cells in the BF-preoptic area and are intermixed with wake-active cells, which predominate.

We have use the immediate-early gene, c-Fos, a marker of neuronal activity, to identify the location, phenotype, and connectivity of the sleep-active neurons. Initially, sleep-active c-Fos-positive neurons were found in the ventral lateral preoptic area (VLPO) (*4*). Then, the median preoptic area (MPOA) was found also to contain sleep-active neurons (*5–8*). These sleep-active neurons contain

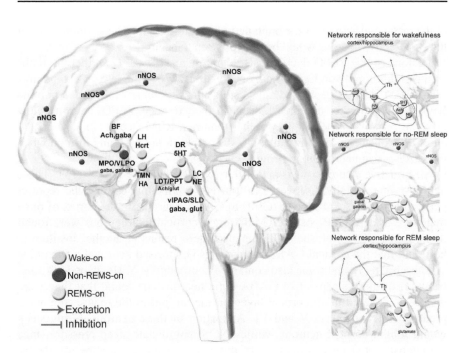

Fig. 1. Neuronal circuitry underlying wake, non-REM (rapid eye movement) sleep, and REM sleep. A distributed group of cells controls the three states. The arousal populations are represented in yellow and comprise the classical neurotransmitters acetylcholine (Ach), histamine (HA), norepinephrine (NE), and serotonin (5HT), and the neuropeptide, hypocretin (Hcrt). When these arousal neurons stop firing, a group of GABA-ergic neurons in the preoptic area (blue) become active, further inhibiting the arousal neurons. There are also sleep-active interneurons in the cortex that are GABA-ergic and contain neuronal nitric oxide synthase (nNOS). These neurons may gauge sleep need based on prior wakefulness. The transition to REM sleep occurs when glutamatergic neurons in the pons (light blue) begin to fire and activate pontine cholinergic neurons. We suggest that some of the arousal neurons (neurons containing Ach, HA, and NE) function as sentinels during sleep, rapidly terminating sleep in the event of danger. *BF* basal forebrain, *DR* dorsal raphé, *GABA* γ-aminobutyric acid, *glut* glutamine, *LC* locus coeruleus, *LDT* lateral dorsal tegmental nucleus, *MPO* median preoptic nucleus, *PPT* pedunculopontine tegmental nucleus, *SLD* sublateral dorsal nucleus, *Th* thalamus, *TMN* tuberomammillary nucleus, *vlPAG* ventral lateral periaquaductual group, *VLPO* ventral lateral preoptic nucleus (*See Color Plates*)

γ-aminobutyric acid (GABA) and galanin and are inhibitory to major arousal populations (see Fig. 1) (*9*). The VLPO neurons are inhibited by the wake-active neurotransmitters acetylcholine, serotonin, and norepinephrine but are unaffected by histamine (*10*). Cessation of the wake-active neurons would allow the sleep-active neurons to become active, releasing inhibitory agents at target wake-active neurons, shutting them off and triggering sleep. Exactly what prompts the wake-active neurons to shut down is not entirely clear but may involve endogenous factors such as adenosine, cytokines, and brain temperature, which rise as a result of the metabolic activity of the brain neurons during waking. Thus, quiescence of the wake-active neurons would be key for sleep to begin.

Lesions of the VLPO decrease sleep and increase wake (11), thereby replicating Nauta's and von Economo's observations. When the lesions extend dorsally, REM sleep is decreased, suggesting that this region influences pontine REM sleep generator neurons. Indeed, in the extended VLPO, neurons show c-Fos in response to REM sleep rather than non-REM sleep (12). The VLPO and MPOA neurons are now linked to sleep pressure (13,14) and turn on when the wake-active neurons stop firing.

Sleep-active neurons have also been identified in the cortex (15). These neurons were initially discovered in transgenic mice that express the reporter gene green fluorescent protein (GFP) in GABA neurons. In the cortex of mice that were asleep, GFP-positive GABA-ergic cortical interneurons were found to express c-FOS. Gerashchenko pursued these results at another institution; he found that the cortical GABA neurons also expressed neuronal nitric oxide synthase (nNOS), and some also contained neuropeptide Y. He mapped the distribution of these sleep-active GABA-ergic neurons and found that they were diffusely scattered in all cortical layers in the rat, but in the mouse they were predominantly in layers V and VI. Activation of these neurons during sleep would inhibit cortical neurons, while nNOS may dictate sleep pressure since the intensity of sleep was found to be directly related to the number of nNOS-expressing GABA-ergic cortical neurons (15).

NEURONAL NETWORK REGULATING WAKEFULNESS

In 1930, von Economo concluded that there was a region in the posterior hypothalamus that was responsible for maintaining daily levels of wake (1). However, it was not until 1999 when the neuropeptide hypocretin was linked to the sleep disorder narcolepsy that von Economo was proved to be correct.

Hypocretin (Orexin)

The discovery of the hypocretin (orexin) peptide and its linkage with narcolepsy is reviewed in Chapter 9 of this volume. Hypocretin neurons are found only in the lateral hypothalamic region of the posterior hypothalamus, from where they innervate virtually the entire brain and spinal cord (see Fig. 1) (16). Two hypocretin receptors have been identified, and their distribution in the brain has been determined (17). Hypocretin receptors are especially dense in areas implicated in wakefulness such as the locus coeruleus (LC), tuberomammillary nucleus (TMN), the dorsal raphé, and the BF (16). Because of these projections to neuronal populations implicated in wakefulness, it is hypothesized that hypocretin promotes wakefulness by driving downstream neurons that have traditionally been implicated in arousal. Hypocretin has a powerful wake-promoting effect, and receptor antagonists that block one or both receptors (18) cause sleepiness. In nonhuman primates, inhalation of orexin produces arousal even after sleep deprivation (19).

The activity of the hypocretin neurons is consistent with promoting arousal. Identified hypocretin neurons are active during wake and silent during sleep (20–22). They begin to fire in anticipation of arousal, and they are easily activated during sleep (21). There is a heavy input from the limbic region, especially the amygdala, and other autonomic regions, and this input would activate the hypocretin neurons. Corticotrophin-releasing factor (CRF), which is released in response to a stressful stimulus, has a potent effect on the hypocretin neurons, primarily via the CRF receptor 1 (23). The neuronal activation is diminished in mice lacking the CRF receptor 1. CRF-1 receptor-deficient mice also show less anxiety (24). Neurotoxin lesions of the perifornical area where the hypocretin neurons are located, by the neurotoxin hypocretin 2 (Hcrt2) saporin (sap) (Hcrt2-sap), in rats abolishes the cardiovascular and behavioral response to the conditioned fear (25). This suggests that during stress the CRF-mediated activation of the hypocretin neurons induces waking and promotes anxiety and conditioned fear.

Basal Forebrain and Acetylcholine

Acetylcholine and the BF are intimately linked to cognitive processing. BF cholinergic neurons innervate the hippocampus and the entire neocortex. Loss of these neurons in Alzheimer's disease is linked to the cognitive dysfunction of that disease (26). Hypocretin neurons innervate the BF, and we hypothesize that release of acetylcholine would facilitate cognitive function during waking. Indeed, acetylcholine is released in the cortex during waking and REM sleep (a time when the cortex is desynchronized) (27–30), c-Fos is present in BF cholinergic neurons in association with waking (31), and juxtacellular recording of the cholinergic neurons shows increased activity associated with cortical desynchronization (32). The release of acetylcholine is evident in the wake-active hemisphere even in mammals that display unihemispheric sleep (33).

The cholinergic neurons in the BF are the source of the acetylcholine release in the cortex because when these neurons are lesioned there is a decrease in cortical acetylcholine levels (34). A direct effect of hypocretin 1 (Hcrt1) on the BF cholinergic neurons has been shown (35). Hypocretin depolarizes BF cholinergic neurons (35) via the Hcrt2 receptor. Moreover, administration of Hcrt1 (orexin A) into the BF via reverse microdialysis produces a dose-dependent increase in acetylcholine in the prefrontal cortex (36). In that study, when the Hcrt1 was applied to the prefrontal cortex, no change in acetylcholine was observed, indicating that the release was from the BF cholinergic neurons.

Infusion of hypocretin to the BF induces wakefulness (37, 38). The wakefulness is produced even in rats with lesions of the cholinergic neurons in the BF, indicating that hypocretin receptors on the noncholinergic neurons can drive wakefulness (39). These wake-active noncholinergic neurons might be GABA-ergic innervating cortical GABA interneurons and may cause arousal through disinhibition (40). The BF also contains sleep-active neurons, some of which contain neuropeptide Y (41). These sleep-active neurons would be disinhibited when the wake-active BF neurons become silent (42). The GABA-ergic neurons increase activity in conjunction with cortical slow waves (43). They project to the cortex (*44*) and to the posterior lateral hypothalamus, where the hypocretin neurons are located. Their activity would suppress activity of the hypocretin wake-active neurons and promote sleep.

Hypocretin neurons are active only during wake (*20–22*), and we hypothesize that their activation would drive downstream targets such as the BF neurons, which release acetylcholine into the cortex and facilitate cognitive function. In our model, the BF is not regulating daily levels of waking as has been hypothesized, but instead its activation during waking is important for memory and cognitive functions. Thus, we hypothesize that the BF neurons serve an important function when one is awakened from sleep, and that is to mobilize cognitive function.

The Tuberomammillary Nucleus and Histamine

In the brain, histamine neurons are located exclusively in the TMN ((*45*). Histamine has a potent arousal effect, and antihistamines produce drowsiness and sedation. Histamine microinjections into projection sites such as the BF produce a dose-dependent increase in wake (*46*). When histamine synthesis in the preoptic area is blocked, sleep increases and wakefulness decreases (*46*). Histamine H1 and H2 receptors are postulated to mediate the arousal (*46*).

Since histamine produces arousal, it is reasonable that histamine neurons should be active during waking. Electrophysiology studies have found that histamine neurons in the TMN region have the highest discharge rate during waking and are virtually silent during sleep (*47*). In narcoleptic canines, TMN neurons are also active only during waking and silent during sleep (*48*).

The hypocretin neurons innervate the TMN, and the Hcrt2 receptor is heavily expressed on these neurons (*17*). Hypocretin stimulates identified histamine neurons (*49*). However, there does not appear to be reciprocal histamine/TMN projections to the hypocretin neurons (*50*) or a direct effect of histamine on identified hypocretin neurons (*51*). This suggests that histamine neurons in the TMN are driven by the hypocretin neurons. The histaminergic neurons would then activate the cortex directly via their widespread hypothalamocortical projections or, indirectly, by stimulating the BF cholinergic system. The net effect of the hypocretin-TMN stimulation would be to arouse the cortex.

This pathway may also be activated in response to a fear-inducing event. Histamine has been implicated in fear conditioning via its action on the basolateral amygdala (BLA), where it may promote the release of acetylcholine (*52*). Microinjection of H3 receptor antagonists into the BLA decreases acetylcholine release and produces an amnesic effect in a fear-conditioning paradigm (*53*), while H3 receptor agonists (R-α-methylhistamine [RAMH] and immepip) augment acetylcholine release and strengthen memory of the context-foot shock association (*54*).

Thus, histaminergic neurons activate the cortex directly via their widespread hypothalamocortical projections or indirectly by stimulating the BF cholinergic system. The net effect of this stimulation would be to arouse the cortex and, in the case of a stressful condition, promote memory of the fearful stimulus.

The Locus Coeruleus and Norepinephrine

The LC contains primarily norepinephrine neurons that innervate virtually the entire brain and spinal cord (*see* Chapter 10, this volume). These neurons are the sole source of norepinephrine input to the hippocampus and cortex, two regions critically involved in cognitive processing. Electrophysiology studies have found that the noradrenergic LC neurons are most active during waking and less active during non-REM sleep, and they stop firing during REM sleep (*55,56*). LC neurons are readily activated by stress and aversive stimuli, and the widespread release of norepinephrine has been hypothesized to sharpen cognitive processing during a stressful condition. CRF has been shown to stimulate LC neurons (*57*).

The LC receives an especially heavy innervation of hypocretin fibers (*16*), but surprisingly, the LC does not project to the hypocretin neurons ((*50*). LC neurons contain primarily the Hcrt1 receptor (*58*). Hypocretin excites LC neurons and potently increases waking and decreases REM sleep (*59,60*).

As reviewed in Chapter 10, this volume, the LC represents a major sympathetic circuit that is activated by stress. Although CRF can stimulate the LC, it is likely that the major source of the activation is from the hypocretin neurons. In response to stress, the sensitivity of the LC neurons may increase; consequently, it would be easier to awaken from sleep. Increased norepinephrine release onto target neurons in the prefrontal cortex and the BLA will enhance memory of the fearful stimulus and subsequent playback of the event. Blocking of the norepinephrine receptors, with propranalol and prazosin, has been shown to be effective in treating the arousal and nightmares associated with PTSD (*see* Chapter 16, this volume).

Serotonin

Serotonin neurons are localized in the raphé. These neurons behave very much like the hypocretin, histamine, and LC neurons in that they are most active in waking and silent during sleep (both non-REM and REM sleep). Hypocretin neurons project heavily to these neurons, and a subpopulation of serotonin neurons (median raphé) feed back onto the hypocretin neurons. It is not clear how this interaction regulates waking, but since the serotonin neurons are silent during REM sleep, they may control REM sleep.

NEURONS REGULATING REM SLEEP

Soon after Aserinsky and Kleitman discovered REM sleep in 1953 (*61*), Jouvet performed a series of experiments that quickly determined that REM sleep originated from the pons (summarized in Ref. *62*). However, the primary signal for REM sleep onset appears to be hypothalamic and requires cessation in activity of the hypocretin neurons. Mice and rats that lack hypocretin enter into REM sleep often (for review, see Ref. *50*). Canines with a mutation of the Hcrt2 receptor also have abnormal onset of REM sleep. In narcolepsy, a disorder characterized by inappropriate intrusion of REM sleep during waking, there is a massive loss of hypocretin neurons. The pons is a target of the hypocretin inhibition since lesion of the hypocretin receptor bearing neurons in the pons increases non-REM and REM sleep (63).

What is less clear is how activity of the hypocretin neurons, which are excitatory (64), arrests REM sleep. One possibility is that hypocretin and other wake-active neurons (such as the LC, serotonin, histamine) turn on GABA-ergic neurons in the pons that are inhibitory to REM sleep. Luppi's group has suggested that these neurons are in the sublateral dorsal (SLD) region, which is just ventral to the LC (65). We lesioned these neurons with Hcrt2-sap and found a potent increase in REM sleep (63). We suggest that an additional group of GABA-ergic neurons residing in the ventral lateral periaqueductal gray (vlPAG) area is also inhibitory to REM sleep and activated by hypocretin. During wake, these pontine GABA-ergic neurons would be activated by hypocretin and inhibit adjacent glutamatergic neurons. When the hypocretin neurons are silent (or destroyed), the pontine GABA neurons do not fire, which then allows the adjacent glutamatergic neurons to become disinhibited and activate REM-on neurons. The chemical identity of the REM on neurons is not known, but it is generally hypothesized that they are cholinergic and represent the neurons in the lateral dorsal tegmentum (LDT) and pedunculopontine tegmental (PPT) region of the pons (see Fig. 1)

BF, TMN, AND LC: AROUSAL TRIGGERS DURING SLEEP

The evidence reviewed indicates that a distributed network of neurons is responsible for generating wake, non-REM, and REM sleep. What is less clear is whether some or all of the arousal neurons awaken a sleeping brain and whether these neurons also keep the brain awake and vigilant during a period of danger. The issue of arousal and vigilance is important because for survival there must be some mechanism to rapidly awaken a sleeping brain. We suggest that in certain disorders such as PTSD this mechanism becomes overly sensitive to the point that the individual becomes hyperaroused and is frequently awakened during sleep.

Current models hypothesize that the hypocretin neurons cause arousal and maintain vigilance. However, hypocretin-null mice stay awake as long as wild-type mice in an unfamiliar environment (66), and they wake up at the correct time in anticipation of feeding time in a forced-feeding schedule (67). These two studies indicated that in the absence of hypocretin the mouse is able to wake up and stay vigilant. We agree that, in a stressful condition, hypocretin neurons are likely to drive arousal since in CRF-1 receptor-null mice fewer hypocretin neurons are activated (23). However, the subsequent hyperarousal and frequent awakenings during sleep in PTSD are likely the result of overactivity of the hypocretin targets, especially BF, TMN, and LC. We reached this conclusion after lesioning these neurons in a series of experiments. Other investigators have tried to lesion these neurons with excitotoxins, but more specific neurotoxins have now been developed, and it is feasible to selectively lesion a particular phenotype of neurons.

In one experiment, the BF cholinergic neurons were lesioned with 192-immunoglobulin G (IgG)-saporin, which kills at least 92% of the cholinergic BF neurons and produces an 80–90% selective decline in activity of the acetylcholine-synthesizing enzyme choline acetyltransferase in rat neocortex and hippocampus (68). We found that the daily levels of sleep or wake were not changed (69), a finding that has subsequently been supported by another group (70).

In another study, the histamine neurons in the TMN were killed by Hcrt2-saporin (71). This neurotoxin binds to the Hcrt2 receptor, which is highly expressed (relative to the Hcrt1 receptor) in the TMN. Hcrt2-saporin lesioned TMN neurons but did not produce hypersomnolence. This is consistent with data from histamine decarboxylase (histamine-synthesizing enzyme) knockout mice studies (72), which did not show an overall change in sleep in knockout mice. However, the histamine decarboxylase knockout mice fell asleep faster in a novel environment, indicating that histamine may be important in maintaining vigilance and arousal in new environments.

In the third study, the noradrenergic LC neurons were killed with anti-dopamine-β-hydroxylase-saporin (DBH-sap). DBH is the norepinephrine-synthesizing enzyme, and its destruction would lead to loss of the norepinephrine neurons in the LC. Lesions of the LC with DBH-sap did not increase total sleep time or increase REM sleep, a finding consistent with previous studies in which the LC was lesioned (73–76) or DBH was genetically removed (77).

The lack of hypersomnolence when the three hypocretin targets were destroyed might be due to compensation from other arousal neuronal populations. Therefore, in a fourth study we lesioned simultaneously all three targets of hypocretin (BF, TMN, and LC) (78). We expected an additive effect on wake (i.e., more sleep) as a result of the combined lesion of three arousal populations, but to our surprise the overall daily levels of wake were not significantly different compared to saline rats. Current models of sleep-wake regulation (79) suggest that hypersomnolence should occur after lesions of the hypocretin targets (such as the TMN and LC). However, our lesion study (78) and the data from knockout mice indicate that this is not the case. Instead, we suggest that the cholinergic, LC, and TMN neurons serve another function, which is to periodically inhibit the sleep neurons and cause arousal. Indeed, in our lesioned rats, there were fewer arousals in sleep and more long bouts (5–10 min long) of non-REM sleep. In other words, the rats woke up less often and stayed asleep longer. This resulted in fewer transitions between the three states and more stable sleep-wake architecture. Mice with deletions of the norepinephrine-synthesizing enzyme DBH (77) or of the histamine-synthesizing enzyme histidine decarboxylase (72) also had fewer arousals.

From our lesion data and evidence from knockout mice, we hypothesize that the LC, histamine TMN, and cholinergic neurons serve a very specific purpose with regard to sleep: They rapidly awaken a sleeping brain and with it turn on cognitive function, attention, and vigilance. We hypothesize that the cholinergic neurons might be responsible for mobilizing cognitive function on awakening from sleep. After all, it would be beneficial to be cognitively aware of one's surroundings on waking up from sleep and be able to escape. Overactivation of these neurons (via the hippocampus and amygdala) might be responsible for replaying of the memories of the traumatic event. On the other hand, LC neurons would facilitate vigilance and be ready to trigger a sympathetic response. The LC and the histamine neurons would act to help maintain vigilance in an unfamiliar environment since mice with deletions of the norepinephrine-synthesizing enzyme DBH (77) or of the histamine-synthesizing enzyme histidine decarboxylase (72) fall asleep much faster than wild-type mice in an unfamiliar environment or after stress.

We suggest that the cholinergic, histamine, and LC neurons are triggers that rapidly terminate a sleep bout. These neurons would monitor the internal and external environment and rapidly stop the sleep neurons in the event of an alarm, either internal (rising carbon dioxide, for example, with sleep apnea) or external (intruder, baby crying). If these neurons are depressed (which might occur with too many sedatives), then there is the risk of death. However, if these neurons are too sensitive, then there would be frequent arousals and difficulty falling asleep, which is the case in PTSD.

ACKNOWLEDGMENTS

This work was supported by National Institutes of Health grants NS30140, NS052287, and MH55772 and the Medical Research Service of the Department of Veterans Affairs.

REFERENCES

1. von Economo, C. (1930) Sleep as a problem of localization. J Nerv Mental Dis 71, 249–59.
2. Nauta, W. J. H. (1946) Hypothalamic regulation of sleep in rats. An experimental study. J Neurophysiol 9, 285–316.
3. McGinty, D., and Szymusiak, R. (2000) The sleep-wake switch: a neuronal alarm clock. Nat Med 6, 510–11.
4. Sherin, J. E., Shiromani, P. J., McCarley, R. W., and Saper, C. B. (1996) Activation of ventrolateral preoptic neurons during sleep. Science 271, 216–19.
5. Alam, M. N., McGinty, D., and Szymusiak, R. (1995) Neuronal discharge of preoptic/anterior hypothalamic thermosensitive neurons: relation to NREM sleep. Am J Physiol 269, R1240–49.
6. Gong, H., Szymusiak, R., King, J., Steininger, T., and McGinty, D. (2000) Sleep-related c-Fos protein expression in the preoptic hypothalamus: effects of ambient warming. Am J Physiol Regul Integr Comp Physiol 279, R2079–88.
7. Suntsova, N., Szymusiak, R., Alam, M. N., Guzman-Marin, R., and McGinty, D. (2002) Sleep-waking discharge patterns of median preoptic nucleus neurons in rats. J Physiol 543, 665–77.
8. Szymusiak, R., Alam, M. N., Steininger, T. L., and McGinty, D. (1998) Sleep-waking discharge patterns of ventrolateral preoptic/anterior hypothalamic neurons in rats. Brain Res 803, 178–88.
9. Chou, T. C., Bjorkum, A. A., Gaus, S. E., Lu, J., Scammell, T. E., and Saper, C. B. (2002) Afferents to the ventrolateral preoptic nucleus. J Neurosci 22, 977–90.

10. Gallopin, T., Fort, P., Eggermann, E., Cauli, B., Luppi, P.-H., Rossier, J., Audino, M. G., Muhlethaler, M., and Serafin, M. (2000) Identification of sleep-promoting neurons in vitro. Nature 404, 992–95.

11. Lu, J., Greco, M. A., Shiromani, P., and Saper, C. B. (2000) Effect of lesions of the ventrolateral preoptic nucleus on NREM and REM sleep. J Neurosci 20, 3830–42.

12. Lu, J., Bjorkum, A. A., Xu, M., Gaus, S. E., Shiromani, P. J., and Saper, C. B. (2002) Selective activation of the extended ventrolateral preoptic nucleus during rapid eye movement sleep. J Neurosci 22, 4568–76.

13. Gvilia, I., Turner, A., McGinty, D., and Szymusiak, R. (2006) Preoptic area neurons and the homeostatic regulation of rapid eye movement sleep. J Neurosci 26, 3037–44.

14. Gvilia, I., Xu, F., McGinty, D., and Szymusiak, R. (2006) Homeostatic regulation of sleep: a role for preoptic area neurons. J Neurosci 26, 9426–33.

15. Gerashchenko, D., Wisor, J. P., Burns, D., Reh, R. K., Shiromani, P. J., Sakurai, T., de la Iglesia, H. O., and Kilduff, T. S. (2008) Identification of a population of sleep-active cerebral cortex neurons. Proc Natl Acad Sci U S A 105, 10227–32.

16. Peyron, C., Tighe, D. K., Van den Pol, A. N., De Lecea, L., Heller, H. C., Sutcliffe, J. G., and Kilduff, T. S. (1998) Neurons containing hypocretin (orexin) project to multiple neuronal systems. J Neurosci 18, 9996–10015.

17. Marcus, J. N., Aschkenasi, C. J., Lee, C. E., Chemelli, R. M., Saper, C. B., Yanagisawa, M., and Elmquist, J. K. (2001) Differential expression of orexin receptors 1 and 2 in the rat brain. J Comp Neurol 435, 6–25.

18. Brisbare-Roch, C., Dingemanse, J., Koberstein, R., Hoever, P., Aissaoui, H., Flores, S., Mueller, C., Nayler, O., van Gerven, J., de Haas, S. L., Hess, P., Qiu, C., Buchmann, S., Scherz, M., Weller, T., Fischli, W., Clozel, M., and Jenck, F. (2007) Promotion of sleep by targeting the orexin system in rats, dogs and humans. Nat Med 13, 150–155.

19. Deadwyler, S. A., Porrino, L., Siegel, J. M., and Hampson, R. E. (2007) Systemic and nasal delivery of orexin-A (Hypocretin-1) reduces the effects of sleep deprivation on cognitive performance in nonhuman primates. J Neurosci 27, 14239–47.

20. Mileykovskiy, B. Y., Kiyashchenko, L. I., and Siegel, J. M. (2005) Behavioral correlates of activity in identified hypocretin/orexin neurons. Neuron 46, 787–98.

21. Takahashi, K., Lin, J. S., and Sakai, K. (2008) Neuronal activity of orexin and non-orexin waking-active neurons during wake-sleep states in the mouse. Neuroscience 153, 860–70.

22. Lee, M. G., Hassani, O. K., and Jones, B. E. (2005) Discharge of identified orexin/hypocretin neurons across the sleep-waking cycle. J Neurosci. 25, 6716–20.

23. Winsky-Sommerer, R., Yamanaka, A., Diano, S., Borok, E., Roberts, A. J., Sakurai, T., Kilduff, T. S., Horvath, T. L., and De Lecea, L. (2004) Interaction between the corticotropin-releasing factor system and hypocretins (orexins): a novel circuit mediating stress response. J Neurosci 24, 11439–48.

24. Timpl, P., Spanagel, R., Sillaber, I., Kresse, A., Reul, J. M., Stalla, G. K., Blanquet, V., Steckler, T., Holsboer, F., and Wurst, W. (1998) Impaired stress response and reduced anxiety in mice lacking a functional corticotropin-releasing hormone receptor 1. Nat Genet 19, 162–66.

25. Furlong, T., and Carrive, P. (2007) Neurotoxic lesions centered on the perifornical hypothalamus abolish the cardiovascular and behavioral responses of conditioned fear to context but not of restraint. Brain Res 1128, 107–19.

26. Whitehouse, P. J., Price, D. L., Struble, R. G., Clark, A. W., Coyle, J. T., and DeLong, M. (1982) Alzheimer's disease and senile dementia: loss of neurons in the basal forebrain. Science 215, 1237–39.

27. Celesia, G. G., and Jasper, H. H. (1966) Acetylcholine released from cerebral cortex in relation to state of activation. Neurology 16, 1053–1063.

28. Jasper, H. H., and Tessier, J. (1971) Acetylcholine liberation from cerebral cortex during paradoxical (REM) sleep Science 172, 601–2.
29. Rasmusson, D. D., Clow, K., and Szerb, J. C. (1992) Frequency-dependent increase in cortical acetylcholine release evoked by stimulation of the nucleus basalis magnocellularis in the rat. Brain Res 594, 150–54.
30. Szerb, J. C. (1967) Cortical acetylcholine release and electroencephalographic arousal. J Physiol 192, 329–43.
31. Greco, M. A., Lu, J., Wagner, D., and Shiromani, P. J. (2000) c-Fos expression in the cholinergic basal forebrain after enforced wakefulness and recovery sleep. Neuroreport 11, 437–40.
32. Manns, I. D., Alonso, A., and Jones, B. E. (2000) Discharge properties of juxtacellularly labeled and immunohistochemically identified cholinergic basal forebrain neurons recorded in association with the electroencephalogram in anesthetized rats. J Neurosci 20, 1505–18.
33. Lapierre, J. L., Kosenko, P. O., Lyamin, O. I., Kodama, T., Mukhametov, L. M., and Siegel, J. M. (2007) Cortical acetylcholine release is lateralized during asymmetrical slow-wave sleep in northern fur seals. J Neurosci 27, 11999–12006.
34. Dekker, A. J., and Thal, L. J. (1993) Independent effects of cholinergic and serotonergic lesions on acetylcholine and serotonin release in the neocortex of the rat. Neurochem Res 18, 277–83.
35. Eggermann, E., Serafin, M., Bayer, L., Machard, D., Saint-Mleux, B., Jones, B. E., and Muhlethaler, M. (2001) Orexins/hypocretins excite basal forebrain cholinergic neurones. Neuroscience 108, 177–81.
36. Fadel, J., Pasumarthi, R., and Reznikov, L. R. (2005) Stimulation of cortical acetylcholine release by orexin A. Neuroscience 130, 541–47.
37. Espana, R. A., Baldo, B. A., Kelley, A. E., and Berridge, C. W. (2001) Wake-promoting and sleep-suppressing actions of hypocretin (orexin): basal forebrain sites of action. Neuroscience 106, 699–715.
38. Thakkar, M. M., Ramesh, V., Strecker, R. E., and McCarley, R. W. (2001) Microdialysis perfusion of orexin-A in the basal forebrain increases wakefulness in freely behaving rats. Arch Ital Biol 139, 313–28.
39. Blanco-Centurion, C. A., Shiromani, A., Winston, E., and Shiromani, P. J. (2006) Effects of hypocretin-1 in 192-IgG-saporin-lesioned rats. Eur J Neurosci 24, 2084–88.
40. Duque, A., Balatoni, B., Detari, L., and Zaborszky, L. (2000) EEG correlation of the discharge properties of identified neurons in the basal forebrain. J Neurophysiol 84, 1627–35.
41. Zaborszky, L., and Duque, A. (2003) Sleep-wake mechanisms and basal forebrain circuitry. Front Biosci 8, d1146–69.
42. Jones, B. E. (2003) Arousal systems. Front Biosci 8, S438–51.
43. Manns, I. D., Alonso, A., and Jones, B. E. (2003) Rhythmically discharging basal forebrain units comprise cholinergic, GABAergic, and putative glutamatergic cells. J Neurophysiol 89, 1057–66.
44. Gritti, I., Mainville, L., Mancia, M., and Jones, B. E. (1997) GABAergic and other noncholinergic basal forebrain neurons, together with cholinergic neurons, project to the mesocortex and isocortex in the rat. J Comp Neurol 383, 163–77.
45. Senba, E., Daddona, P. E., Watanabe, T., Wu, J. Y., and Nagy, J. I. (1985) Adenosine deaminase is a marker for histamine neurons in the rat. J Neurosci 5, 3393–3402.
46. Lin, J. S., Sakai, K., and Jouvet, M. (1994) Hypothalamo-preoptic histaminergic projections in sleep-wake control in the cat. Eur J Neurosci 6, 618–25.

47. Takahashi, K., Lin, J. S., and Sakai, K. (2006) Neuronal activity of histaminergic tubero-mammillary neurons during wake-sleep states in the mouse. J Neurosci 26, 10292–98.

48. John, J., Wu, M. F., Boehmer, L. N., and Siegel, J. M. (2004) Cataplexy-active neurons in the hypothalamus: implications for the role of histamine in sleep and waking behavior. Neuron 42, 619–34.

49. Eriksson, K. S., Sergeeva, O., Brown, R. E., and Haas, H. L. (2001) Orexin/hypocretin excites the histaminergic neurons of the tuberomammillary nucleus. J Neurosci 21, 9273–79.

50. Sakurai, T., Nagata, R., Yamanaka, A., Kawamura, H., Tsujino, N., Muraki, Y., Kageyama, H., Kunita, S., Takahashi, S., Goto, K., Koyama, Y., Shioda, S., and Yanagi-sawa, M. (2005) Input of orexin/hypocretin neurons revealed by a genetically encoded tracer in mice. Neuron 46, 297–308.

51. Li, Y, Gao, X. B., Sakurai, T., and Van den Pol, A. N. (2002) Hypocretin/Orexin excites hypocretin neurons via a local glutamate neuron- a potential mechanism for orchestrating the hypothalamic arousal system. Neuron 35, 1169–81.

52. Passani, M. B., Bacciottini, L., Mannaioni, P. F., and Blandina, P. (2000) Central histaminergic system and cognition. Neurosci Biobehav Rev 24, 107–13.

53. Passani, M. B., Cangioli, I., Baldi, E., Bucherelli, C., Mannaioni, P. F., and Blandina, P. (2001) Histamine H3 receptor-mediated impairment of contextual fear conditioning and in-vivo inhibition of cholinergic transmission in the rat basolateral amygdala. Eur J Neurosci 14, 1522–32.

54. Cangioli, I., Baldi, E., Mannaioni, P. F., Bucherelli, C., Blandina, P., and Passani, M. B. (2002) Activation of histaminergic H3 receptors in the rat basolateral amygdala improves expression of fear memory and enhances acetylcholine release. Eur J Neurosci 16, 521–28.

55. Hobson, J. A., McCarley, R. W., and Wyzinski, P. W. (1975) Sleep cycle oscillation: reciprocal discharge by two brainstem neuronal groups. Science 189, 55–58.

56. McGinty, D. J., and Harper, R. M. (1976) Dorsal raphe neurons: depression of firing during sleep in cats. Brain Res 101, 569–75.

57. Valentino, R. J., Foote, S. L., and Aston-Jones, G. (1983) Corticotropin-releasing factor activates noradrenergic neurons of the locus coeruleus. Brain Res 270, 363–67.

58. Greco, M. A., and Shiromani, P. J. (2001) Hypocretin receptor protein and mRNA expression in the dorsolateral pons of rats. Brain Res Mol Brain Res 88, 176–82.

59. Horvath, T. L., Peyron, C., Diano, S., Ivanov, A., Aston-Jones, G., Kilduff, T. S., and Van den Pol, A. N. (1999) Hypocretin (orexin) activation and synaptic innervation of the locus coeruleus noradrenergic system. J Comp Neurol 415, 145–59.

60. Hagan, J. J., Leslie, R. A., Patel, S., Evans, M. L., Wattam, T. A., Holmes, S., Benham, C. D., Taylor, S. G., Routledge, C., Hemmati, P., Munton, R. P., Ashmeade, T. E., Shah, A. S., Hatcher, J. P., Hatcher, P. D., Jones, D. N., Smith, M. I., Piper, D.C., Hunter, A. J., Porter, R. A., and Upton, N. (1999) Orexin A activates locus coeruleus cell firing and increases arousal in the rat. Proc Natl Acad Sci U S A. 96, 10911–16.

61. Aserinsky, E., and Kleitman, N. (1953) Regularly occurring periods of eye motility and concomitant phenomenon during sleep. Science 118, 273–74.

62. Jones, B. E. (2004) Paradoxical REM sleep promoting and permitting neuronal networks. Arch Ital Biol 142, 379–96.

63. Blanco-Centurion, C., Gerashchenko, D., Salin-Pascual, R. J., and Shiromani, P. J. (2004) Effects of hypocretin2-saporin and antidopamine-beta-hydroxylase-saporin neurotoxic lesions of the dorsolateral pons on sleep and muscle tone. Eur J Neurosci 19, 2741–2752.

64. Burlet, S., Tyler, C. J., and Leonard, C. S. (2002) Direct and indirect excitation of latero-dorsal tegmental neurons by Hypocretin/Orexin peptides: implications for wakefulness and narcolepsy. J Neurosci 22, 2862–72.
65. Boissard, R., Fort, P., Gervasoni, D., Barbagli, B., and Luppi, P. H. (2003) Localiza-tion of the GABAergic and non-GABAergic neurons projecting to the sublaterodorsal nucleus and potentially gating paradoxical sleep onset. Eur J Neurosci 18, 1627–39.
66. Mochizuki, T., Crocker, A., McCormack, S., Yanagisawa, M., Sakurai, T., and Scammell, T. E. (2004) Behavioral state instability in orexin knock-out mice. J Neurosci 24, 6291–6300.
67. Kaur, S., Thankachan, S., Begum, S., Blanco-Centurion, C., Sakurai, T., Yanagisawa, M., and Shiromani, P. J. (2008) Entrainment of temperature and activity rhythms to restricted feeding in orexin knock out mice. Brain Res 1205, 47–54.
68. Heckers, S., Ohtake, T., Wiley, R. G., Lappi, D. A., Geula, C., and Mesulam, M. M. (1994) Complete and selective cholinergic denervation of rat neocortex and hippocampus but not amygdala by an immunotoxin against the p75 NGF receptor. J Neurosci 14, 1271–89.
69. Blanco-Centurion, C., Xu, M., Murillo-Rodriguez, E., Gerashchenko, D., Shiromani, A. M., Salin-Pascual, R. J., Hof, P. R., and Shiromani, P. J. (2006) Adenosine and sleep home-ostasis in the basal forebrain. J Neurosci 26, 8092–8100.
70. Kaur, S., Junek, A., Black, M. A., and Semba, K. (2008) Effects of ibotenate and 192IgG-saporin lesions of the nucleus basalis magnocellularis/substantia innominata on spontaneous sleep and wake states and on recovery sleep after sleep deprivation in rats. J Neurosci 28, 491–504.
71. Gerashchenko, D., Chou, T. C., Blanco-Centurion, C. A., Saper, C. B., and Shiromani, P. J. (2004) Effects of lesions of the histaminergic tuberomammillary nucleus on spontaneous sleep in rats. Sleep 27, 1275–81.
72. Parmentier, R, Ohtsu, H, Djebbara-Hannas, Z, Valatx, J-L., Watanabe, T., and Lin, J.-S. (2002) Anatomical, physiological, and pharmacological characteristics of histidine decarboxylase knock-out mice: evidence for the role of brain histamine in behavioral and sleep-wake control. J Neurosci 22, 7695–7711.
73. Roussel, B., Pujol, J. F., and Jouvet, M. (1976) [Effects of lesions in the pontine tegmen-tum on the sleep stages in the rat]. Arch Ital Biol 114, 188–209.
74. Jones, B. E., Harper, S. T., and Halaris, A. E. (1977) Effects of locus coeruleus lesions upon cerebral monoamine content, sleep-wakefulness states and the response to amphet-amine in the cat. Brain Res. 124, 473–96.
75. Webster, H. H., and Jones, B. E. (1988) Neurotoxic lesions of the dorsolateral pontomes-encephalic tegmentum-cholinergic cell area in the cat. II. Effects upon sleep-waking states. Brain Res 458, 285–302.
76. Gonzalez, M. M., Debilly, G., and Valatx, J. L. (1998) Noradrenaline neurotoxin DSP-4 effects on sleep and brain temperature in the rat. Neurosci Lett 248, 93–96.
77. Hunsley, M. S., and Palmiter, R. D. (2003) Norepinephrine-deficient mice exhibit nor-mal sleep-wake states but have shorter sleep latency after mild stress and low doses of amphetamine. Sleep 26, 521–26.
78. Blanco-Centurion, C., Gerashchenko, D., and Shiromani, P. J. (2007) Effects of saporin-induced lesions of three arousal populations on daily levels of sleep and wake. J Neuro-sci 27, 14041–48.
79. Saper, C. B., Scammell, T. E., and Lu, J. (2005) Hypothalamic regulation of sleep and circadian rhythms. Nature 437, 1257–63.

9

Hyperarousal and Post-Traumatic Stress Disorder: A Role for the Hypocretin System

Matt Carter and Luis de Lecea

CONTENTS

INTRODUCTION
THE HYPOCRETINS
THE ROLE OF HYPOCRETINS IN AROUSAL
THE HYPOCRETINS AND STRESS
THE HYPOCRETINS INTERACT WITH THE NEURAL
    CIRCUITRY ASSOCIATED WITH STRESS/ANXIETY
A ROLE FOR HYPOCRETINS IN PTSD
REFERENCES

Abstract

The hypocretins are a pair of neuropeptides produced in a few thousand neurons in the lateral hypothalamus. Extensive evidence suggests that one of the main functions of hypocretin neurons is to stabilize arousal/alertness during periods of wakefulness and to increase arousal-related behaviors, including eating, drinking, grooming, and locomotor activity. The ability of hypocretin neurons to increase arousal-associated behaviors suggests the possibility that these neurons may play a role in the hyperarousal state observed when an animal is exposed to an acute stressor. Consistent with this hypothesis is a variety of observations indicating that centrally administered hypocretins mimic the behavioral and physiological response to stress. In addition, hypocretin neurons receive prominent input and are activated by terminals containing corticotropin-releasing factor (CRF), a neuropeptide that is secreted in response to an acute stressor. There is abundant evidence demonstrating a reciprocal

From: *Post-Traumatic Stress Disorder: Basic Science and Clinical Practice*
Edited by: P. J. Shiromani et al., DOI: 10.1007/978-1-60327-329-9_9
© Humana Press, a part of Springer Science+Business Media, LLC 2009

connection between hypocretin and CRF neurons, which may be important in the regulation of the hypothalamic-pituitary-adrenal (HPA) axis and the acute stress response. Given that CRF secretion and hyperarousal are both important symptoms of post-traumatic stress disorder (PTSD), hypocretin neurons may play a prominent role in causing many of the other physiological symptoms of the disease. We review the possible role of hypocretin neurons in the allostatic pathophysiology of PTSD, including dysregulation of the stress response, and in the circuitry that regulates sleep and wakefulness.

Key Words: Corticotropin-releasing factor (CRF), HPA axis, hyperarousal, hypocretin, hypothalamus.

INTRODUCTION

One of the major hallmarks of post-traumatic stress disorder (PTSD) is a state of heightened arousal characterized by interrupted sleep, hypervigilance, and an exaggerated startle response *(1)*. This hyperarousal state can also be characterized as changes in physiological indicators of stress, such as higher blood pressure, heart rate, and body temperature *(1,2)*. Much research into the neurobiology of PTSD has focused on the corticotropin-releasing factor (CRF) system and hypothalamus-pituitary-adrenal (HPA) axis, as these systems play an important role in the response to acute and chronic stressors. Indeed, hyperactivity of CRF and the HPA axis has been proposed as contributing to the hyperarousal and physiological symptoms of PTSD *(1–4)*. However, a recently discovered pair of peptides, the hypocretins, has also been shown to play a crucial role in the stability of arousal and alertness *(5)*. Perturbing the hypocretin system can lead to higher indices of arousal and anxiety that mimic the hyperarousal state exhibited in PTSD. In this chapter, we review the data suggesting that hypocretin peptides play a role in arousal and stress and propose a model for hyperactivity of the hypocretin system in PTSD.

THE HYPOCRETINS

The hypocretins (also known as orexins) were discovered independently by two groups in the late 1990s *(6,7)*. They consist of a pair of secreted peptides, hypocretin 1 and hypocretin 2 (Hcrt1 and Hcrt2; also known as orexin A and orexin B, respectively) that are processed from the same precursor, preprohypocretin (ppHcrt) *(6,7)*. The two peptides are produced exclusively in a few thousand neurons in the lateral hypothalamus (LH), distinct from cells in the LH that express melanin-concentrating hormone (MCH) *(6,7)*.

Hypocretin neurons project diffusely throughout the brain to two receptors, Hcrt-r1 and Hcrt-r2 *(6,7)*. Initial work demonstrated that Hcrt-r1 bound Hcrt1 with high affinity and Hcrt2 with 100- to 1,000-fold lower affinity *(7)*. However, Hcrt-r2 was shown to have high affinity for both Hcrt1 and Hcrt2. Hcrt-r1 messenger ribonucleic acid (mRNA) levels are found within the hypothalamus, the locus coeruleus (LC), the cerebral cortex, and several brain stem nuclei. In contrast, Hcrt-r2 mRNA is expressed in cholinergic nuclei in the brain stem, the ventral tegmental area, and histaminergic neurons in the tuberomammilary nucleus (TMN), as well as overlapping expression with Hcrt-r1 in the hypothalamus *(6–10)*. The in situ hybridization pattern of these receptors is consistent with the map of Hcrt-containing fibers *(8)*. Dense projections to the ventrolateral preoptic area (VLPO), TMN, pedunculopontine tegmental (PPT) area, laterodorsal tegmental (LDT) area, and LC suggest that hypocretins may play a role in regulating arousal as all these nuclei play a role in regulating sleep and wakefulness. Thus, initial study of the physiological function of hypocretins involved the role of Hcrts in arousal and vigilance.

THE ROLE OF HYPOCRETINS IN AROUSAL

Extensive evidence now suggests that a main function of hypocretins is to enhance arousal and wakefulness. Shortly after their discovery, a mutation in Hcrt-r2 was demonstrated to be the cause of the sleep disorder narcolepsy in a canine model of the disease *(11)*. Hcrt knockout animals also display a striking narcolepsy phenotype, including a dysregulation of REM (rapid eye movement) sleep and "cataplexy-like" attacks, a hallmark of human narcolepsy *(12)*. Genetic ablation of Hcrt neurons also results in a narcolepsy phenotype *(13)*. Indeed, human narcoleptic patients were shown to have decreased hypocretin levels in their cerebrospinal fluid, and postmortem analysis of narcoleptic brains revealed a loss of hypocretin neurons in the hypothalamus *(14–16)*. Abnormal states of arousal due to mutations in the hypocretin system have even been documented in zebrafish *(17)*. Thus, the impairment of the Hcrts or their receptors demonstrates the necessity of this system to sustain normal states of arousal and alertness.

In addition to these loss-of-function studies, several gain-of-function studies also demonstrated that these peptides are sufficient to cause a state of hyperarousal. Intracerebroventricular injection of Hcrt1 or Hcrt2 increases the time spent awake and decreases the time spent in slow-wave and REM sleep *(18–20)*. Hcrt-induced increases in time spent awake are correlated with a relative increase in arousal-related behaviors, including eating, drinking, grooming, and locomotor activity *(18–21)*. In addition to intracerebroventricular injection of Hcrt1 and Hcrt2 peptides, artificial stimulation of Hcrt neurons using a light-activated cation channel, channelrhodopsin 2, increases the probability of transitions from sleep to wakefulness during both slow-wave and REM sleep *(22)*.

Taken together, these studies demonstrate that the Hcrt system mediates an arousal continuum from sleep to hypervigilance. Not only is hypocretin necessary for normal states of arousal and alertness, but overactivity of the hypocretin system leads to a hyperarousal phenotype in which animals not only spend more time in an awake state but also display an increase in arousal-associated behaviors. Because arousal is a prominent component in the biological stress response, it has been hypothesized that Hcrts can play a role in stress and anxiety-like states. This hypothesis is supported by data suggesting that overactivity of hypocretins may induce behavioral and physiological indicators of stress *(5)*.

THE HYPOCRETINS AND STRESS

A variety of observations indicate that centrally administered Hcrts mimic the behavioral and physiological responses to stress *(5,23)*. For example, intracerebral ventricular injection of Hcrt1 in rodents elicits a majority of stress-related behaviors, including grooming, chewing of inedible material, increased locomotor activity, and food consumption *(18,19,24–27)*. Furthermore, hyperactivity of the Hcrt system is also correlated with a variety of autonomic processes associated with high levels of arousal or stress, such as elevation of heart rate, body temperature, mean arterial blood pressure, and oxygen consumption *(28–32)*. Interestingly, all of these behavioral and physiological responses are observed in animal models of stress and anxiety *(33–37)*. These physiological responses and states of hyperarousal are also observed in human anxiety disorders, including PTSD *(1–4,38)*.

Hypocretin cells also seem to be activated by environmental stressors. Many studies showed an increase in c-Fos, an immediate early gene and marker of neural activity, in Hcrt cells in response to acute stressful stimuli, including a brightly lit, novel environment, food deprivation, and cold exposure, in addition to more chronic stressors such as foot shock and immobilization stress *(5,23,25,39–41)*.

How do Hcrts affect arousal and the stress response? As mentioned, Hcrts probably affect arousal by projecting to different arousal-promoting nuclei in the brain, including the LC, TMN, raphé nuclei, and cholinergic nuclei of the brain stem, as well as multiple regions of the cortex *(6–10)*. The Hcrt system has also been shown to directly interact with circuitry associated with the stress response, including the HPA axis and amygdala.

THE HYPOCRETINS INTERACT WITH THE NEURAL CIRCUITRY ASSOCIATED WITH STRESS/ANXIETY

One of the best-studied systems into the neurobiology of stress, anxiety, and PTSD disorders is that of CRF and the HPA axis. In response to environmental stressors, CRF is secreted by the paraventricular hypothalamic nucleus (PVN) *(42–47)*. Stimulation of pituitary corticotroph cells by CRF results in the production of adrenocorticotropic hormone (ACTH), which elicits the release of glucocorticoids, such as cortisol, from the adrenal gland *(48)*. Cortisol then acts on peripheral and visceral physiological responses to support "fight-or-flight" reactions, such as increasing heart rate, blood pressure, body temperature, and oxygen consumption, all hallmarks of the hyperarousal state of PTSD *(1–4,38,47,48)*. Indeed, patients with PTSD exhibit higher levels of CRF compared to healthy controls *(1–3)*. However, these patients also exhibit a *decreased* level of baseline plasma cortisol, suggesting hyperactivity in the central release of CRF and a hyperfeedback of ACTH levels secreted by the pituitary *(1–3)*. The exact dysregulation of this negative feedback is unknown.

Interestingly, the hypocretins have been shown to functionally interact with the HPA axis. Hypocretin receptors, especially Hcrt-r2, are abundantly present in the PVN *(49)*. Bath application of Hcrt1 and Hcrt2 depolarizes a majority of magnocellular and parvocellular PVN neurons in vitro (50). The effect of hypocretins on magnocellular PVN neurons is likely indirect, as tetrodotoxin (TTX) treatment blocks Hcrt1-elicited depolarizations (51). Furthermore, these effects are also blocked by kynurenic acid, demonstrating the role of glutaminergic interneurons in the action of Hcrt1 (51). In contrast, Hcrt1 depolarizes parvocellular neurons, and this effect is not blocked by TTX (51). While the exact biochemical identity of neurons in the PVN that respond to Hcrt administration is unknown, it is clear that Hcrt can stimulate the release of CRF into the portal vessels (52). Intracerebroventricular Hcrt1 administration increases plasma levels of both glucocorticoids and ACTH release (5,25,52–54).

Not only can the hypocretins depolarize CRF-containing cells in the PVN, but CRF can also affect hypocretin cells in the LH. CRF-immunoreactive boutons are found adjacent to Hcrt cells, and Hcrt cells express CRF receptors (55). Application of CRF to hypothalamic slices depolarizes the membrane potential and increases firing rate in a subpopulation of hypocretinergic cells (55). These CRF-induced depolarizations are dose dependent and blocked by astressin, a CRF receptor 1 antagonist (55). Furthermore, behavioral stressors such as intermittent foot shock and restraint can induce the activation of Hcrt cells in mice but not in CRF receptor 1-deficient animals. Taken together, these studies demonstrate that CRF neurons and Hcrt neurons form a circuit that may mediate the neuroendocrine and hyperarousal responses to stress. These studies also demonstrate that an increase in CRF release, as is documented in PTSD, could lead to an increase in Hcrt-cell activity and consequently a state of hyperarousal.

Retrograde tracing studies suggest that hypocretin cells receive not only CRF projections from the PVN but also strong projections from CRF-containing cells in the central nucleus of the amygdala (CE) and bed nucleus of the stria terminalis (BNST) (56). These two structures serve as output structures of the amygdala and play a role in regulating anxiety (1–4). It has been suggested that altered plasticity within the amygdaloid complex is responsible for the chronic anxiety experienced in PTSD (4).

Another subregion within the amygdala, the basolateral nucleus (BLA), seems to serve as an integrator and relay center for incoming sensory, memory, and limbic information necessary for anxiety responses (57). Much research has demonstrated that the BLA is a crucial site of synaptic plasticity that contributes to changes in behavior following a stressful or traumatic event (58–64). The BLA sends direct, excitatory projections to the CE and BNST, suggesting that altered plasticity in anxiety disorders causes hyperactivity of the amygdala and its efferent subregions (1).

Consistent with this hypothesis are the consistent findings in functional magnetic resonance imaging (fMRI) studies that increased amygdala activation is associated with several anxiety and mood states (65–67). In rodent models, CRF mRNA is increased in the amygdala following stressful paradigms (68). Restraint, drug withdrawal, and neonatal stressors cause an increase of CRF in the amygdala (69–70). These studies suggest that altered plasticity causes hyperactivity in the amygdala, with Hcrt cells in the LH receiving direct efferent projections from CRF-containing cells in the CE and BNST.

A ROLE FOR HYPOCRETINS IN PTSD

Taken together, there is much evidence suggesting that hyperactivity of the Hcrt system may contribute to the hyperarousal state experienced in PTSD:

- PTSD is a hyperarousal disorder, and hyperactivity of the Hcrt system causes a state of hyperarousal in all animals tested, including mice, rats, fish, and birds.
- Hyperactivity of the Hcrt system also causes autonomic and neuroendocrine changes that are symptoms of PTSD in human patients.
- PTSD patients have an overabundance of CRF resulting from stressful stimuli, and CRF directly excites Hcrt neurons.
- The CE and BNST, structures of the amygdaloid complex that are hyperactive in PTSD, send direct projections to Hcrt cells.

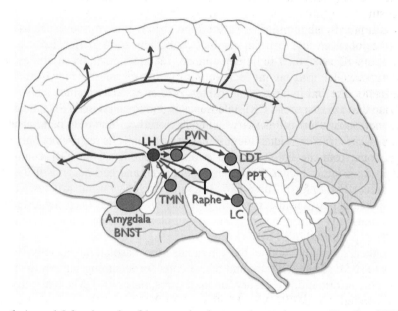

Fig. 1. A model for the role of hypocretins in post-traumatic stress disorder (PTSD). Altered plasticity in the amygdala causes an increase in activity in corticotrophin-releasing factor (CRF)-containing neurons of the central nucleus of the amygdala and bed nucleus of the stria terminalis (BNST). These nuclei send robust projections to hypocretin neurons in the lateral hypothalamus (LH). The hypocretin neurons are well positioned to cause a heightened state of arousal, projecting to multiple brain systems that promote arousal and the response to stress, such as CRF-containing neurons in the paraventricular hypothalamic nucleus (PVN), histaminergic neurons in the tuberomammilary nucleus (TMN), serotoninergic neurons in the raphé nuclei, cholinergic neurons in the lateral dorsal tegmental nucleus (LDT) and pedunculopontine tegmental nucleus (PPT), and noradrenergic neurons in the locus coeruleus (LC). Thus, hyperexcitation of hypocretin neurons could orchestrate the hyperarousal state of PTSD (*See Color Plates*)

Because the CE and BNST send robust projections to Hcrt cells in the LH, we propose a simple model in which hyperexcitability of CRF cells in the amygdala, as has been shown in PTSD, causes an increase in activity in Hcrt cells (Fig. 1). This increase would in turn result in a hyperarousal state such as seen with stimulation of the Hcrt system. The Hcrt cells are perfectly situated to cause an increase in arousal and a stress-like state as they project to multiple nuclei that promote arousal (such as the LC, TMN, and raphé nuclei), as well as the PVN and HPA axis.

The hypocretin cells are also perfectly situated to contribute to the sleep disturbances found in PTSD. It is estimated that 70–91% of patients with PTSD have difficulty falling asleep or staying asleep (71). Individuals with PTSD are more likely to report waking up restless with excessive body movements during sleep compared to individuals with insomnia and no PTSD (72). Furthermore, patients with PTSD exhibit inappropriate awakenings from normal REM sleep (73). As mentioned, these are the same effects seen in animal models in which artificial stimulation of hypocretin neurons causes an increase in the probability of a transition from sleep to wakefulness (22). Intracerebroventricular injection of hypocretins increases the time spent awake and decreases the time spent in slow-wave and REM sleep (18–20). Some have hypothesized that overactivity of the LC/noradrenergic system is responsible for the sleep disturbances observed in PTSD; indeed, some reports indicated that PTSD patients exhibit an increase in noradrenergic activity (74,75). The LC receives robust projections from hypocretin cells, yet so far no study has examined an increase in hypocretin tone as causal or correlational with the sleep disturbances experienced in PTSD.

Future studies should directly examine a role for hypocretin cells in PTSD. It will be interesting to find out if PTSD patients have hyperactivity in the LH and an increase in cerebrospinal fluid hypocretin concentration as compared with healthy controls, especially following stressful stimuli. In animal models, it will be necessary to test whether stimulation of the CE or BNST causes an increase in activity of hypocretin neurons. Finally, a growing number of pharmacological agents target the hypocretin system in humans (76). It will be clinically important to examine the effects of a hypocretin antagonist in patients suffering from PTSD and other anxiety disorders to see if a decrease in hypocretin activity helps to moderate an abnormal hyperarousal state.

REFERENCES

1. Yehuda, R., and LeDoux, J. (2007) Response variation following trauma: a translational neuroscience approach to understanding PTSD. Neuron 56(1), 19–32.
2. Newport, D. J., and Nemeroff, C. B. (2000) Neurobiology of posttraumatic stress disorder. Curr Opin Neurobiol 10(2), 211–18.
3. Risbrough, V. B., and Stein, M. B. (2006). Role of corticotropin releasing factor in anxiety disorders: a translational research perspective. Horm Behav 50(4), 550–61.
4. Shekhar, A., Truitt, W., Rainnie, D., and Sajdyk, T. (2005) Role of stress, corticotrophin releasing factor (CRF) and amygdala plasticity in chronic anxiety. Stress 8(4), 209–19.

5. Berridge, C. W., and Espana, R. A. (2005) Hypocretin/orexin in stress and arousal. In de Lecea, L., and Sutcliffe, J. G., Hypocretins: Integrators of Physiological Functions. New York: Springer-Verlag.
6. de Lecea, L., Kilduff, T. S., Peyron, C., et al. (1998) The hypocretins: hypothalamus-specific peptides with neuroexcitatory activity. Proc Natl Acad Sci U S A 95(1), 322–27.
7. Sakurai, T., Amemiya, A., Ishii, M., et al. (1998) Orexins and orexin receptors: a family of hypothalamic neuropeptides and G protein-coupled receptors that regulate feeding behavior. Cell 92(5), 573–85.
8. Peyron, C., Tighe, D. K., van den Pol, A. N., et al. (1998) Neurons containing hypocretin (orexin) project to multiple neuronal systems. J Neurosci 18(23), 9996–10015.
9. Sakurai, T. (2007) The neural circuit of orexin (hypocretin), maintaining sleep and wakefulness. Nat Rev Neurosci 8(3), 171–81.
10. Date, Y., Ueta, Y., Yamashita, H., et al. (1999) Orexins, orexigenic hypothalamic peptides, interact with autonomic, neuroendocrine and neuroregulatory systems. Proc Natl Acad Sci U S A 96(2), 748–53.
11. Lin, L., Faraco, J., Li, R., et al. (1999) The sleep disorder canine narcolepsy is caused by a mutation in the hypocretin (orexin) receptor 2 gene. Cell 98(3), 365–76.
12. Chemelli, R. M., Willie, J. T., Sinton, C. M., et al. (1999) Narcolepsy in orexin knockout mice: molecular genetics of sleep regulation. Cell 98(4), 437–51.
13. Hara, J., Beuckmann, C. T., Willie, J. T., et al. (2001) Genetic ablation of orexin neurons in mice results in narcolepsy, hypophagia, and obesity. Neuron 30(2), 345–54.
14. Nishino, S., Ripley, B., Overeem, S., Lammers, G. J., and Mignot, E. (2000) Hypocretin (orexin) deficiency in human narcolepsy. Lancet 355(9197), 39–40.
15. Peyron, C., Faraco, J., Rogers, W., et al. (2000) A mutation in a case of early onset narcolepsy and a generalized absence of hypocretin peptides in human narcoleptic brains. Nat Med 6(9), 991–97.
16. Thannickal, T. C., Moore, R. Y., Nienhuis, R., et al. (2000) Reduced number of hypocretin neurons in human narcolepsy. Neuron 27(3), 469–74.
17. Yokogawa, T., Marin, W., Faraco, J., et al. (2007) Characterization of sleep in zebrafish and insomnia in hypocretin receptor mutants. PLoS Biol 5(10), 2379–97.
18. Espana, R. A., Baldo, B. A., Kelley, A. E., and Berridge, C. W. (2001) Wake-promoting and sleep-suppressing actions of hypocretin (orexin), basal forebrain sites of action. Neuroscience 106(4), 699–715.
19. Espana, R. A., Plahn, S., and Berridge, C. W. (2002) Circadian-dependent and circadian-independent behavioral actions of hypocretin/orexin. Brain Res 943(2), 224–36.
20. Piper, D. C., Upton, N., Smith, M. I., and Hunter, A. J. (2000) The novel brain neuropeptide, orexin-A, modulates the sleep-wake cycle of rats. Eur J Neurosci 12(2), 726–30.
21. da Silva, E. S., Dos Santos, R. V., Hoeller, A. A., et al. (2008) Behavioral and metabolic effects of central injections of orexins/hypocretins in pigeons (Columba livia). Regul Pept 147, 9–18, Epub 2007 Dec 26.
22. Adamantidis, A. R., Zhang, F., Aravanis, A. M., Deisseroth, K., and de Lecea, L. (2007) Neural substrates of awakening probed with optogenetic control of hypocretin neurons. Nature. 450(7168), 420–424.
23. Winsky-Sommerer, R., Boutrel, B., and de Lecea, L. (2005) Stress and arousal: the corticotropin releasing factor/hypocretin circuitry. Mol Neurobiol 32(3), 285–94.
24. Ida, T., Nakahara, K., Katayama, T., Murakami, N., and Nakazato, M. (1999) Effect of lateral cerebroventricular injection of the appetite-stimulating neuropeptide, orexin and neuropeptide Y, on the various behavioral activities of rats. Brain Res 821(2), 526–29.

25. Ida, T., Nakahara, K., Murakami, T., Hanada, R., Makazato, M., and Murakami, N. (2000) Possible involvement of orexin in the stress reaction in rats. Biochem Biophys Res Commun 270(1), 318–23.
26. Espana, R. A., Valentino, R. J., and Berridge, C. W. (2003) Fos immunoreactivity in hypocretin-synthesizing and hypocretin-1 receptor-expressing neurons: effects of diurnal and nocturnal spontaneous waking, stress, and hypocretin-1 administration. Neuroscience 121(1), 201–17.
27. Martins, P. J., D'Almeida, V., Pedrazzoli, M., Lin, L., Mignot, E., and Tufik, S. (2004) Increased hypocretin-1 (orexin-a) levels in cerebrospinal fluid of rats after short-term forced activity. Regul Pept 117(3), 155–58.
28. Chen, C. T., Hwang, L. L., Chang, J. K., and Dun, N. J. (2000) Pressor effects of orexins injected intracisternally and to rostral ventrolateral medulla of anesthetized rats. Am J Physiol Regul Integr Comp Physiol 278(3), R692–97.
29. Lubkin, M., and Stricker-Krongrad, A. (1998) Independent feeding and metabolic actions of orexins in mice. Biochem Biophys Res Commun 253(2), 241–45.
30. Samson, W. K., Gosnell, B., Chang, J. K., Resch, Z. T., and Murphy, T. C. (1999) Cardiovascular regulatory actions of the hypocretins in brain. Brain Res 831(1–2), 248–53.
31. Shirasaka, T., Nakazato, M., Matsukura, S., Takasaki, M., and Kannan, H. (1999) Sympathetic and cardiovascular actions of orexins in conscious rats. Am J Physiol 277(2), R1780–85.
32. Yoshimichi, G., Yoshimatsu, H., Masaki, T., and Sakata, T. (2001) Orexin-A regulates body temperature in coordination with arousal status. Exp Biol Med 226(5), 468–476.
33. Levine, S., and Ursin, H. (1991). In Brown, M. R., and Knob, G. F., eds., Stress Neurobiology and Neuroendocrinology. New York: Rivier Marcel Dekker.
34. Chrousos, G. P., and Gold, P. W. (1992) The concepts of stress and stress system disorders: Overview of physical and behavioral homeostasis. JAMA 267, 1244–52.
35. McEwen, B.S. (2000). In: Fink, G., , Encyclopedia of Stress. San Diego, CA: Academic.
36. McEwen, B. S. (2003) Mood disorders and alalostatic load. Biol Psychiatry 54(3), 200–7.
37. Van Praag, H. M. (2004) de Kloet, E. R., and Van Os J., Stress, the Brain and Depression. Cambridge: Cambridge University Press.
38. Yehuda, R. (2002) Post-traumatic stress disorder. N Engl J Med 346(2), 108–14.
39. Sakamoto, F., Yamada, S., and Ueta, Y. (2004) Centrally administered orexin-A activates corticotropin-releasing factor-containing neurons in the hypothalamic paraventricular nucleus and central amygdaloid nucleus of rats: possible involvement of central orexins on stress-activated central CRF neurons. Regul Pept 118(3), 183–91.
40. Sakurai, T., Moriguchi, T., Furuya, K., et al. (1999) Structure and function of human prepro-orexin gene. J Biol Chem 27425, 17771–76.
41. Zhu, L., Onaka, T., Sakurai, T., and Yada, T. (2002) Activation of orexin neurons after noxious but not conditioned fear stimuli in rats. Neuroreport 13(10), 1351–53.
42. Owens, M. J., and Nemeroff, C. B. (1990) Physiology and pharmacology of corticotropin-releasing factor. Pharmacol Rev 43, 425–73.
43. Dunn, A. J., and Berridge, C. W. (1990) Is corticotropin-releasing factor a mediator of stress responses? Ann NY Acad Sci 579, 183–91.
44. Dunn, A. J., and Berridge, C. W. (1990) Physiological and behavioral responses to corticotropin-releasing factor administration: is CRF a mediator of anxiety or stress responses? Brain Res Brain Res Rev 15(2), 71–100.
45. Chang, F. C., and Opp, M. R. (2001) Corticotropin releasing hormone (CRH) as a regulator of waking. Neurosci Biobehav Rev 25, 445–53.

46. Chang, F. C., and Opp, M. R. (2005) A corticotropin-releasing hormone antisense oligo-deoxynucleotide reduces spontaneous waking in the rat. Regul Pept 117(1), 43–52.

47. Koob, G. F., and Bloom, F. E. (1985) Corticotropin-releasing factor and behavior. Fed Proc 44, 259–63.

48. Sapolsky, R. M., Romero, L. M., and Munck, A. U. (2000) How do glucocorticoids influence stress responses? Integrating permissive, suppressive, simulatory, and prepara-tive actions. Endocr Rev 21, 55–89.

49. Lu, X. Y., Bagnol, D., Burke, S., Akil, H., and Watson, S. J. (2000) Differential distribu-tion and regulation of OC1 and OX2 orexin/hypocretin receptor messenger RNA in the brain upon fasting. Horm Behav 37(4), 335–44.

50. Shirasaka, T., Miyahara, S., Kunitake, T., et al. (2001) Orexin depolarizes rat hypotha-lamic paraventricular nucleus neurons. Am J Physiol Regul Integr Comp Physiol 281(4), R1114–18.

51. Follwell, M. J., and Ferguson, A. V. (2002) Cellular mechanisms of orexin actions on paraventricular nucleus neurons in rat hypothalamus. J Physiol 545(pt 3), 855–67.

52. Al-Barazanji, K. A., Wilson, S., Baker, J., Jessop, D. S., and Harbuz, M. S. (2001) Cen-tral orexin-A activates hypothalamic-pituitary-adrenal axis and stimulates hypothalamic corticotropin releasing factor and arginine vasopressin neurons in conscious rats. J Neu-roendocrinol 13(5), 421–24.

53. Jaszberenyi, M., Bujdoso, E., Pataki, I., and Telegdy, G. (2000) Effects of orexins on the hypothalamic-pituitary-adrenal system. J Neuroendocrinol 12(12), 1174–78.

54. Kuro, M., Ueta, Y., Serino, R., et al. (2000) Centrally administered orexin/hypocretin activates HPA axis in rats. Neuroreport 11(9), 1977–80.

55. Winsky-Sommerer, R., Yamanaka, A., Diano, S., et al. (2004) Interaction between the corticotropin-releasing factor system and hypocretins (orexins), a novel circuit mediat-ing stress response. J Neurosci 24(50), 11439–48.

56. Mochizuki, T., and Scammell, T. E. (2003) Orexin/hypocretin: wired for wakefulness. Curr Biol 13(14), R563–64.

57. Campeau, S., and Davis, M. (1995) Involvement of the central nucleus and basolateral complex of the amygdala in fear conditioning measured with fear-potentiated startle in rats trained concurrently with auditory and visual conditioned stimuli. J Neurosci 15(3), 2301–11.

58. Sanders, S. K., and Shekhar, A. (1991) Blockade of GABAA receptors in the region of the anterioir basolateral amygdala of rats elicits increases in heart rate and blood pres-sure. Brain Res 567(1), 101–10.

59. Sanders, S. K., and Shekhar, A. (1995) Anxiolytic effects of chlordiazepoxide blocked by injection of GABAA and benzodiazepine receptor antagonists in the region of the anterior basolateral amygdala of rats. Biol Psychiatry 37(7), 473–76.

60. Shekhar, A., Sajdyk, T. S., Keim, S. R., Yoder, K. K., and Sanders, S. K. (1999) Role of the basolateral amygdala in panic disorder. Ann N Y Acad Sci 877:747–50.

61. Sajdyk, T. J., and Shekhar, A. (2000) Sodium lactate elicits anxiety in rats after repeated GABA receptor blockade in the basolateral amygdala. Eur J Pharmacol 394(2–3), 265–73.

62. Shekhar, A., Sajdyk, T. J., Gehlert, D. R., and Rainnie, D. G. (2003) The amygdala, panic disorder, and cardiovascular responses. Ann N Y Acad Sci 985:308–25.

63. Rainnie, D. G., Bergeron, R., Sajdyk, T. J., Patil, M., Hehlert, D. R., and Shekhar, A. (2004) Corticotrophin releasing factor-induced synaptic plasticity in the amygdala trans-lates stress into emotional disorders. J Neurosci 24(14), 3471–79.

64. Vyas, A., Mitra, R., Shankaranarayana Rao, B. S., and Chattarji, S. (2002) Chronic stress induces contrasting patterns of dendritic remodeling in hippocampal and amygdaloid neurons. J Neurosci 22, 6810–18.

65. Rauch, S. L., Whalen, P. J., Shin, L. M., et al. (2000) Exaggerated amygdala response to masked facial stimuli in posttraumatic stress disorder: a functional MRI study. Biol Psychiatry 47(9), 769–76.

66. Williams, L. M., Kemp, A. H., Felmingham, K., et al. (2006) Trauma modulates amygdala and medial prefrontal responses to consciously attended fear. Neuroimage 29(2), 347–57.

67. Liberzon, I., and Sripada, C. S. (2008) The functional neuroanatomy of PTSD: a critical review. Prog Brain Res 167, 151–69.

68. Herringa, R. J., Nanda, S. A., Hsu, D. T., Roseboom, P. H., and Kalin, N. H. (2004) The effects of acute stress on the regulation of central and basolateral amygdala CRF-binding protein gene expression. Brain Res Mol Brain Res 131, 17–25.

69. Merlo Pich, E., Lorang, M., Yeganeh, M., et al. (1995) Increase of extracellular corticotropin-releasing factor-like immunoreactivity levels in rats during restraint stress and ethanol withdrawal as measured by microdialysis. J Neurosci 15(8), 5439–47.

70. Cratty, M. S., Ward, H. E., Johnson, E. A., Azzaro, A. J., and Birkle, D. L. (1995) Prenatal stress increases corticotropin-releasing factor (CRF) content and release in rat amygdala minces. Brain Res 675(1–2), 297–302.

71. Maher, M. J., Rego, S. A., and Asnis, G. M. (2006) Sleep disturbances in patients with post-traumatic stress disorder: epidemiology, impact, and approaches to management. CNS Drugs 20(7), 567–90.

72. Inman, D., Silver, S., and Doghramji, K. (1990) Sleep disturbances in patients with post-traumatic stress disorder: a comparison with non-PTSD insomnia. J Trauma Stress 3, 429–37.

73. Ross, R. J., Ball, W. A., Sullivan, K. A., and Caroff, S. N. (1989) Sleep disturbance as the hallmark of posttraumatic stress disorder. Am J Psychiatry 146(6), 697–707.

74. Mellman, T. A., Kumar, A., Kulick-Bell, R., Kumar, M., and Nolan, B. (1995) Nocturnal/daytime urine noradrenergic measures and sleep in combat-related PTSD. Biol Psychiatry 38(3), 174–79.

75. Lamarche, L. J., and De Koninck, J. (2007) Sleep disturbance in adults with posttraumatic stress disorder: a review. J Clin Psychiatry 68(8), 1257–70.

76. Brisbare-Roch, C., Dingemanse, J., Koberstein, R., et al. (2007) Promotion of sleep by targeting the orexin system in rats, dogs, and humans. Nat Med 13, 150–55.

10 The Locus Coeruleus-Noradrenergic System and Stress: Implications for Post-Traumatic Stress Disorder

Craig W. Berridge

CONTENTS

OVERVIEW
THE LOCUS COERULEUS-NORADRENERGIC SYSTEM
AROUSAL-ENHANCING ACTIONS OF THE
 LC-NORADRENERGIC SYSTEM
THE LC-NORADRENERGIC SYSTEM MODULATES
 SENSORY INFORMATION PROCESSING WITHIN
 CORTICAL AND THALAMIC CIRCUITS
MODULATORY ACTIONS OF THE LC-NORADRENERGIC
 SYSTEM ON NEURONAL PLASTICITY
MODULATORY ACTIONS OF THE LC-NORADRENERGIC
 SYSTEM ON COGNITIVE PROCESSES
THE LC IN STRESS-RELATED DISORDERS: PTSD
SUMMARY
REFERENCES

Abstract

Stress is associated with the activation of a number of central physiological systems, which act to enhance arousal and modulate attentional, memory, and other behavioral processes. The net consequence of these actions better permits the organism to contend with a challenging situation and react promptly and effectively when similar conditions are reencountered. It has long been known that stress is associated with a robust activation of the locus coeruleus and other

From: *Post-Traumatic Stress Disorder: Basic Science and Clinical Practice*
Edited by: P. J. Shiromani et al., DOI: 10.1007/978-1-60327-329-9_10
© Humana Press, a part of Springer Science+Business Media, LLC 2009

noradrenergic systems. Moreover, evidence indicates a prominent involvement of central noradrenergic systems in a variety of behavioral and cognitive processes associated with stress, including arousal, memory, and attention. Under normal conditions, these actions are likely beneficial to the individual. However, under conditions of extreme stress/trauma, stressor-induced sensitization of noradrenergic systems and long-term actions of norepinephrine may well prove maladaptive. Consistent with this hypothesis, available evidence indicates a prominent involvement of noradrenergic systems in the behavioral pathology associated with various stress-related disorders, particularly post-traumatic stress disorder (PTSD). In particular, there is strong evidence for an involvement of noradrenergic systems in PTSD-related hyperarousal, intrusive memories, and sleep disturbances. Consistent with this, recent studies suggest that pharmacological disruption of noradrenergic neurotransmission may well be efficacious in treating these symptoms of PTSD. Combined, available information indicates that the central noradrenergic systems likely contribute to a broad spectrum of behavioral symptoms of PTSD and that pharmacological treatments targeting noradrenergic neurotransmission will prove clinically beneficial.

Key Words: α-Receptor, basal forebrain, β-receptor, locus coeruleus, long-term potentiation, norepinephrine.

OVERVIEW

The current conceptualization of stress as a behavioral state elicited by challenging or threatening events arises from nearly a century of research, starting with the seminal work of Cannon (*1*) and Selye (*2*). These studies identified physiological systems that were similarly affected by disparate environmental events, which had in common a potential to threaten animal well-being. Initially, emphasis was placed on stressor-induced activation of peripheral systems, primarily endocrine systems. This work identified the activation of both peripheral catecholamine systems and the pituitary-adrenal axis as hallmark features of the state of stress. The activation of these systems results in enhanced ability of the animal to physically contend with a challenging situation. More recently, emphasis has been placed on the neurobiology of the affective, cognitive, and behavioral components of stress.

This raises the long-standing issue of which psychological features define the state of stress. In contrast to the well-delineated physiological indices of stress, the affective and cognitive features of stress remain less clear. The extent to which stress has an affective component that can or cannot be dissociated from anxiety is not clear. Regardless of the exact configuration of cognitive and affective responses associated with stress, it appears that a heightened level of readiness for action is paramount to a state of stress. A prominent component of this preparatory state is an *elevated level of arousal*, defined for the purposes of this review as a heightened sensitivity to environmental stimuli.

Sustained arousal can be a considerable drain on physiological resources, regardless of whether it is precipitated by aversive or pleasant events. Indeed, the concept of eustress was introduced to acknowledge that pleasant events that are nonetheless challenging and arousing can produce a physiological state similar to that seen in the presence of aversive conditions (distress; *3*). Regardless of whether negative affect is an obligatory component to the state of stress, there is a strong relationship between arousal level and a variety of state-dependent processes affected in stress, including attention, memory, and sensory information processing. These observations suggest the working hypothesis that at least a subset of the physiological and cognitive/behavioral components of stress may be independent of affective valence (pleasant vs. unpleasant) and more closely aligned with arousal level, motivational state, or the need for action.

It has long been known that stress is associated with a robust activation of the locus coeruleus (LC) and other noradrenergic systems, resulting in increased rates of norepinephrine (NE) release widely throughout the brain. Moreover, these noradrenergic systems are known to modulate a variety of behavioral and cognitive processes associated with stress. Consistent with this, evidence demonstrates a causal role of brain noradrenergic systems in a variety of behavioral and cognitive components of stress. Under normal conditions, these actions are likely beneficial to the individual. However, under conditions of extreme stress/trauma, actions of NE may well prove maladaptive. Consistent with this hypothesis, available evidence indicates a prominent involvement of noradrenergic systems in the behavioral pathology associated with various stress-related disorders, particularly post-traumatic stress disorder (PTSD).

THE LOCUS COERULEUS-NORADRENERGIC SYSTEM

Norepinephrine is a prominent neuromodulatory transmitter within the brain. NE acts at three major receptor families, α_1, α_2, and β, each comprised of multiple subtypes. The α_1- and β-receptors exist primarily postsynaptically, whereas α_2-receptors are present both pre- and postsynaptically. The LC is the major source of brain NE (*4*). This nucleus is composed of a small number of neurons, approximately 1,500 per nucleus in rat, several thousand in monkey, and 10,000–15,000 in humans. Despite these relatively small numbers, LC neurons possess immensely ramified axons, permitting the nucleus to project broadly throughout the neuraxis (*4*), excluding the basal ganglia. Importantly, the LC is the sole provider of NE to hippocampus and neocortex, regions critical for higher cognitive and affective function. Despite the widespread distribution of noradrenergic efferent fibers within the brain, there is substantial regional specificity of noradrenergic fiber distribution across cortical and subcortical structures (*5*). This regional heterogeneity likely has important functional ramifications.

Discharge Activity of LC Neurons

LC neurons fire in two distinct activity modes: tonic and phasic. *Tonic* activity is characterized by relatively low-frequency, sustained, and highly regular discharge patterns. Tonic discharge activity is state dependent, with LC neurons displaying highest discharge rates during waking, slower rates during slow-wave sleep, and minimal activity during rapid eye movement (REM) sleep (6, 7). Within waking, sustained increases in tonic discharge rates are elicited by environmental stimuli that elicit sustained increases in electroencephalographic (EEG) and behavioral indices of arousal (7,8).

LC neurons also display *phasic* alterations in discharge rates in response to both unconditioned and conditioned salient sensory stimuli (7,9). These phasic responses are observed with a relatively short latency and are comprised of a brief burst of two or three action potentials followed by a sustained period of suppression of discharge activity (approximately 300–700 ms). Phasic responses are observed in association with overt attending to a novel stimulus within a particular environmental location (e.g., an orienting response). Phasic responses are less robust during lower levels of arousal/vigilance (10) as well as higher levels of tonic discharge activity, including in stress. For example, both hypotension stress and corticotropin-releasing hormone elevate tonic discharge activity and reduce sensory-driven phasic discharge (11). Thus, stress likely interferes with behavioral processes dependent on phasic LC discharge.

Plasticity of the LC-Noradrenergic System in Stress

Central noradrenergic systems possess robust compensatory mechanisms that permit adjustment to long-term alterations in activity. These alterations are observed in response to damage (e.g., lesions) as well as environmental (e.g., stress) and pharmacological (e.g., antidepressant) manipulations. In the case of stress, prolonged or repeated exposure to stressors such as foot shock, cold, or restraint decrease β-receptor-driven accumulation of cyclic adenosine monophosphate (cAMP) (12) The stressor-induced downregulation of the β-dependent cAMP response appears to result largely from a reduction in α_1-receptor potentiation of the β-receptor cAMP response (12). Repeated exposure to a stressor also attenuates LC neuronal responsivity and NE release to the same (homotypic) stressor (13,14). Although repeated presentation of certain stressors results in tolerance to the LC-activating actions of those stressors, enhanced responsivity of LC neurons to repeated immobilization stress has been observed (15), indicating that tolerance to a given stressor is not obligatory.

Tolerance to stressor-induced LC activation is in contrast to the ability of both acute and chronic stressors to increase levels of the rate-limiting enzyme in NE biosynthesis, tyrosine hydroxylase (16). Thus, although chronic/repeated stressors do not tend to increase LC neuronal discharge, they do result in increased capacity of the system to release NE due to elevated rates of NE synthesis (for review, see Ref. 5). These observations raise the question of which conditions would utilize an increase in NE synthetic capacity. Insight into this issue is provided by the observation that, in contrast to homotypic stressors, repeated/chronic stress results in an increased responsiveness of the LC-noradrenergic system to presentation of a *different* (heterotypic) stressor. For example, chronic cold stress results in larger increases in NE efflux in response to tail shock (14) or tail pinch (17). These observations are consistent with an increase in responsivity of LC neurons to excitatory input seen in anesthetized animals that had been previously exposed to chronic stress (*18*).

Thus, during prolonged exposure to a stressor, the LC-noradrenergic system develops an increased capacity to respond to additional challenges. As reviewed later, stress-related sensitization of noradrenergic systems may play a critical role in PTSD.

Sensitivity of the LC-Noradrenergic System to Appetitive Stimuli

Extensive evidence indicates a robust activation of the LC-noradrenergic system by a variety of stressors (for review, *see* Ref. *5*). The early demonstration of a sensitivity of LC neurons to stressors suggested a possibly selective role of the LC in stress and led to a number of hypotheses concerning alarm- or anxiety-specific functions of these neurons. However, subsequent studies in unanesthetized animals demonstrated a sensitivity of tonic and phasic LC discharge as well as NE release to both appetitive as well as aversive stimuli (*7,19,20*). Combined, these observations suggest that both tonic and phasic LC-NE neurotransmission is more closely related to the overall salience, arousing or motivating nature of a given stimulus rather than affective valence.

AROUSAL-ENHANCING ACTIONS OF THE LC-NORADRENERGIC SYSTEM

Enhanced arousal is a primary component of the state of stress. The fact that LC neurons increase firing rates in anticipation of waking and waking-associated forebrain activation suggests the hypothesis that LC neurons help induce the waking state. Substantial evidence collected since 1990 provides strong support for this hypothesis.

Noradrenergic Modulation of Cortical and Thalamic Neuronal Activity State In Vitro

Cortical and thalamic neurons display distinct activity modes during sleeping and waking. Thus, during slow-wave sleep, these neurons are hyperpolarized and display a burst-type activity mode that is associated with a relative insensitivity to incoming sensory information. In contrast, during waking these neurons display a single-spike mode associated with the efficient and accurate processing of sensory information (*21,22*). Consistent with the described increase in LC discharge rates during waking, in vitro, NE induces a shift in the firing pattern of cortical and thalamic neurons from a burst mode to a waking-like single spike mode (*23*).

Effects of LC Neuronal Discharge Activity on EEG and Behavioral Indices of Arousal

The small size of the LC, situated in close proximity to a variety of brain stem structures, presents a substantial challenge for the selective manipulation of LC neuronal discharge rates. A combined recording/infusion probe was developed that permitted a greater degree of anatomical localization of intratissue infusions (24). Using this approach, it was demonstrated that *unilateral* LC activation, produced by a small infusion of the cholinergic agonist bethanechol, elicits a robust *bilateral* activation of cortical and hippocampal EEG (25). In contrast, bilateral suppression of LC neuronal discharge activity via infusion of an α_2-agonist produces a robust increase in slow-wave activity in cortical and hippocampal EEG (78). Combined, these and other observations indicate the LC is a potent modulator of forebrain EEG state, with unilateral LC neuronal discharge activity causally related to the bilateral maintenance of EEG activity patterns associated with arousal.

NE Acts Within the Basal Forebrain to Promote Arousal

A number of subcortical structures have been implicated in the regulation of cortical and hippocampal activity state, including the general region of the basal forebrain encompassing the medial septal area (MSA)/diagonal band of Broca, the general region of the anterior-medial hypothalamus, encompassing the medial preoptic area (MPOA), and the substantia innominata (SI; for review, *see* Ref. 5). Moreover, each of these regions receives a prominent noradrenergic innervation from the LC (26). Therefore, a series of microinfusion studies was conducted to assess the degree to which NE acts within these regions to modulate the behavioral state.

These studies demonstrated potent EEG-activating and wake-promoting actions of NE via actions at both β- and α_1-receptor subtypes located within MSA and MPOA, but not SI. For example, in sleeping, unanesthetized rats, β- and α_1-receptor stimulation within MSA and MPOA produced a robust and additive increase in time spent awake (for review, *see* Ref. 5). In contrast, when infused into SI, neither NE, a β-agonist, an α_1-agonist, or the indirect noradrenergic agonist amphetamine exerted wake-promoting actions (for review, *see* Ref. 5). It is important to note that although the LC provides a majority of noradrenergic input to the MPOA and MSA, two areas within which NE acts to promote arousal, other noradrenergic nuclei also contribute to the noradrenergic innervation of these regions (e.g., 26). Thus, although the LC plays a critical role in the regulation of arousal, other noradrenergic systems likely also exert arousal-promoting actions.

NE Is Necessary for Alert Waking: Synergistic Sedative Actions of α1- and β-Receptor Blockade

As described, α_1- and β-receptors exert additive wake-promoting actions. Consistent with this, combined β-receptor and α_1-blockade blockade (intracerebroventricular timolol and intraperitoneal prazosin, respectively) exerts additive sedative actions, resulting in a profound increase in large-amplitude slow-wave activity in cortical EEG in animals exposed to an arousal-increasing and stress-inducing, brightly lit novel environment (27). This increase in slow-wave activity is in contrast to the minimal EEG effects observed with β-receptor blockade alone or the high-voltage spindles elicited by α_1-receptor blockade (27).

Enhanced LC Discharge Activity Contributes to Stressor-Induced Activation of the Forebrain

The described observations suggest a potentially critical role of the LC-NE system in stressor-induced arousal. Consistent with this hypothesis, bilateral suppression of LC neuronal activity, via peri-LC infusions of an α_2-agonist (clonidine), prevented EEG activation elicited by hypotension-stress in the anesthetized rat (28). These results provide direct support for a causal role of the LC-noradrenergic system in stressor-induced arousal.

Summary: LC Modulation of Arousal in Stress

A large body of information demonstrates a prominent role for the LC-noradrenergic system in the modulation of EEG and behavioral indices of arousal. Additional evidence demonstrates a critical role of the LC in stressor-induced activation of the forebrain. Combined, these observations suggest the prominent participation of this neurotransmitter system in stressor-induced increases in arousal. Stressor-induced sensitization of the LC-NE system could contribute to elevated arousal levels associated with PTSD and other stress-related disorders.

THE LC-NORADRENERGIC SYSTEM MODULATES SENSORY INFORMATION PROCESSING WITHIN CORTICAL AND THALAMIC CIRCUITS

During periods of environmental demand (e.g., stress), information collection and processing are critical for guidance of appropriate behavior. Sensory information processing is highly state-dependent (for review, see Ref. 5). Given the described state-dependent nature of the LC-NE system, this system may well contribute to state-dependent modulation of sensory information processing during stress.

A large body of work indicates complex modulatory actions of NE on discharge properties of cortical and thalamic sensory neurons (for review, see Ref. 5). These actions include increasing the "signal-to-noise" ratio of evoked responding (both excitatory and inhibitory responses) as well as "gating" of neuronal responses to previously subthreshold stimuli. Importantly, the electrophysiological actions of NE on sensory cortical neuronal activity follows a nonmonotonic, inverted U-shaped dose-response relationship, similar to that described for noradrenergic modulation of cognitive function (29). Combined, these observations indicate that, within neocortex, NE exerts a complicated array of modulatory actions. Such actions are likely of particular importance under conditions of threat/stress when a rapid and accurate behavioral response is required.

MODULATORY ACTIONS OF THE LC-NORADRENERGIC SYSTEM ON NEURONAL PLASTICITY

Long-term survival requires behavioral, and thus neural, plasticity. As described, the LC-noradrenergic system displays long-term, stressor-induced alterations in a variety of cellular processes. Additional information indicates that the LC system modulates long-term alterations in synaptic efficacy and gene transcription posited to underlie learning and memory. Combined, these actions may contribute to stress-related long-term alterations in behavior.

Long-Term Modulatory Actions of the LC-Noradrenergic System on Synaptic Efficacy Within Neuronal Ensembles

Long-lasting, experience-dependent alterations in responsiveness to afferent information are observed within large-population neuronal ensembles. For example, long-term potentiation (LTP) refers to a long-lasting increase in synaptic strength that results when excitatory synapses are rapidly and repetitively stimulated for brief periods (tetanic stimulation). Experimentally, this has been most intensively studied within the hippocampal formation and is manifested as an increase in the population spike to subsequent punctate stimulation of hippocampal afferent paths. That LTP is readily observed in a structure believed to be critical for memory function has stimulated interest in LTP as a possible mechanism underlying memory.

The LC-NE system is a potent modulator of LTP. For example, when tested in vitro, depletion of NE decreases LTP in the dentate gyrus (*30*), whereas NE application elicits a β-receptor-dependent enhancement of LTP in CA3 (*31*). NE also produces a long-lasting enhancement of synaptic efficacy in both the dentate gyrus and CA1 region of the hippocampus in the absence of tetanic stimulation (*32,33*). In vivo, enhancement of NE neurotransmission by LC activation, α_2-antagonist administration, or direct application of NE results in an increase in the population spike recorded in the dentate gyrus (*32,34*). These last actions involve both β- and α_1-receptors (*35,36*).

An additional form of NE-dependent plasticity has also been described in neocortex in which NE elicits a long-term synaptic depression of the population response recorded from layer III of visual cortex (*37*). Overall, these observations indicate a potentially prominent role of the LC-NE system in mediating long-lasting modifications in neurotransmission within large populations of forebrain neurons. It is particularly intriguing that these actions are observed in structures implicated in learning and memory. Such actions may be particularly critical for dealing rapidly and effectively when environmental situations that pose a threat (e.g., stress) are reencountered. Excessive activation of these systems may manifest in an excessive and potentially detrimental sensitivity to otherwise mild environmental events/stressors.

Facilitatory Actions of the LC-Noradrenergic System on Transcription Rates of Immediate-Early and Other Plasticity-Related Genes

Long-term alterations in behavior likely involve alterations in rates of gene transcription and protein production. A set of immediate-early genes (IEGs) has been identified that are activated rapidly by a variety of neuromodulators. Many of these genes act as "transcription regulators," regulating gene transcription rates. Through these actions, IEGs may provide an intervening step through which relatively short-term alterations in neuronal activity are transduced into long-term alterations in neuronal function and behavior (*38*).

Evidence indicates a prominent role of the LC-NE system in the regulation of IEGs. For example, increases in NE release result in an increase in messenger ribonucleic acid (mRNA) and protein levels for a variety of IEGs in the neocortex and amygdala (for review, *see* Ref. *5*). Interestingly, stress is associated with similar activating effects on IEG expression (*39–41*). Importantly, the activating effects of stressor-induced increases in NE neurotransmission on IEG expression are attenuated with pretreatment of either β- or α_1-antagonists or LC lesions (*42*). These observations indicate that stressor-induced alterations in IEG expression are dependent on stressor-induced increases in NE release.

MODULATORY ACTIONS OF THE LC-NORADRENERGIC SYSTEM ON COGNITIVE PROCESSES

The described actions of the LC efferent system suggest a widespread influence of this neurotransmitter pathway on information processing within a variety of LC terminal fields. Indeed, substantial evidence suggests the LC-noradrenergic system plays a prominent role in a variety of behavioral/cognitive processes related to the collection, processing, retention, and utilization of sensory information. Importantly, actions of NE appear to play a prominent role in stressor-induced alterations in at least a subset of these processes.

The LC-Noradrenergic System Modulates Attention

The ability to regulate attention is an important aspect of behavior. This may be particularly true under stressful conditions that pose a threat to the animal. The actions of NE on cortical/thalamic neuronal activity reviewed indicate that NE facilitates processing of relevant sensory signals. These observations suggest that the LC-noradrenergic system might enhance cognitive function under "noisy" conditions in which irrelevant stimuli could impair performance. Results from pharmacological and lesion studies conducted in rodents, monkeys, and humans largely support these hypotheses. For example, NE depletion produces deficits in the performance on a variety of tasks when irrelevant stimuli are presented during testing (for review, *see* Ref. *43*). Thus, the addition of distracting visual stimuli at the choice point in a T maze produces a greater disruption of performance in NE-depleted rats than in sham-treated animals (for review, see Ref. 5). Similarly, the presentation of irrelevant auditory stimuli impairs sustained attention in rats with forebrain NE depletion, although these animals perform normally under nondistracting conditions (44). Further, NE depletion increases conditioned responses to irrelevant stimuli while decreasing responses to relevant stimuli (45–47). Thus, overall, impairment of noradrenergic neurotransmission has an impact on attentional and other cognitive tasks under conditions associated with high-demand or increased arousal.

The LC-noradrenergic system may be particularly sensitive to novel environmental stimuli. For example, enhanced LC discharge rates are observed when rats encounter novel stimuli within a familiar environment (48). Further, pharmacological manipulations that enhance NE release increase physical contact/interaction with a novel stimulus located within a familiar environment (49). In contrast, when examined in a novel environment, enhanced NE neurotransmission decreases attention to an individual object, possibly reflecting enhanced scanning of the environment (50,51). Interestingly, stress produces a similar decrease in focused attention that is reversed by α_1-receptor blockade (51).

Combined, these observations suggest an involvement of noradrenergic systems in the regulation of attentional processes, including sustained or focused attention. Initial electrophysiological recordings suggested the potential involvement of both phasic and tonic LC discharge and performance in a vigilance task (9). In these studies, moderate levels of tonic discharge, correlating with moderate arousal levels, were associated with high levels of performance and robust phasic LC responses. When tonic levels were too low (sedation) or too high (high arousal, scanning attention), phasic discharge was reduced, and performance was impaired. Although this was originally interpreted to suggest a role for both phasic and tonic discharge in sustained attention, subsequent work indicated that phasic LC discharge most closely correlates with behavioral responding in this task rather than attention to a sensory stimulus (52). Nonetheless, these studies indicate a sensitivity of sustained attention to fluctuations in tonic LC discharge, indicating an optimal level of tonic LC discharge is necessary for maximal levels of sustained attention.

The LC-Noradrenergic System Modulates Working Memory

The prefrontal cortex (PFC) is involved in a variety of cognitive, behavioral, and physiological processes, many of which are affected in stress. NE modulates PFC neuronal activity and PFC-dependent behavior (for review, see Ref. 53). The actions of NE on PFC-dependent behavior have been most comprehensively studied in the context of working memory. A large body of work demonstrates NE acts directly within the PFC to produce an inverted U-shaped modulation of working memory, with both low and high levels of NE neurotransmission associated with impaired working memory (for review, see Ref. 53). For example, decreased NE neurotransmission impairs working memory, an effect that is reversed by local infusion of postsynaptic-preferring α_2-agonists (e.g., guanfacine; *53*). Conversely, stressor-induced impairment in working memory is reversed by intra-PFC infusion of α_1-antagonists (*54,55*). Based on these and other observations, it has been hypothesized that moderate levels of NE release associated with nonstress conditions activate high-affinity α_{2A}-receptors, whereas release of higher levels of NE (i.e., stress) activates lower-affinity α_1-receptors (*53*).

LC-Noradrenergic System Modulates Arousal-Related Memory

Memory strength can be enhanced by stressful and emotionally arousing conditions. Steroid (e.g., glucocorticoids) and catecholamine (e.g., epinephrine) hormones participate in this arousal-related enhancement of memory (for review, *see* Ref. *56*). Circulating epinephrine stimulates release of central NE via stimulation of β-receptors located on vagal afferents (*56*). Evidence indicates that NE action at β-receptors within the amygdala plays a critical role in the memory-enhancing actions of both arousing stimuli and circulating epinephrine (*56*). The basolateral nucleus of the amygdala appears to be a critical site within the amygdala for the memory-modulating effects of NE. Thus, posttraining infusions of NE into the basolateral nucleus of the amygdala enhance spatial learning, while β-antagonist infusions impair performance in this task (*57*) as well as an inhibitory avoidance task (*58,58*). Further, glucocorticoid-induced enhancement of performance in an inhibitory avoidance task is prevented by the blockade of basolateral amygdala β_1- or β_2-receptors (*60*). Basolateral amygdala α_1-receptors also facilitate performance in an inhibitory avoidance task (*61*). This facilitatory action of α_1-receptors on memory appears to result from the α_1-dependent enhancement of β-receptor-mediated cAMP production (*61,62*). In support of a role of NE in emotion-related memory in humans, Cahill, Prins, Weber, and McGaugh (*63*) demonstrated that β-receptor blockade in human subjects blocks the enhanced memory typically observed with emotionally activating images.

These observations indicate a prominent role of NE, via actions within the basolateral amygdala, in the consolidation of memory under high-arousal, stressful conditions. Memory involves not only the consolidation of information following an event, but also the retrieval and subsequent reconsolidation of that information (*64*). Additional information suggests that the modulatory actions of basolateral amygdala NE on memory consolidation are not universally observed across different types of memories. Thus, in a conditioned fear (conditioned freezing) paradigm, posttraining blockade of basolateral amygdala β-receptors had minimal effects on auditory fear conditioning (*65*). In contrast, intrabasolateral amygdala β-receptor blockade interfered with reconsolidation in this paradigm (*65*).

Combined, these observations suggest NE acts within the basolateral amygdala to strengthen consolidation or reconsolidation of aversive and emotionally arousing events.

THE LC IN STRESS-RELATED DISORDERS: PTSD

Introduction

The information reviewed indicates noradrenergic systems have an impact on widespread neural circuits involved in the regulation of arousal and the collection, processing, and responding to sensory information. Moreover, noradrenergic systems participate in a variety of behavioral, cognitive, and physiological responses associated with stress. These observations suggest a potentially prominent role of NE in stress-related disorders, including PTSD. In this discussion, it is worth noting that much of the impetus behind the initial speculation of an anxiogenic action of NE was the observation that stressors were particularly potent at activating the LC-NE system. As reviewed, subsequent work demonstrated comparable sensitivity/responsivity of LC neurons to both aversive and appetitive stimuli. These observations indicate that increased release of NE per se does not produce a negative affective state, such as anxiety. Such a conclusion apparently contradicts results from studies in humans that indicate increased anxiety following peripheral manipulations that increase NE neurotransmission (66). However, the relationship between generalized arousal, which is likely sensitive to peripheral manipulations of noradrenergic neurotransmission, and anxiety has not been fully explored in humans. Thus, the extent to which results obtained in humans indicate direct versus indirect actions of central noradrenergic systems on anxiety-related circuits remains unclear.

Despite these caveats, it is clear that noradrenergic systems are highly responsive to stressful stimuli and mediate a variety of stress-related physiological, behavioral, and cognitive processes. These observations suggest that, at the very least, the LC and other noradrenergic systems may contribute to certain *affect-independent* components of stress-related disorders.

Norepinephrine and PTSD

Among stress-related disorders, the strongest case for an involvement of noradrenergic systems can be made for PTSD (for review, *see* Ref. *67*). For example, PTSD is associated with the dysregulation of a variety of processes influenced by central noradrenergic systems. This includes dysregulation of arousal and long-term memory as well as working memory, attention and other PFC-dependent processes (*68–70*). As reviewed, NE not only acutely modulates a variety of behavioral processes but also can induce long-term alterations in plasticity-related gene transcription, neuronal reactivity, and memory. Thus, the activation of central noradrenergic systems under intense/traumatic stressful events could contribute to certain long-lasting behavioral attributes of PTSD that result from trauma exposure.

The described work indicates that via actions at β-receptors located within the basolateral amygdala, NE strengthens memories for emotionally arousing events. It has been posited that this mechanism may contribute to certain symptoms associated with PTSD, including long-lasting and intrusive memories. Consistent with this hypothesis, clinical studies indicated that the administration of the β-antagonist propranolol within close proximity of a traumatic event, or while remembering that event, lessens behavioral and physiological symptoms of PTSD (71–73).

Beyond long-term alterations in neuronal circuitry induced by NE at the time of a traumatic event, evidence further indicates that noradrenergic systems may be dysregulated in PTSD. Specifically, noradrenergic systems appear to be hyperreactive in PTSD (for review, see Ref. 74). Hyperactivity of peripheral NE systems is observed in response to auditory reminders of trauma (75) and in response to pharmacological challenge with the α_2-antagonist yohimbine (74). Based on the preclinical evidence reviewed, it is expected that excessive activity/reactivity of noradrenergic systems in PTSD would have a broad impact on arousal, memory, and attentional systems. Thus, noradrenergic hyperactivity could well contribute to a variety of symptoms associated with PTSD. Consistent with this, α_2-antagonist challenge (to increase NE release) has been documented to cause both panic attacks and flashbacks in a large proportion of the PTSD patients, effects not seen with either placebo or yohimbine treatment in control subjects (74). Moreover, α_1-antagonist treatment has been demonstrated to reduce trauma-related nightmares and other sleep-related disturbances seen in PTSD (76,77).

SUMMARY

A defining feature of stressful conditions is the need to confront challenging, or threatening, conditions. Associated with this is the need to acquire and process sensory information rapidly and efficiently to make an accurate response selection. Long-term survival may be dependent on behavioral plasticity to better contend with, or avoid, a threatening environmental stimulus when it is reencountered. Evidence reviewed in this chapter argues for a prominent role of the LC-noradrenergic system in a variety of physiological, cognitive, and behavioral processes associated with information processing, response selection, and behavioral plasticity. Stress is associated with elevated rates of NE release. Thus, it is not surprising that evidence indicates an involvement of the LC-noradrenergic system in stressor-induced alterations in a variety of these processes (e.g., arousal, working memory, high-arousal-related memory, IEG expression). These actions of the LC-noradrenergic system are likely independent of affective valence (e.g., appetitive vs. aversive) and are dependent only on whether a stimulus is salient (relevant) to the organism.

Under normal conditions, the long-term actions of NE, whether at the level of the gene (IEGs), neural ensembles (LTP), or behavior (memory) likely facilitate rapid and accurate response selection when a stimulus is reencountered. However, under extreme conditions associated with extreme activation of the LC-NE system, these long-term changes may result in an excessive sensitivity of arousal, memory, or other systems. In addition, these extreme conditions may result in a sensitization of the LC-NE system to otherwise innocuous stimuli. In support of these hypotheses, available evidence indicates hyperactivity/reactivity of noradrenergic systems in PTSD. Moreover, symptoms associated with PTSD are reduced by pharmacological interference with noradrenergic neurotransmission. Combined, this information indicates a prominent role for central noradrenergic systems in PTSD.

ACKNOWLEDGMENTS

The author gratefully acknowledge support by the University of Wisconsin Graduate School and Public Health Service grants DA10681, DA00389, and MH62359.

REFERENCES

1. Cannon, W. B. (1914) The emergency function of the adrenal medulla in pain and the major emotions. Am J Physiol 33, 356–72.
2. Selye, H. (1946) The general adaptation syndrome and the diseases of adaptation. J Clin Endocrinol Metab 6, 117–230.
3. Selye, H. (1975) Confusion and controversy in the stress field. J Human Stress 1, 37–44.
4. Foote, S. L., Bloom, F. E., and Aston-Jones, G. (1983) Nucleus locus ceruleus: new evidence of anatomical and physiological specificity. Physiol Rev 63, 844–914.
5. Berridge, C. W., and Waterhouse, B. D. (2003) The locus coeruleus-noradrenergic system: modulation of behavioral state and state-dependent cognitive processes. Brain Res Brain Res Rev 42, 33–84.
6. Hobson, J. A., McCarley, R. W., and Wyzinski, P. W. (1975) Sleep cycle oscillation: reciprocal discharge by two brainstem neuronal groups. Science 189, 55–58.
7. Foote, S. L., Aston-Jones, G., and Bloom, F. E. (1980) Impulse activity of locus coeruleus neurons in awake rats and monkeys is a function of sensory stimulation and arousal . Proc Natl Acad Sci U S A 77, 3033–37.
8. Aston-Jones, G., and Bloom, F. E. (1981) Activity of norepinephrine-containing locus coeruleus neurons in behaving rats anticipates fluctuations in the sleep-waking cycle. J Neurosci 1, 876–886.
9. Rajkowski, J., Kubiak, P., and Aston-Jones, G. (1994) Locus coeruleus activity in monkey: phasic and tonic changes are associated with altered vigilance. Brain Res Bull 35, 607–16.
10. Aston-Jones, G., and Bloom, F. E. (1981) Norepinephrine-containing locus coeruleus neurons in behaving rats exhibit pronounced responses to non-noxious environmental stimuli. J Neurosci 1, 887–900.
11. Valentino, R. J., and Foote, S. L. (1987) Corticotropin-releasing factor disrupts sensory responses of brain noradrenergic neurons. Neuroendocrinology 45, 28–36.
12. Stone, E. A. (1987) Central cyclic-AMP-linked noradrenergic receptors: new findings on properties as related to the actions of stress. Neurosci Biobehav Rev 11, 391–98.
13. Abercrombie, E. D., and Jacobs, B. L. (1987) Single-unit response of noradrenergic neurons in the locus coeruleus of freely moving cats. II. Adaptation to chronically presented stressful stimuli. J Neurosci 7, 2844–48.
14. Nisenbaum, L. K., Zigmond, M. J., Sved, A. F., and Abercrombie, E. D. (1991) Prior exposure to chronic stress results in enhanced synthesis and release of hippocampal norepinephrine in response to a novel stressor. J Neurosci 11, 1478–84.

15. Pavcovich, L. A., Cancela, L. M., Volosin, M., Molina, V. A., and Ramirez, O. A. (1990) Chronic stress-induced changes in locus coeruleus neuronal activity. Brain Res Bull 24, 293–96.

16. Stone, E. A., Freedman, L. S., and Morgano, L. E. (1978) Brain and adrenal tyrosine hydroxylase activity after chronic footshock stress. Pharmacol Biochem Behav 9, 551–53.

17. Finlay, J. M., Zigmond, M. J., and Abercrombie, E. D. (1995) Increased dopamine and norepinephrine release in medial prefrontal cortex induced by acute and chronic stress: effects of diazepam. Neuroscience 64, 619–28.

18. Simson, P. E., and Weiss, J. M. (1988) Altered activity of the locus coeruleus in an animal model of depression. Neuropsychopharmacology 1, 287–295.

19. Feenstra, M. G., Teske, G., Botterblom, M. H., and de Bruin, J. P. (1999) Dopamine and noradrenaline release in the prefrontal cortex of rats during classical aversive and appetitive conditioning to a contextual stimulus: interference by novelty effects. Neurosci Lett 272, 179–82.

20. Feenstra, M. G. (2000) Dopamine and noradrenaline release in the prefrontal cortex in relation to unconditioned and conditioned stress and reward. Prog Brain Res 126, 133–63.

21. Steriade, M., Domich, L., and Oakson, G. (1986) Reticularis thalami neurons revisited: activity changes during shifts in states of vigilance. J Neurosci 6, 68–81.

22. McCormick, D. A., and Bal, T. (1997) Sleep and arousal: thalamocortical mechanisms. Annu Rev Neurosci 20, 185–215.

23. McCormick, D. A., Pape, H. C., Williamson, A. (1991) Actions of norepinephrine in the cerebral cortex and thalamus: implications for function of the central noradrenergic system. Prog Brain Res 88, 293–305.

24. Adams, L. M., and Foote, S. L. (1988) Effects of locally infused pharmacological agents on spontaneous and sensory-evoked activity of locus coeruleus neurons. Brain Res Bull 21, 395–400.

25. Berridge, C. W., and Foote, S. L. (1991) Effects of locus coeruleus activation on electroencephalographic activity in neocortex and hippocampus. J Neurosci 11, 3135–45.

26. España, R. A., and Berridge, C. W. (2006) Organization of noradrenergic efferents to arousal-related basal forebrain structures. J Comp Neurol 496, 668–83.

27. Berridge, C. W., and España, R. A. (2000) Synergistic sedative effects of noradrenergic alpha(1)- and beta- receptor blockade on forebrain electroencephalographic and behavioral indices. Neuroscience 99, 495–505.

28. Page, M. E., Berridge, C. W., Foote, S. L., and Valentino, R. J. (1993) Corticotropin-releasing factor in the locus coeruleus mediates EEG activation associated with hypotensive stress. Neurosci Lett 164, 81–84.

29. Devilbiss, D. M., and Waterhouse, B. D. (2000) Norepinephrine exhibits two distinct profiles of action on sensory cortical neuron responses to excitatory synaptic stimuli. Synapse 37, 273–82.

30. Stanton, P. K., and Sarvey, J. M. (1985) Depletion of norepinephrine, but not serotonin, reduces long-term potentiation in the dentate gyrus of rat hippocampal slices. J Neurosci 5, 2169–76.

31. Hopkins, W. F., and Johnston, D. (1984) Frequency-dependent noradrenergic modulation of long-term potentiation in the hippocampus. Science 226, 350–52.

32. Stanton, P. K., and Sarvey, J. M. (1987) Norepinephrine regulates long-term potentiation of both the population spike and dendritic EPSP in hippocampal dentate gyrus. Brain Res Bull 18, 115–19.

33. Heginbotham, L. R., and Dunwiddie, T. V. (1991) Long-term increases in the evoked population spike in the CA1 region of rat hippocampus induced by beta-adrenergic receptor activation. J Neurosci 11, 2519–27.

34. Harley, C. W., and Sara, S. J. (1992) Locus coeruleus bursts induced by glutamate trigger delayed perforant path spike amplitude potentiation in the dentate gyrus. Exp Brain Res 89, 581–87.

35. Chaulk, P. C., and Harley, C. W. (1998) Intracerebroventricular norepinephrine potentiation of the perforant path-evoked potential in dentate gyrus of anesthetized and awake rats: A role for both alpha- and beta-adrenoceptor activation. Brain Res 787, 59–70.

36. Kitchigina, V., Vankov, A., Harley, C., and Sara, S. J. (1997) Novelty-elicited, noradrenaline-dependent enhancement of excitability in the dentate gyrus. Eur J Neurosci 9, 41–47.

37. Kirkwood, A., Rozas, C., Kirkwood, J., Perez, F., and Bear, M. F. (1999) Modulation of long-term synaptic depression in visual cortex by acetylcholine and norepinephrine. J Neurosci 19, 1599–1609.

38. Milbrandt, J. (1987) A nerve growth factor-induced gene encodes a possible transcriptional regulatory factor. Science 238, 797–99.

39. Gubits, R. M., Smith, T. M., Fairhurst, J. L., and Yu, H. (1989) Adrenergic receptors mediate changes in c-fos mRNA levels in brain. Brain Res Mol Brain Res 6, 39–45.

40. Bing, G. Y., Filer, D., Miller, J. C., and Stone, E. A. (1991) Noradrenergic activation of immediate early genes in rat cerebral cortex. Brain Res Mol Brain Res 11, 43–46.

41. Bing, G., Stone, E. A., Zhang, Y., and Filer, D. (1992) Immunohistochemical studies of noradrenergic-induced expression of c- fos in the rat. CNS Brain Res 592, 57–62.

42. Stone, E. A., Zhang, Y., John, S., Filer, D., and Bing, G. (1993) Effect of locus coeruleus lesion on c-fos expression in the cerebral cortex caused by yohimbine injection or stress. Brain Res 603, 181–85.

43. Mehta, M. A., Sahakian, B. J., and Robbins, T. W. (2001) Comparative psychopharmacology of methylphenidate and related drugs in human volunteers, patients with ADHD, and experimental animals. Solanto, M. V., Arnsten, A. F. T., and Castellanos, F. X., ed., Stimulant Drugs and ADHD: Basic and Clinical Neuroscience. New York: Oxford University Press; 303–31.

44. Carli, M., Robbins, T. W., Evenden, J. L., and Everitt, B. J. (1983) Effects of lesions to ascending noradrenergic neurones on performance of a 5-choice serial reaction task in rats; implications for theories of dorsal noradrenergic bundle function based on selective attention and arousal. Behav Brain Res 9(3), 361–80.

45. Lorden, J. F., Callahan, M., and Dawson, R., Jr.. (1980) Depletion of central catecholamines alters amphetamine- and fenfluramine-induced taste aversions in the rat. J Comp Physiol Psychol 94, 99–114.

46. Selden, N. R., Robbins, T. W., and Everitt, B. J. (1990) Enhanced behavioral conditioning to context and impaired behavioral and neuroendocrine responses to conditioned stimuli following ceruleocortical noradrenergic lesions: support for an attentional hypothesis of central noradrenergic function. J Neurosci 10, 531–39.

47. Selden, N. R., Everitt, B. J., and Robbins, T. W. (1991) Telencephalic but not diencephalic noradrenaline depletion enhances behavioural but not endocrine measures of fear conditioning to contextual stimuli. Behav Brain Res 43, 139–54.

48. Vankov, A., Herve-Minvielle, A., and Sara, S. J. (1995) Response to novelty and its rapid habituation in locus coeruleus neurons of the freely exploring rat. Eur J Neurosci 7, 1180–87.

49. Devauges, V., and Sara, S. J. (1990) Activation of the noradrenergic system facilitates an attentional shift in the rat,. Behav Brain Res 39, 19–28.

50. Arnsten, A. F., Segal, D. S., Loughlin, S. E., and Roberts, D. C. (1981) Evidence for an interaction of opioid and noradrenergic locus coeruleus systems in the regulation of environmental stimulus-directed behavior. Brain Res 222, 351–63.

51. Berridge, C. W., and Dunn, A. J. (1989) Restraint-stress-induced changes in exploratory behavior appear to be mediated by norepinephrine-stimulated release of CRF. J Neurosci 9, 3513–21.

52. Clayton, E. C., Rajkowski, J., Cohen, J. D., and Aston-Jones, G. (2004) Phasic activation of monkey locus ceruleus neurons by simple decisions in a forced-choice task. J Neurosci 24, 9914–20.

53. Arnsten, A. F. (2007) Catecholamine and second messenger influences on prefrontal cortical networks of "representational knowledge": a rational bridge between genetics and the symptoms of mental illness. Cereb Cortex 17(suppl 1), i6–15.

54. Arnsten, A. F., and Goldman-Rakic, P. S. (1998) Noise stress impairs prefrontal cortical cognitive function in monkeys: evidence for a hyperdopaminergic mechanism. Arch Gen Psychiatry 55, 362–68.

55. Birnbaum, S., Gobeske, K. T., Auerbach, J., Taylor, J. R., and Arnsten, A. F. (1999) A role for norepinephrine in stress-induced cognitive deficits: alpha-1-adrenoceptor mediation in the prefrontal cortex. Biol Psychiatry 46, 1266–74.

56. McGaugh, J. L. (2000) Memory—a century of consolidation. Science 287, 248–51.

57. Hatfield, T., and McGaugh, J. L. (1999) Norepinephrine infused into the basolateral amygdala posttraining enhances retention in a spatial water maze task. Neurobiol Learn Mem 71, 232–39.

58. Ferry, B., and McGaugh, J. L. (1999) Clenbuterol administration into the basolateral amygdala post-training enhances retention in an inhibitory avoidance task. Neurobiol Learn Mem 72, 8–12.

59. Ferry, B., Roozendaal, B., and McGaugh, J. L. (1999) Role of norepinephrine in mediating stress hormone regulation of long- term memory storage: a critical involvement of the amygdala. Biol Psychiatry 46, 1140–52.

60. Quirarte, G. L., Roozendaal, B., and McGaugh, J. L. (1997) Glucocorticoid enhancement of memory storage involves noradrenergic activation in the basolateral amygdala. Proc Natl Acad Sci U S A 94, 14048–53.

61. Ferry, B., Roozendaal, B., and McGaugh, J. L. (1999) Involvement of alpha1-adrenoceptors in the basolateral amygdala in modulation of memory storage. Eur J Pharmacol 372, 9–16.

62. Ferry, B., Roozendaal, B., and McGaugh, J. L. (1999) Basolateral amygdala noradrenergic influences on memory storage are mediated by an interaction between beta- and alpha1-adrenoceptors. J Neurosci 19, 5119–23.

63. Cahill, L., Prins, B., Weber, M., and McGaugh, J. L. (1994) Beta-adrenergic activation and memory for emotional events. Nature 371, 702–4.

64. Dudai, Y. (2004) The neurobiology of consolidations, or, how stable is the engram?. Annu Rev Psychol 55, 51–86.

65. Debiec, J., and Ledoux, J. E. (2004) Disruption of reconsolidation but not consolidation of auditory fear conditioning by noradrenergic blockade in the amygdala. Neuroscience 129, 267–72.

66. Charney, D. S., Heninger, G. R., and Redmond, D. E. Jr.. (1983) Yohimbine induced anxiety and increased noradrenergic function in humans: effects of diazepam and clonidine. Life Sci 33, 19–29.

67. Southwick, S. M., Bremner, J. D., Rasmusson, A., Morgan, C. A., III, Arnsten, A., and Charney, D. S. (1999) Role of norepinephrine in the pathophysiology and treatment of posttraumatic stress disorder. Biol Psychiatry 46, 1192–1204.

68. Barrett, D. H., Green, M. L., Morris, R., Giles, W. H., and Croft, J. B. (1996) Cognitive functioning and posttraumatic stress disorder. Am J Psychiatry 153, 1492–94.

69. Bremner, J. D., Scott, T. M., Delaney, R. C., et al. (1993) Deficits in short-term memory in posttraumatic stress disorder. Am J Psychiatry 150, 1015–19.

70. Clark, C. R., McFarlane, A. C., Morris, P., et al. (2003) Cerebral function in posttraumatic stress disorder during verbal working memory updating: a positron emission tomography study. Biol Psychiatry 53, 474–81.

71. Pitman, R. K., Sanders, K. M., Zusman, R. M. et al. (2002) Pilot study of secondary prevention of posttraumatic stress disorder with propranolol. Biol Psychiatry 51, 189–92.

72. Vaiva, G., Ducrocq, F., Jezequel, K. et al. (2003) Immediate treatment with propranolol decreases posttraumatic stress disorder two months after trauma. Biol Psychiatry 54, 947–49.

73. Brunet, A., Orr, S. P., Tremblay, J., Robertson, K., Nader, K., and Pitman, R. K. (2008) Effect of post-retrieval propranolol on psychophysiologic responding during subsequent script-driven traumatic imagery in post-traumatic stress disorder. J Psychiatr Res 42, 503–6.

74. Southwick, S. M., Krystal, J. H., Morgan, C. A., et al. (1993) Abnormal noradrenergic function in posttraumatic stress disorder. Arch Gen Psychiatry 50(4):266–74.

75. Blanchard, E. B., Kolb, L. C., Prins, A., Gates, S., and McCoy, G. C. (1991) Changes in plasma norepinephrine to combat-related stimuli among Vietnam veterans with posttraumatic stress disorder. J Nerv Ment Dis 179, 371–73.

76. Taylor, F., and Raskind, M. A. (2002) The alpha1-adrenergic antagonist prazosin improves sleep and nightmares in civilian trauma posttraumatic stress disorder. J Clin Psychopharmacol 22, 82–85.

77. Raskind, M. A., Peskind, E. R., Hoff, D. J., et al. (2007) A parallel group placebo controlled study of prazosin for trauma nightmares and sleep disturbance in combat veterans with post-traumatic stress disorder. Biol Psychiatry 61, 928–34.

78. Berridge, C. W., Page, M. E., Valentino R. J., and Foote S. L. (1993) Effects of locus coeruleus inactivation on electroencephalographic activity in neocortex and hippocampus, Neuroscience 55, 381–393.

11

Effect of Stress on Sleep and Its Relationship to Post-Traumatic Stress Disorder

L. D. Sanford and X. Tang

CONTENTS

INTRODUCTION
SLEEP DISTURBANCES IN POST-TRAUMATIC STRESS
    DISORDER
EFFECTS OF STRESS ON SLEEP IN ANIMALS
STRESS, SLEEP, AND THE DEVELOPMENT OF PTSD
CONDITIONED FEAR AND ALTERATIONS IN SLEEP
FEAR EXTINCTION AND SLEEP
ROLE OF THE AMYGDALA IN MODULATING
    THE EFFECTS OF STRESS ON SLEEP
CRH, STRESS, AND ALTERATIONS IN SLEEP
SUMMARY
REFERENCES

Abstract

Stress-induced alterations in sleep have been linked to the development of post-traumatic stress disorder (PTSD), and sleep complaints and disturbances in arousal are continuing symptoms in patients. PTSD-related changes in sleep have not been fully characterized but appear to involve persistent disturbances in both rapid eye movement (REM) and non-REM (NREM). Intense conditioned fear training, which may model PTSD in rodents, can produce reductions in REM without recovery as well as significant alterations in NREM that may vary with mouse and rat strains. These variants of conditioned fear paradigms and strain differences have not been fully exploited, but they appear to hold promise for modeling responses to stress that may provide insight into the role sleep

From: *Post-Traumatic Stress Disorder: Basic Science and Clinical Practice*
Edited by: P. J. Shiromani et al., DOI: 10.1007/978-1-60327-329-9_11
© Humana Press, a part of Springer Science + Business Media, LLC 2009

plays in the neurobiology of PTSD. The amygdala and corticotropin-releasing hormone (CRH) play significant roles in regulating the stress response and have been implicated in PTSD. Recent work suggests that the amygdala and CRH may also play roles in regulating stress-induced changes in arousal and sleep. This chapter reviews the effects of stress on sleep with a specific emphasis on factors that may be important in modeling PTSD.

Key Words: Amygdala, conditioned fear, non-rapid eye movement sleep, rapid eye movement sleep, sleep, stress.

INTRODUCTION

Stress can have a significant, long-lasting negative impact on health (1), and severe stress has been linked to the genesis of post-traumatic stress disorder (PTSD) and other anxiety and mood disorders. However, stressors are commonly encountered in daily life without producing permanent or pathological changes. Even the traumatic life events that can give rise to PTSD do so in only a percentage of the population (2,3), whereas the majority may cope with similar situations with only transitory effects. The difference between successful and unsuccessful coping with stress and whether it has transitory or lasting effects can vary with characteristics of the stressful event, including its duration, intensity (4), predictability (5), and controllability (6). The effects also may involve individual differences in resilience and vulnerability to stressful events (7).

Stress-related conditioning processes are thought to play significant roles in the development of anxiety disorders (8,9) and thus provide a significant pathway by which traumatic events can produce lasting changes in behavior. Specifically, fear conditioning is thought to play a significant role in the development of PTSD (10,11). However, it is important to note that conditioned fear also can underlie adaptive behavior that typically is extinguished when the fear-inducing situation is removed. Fear "extinction" is considered a type of new learning that inhibits subsequent fear without erasing the original memory for fear conditioning (12). It is the failure of extinction that has been linked to persisting symptoms of PTSD (13).

Stress also has an impact on sleep, and traumatic life events virtually always produce at least temporary sleep disturbances that may include insomnia or subjective sleep problems (14). The persistence of sleep disturbances after a traumatic event may be predictive of future development of emotional and physical disorders (14). Sleep disturbances are also a core feature of PTSD, and insomnia is the most common grievance (15). PTSD also is characterized by disturbed REM, hypervigilance to unfamiliar stimuli, and stereotypical anxiety dreams (16,17). These factors suggest that disturbed sleep may be involved in the development of PTSD as well as being one of its persisting symptoms, and that determining how the sleep and arousal system are impacted by stressful events could lead to new avenues for understanding and treating stress-related disorders, including PTSD.

Our work over the last several years has focused on examining the effects of stress on sleep using a variety of stress paradigms but primarily aimed at understanding the effects of stress-related learning and stressful memories on sleep using variations of conditioned fear and other stress-motivated paradigms. We have also examined the role of the amygdala, a region strongly implicated in the regulation of stress and in PTSD, in regulating spontaneous and stress-induced alterations in arousal and sleep. In this chapter, we provide a general overview of the relationship between stress and sleep and its regulation by the amygdala, with a primary focus on our work and that of others examining the effects of fear conditioning on sleep. However, the relationship between stress and sleep as they relate to PTSD and other stress-related disorders is a significantly understudied problem, and current work, including our own, has a number of weaknesses in adequately modeling the effects of stress on sleep as it relates to the development of stress-related disorders. These are also discussed.

SLEEP DISTURBANCES IN POST-TRAUMATIC STRESS DISORDER

The nature of the sleep disturbance in patients with PTSD has been reviewed (16,17), and we only briefly address the topic here. Much of the work on sleep disturbances in PTSD has focused on REM, and some early polysomnographic studies reported a heightened tendency to enter and remain in REM in patients with PTSD. Among these studies, Greenberg, Pearlman, and Gampel (18) reported shortened REM latency (time from sleep onset to the first REM period) and increased REM density (number of rapid eye movements/total REM time) in Vietnam veterans with "war neurosis," and van der Kolk, Blitz, Burr, Sherry, and Hartmann reported increased REM percentage (total REM time/total sleep time) in a group of elderly ex-prisoners of war with PTSD (19). Other early studies reported reduced REM in PTSD (e.g., 20).

Ross et al. (21,22) found abnormalities in the internal structure of REM rather than in the amount of REM in patients with combat-related PTSD. Tonic REM measures, indications of physiological processes that occur continuously throughout an REM period, showed internight variability and did not reliably discriminate PTSD patients from normal control subjects. However, measures of REM phasic events, exemplified by REM density, were elevated in PTSD compared to control subjects on the adaptation night and on two subsequent recording nights. Other researchers (e.g., 23,24) have observed increased REM density in PTSD patients; however, increased REM density was also found in patients with both PTSD and major depression and with depression alone compared to healthy controls.

Mellman et al. (25,26) have made the point that studies conducted months, years, or even decades after the traumatic event may be influenced by factors not related to the development of PTSD, and few studies have examined sleep in the initial stages of PTSD. One early polysomnographic study (20) of three patients hospitalized for "acute combat fatigue" reported that sleep was reduced in duration and consisted primarily of stage 2 sleep with an absence of stage 4 sleep. REM episodes were described as "rare and short." The electromyograph (EMG) was reported as usually high, with numerous body movements and bursts of tachycardia occurring during the night. However, even this study was potentially influenced by other factors as the patients had experienced chronic partial sleep deprivation before they experienced a breakdown prior to the sleep studies being conducted (20).

Mellman and his colleagues (25,26) conducted more extensive polysomnographic studies within a month of the traumatic experience. These studies generally found a more fragmented pattern of REM characterized by shorter average duration REM episodes before shifting stage or awakening in PTSD patients compared to patients without PTSD and a nontraumatized comparison group. There was also a greater number of REM sleep episodes in the PTSD patients than in patients who experienced trauma without developing PTSD. These findings led Mellman et al. to speculate that intact REM may perform an adaptive function in aiding in the processing of the memory for trauma. We also have suggested that REM may play an adaptive function in recovery from stress in our work with animals (27).

The findings of changes in NREM in PTSD have also been emphasized. Specifically, both visually scored delta sleep and electroencephalographic (EEG) delta amplitude are reduced in patients with PTSD (reviewed in 16). Neylan, Otte, Yehuda, and Marmar (16) suggested that the changes in NREM and delta may involve persistent increases in corticotropin-releasing hormone (CRH) activity coupled with either enhanced negative feedback or downregulated CRH receptors. Taken together, the studies on sleep in PTSD patients suggest that that it will be important to determine alterations in REM and NREM as well as microarchitectural changes in each state to fully understand the changes in sleep that occur after traumatic stress.

EFFECTS OF STRESS ON SLEEP IN ANIMALS

Animal experiments have repeatedly demonstrated that stressful experiences during wakefulness can have a significant impact on subsequent sleep. Sleep has been recorded after a great number of stressors, including avoidable foot shock (28), restraint (29,30), water maze (31), exposure to novel objects (32), open field (33,34), ether exposure (35), cage change (33,34), and social stress (36). This work provides descriptive data of the effects of a variety of stressors on sleep and demonstrates that the extent of the changes in arousal and sleep varies with the type and intensity of stressor that is used. Exposure to these stressors typically induces a stress-induced period of arousal (37) followed by subsequent rebound sleep (increases in REM or NREM) that occur at various latencies after the stressor is removed. REM appears to be particularly susceptible to the effects of stress, and an initial decrease in REM is observed in response to all stressors (presented in the light-on sleep period) of which we are aware.

While there are many unanswered questions regarding the relationship between sleep and the development of PTSD in humans, the rebound REM or NREM found after various stressors is not consistent with the decreased REM and decreased delta sleep reported in PTSD patients after the initial traumatic stressor is no longer experienced. The rebound sleep also occurs in response to relatively mild stressors that animals may experience repeatedly, thus suggesting that this sleep response to a stressor is not indicative of developing pathology. An example of a repeated mild stressor is the routine cage changes that experimental animals experience as part of normal husbandry and that produce significant alterations in their sleeping and living environments. The stress induced by cage change may be related to fear and novelty (38), a view supported by behavioral and physiological observations, including increased rearing and grooming, increased exploratory behavior, and increased heart rate and blood pressure in rats after a cage change (38). These responses are consistent with recurring cage changes in animals on weekly change schedules, suggesting that the animals do not habituate over time (38).

Another example of a mild stressor is open-field exposure, which is thought to produce anxiety and an opportunity for exploration. Sleep after exposure to an open field also is characterized by an initial decrease followed by an increase in REM (33). We showed that the increases in REM are positively correlated to the amount of exploration in the open field in mice (33), which we have suggested may reflect an adaptive process of small rodents as they cope with potential challenges posed by a new environment (33). Thus, poststress increases in REM and sleep, in general, may play a positive functional role in responses to stressors that are experienced during wakefulness.

STRESS, SLEEP, AND THE DEVELOPMENT OF PTSD

The preceding discussion reveals some of the more significant problems in studying the effects of stress on sleep in animals with respect to modeling the development of PTSD. That is, there is a paucity of data describing the immediate and short-term effects of traumatic stress on sleep in humans, and the relationship of sleep disturbances to the development of PTSD is not fully known. It is also not known whether the initial stress-induced alterations in sleep are the same as those that occur in later stages of PTSD or how they may be modified over time by subsequent life experiences. In addition, work in animals has generally focused on acute stress manipulations and their immediate effects on sleep. Potential longer-term changes in sleep and their relationship to behaviors indicative of PTSD have received much less attention. These factors suggest that refinement is needed in the way that stress and sleep are studied if successful models are to be developed.

Stressors may be defined as stimuli that disrupt homeostasis (39), whereas the stress response is an attempt by the organism to restore homeostasis (37). In a review, Yehuda and LeDoux (2) emphasized that understanding the neurobiology of PTSD will require examining "atypical" responses to stress as well as determining individual differences in pre- and post-traumatic risk factors related to the genesis of PTSD and to the failure to restore physiological homeostasis. Obvious corollaries of these requirements are the need to understand normal responses to stressors as well as how the stress response may normally vary among individuals in order to identify those that are atypical.

We have suggested that the subsequent increases in sleep after many stressors may reflect restoration of homeostasis as the stress response follows its normal course *(27)*. If this hypothesis is true, identifying either stressful situations or individual responses to those situations characterized by lack of recovery REM and abnormal changes in NREM compared to those reported after many stressors may reflect the failure of the stress response to restore homeostasis and may thus be a factor in the development of pathology. This also would be consistent with findings of decreased REM *(20,25,26)* and abnormalities in NREM *(16)* in PTSD patients.

Genetic differences are an important factor in the development of stress-related pathology as approximately 20–30% of individuals who experience traumatic events may develop PTSD, whereas others do not appear to suffer significant long-lasting effects *(3,40)*. A few attempts to develop animal models that better represent individual differences in clinical populations have included selecting low and high responders to stressors in outbred rat strains *(3,41)*. Examining individual differences has not often been considered in animal studies of stress and sleep or of sleep in general *(42)*. An approach we have taken is to compare inbred strains, which are genetically identical within strain but that vary genetically and phenotypically across strain, to identify animals that vary in level of responsiveness to conditioned fear and other stressors. Our work in mice and rats has demonstrated that strains that exhibited greater anxiety-like behaviors in response to challenges in wakefulness exhibited correspondingly greater and longer duration alterations in sleep after training with inescapable shock and after fearful cues *(43)* and contexts *(44)*. In general, more "anxious" mouse strains also showed greater decreases in sleep in situations with unlearned responses, including after exposure to an open field *(33)*, after cage change, and after novel objects placed in the home cage *(32)*. These findings led us to suggest that mouse strains that have greater emotional responses when faced with various types of environmental challenges also have greater reductions in subsequent sleep *(32,33)*.

The following section describes work examining the effects of conditioned fear on sleep and some variants of the paradigm that show promise for producing alterations in sleep that differ from those seen with many of the stressors that have been examined.

CONDITIONED FEAR AND ALTERATIONS IN SLEEP

The conditioned fear paradigm is a classical conditioning procedure in which an association is formed between an explicit neutral stimulus (generally a light or auditory stimulus) or situational context and an aversive stimulus (usually foot shock). In typical experiments, the light or auditory stimulus serves as an initially emotionally neutral conditioned stimulus (CS) and the foot shock as an aversive unconditioned stimulus (US). Through pairing of the CS and US, an association is made, resulting in the previously neutral CS having fear-inducing qualities similar to those of the US and producing similar physiologic outcomes. Studies on conditioned fear have typically measured immediate responses to fearful cues or contexts or their effects on modifying responses to other stimuli. Thus, responses such as behavioral freezing (absence of all movement except respiration) (e.g., *45*) and fear-potentiated startle amplitude are well established, as are the effects on a variety of physiological signals indicative of fear (reviewed in *46*). The resemblance of the behavioral effects of fear conditioning to the symptoms of anxiety and other affective disorders has led to fear conditioning being an important model for examining how stressful and fearful memories can have an impact on behavior, and it is of particular interest as a factor in the development of anxiety disorders, including PTSD *(1,6)*

The effects of fear conditioning on sleep have received attention only in the last few years. A few studies have examined the relationship between conditioned fear and sleep, with the goal of understanding the potential role of sleep in fear memory consolidation. These studies have typically used training procedures with single, or at most a few, tone-shock or context-shock pairings as this type of paradigm may be more conducive to studies of memory consolidation *(47)*. For example, with a single-shock presentation procedure, Graves, Heller, Pack, and Abel *(47)* found that total sleep deprivation performed by a gentle handling procedure impaired memory consolidation for contextual fear when sleep was deprived from 0 to 5 h after training but had no effect when sleep was deprived from 5 to 10 h after training. Cued fear was not altered by sleep deprivation in either time window. More recently, Hellman and Abel *(48)* found that NREM was increased by approximately 1 h over the 24 h after training in fear-conditioned mice compared to those exposed to conditioning stimuli without shock or to an immediate shock treatment that did not produce conditioned fear. In addition, mice experiencing conditioning stimuli alone had more delta power during NREM, whereas those receiving fear conditioning had less theta power during REM. An important point made by Hellman and Abel is that even a single trial of conditioned fear can produce alterations in sleep and EEG spectra that can persist for up to 24 h, whereas the behavioral effects (e.g., freezing) are much more transitory.

The studies described above suggested that sleep plays a role in the consolidation of fear memory. As conditioned fear typically extinguishes when the fear-inducing situation is removed, it is unlikely that brief, stressful experiences will produce the lasting changes necessary for the development of persisting changes in behavior. Indeed, the studies described above used training procedures with mild or brief foot shock stress and induced fear responses that typically are readily extinguishable with reexposure to the CS without reoccurrence of the US. By comparison, our own work is aimed at modeling and understanding how stress-related learning and memories can lead to persistent changes in behavior that are resistant to extinction and the potential role that stress-induced alterations in sleep play in those changes. As such, we have used training procedures with multiple-shock presentations and are beginning to examine the role of other stress parameters such as shock intensity and controllability in the persisting effects of stress. Thus, a distinction should be made between the procedures used in studies examining the relationship between sleep and fear memory consolidation and the procedures of studies aimed at understanding the lasting effects of traumatic stressors for which the memories are resistant to extinction.

The models we use have similarities to learned helplessness in that mice or rats are placed in a situation in which they repeatedly receive inescapable foot shock and cannot learn an adaptive response. In learned helplessness, rats exposed to inescapable foot shock later fail to learn an escape response in a situation for which their actions could let them avoid foot shock (reviewed in *49*). These rats also may respond more anxiously in behavioral anxiety tests, and they may have greater responses to drugs of abuse. The training portion of the paradigm we use is essentially identical to training in learned helplessness with the difference that we usually do not test for performance on other tests. Instead, the animal is "reminded" of the shock situation in a manner similar to testing in cued or contextual fear; most importantly, we record the EEG and EMG as well as other physiological indicators across conditions. This gives a continual readout of changes in the animal's behavioral state after experiencing the stressor. This continual readout in the form of sleep and wake states and EEG spectra provides indicators of the longer-term effects of stress that may reflect the successful or unsuccessful resolution of the stress response and could ultimately provide predictors for changes in sleep involved in the development of PTSD.

Adrien, Dugovic, and Martin *(50)* provided the first report, of which we are aware, that examined the effects of learned helplessness training on sleep. In their study, rats were presented with 60 inescapable foot shocks of relatively high intensity (0.8 mA) and duration (15 s) over the course of 1 h. Compared to handling control rats that experienced the shock chamber without receiving foot shock, rats trained with inescapable shock showed greater REM latency, and during the first 3 h after training, shock-trained rats also showed reduced REM and increased light NREM compared to the control group and their own baseline sleep. Afterward, REM returned to control amounts, but no REM rebound was observed in recordings that night or the following day. Light NREM also was enhanced over the dark period recordings. This suggests that this paradigm results in significant differences in poststress sleep compared to most stressors described in the literature.

Our work with multitrial shock training procedures also has found significant posttraining alterations in sleep architecture in mice *(43,44)* and rats *(27)*, although to date we have typically used less-intense shock of shorter duration. The most important outcome of this work has been the demonstration that cues and contexts associated with the foot shock can produce changes in sleep that are directionally similar to those produced when foot shock is presented. Thus, fear-conditioned stimuli (reminders of the shock) can produce significant changes in sleep similar to those when the foot shock stressor was presented just as they can produce the more immediate signs of fear that have been amply demonstrated.

In mice, multiple-shock training trials in both cued (43) and contextual (44) fear produced significant reductions in REM that can occur without recovery, and similar reductions without recovery can be seen with subsequent presentation of the fearful cue and fearful context. Hourly plots of NREM and REM amounts demonstrating this effect for cued fear in BALB/cJ mice are provided in (Fig. 1) Across studies, changes in NREM have been more variable, with some strains showing increases and some showing overall decreases compared to handling controls. Unfortunately, the EEG spectra across studies and strains have not been fully characterized, although there is some evidence that delta amplitude may vary as well, and we have found that NREM delta was relatively less in mice that showed greater reductions in REM (51). By comparison, NREM delta has been reported to be increased in rats after social stress (36) and

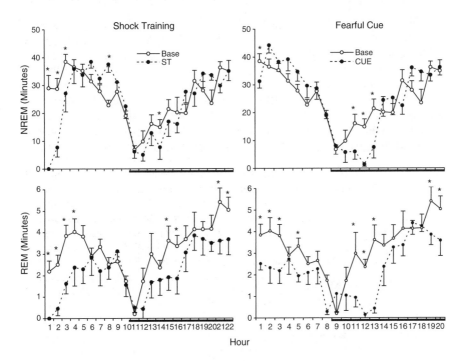

Fig. 1. Non-rapid eye movement (NREM) and rapid eye movement (REM) sleep in BALB/cJ mice ($n = 8$) plotted hourly after shock training (*left panels*) and after the presentation of an auditory fearful cue (*right panels*) compared to baseline. For training, the mice received 15 tone-shock pairings (90-dB, 4.0-kHz, 5-s tone; 0.2-mA shock presented during the last 0.5 s). Testing with the fearful cue alone occurred 5 full days after shock training, and it was presented to the mice as they were otherwise undisturbed in their home cages. Note that 10 h of light period sleep were presented for the shock training day and 8 h of light period sleep were presented for the cue day due to a time difference between training and testing. Horizontal bar on the *X*-axis indicates the dark period. *Base* baseline, *ST* shock training, *CUE* fearful cue. Values are mean hourly total ± SEM, *$p < .05$ compared to baseline. (Adapted from Ref. 53)

after stress induced by a simulated predator *(52)*. The decrease in delta sleep in patients with PTSD (reviewed in *16*) suggests that it is important to determine stress-induced alterations in NREM as well as those in REM to understand the role sleep may play in the long-term effects of a traumatic event.

The amount of training may also be an important factor as there appears to be a graded response in poststress sleep with greater or lesser numbers of pairings. For example, we found that the initial presentation of fearful cues after 4 days of training produced an 85% and a 55% reduction in REM and NREM, respectively, in the hour immediately after presentation *(43)*. By comparison, the presentation of a fearful cue after a single day of training produced a 34% and a 19% reduction in REM and NREM, respectively, in the hour immediately after presentation *(53)*. In contrast, REM and NREM mice trained with a single cue-shock pairing did not significantly differ from baseline levels after presentation of the cue. These differences also suggest variations in the relative strength of the association that was made between the cue and the shock across different amounts of training.

We have not fully replicated Adrien et al.'s *(50)* findings in rats; however, we have found reduced REM without rebound after multitrial training with a mild shock and reexposure to the fearful context (see Fig. 2), although there were differences among rat strains that may be related to differences in emotional reactivity as well as to differences in the stress axis *(27)*. We have also found reductions in NREM after shock training and fearful contexts in some strains and not in others.

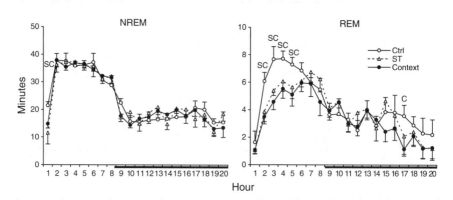

Fig. 2. Non-rapid eye movement (NREM) (*left panel*) and rapid eye movement (REM) (*right panel*) in Wistar rats (*n* = 8) plotted hourly after a handling and nonfearful, context control condition (Ctrl), after shock training (ST), and after reexposure to the shock training context without shock (context). For training, the rats were presented with 20 foot shocks (0.2 mA, 0.5-s duration) at 1.0-min intervals over the course of 20 min on two separate days (day 2 of training is plotted). For testing, they were placed back into the shock context for an equivalent period without receiving shock. Horizontal bar on the *X*-axis indicates the dark period. Values are mean ± SEM. S and C above the Ctrl line indicate significant differences compared for ST and Context, respectively. (Adapted from Ref. *27*)

Unfortunately, no one has conducted a full study of EEG spectra across rat strains and with different types of shock paradigms. Thus, while NREM amounts can be variable across studies, it remains to be seen whether there are differences in light and deep NREM or changes in EEG spectra in specific types of training paradigms that covary with the persistence of fearful behaviors.

Morrison, Ross, and their colleagues *(11,54,55)* have focused primarily on the changes in REM that occur within the first 4 h after relatively mild fear training and subsequent presentation of fearful cues or contexts. These studies have also examined the recordings for the relative occurrence of sequential (<3 min between) and single (>3 min between) REM episodes based on findings that stressors like thermal load *(56)* and immobilization stress *(30)* have differential effects on sequential and single-REM episodes. In a study of cued fear, these authors *(11)* reported that the decrease in REM after presentation of the fearful cue was due to fewer single-REM episodes, whereas rats trained with an unpaired cue showed an increase in REM characterized by an increase in the number of sequential REM episodes. In a more recent study *(55)*, they reported reduced sequential REM and increased single-REM episodes after presenting fear-inducing cues on day 14 after shock training. They also found significantly increased myoclonic twitches during REM, an important finding because increased phasic muscle activity during REM has been reported in veterans with PTSD *(21,24)*. These studies indicate that determining simple changes in REM amounts will not be sufficient to fully understand the effects of stressors. It also remains to be determined how these conditioned changes in REM compare to those induced by other stressors.

Learning is often associated with increases in REM *(57)*, and one might have predicted increased REM following fear conditioning. Rats *(57)* and mice *(58)* do exhibit increased REM (and rats also have more clusters of ponto-geniculo-occipital (PGO) waves, a signature characteristic of REM *(57)*) at various latencies after shock avoidance training in a shuttlebox. In the avoidance paradigm, animals are signaled of imminent shock and can learn to jump to safety without shock ever being delivered. The increases in REM have typically been viewed in the context of learning and interpreted as indicating a role for REM in memory consolidation. However, performance in this paradigm is motivated by foot shock and could involve significant stress.

While the reason for the difference between the two training procedures is unknown, the clearest difference is that shuttlebox training allows the animal to learn to avoid shock, whereas in fear conditioning the foot shock is inescapable. The fact that animals can learn to avoid shock in shuttlebox training implies that the animals have some control over the situation. By comparison, in fear conditioning, the animal has no control over whether it receives shock, although its occurrence may be predictable. Thus, there are significant differences in sleep after uncontrollable shock compared to after controllable shock, suggesting that understanding these differences may provide clues regarding the role poststress sleep may play in deterring or promoting the development of stress-related pathology. Intensity *(4)*, predictability *(5)*, and controllability *(6)* are important factors in the influence of stressors on behavior and physiology, and stressor intensity *(4)* and lack of controllability *(6)* have been suggested to be factors in the development of PTSD.

While the research on conditioned fear and sleep is not yet conclusive, work to date suggests that variations of this paradigm may provide models that have significant parallels to sleep in the development of PTSD as well as in the persisting alterations in sleep and arousal and may provide models that lead to better understanding of the underlying neurobiology. This work is also consistent with the suggestion of Yehuda and LeDoux *(2)* that understanding the neurobiology of PTSD will require identifying and characterizing atypical responses to stressors. This will likely require determining the relevant stressor qualities as well as determining individual differences in stress-induced changes in sleep that predict long-term changes in behavior in either inbred or outbred animals.

FEAR EXTINCTION AND SLEEP

Conditioned fear responses produced by fearful cues and contexts can typically be blocked through extended presentations of either type of stimuli without the reoccurrence of foot shock. This fear extinction is considered a type of new learning that inhibits subsequent fear without erasing the original memory for fear conditioning *(12)*. The failure of extinction is thought to be a significant factor in persisting fear responses and anxiety *(13)*, and extinction based therapy is used to treat PTSD patients *(59)*. However, even though sleep disturbances are a significant complaint in PTSD, and several studies have demonstrated the effects of conditioned fear on sleep in animals, the relationship of fear extinction to subsequent sleep is not yet known.

Silvestri *(60)* trained rats for cued fear conditioning with light-shock pairings followed by 6 h of REM deprivation produced by the inverted flowerpot method. On extinction trials when the light alone was presented, compared to controls, REM-deprived rats showed greater overall freezing and less decrease in freezing across presentations of the light. The groups did not differ in freezing on a second session when the light alone was presented. No significant difference was found between REM-deprived and control rats in extinction to contextual fear. By comparison, Fu et al. *(61)* trained rats using an auditory cue to signal shock and found that 6 h of REM deprivation immediately after training did not alter extinction learning compared to control rats; however, REM-deprived rats did show greater spontaneous recovery of freezing on a second day with presentation of the fearful cue alone. REM deprivation performed from 7 to 12 h after shock training had no significant effects. There are a number of procedural differences in the studies that may be linked to relative differences in results in these two studies. However, both studies found effects for extinction of cued fear, and neither found that REM deprivation significantly altered contextual fear extinction learning or spontaneous recovery of freezing on a second day of testing *(60,61)*. A limitation of these studies is that they were conducted without recording sleep and thus do not provide information regarding the relationship between electrophysiologically determined sleep and extinction.

We completed the first study that we are aware of to determine whether fear extinction is followed by different patterns of sleep compared to those after continued fear *(62)*. We trained two groups of rats in contextual fear using a foot shock stressor and then reexposed both groups to the fearful context alone. One group was removed from the context before extinction occurred, and the other was allowed to remain in the fearful context until behavioral signs of fear (freezing) had completely subsided. This allowed comparison of sleep in rats with extinguished fear behavior to that in rats that continued to show fear. We also examined both groups for similarities and differences in freezing during shock training and on reexposure to the context. Figure 3 demonstrates increased sleep (both NREM and REM) following extinction to levels indicative of normal sleep, whereas rats that continued to show freezing in the fearful context exhibited reductions in REM similar to those previously reported *(11,27)*. All rats experienced the same stressor; afterward, all were returned to the safety of their home cages. Animals that experienced identical handling and time in the context compared to the rats that exhibited continued fear or extinguished fear but never received shock sleep did not show significant differences in sleep. Thus, rats that were allowed to extinguish fear in the shock context showed different sleep than those that continued to show fear in the shock chamber, even though all were returned to the safety of their home cage. These data complement findings demonstrating fear-conditioned alterations in sleep and further suggest that poststress sleep is an important reflection of how the fear was processed. While this issue has not been examined in humans, these data also suggest that exposure therapy in PTSD patients may not only decrease their behavioral symptoms but also could play a role in alleviating their sleep disturbances as well *(62)*.

ROLE OF THE AMYGDALA IN MODULATING THE EFFECTS OF STRESS ON SLEEP

The role of the amygdala in identifying aversive stimuli, mediating conditioned fear responses, and storing fearful memories has long been recognized *(46,63)*. The amygdala also is a critical region for mediating the effects of stress, and it has been implicated in the psychopathology of PTSD *(64)*. Several lines of research demonstrate that the amygdala plays a significant role in regulating sleep and arousal, and it is likely to play a role in regulating changes in arousal induced by stress.

The majority of research on the role of the amygdala in regulating sleep has been focused on its influence on REM; however, a number of studies indicated that the amygdala may be able to influence all sleep-wakefulness states. Evidence also indicates that inhibition of the central nucleus of the amygdala (CNA) suppresses REM, and that activation of CNA can promote REM in some situations. Functional inactivation of CNA with microinjections of the γ-aminobutyric acid A (GABA$_A$) agonist muscimol produces a relatively selective decrease in REM, whereas blocking GABA-ergic inhibition with the GABA$_A$ antagonist bicuculline enhances REM. Functional lesions of the CNA by tetrodotoxin (TTX),

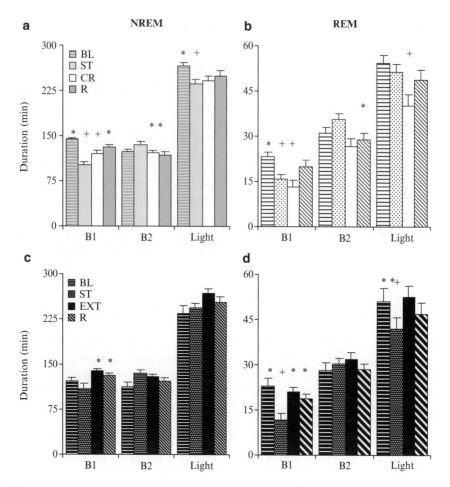

Fig. 3. Comparison of non-rapid eye movement (NREM) and rapid eye movement (REM) sleep recorded in Wistar rats after exposure to a fearful context without fear extinction (*top panels*) as indicated by continued freezing and with fear extinction (*bottom panels*) as indicated by cessation of freezing. NREM and REM sleep are plotted in two 4-h blocks (*B1 and B2*) and the entire 8-h light period (*LIGHT*). *BL* baseline sleep, *ST* shock training, *FR* (*n* = 7) 30-min context reexposure that did not produce extinction, *EXT* (*n* = 7) 60-min context reexposure that did produce extinction, *R* retest of both with a second fearful context exposure. For training, the rats were presented with 20 foot shocks (0.8 mA, 0.5-s duration) at 1.0-min intervals on a single day. Values are mean ± SEM. Differences relative to BL: +, *p* ≤ .05; differences relative to ST: *, *p* ≤ .05. (Adapted from Ref. *62*)

which inactivates both cell bodies and fibers of passage, also decrease REM and reduce arousal (*65*). The decrease in REM can occur without recovery (see Fig. 4), a finding also seen with training with inescapable shock and fearful cues and contexts. In addition, putative inhibition of CNA by microinjections

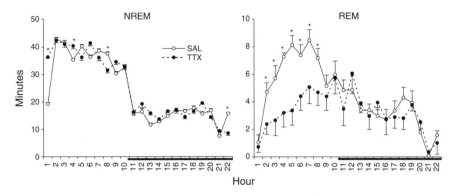

Fig. 4. Non-rapid eye movement (NREM) (*left panel*) and rapid eye movement (REM) (*right panel*) sleep in Wistar rats ($n = 9$) plotted hourly after microinjection of saline (*SAL*: 0.2 µL) and tetrodotoxin (*TTX*; 5.0 ng/0.2 µL) bilaterally into the central nucleus of the amygdala. Horizontal bar under X-axis indicates dark period. Error bars indicate SEM. *, $p < .05$ differences between SAL and TTX. (Adapted from Ref. *65*)

of serotonin terminate ongoing REM episodes *(66)*, and electrical stimulation of the serotonergic dorsal raphé nucleus inhibits REM-on neurons in CNA *(11)*. By comparison, electrical stimulation of CNA promotes REM in rats *(67)*. In cats, microinjections of vasoactive intestinal peptide *(68)* and the cholinergic agonist carbachol *(68)* into CNA and basal amygdaloid nuclei can increase REM and related phenomena, although acetylcholine appears to play a role in reducing REM in rats *(69)*.

Some of the effect of TTX may involve blocking fibers from the basal amygdala (BA) that pass through CNA to the bed nucleus of the stria terminalis *(63)*. TTX inactivation of CNA, including fibers of passage, prior to dark onset shortened sleep latency, increased NREM time, decreased REM time, and decreased activity in rats *(70)*. The effects of TTX inactivation on dark period sleep amounts are shown in Fig. 5. The involvement of BA also is suggested by reports that bilateral electrolytic and chemical lesions of the basolateral amygdala (BLA) increase NREM and total sleep time in rats *(71)* and that bilateral chemical lesions of the amygdala produce more consolidated sleep in chair-restrained Rhesus monkeys *(72)*. In contrast, electrical and chemical stimulation of the BLA increased low-voltage, high-frequency activity in the cortical EEG and decreased NREM and total sleep time, respectively *(71)*. An early study reported that electrical stimulation of the dorsal and ventral regions of BLA desynchronized and synchronized the EEG, respectively *(73)*.

The human PTSD literature generally considers the amygdala as a single structure whose activation is important in PTSD symptoms. Indeed, neuroimaging studies have reported increased activation in the amygdala of PTSD patients in response to threat stimuli compared to nontrauma controls and trauma-exposed people who did not develop PTSD (reviewed in *74*). However activation of the amygdala has also been found in association with REM in humans (e.g., *75*).

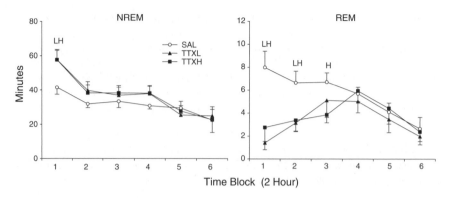

Fig. 5. Dark period non-rapid eye movement (NREM) (*left panel*) and rapid eye movement (REM) (*right panel*) sleep in Wistar rats (*n* = 8) plotted in 2-h intervals after microinjections of saline (*SAL*: 0.2 µL) and two volumes of tetrodotoxin (*TTXL*: 2.5 ng/0.1
µL; *TTXH*: 5.0 ng/0.2 µL) to the central nucleus of the amygdala. Error bars indicate
SEM. *L* and *H* indicate significant differences for TTXL and TTXH, respectively, compared to SAL (Tukey test, $p < .05$). (Adapted from Ref. *70*)

This suggests a refinement is needed regarding how the amygdala is viewed in
regulating arousal state. This may be found in animal work that indicates that
regions of the amygdala may be differentially involved in modulating different
sleep states. For example, consistent with microinjection data, training with
inescapable shock produced increased Fos activation in several regions of the
amygdala (e.g., medial amygdala, cortical amygdala, BA, lateral amygdala, and
amygdalostriatal transition region), but not in CNA *(76)*, where muscimol and
TTX microinjections decreased REM. This suggests that the probable role of
the amygdala in influencing poststress sleep may involve differential activation
and inactivation in various nuclei, and that multiple regions of the amygdala can
be activated at the same time that REM is reduced.

CRH, STRESS, AND ALTERATIONS IN SLEEP

CRH has a major role in mediating central nervous system as well behavioral, autonomic, and physiological responses to stressors *(77)*. It thus has been of
significant interest as a factor in anxiety and mood disorders. Elevated levels of
CRH have been found in the cerebrospinal fluid *(78)* and plasma *(79)* of PTSD
patients, and elevated CRH has been hypothesized to play a role in the reduced
delta sleep found in patients with PTSD *(16)*.

Also, CRH has been implicated in stress-induced alterations in sleep, particularly in the control of REM *(80)*. For example, administration of CRH antagonists have been reported to eliminate REM rebound after immobilization stress
(80) and to decrease REM rebound after sleep deprivation *(29)*. In the absence

of stressors, CRH may contribute to the regulation of spontaneous waking *(81)*, as evidenced by findings that the intracerebroventricular administration of CRH increases wakefulness in rats *(82)*. The enhancement of wakefulness by CRH may occur at dosages too low to stimulate the hypothalamic-pituitary-adrenal (HPA) axis or produce behavioral effects *(83)*. These findings indicate that CRH may produce changes in arousal and sleep in otherwise undisturbed conditions.

Opp and his colleagues have conducted an extensive series of studies examining the role of CRH in modulating arousal. These studies demonstrated that rat strains differing in the synthesis and secretion of CRH and in basal plasma concentrations of corticosterone show significant differences in amounts of sleep *(83)*. Specifically, Lewis strain rats have a deficiency in the synthesis and secretion of hypothalamic CRH. These rats exhibit less wakefulness and more NREM than genetically related inbred Fischer 344 rats, outbred Spague-Dawley rats *(33,83)*, or Wistar strain rats *(33)*. Opp's laboratory also found that rats recorded in their home cages under well-habituated conditions, and without the presence of stressors, showed selective increases in wakefulness and decreases in NREM but no significant changes in REM after the intracerebroventricular administration of CRH *(84)*. In addition, in rats in nonstressful conditions, the intracerebroventricular administration of CRH enhanced wakefulness when given at the beginning of either the light or the dark period, whereas intracerebroventricular administration of the nonspecific CRH antagonists astressin and αHelCRH (α-helical CRH_{9-41}) reduced wakefulness and increased NREM only when administered in the dark period *(84)*.

We examined the effects of CRH and astressin on wakefulness and sleep using two mouse strains with differential responsiveness to stress to determine whether CRH might also differentially affect undisturbed sleep and activity *(85)*. Less-reactive C57BL/6J and high-reactive BALB/cJ mice were implanted with transmitters for determining sleep via telemetry and with guide cannulae for delivering drug into the lateral ventricles. In C57BL/6J mice, REM was significantly decreased after microinjections of 0.2 μg CRH and 0.4 μg CRH, and NREM and total sleep were decreased after microinjection of 0.4 μg CRH. Astressin did not significantly change wakefulness or sleep. In BALB/cJ mice, 0.4 μg CRH increased wakefulness and decreased NREM, REM, and total sleep. Astressin decreased active wakefulness and significantly increased REM at the low and high dosages. These strain differences in the effects of CRH and astressin may be linked to the relative responsiveness of C57BL/6J and BALB/cJ mice to stressors and to underlying differences in the CRH system.

The amygdala is a critical region for the central effects of CRH, and it appears to mediate a number of its anxiogenic effects, as evidenced by intra-amygdala microinjections of CRH agonists and antagonists (reviewed in *63*). There has been very little work with respect to the effects on sleep of local application of CRH compounds into the brain; however, microinjections of 1.0-ng dosage of CRH into CNA of rats decreased average amount of REM over 4 h postinjection *(11)*. Ongoing work in our lab conducted in rats also suggests that the

CRH system in the amygdala can influence fear-induced alterations in sleep. For instance, microinjections of the relatively specific CRH receptor 1 antagonist antalarmin into CNA of rats attenuated reductions in REM and NREM that occur after exposure to a fearful context *(86)*. While preliminary, these data indicate that the amygdala could be an important site for the influence of CRH on arousal and sleep in stressful conditions, and that it could be involved in potential effects on sleep produced by enhanced central CRH in PTSD patients. Recent in vitro work has implicated CRH in the modulation of excitatory glutamatergic synaptic transmission in CNA, with CRH_1 and CRH_2 receptors apparently playing inhibitory and facilitatory roles, respectively *(87)*, a finding consistent with studies demonstrating that inactivation of CNA decreases REM.

SUMMARY

Stress-induced alterations in sleep have been linked to the development of PTSD in humans, and sleep complaints and disturbances in arousal are continuing symptoms in patients. Stress-induced changes in sleep related to PTSD have not been fully characterized but appear to involve persisting changes in both REM and NREM. A number of animal models of stress are characterized by initial decreases in sleep followed by recovery sleep, which may indicate a restoration of homeostasis and successful resolution of the stress response. By comparison, intense conditioned fear training can produce reductions in REM without recovery as well as significant alterations in NREM that may vary with mouse and rat strains. These variants of conditioned fear paradigms and strain differences have not been fully exploited, but they appear to hold promise for modeling responses to stress that may provide insight into the role sleep plays in the neurobiology of PTSD. The amygdala and CRH have been implicated in PTSD and play significant roles in regulating the stress response that most likely includes regulating stress-induced changes in arousal and sleep. Determining normal and atypical responses to stress, including poststress sleep, may lead to the development of significantly improved models for examining how stress produces long-term alterations in behavior.

REFERENCES

1. Shalev, A. Y. (2000) Biological responses to disasters. Psychiatric Q 71, 277–88.
2. Yehuda, R., and LeDoux, J. (2007) Response variation following trauma: a translational neuroscience approach to understanding PTSD. Neuron 56, 19–32.
3. Cohen, H., Zohar, J., and Matar, M. (2003) The relevance of differential response to trauma in an animal model of posttraumatic stress disorder. Biol Psychiatry 53, 463–73.
4. Buydens-Branchey, L., Noumair, D., and Branchey, M. (1990) Duration and intensity of combat exposure and posttraumatic stress disorder in Vietnam veterans. J Nerv Ment Dis 178, 582–87.
5. Abbott, B. B., Schoen, L. S., and Badia, P. (1984) Predictable and unpredictable shock: behavioral measures of aversion and physiological measures of stress. Psychol Bull 96, 45–71.

6. Foa, E. B., Zinbarg, R., and Rothbaum, B. O. (1992) Uncontrollability and unpredictability in post-traumatic stress disorder: an animal model. Psychol Bull 112, 218–38.

7. Yehuda, R., Flory, J. D., Southwick, S., and Charney, D. S. (2006) Developing an agenda for translational studies of resilience and vulnerability following trauma exposure. Ann N Y Acad Sci 1071, 379–96.

8. Rauch, S. L., Shin, L. M., and Phelps, E. A. (2006) Neurocircuitry models of posttraumatic stress disorder and extinction: human neuroimaging research—past, present, and future. Biol Psychiatry 60, 376–82.

9. Charney, D., and Deutch, A. (1996) A functional neuroanatomy of anxiety and fear: implications for the pathophysiology and treatment of anxiety disorders. Crit Rev Neurobiol 10, 419–46.

10. Pynoos, R., Ritzmann, R., Steinberg, A., Goenjian, A., and Prisecaru, I. (1996) A behavioral animal model of posttraumatic stress disorder featuring repeated exposure to situational reminders. Biol Psychiatry 39, 129–34.

11. Jha, S. K., Brennan, F. X., Pawlyk, A. C., Ross, R. J., and Morrison, A. R. (2005) REM sleep: a sensitive index of fear conditioning in rats. Eur J Neurosci 21, 1077–80.

12. Bouton, M. E. (2004) Context and behavioral processes in extinction. Learn Mem 11, 485–94.

13. Myers, K. M., and Davis, M. (2007) Mechanisms of fear extinction. Mol Psychiatry 12, 120–50.

14. Lavie, P. (2001) Sleep disturbances in the wake of traumatic events. N Engl J Med 345, 1825–32.

15. Harvey, A. G., Jones, C., and Schmidt, D. A. (2003) Sleep and posttraumatic stress disorder: a review. Clin Psychol Rev 23, 377–407.

16. Neylan, T. C., Otte, C., Yehuda, R., and Marmar, C. R. (2006) Neuroendocrine regulation of sleep disturbances in PTSD. Ann N Y Acad Sci 1071, 203–15.

17. Germain, A., Buysse, D. J., and Nofzinger, E. (2007) Sleep-specific mechanisms underlying posttraumatic stress disorder: integrative review and neurobiological hypotheses. Sleep Med Rev 12, 185–95.

18. Greenberg, R., Pearlman, C. A., and Gampel, D. (1972) War neuroses and the adaptive function of REM sleep. Br J Med Psychol 45, 27–33.

19. van der Kolk, B., Blitz, R., Burr, W., Sherry, S., and Hartmann, E. (1984) Nightmares and trauma: a comparison of nightmares after combat with lifelong nightmares in veterans. Am J Psychiatry 141, 187–90.

20. Schlosberg, A., and Benjamin, M. (1978) Sleep patterns in three acute combat fatigue cases. J Clin Psychiatry 39, 546–49.

21. Ross, R. J., Ball, W. A., Dinges, D. F., et al. (1994) Rapid eye movement sleep disturbance in posttraumatic stress disorder. Biol Psychiatry 35, 195–202.

22. Ross, R. J., Ball, W. A., Sanford, L. D., et al. (1999) Rapid eye movement sleep changes during the adaptation night in combat veterans with posttraumatic stress disorder. Biol Psychiatry 45, 938–41.

23. Dow, B. M., Kelsoe, J. R., Jr., and Gillin, J. C. (1996) Sleep and dreams in Vietnam PTSD and depression. Biol Psychiatry 39, 42–50.

24. Mellman, T. A., Nolan, B., Hebding, J., Kulick-Bell, R., and Dominguez, R. (1997) A polysomnographic comparison of veterans with combat-related PTSD, depressed men, and non-ill controls. Sleep (abstract suppl) 20, 46–51.

25. Mellman, T. A., Bustamante, V., Fins, A. I., Pigeon, W. R., and Nolan, B. (2002) REM sleep and the early development of posttraumatic stress disorder. Am J Psychiatry 159, 1696–1701.

26. Mellman, T. A., Pigeon, W. R., Nowell, P. D., and Nolan, B. (2007) Relationships between REM sleep findings and PTSD symptoms during the early aftermath of trauma. J Trauma Stress 20, 893–901.
27. Tang, X., Yang, L., and Sanford, L. D. (2005) Rat strain differences in freezing and sleep alterations associated with contextual fear. Sleep 28, 1235–44.
28. Sanford, L. D., Xiao, J., Liu, X., Yang, L., and Tang, X. (2005) Influence of avoidance training (AT) and AT cues on sleep in C57BL/6J (B6) and BALB/cJ (C) mice. Sleep (abstract suppl) 28, A6.
29. Gonzalez, M. M., Debilly, G., Valatx, J. L., and Jouvet, M. (1995) Sleep increase after immobilization stress: role of the noradrenergic locus coeruleus system in the rat. Neurosci Lett 202, 5–8.
30. Dewasmes, G., Loos, N., Delanaud, S., Dewasmes, D., and Ramadan, W. (2004) Pattern of rapid-eye movement sleep episode occurrence after an immobilization stress in the rat. Neurosci Lett 355, 17–20.
31. Smith, C. (1995) Sleep states and memory processes. Behav Brain Res 69, 137–45.
32. Tang, X., Xiao, J., Parris, B. S., Fang, J., and Sanford, L. D. (2005) Differential effects of two types of environmental novelty on activity and sleep in BALB/cJ and C57BL/J mice. Physiol Behav 85, 419–29.
33. Tang, X., Xiao, J., Liu, X., and Sanford, L. D. (2004) Strain differences in the influence of open field exposure on sleep in mice. Behav Brain Res 154, 137–47.
34. Tang, X., Liu, X., Yang, L., and Sanford, L. D. (2005) Rat strain differences in sleep after acute mild stressors and short-term sleep loss. Behav Brain Res 160, 60–71.
35. Bodosi, B., Obal, F., Jr., Gardi, J., Komlodi, J., Fang, J., and Krueger, J. M. (2000) An ether stressor increases REM sleep in rats: possible role of prolactin. Am J Physiol Regul Integr Comp Physiol 279, R1590–98.
36. Meerlo, P., Pragt, B. J., and Daan, S. (1997) Social stress induces high intensity sleep in rats. Neurosci Lett 225, 41–44.
37. Chrousos, G. P. (1998) Stressors, stress, and neuroendocrine integration of the adaptive response. Ann N Y Acad Sci 851, 311–35.
38. Duke, J. L., Zammit, T. G., and Lawson, D. M. (2001) The effects of routine cage-changing on cardiovascular and behavioral parameters in male Sprague-Dawley rats. Contemp Top Lab Anim Sci 40, 17–20.
39. Pacak, K., and Palkovits, M. (2001) Stressor specificity of central neuroendocrine responses: implications for stress-related disorders. Endocr Rev 22, 502–48.
40. Kerns, J. G., Cohen, J. D., MacDonald, A. W., 3rd, Cho, R. Y., Stenger, V. A., and Carter, C. S. (2004) Anterior cingulate conflict monitoring and adjustments in control. Science 303, 1023–26.
41. Bush, D. E., Sotres-Bayon, F., and LeDoux, J. E. (2007) Individual differences in fear: isolating fear reactivity and fear recovery phenotypes. J Trauma Stress 20, 413–22.
42. Tang, X., Yang, L., and Sanford, L. D. (2007) Individual variation in sleep and motor activity in rats. Behav Brain Res 180, 62–68.
43. Sanford, L. D., Tang, X., Ross, R. J., and Morrison, A. R. (2003) Influence of shock training and explicit fear-conditioned cues on sleep architecture in mice: strain comparison. Behav Genet 33, 43–58.
44. Sanford, L. D., Yang, L., and Tang, X. (2003) Influence of contextual fear on sleep in mice: a strain comparison. Sleep 26, 527–40.
45. Blanchard, R. J., and Blanchard, D. C. (1969) Crouching as an index of fear. J Comp Physiol Psychol 67, 370–75.

46. Davis, M. (1992) The role of the amygdala in conditioned fear. In: Aggleton, J., ed. The Amygdala: Neurobiological Aspects of Emotion, Memory, and Mental Dysfunction. New York: Wiley-Liss; 255–305.

47. Graves, L. A., Heller, E. A., Pack, A. I., and Abel, T. (2003) Sleep deprivation selectively impairs memory consolidation for contextual fear conditioning. Learn Mem 10, 168–76.

48. Hellman, K., and Abel, T. (2007) Fear conditioning increases NREM sleep. Behav Neurosci 121, 310–23.

49. Maier, S. F., Amat, J., Baratta, M. V., Paul, E., and Watkins, L. R. (2006) Behavioral control, the medial prefrontal cortex, and resilience. Dialogues Clin Neurosci 8, 397–406.

50. Adrien, J., Dugovic, C., and Martin, P. (1991) Sleep-wakefulness patterns in the helpless rat. Physiol Behav 49, 257–62.

51. Tang, X., Yang, L., and Sanford, L. D. (2006) Spectral EEG power after uncontrollable shock (US) and fearful context (FC): variability amongst mouse strains. Sleep 29, A11.

52. Lesku, J. A., Bark, R. J., Martinez-Gonzalez, D., Rattenborg, N. C., Amlaner, C. J., and Lima, S. L. (2008) Predator-induced plasticity in sleep architecture in wild-caught Norway rats (Rattus norvegicus). Behav Brain Res 189, 298–305.

53. Sanford, L. D., Fang, J., and Tang, X. (2003) Sleep after differing amounts of conditioned fear training in BALB/cJ mice. Behav Brain Res 147, 193–202.

54. Pawlyk, A. C., Jha, S. K., Brennan, F. X., Morrison, A. R., and Ross, R. J. (2005) A rodent model of sleep disturbances in posttraumatic stress disorder: the role of context after fear conditioning. Biol Psychiatry 57, 268–77.

55. Madan, V., Brennan, F. X., Mann, G. L., et al. (2008) Long-term effect of cued fear conditioning on REM sleep microarchitecture in rats. Sleep (abstract suppl) 31, 497–305.

56. Amici, R., Zamboni, G., Perez, E., Jones, C. A., and Parmeggiani, P. L. (1998) The influence of a heavy thermal load on REM sleep in the rat. Brain Res 781, 252–58.

57. Datta, S. (2000) Avoidance task training potentiates phasic pontine-wave density in the rat: a mechanism for sleep-dependent plasticity. J Neurosci 20, 8607–13.

58. Smith, C., Kitahama, K., Valatx, J. L., and Jouvet, M. (1974) Increased paradoxical sleep in mice during acquisition of a shock avoidance task. Brain Res 77, 221–30.

59. Pitman, R. K., Shin, L. M., and Rauch, S. L. (2001) Investigating the pathogenesis of posttraumatic stress disorder with neuroimaging. J Clin Psychiatry 62, 47–54.

60. Silvestri, A. J. (2005) REM sleep deprivation affects extinction of cued but not contextual fear conditioning. Physiol Behav 84, 343–49.

61. Fu, J., Li, P., Ouyang, X., et al. (2007) Rapid eye movement sleep deprivation selectively impairs recall of fear extinction in hippocampus-independent tasks in rats. Neuroscience 144, 1186–92.

62. Wellman, L. L., Holbrook, B. D., Yang, L., Tang, X., and Sanford, L. D. (2008) Contextual fear extinction eliminates sleep disturbances found following fear conditioning in rats. Sleep 31, 1035–42.

63. Davis, M., and Whalen, P. J. (2001) The amygdala: vigilance and emotion. Mol Psychiatry 6, 13–34.

64. Bremner, J. D. (2005) Effects of traumatic stress on brain structure and function: relevance to early responses to trauma. J Trauma Dissociation 6, 51–68.

65. Tang, X., Yang, L., Liu, X., and Sanford, L. D. (2005) Influence of tetrodotoxin inactivation of the central nucleus of the amygdala on sleep and arousal. Sleep 28, 923–30.

66. Sanford, L. D., Tejani-Butt, S. M., Ross, R. J., and Morrison, A. R. (1995) Amygdaloid control of alerting and behavioral arousal in rats: involvement of serotonergic mechanisms. Arch Ital Biol 134, 81–99.
67. Smith, C. T., and Miskiman, D. E. (1975) Increases in paradoxical sleep as a result of amygdaloid stimulation. Physiol Behav 15, 17–19.
68. Calvo, J., Simón-Arceo, K., and Fernández-Mas, R. (1996) Prolonged enhancement of REM sleep produced by carbachol microinjection into the amygdala. NeuroRep 7, 577–80.
69. Sanford, L. D., Yang, L., Tang, X., Dong, E., Ross, R. J., and Morrison, A. R. (2006) Cholinergic regulation of the central nucleus of the amygdala in rats: effects of local microinjections of cholinomimetics and cholinergic antagonists on arousal and sleep. Neuroscience 141, 2167–76.
70. Sanford, L. D., Yang, L., Liu, X., and Tang, X. (2006) Effects of tetrodotoxin (TTX) inactivation of the central nucleus of the amygdala (CNA) on dark period sleep and activity. Brain Res 1084, 80–88.
71. Zhu, G. Q., Zhong, M. K., Zhang, J. X., et al. (1998) [Role of basolateral amygdaloid nuclei in sleep and wakeful state regulation]. Sheng Li Xue Bao 50, 688–92.
72. Benca, R. M., Obermeyer, W. H., Shelton, S. E., Droster, J., and Kalin, N. H. (2000) Effects of amygdala lesions on sleep in rhesus monkeys. Brain Res 879, 130–38.
73. Kreindler, A., and Steriade, M. (1964) EEG patterns of arousal and sleep induced by stimulating various amygdaloid levels in the cat. Arch Ital Biol 102, 576–86.
74. Shin, L. M., Rauch, S. L., and Pitman, R. K. (2006) Amygdala, medial prefrontal cortex, and hippocampal function in PTSD. Ann N Y Acad Sci 1071, 67–79.
75. Maquet, P., Peters, J., Aerts, J., et al. (1996) Functional neuroanatomy of human rapid-eye-movement sleep and dreaming. Nature 383, 163–66.
76. Liu, X., Tang, X., and Sanford, L. D. (2003) Fear-conditioned suppression of REM sleep: relationship to Fos expression patterns in limbic and brainstem regions in BALB/cJ mice. Brain Res 991, 1–17.
77. Koob, G. F. (1999) Corticotropin-releasing factor, norepinephrine, and stress. Biol Psychiatry 46, 1167–80.
78. Bremner, J. D., Licinio, J., Darnell, A., et al. (1997) Elevated CSF corticotropin-releasing factor concentrations in posttraumatic stress disorder. Am J Psychiatry 154, 624–29.
79. de Kloet, C. S., Vermetten, E., Geuze, E., et al. (2007) Elevated plasma corticotrophin-releasing hormone levels in veterans with posttraumatic stress disorder. Prog Brain Res 167, 287–91.
80. Gonzalez, M. M., and Valatx, J. L. (1997) Effect of intracerebroventricular administration of alpha-helical CRH (9–41) on the sleep/waking cycle in rats under normal conditions or after subjection to an acute stressful stimulus. J Sleep Res 6, 164–70.
81. Chang, F. C., and Opp, M. R. (2001) Corticotropin-releasing hormone (CRH) as a regulator of waking. Neurosci Biobehav Rev 25, 445–53.
82. Ehlers, C. L., Reed, T. K., and Henriksen, S. J. (1986) Effects of corticotropin-releasing factor and growth hormone-releasing factor on sleep and activity in rats. Neuroendocrinology 42, 467–74.
83. Opp, M. R. (1997) Rat strain differences suggest a role for corticotropin-releasing hormone in modulating sleep. Physiol Behav 63, 67–74.
84. Chang, F. C., and Opp, M. R. (1998) Blockade of corticotropin-releasing hormone receptors reduces spontaneous waking in the rat. Am J Physiol 275, R793–R802.

85. Sanford, L. D., Yang, L., Wellman, L. L., Dong, E., and Tang, X. (2008) Mouse strain differences in the effects of corticotropin releasing hormone (CRH) on sleep and wakefulness. Brain Res 1190, 94–104.
86. Liu, X., Dong, E., Yang, L., Tang, X., and Sanford, L. D. (2008) Antagonizing corticotropin releasing hormone (CRH) 1 receptors in the central nucleus of the amygdala (CNA) attenuates fear-induced reductions in sleep. Sleep (abstract suppl) 31, A16.
87. Liu, J., Yu, B., Neugebauer, V., et al. (2004) Corticotropin-releasing factor and Urocortin I modulate excitatory glutamatergic synaptic transmission. J Neurosci 24, 4020–29.

Stress Hormones in Post-Traumatic Stress Disorder

12 Stress Hormones and PTSD

Rachel Yehuda

CONTENTS

INTRODUCTION
RELEVANCE OF NEUROENDOCRINOLOGY
    OF STRESS TO PTSD
CORTISOL LEVELS IN PTSD
COULD CORTISOL ALTERATIONS CONTRIBUTE
    TO PTSD RISK?
CIRCADIAN RHYTHM ALTERATIONS IN PTSD
RESULTS OF NEUROENDOCRINE CHALLENGES
    IN PTSD: FOCUS ON THE DEXAMETHASONE
    SUPPRESSION TEST
GLUCOCORTICOID RESPONSIVENESS IN PTSD
PUTATIVE MODELS OF HPA AXIS ALTERATIONS IN PTSD
FUTURE DIRECTIONS: THE POTENTIAL
    RELEVANCE OF EPIGENETICS
CONCLUSIONS
REFERENCES

Abstract

There are now several hundred peer-reviewed journal articles that report on various aspects of hypothalamic-pituitary-adrenal (HPA) axis functioning in post-traumatic stress disorder (PTSD). Yet, published reports do not always show agreement. This review discusses approaches to the interpretation of neuroendocrine results in consideration of discrepant observations. A disturbing tendency in the literature has been to dismiss HPA axis findings as directly relevant to PTSD pathophysiology or to try to reach consensus regarding contrasting views in the literature by designating majority findings as more true than findings occurring less frequently. There have been few attempts to evaluate the meaning of disparate observations or determine whether specific

From: *Post-Traumatic Stress Disorder: Basic Science and Clinical Practice*
Edited by: P. J. Shiromani et al., DOI: 10.1007/978-1-60327-329-9_12
© Humana Press, a part of Springer Science+Business Media, LLC 2009

methodological considerations compromise the findings or their interpretation. There has been a reluctance to assign a rank ordering to observations that are more definitive because they use a superior endocrine strategy that might result in weighting some studies more heavily than others. Finally, there have been few attempts to incorporate the observed discrepancies into a coherent model of neuroendocrine functioning in PTSD. This chapter attempts to analyze the literature from this framework.

Key Words: Adrenocorticotropin hormone (ACTH), circadian rhythm, cortisol, dexamethasone, epigenetic, glucocorticoids, hypothalamic-pituitary adrenal, stress.

INTRODUCTION

There has been substantial interest in examining stress hormones in post-traumatic stress disorder (PTSD). Several hundred journal articles on this topic have been published in the last decade (i.e., since 1998). Given that PTSD is a disorder that is precipitated by stress and that the neuroendocrine stress response has been well characterized, inquiries regarding the neuroendocrinology of PTSD should have arguably generated a rather straightforward set of results. This has not been the case, much to the bafflement of clinical investigators. Indeed, in reviewing any of the many articles on the topic of cortisol-related alterations in PTSD, the reader will almost certainly find that while there is agreement that hypothalamic-pituitary-adrenal (HPA) alterations are present in PTSD, the nature of the alterations in PTSD are not well understood or integrated into a cohesive model. In part, this difficulty stems from the presence of disparate findings. However, even among findings that have been replicated, interpretative problems arise from discrepancies between observations in PTSD and those that have been more classically attributable to stress responses and the basic neuroendocrine mechanisms described in other conditions. This review briefly summarizes findings of HPA axis alterations in PTSD.

RELEVANCE OF NEUROENDOCRINOLOGY
OF STRESS TO PTSD

In response to a stressor, the body mobilizes a series of coordinated biological responses via activation of the sympathetic nervous system (SNS) and HPA axis to deal effectively with the challenges imposed on it. Whereas the SNS is important in facilitating the mobilization of physiological resources to respond to stress, activation of the HPA axis also contributes to maintaining physiological homeostasis. The mechanics of the HPA axis are well understood. Stress activates the parvocellular neurons of the hypothalamus, which are stimulated to secrete the neuropeptides corticotropin-releasing factor (CRF) and vasopressin (AVP) into the portal vessel system to activate the synthesis and release of adrenocorticotropic hormone (ACTH) from the anterior pituitary. ACTH in turn stimulates the adrenal cortex to synthesize and release glucocorticoids, in particular cortisol. The release of cortisol contributes to the mobilization of energy to the body's vital organs. In addition, stress-activated cortisol release helps contain sympathetic activation and other neuronal defensive reactions that are initiated by stress (*1*). Furthermore, elevated cortisol levels also suppress the further release of cortisol itself through negative feedback inhibition, acting at glucocorticoid receptors (GRs). Occupation of GRs in the paraventricular nucleus (PVN) of the hypothalamus and at the pituitary suppress release of CRF and ACTH, respectively, resulting in a reduction in cortisol release and a restoration in basal hormone levels (*2,3*). Accordingly, in the absence of sustained provocation or multiple stressors, the physiological reactivity associated with stress is not maintained.

In contrast to this model that predicts eventual recovery of biological responses to stress, initial descriptions of combat veterans suggested a chronic and sustained physiological hyperarousal that could be observed years after trauma exposure (*4*). As early as 1918, World War I veterans with "irritable heart of soldiers" were reported as having increased heart rate responses to experimentally induced sounds of gunfire and exaggerated behavioral responses to epinephrine injections (*5,6*). The first formal neurochemical and psychophysiological studies in PTSD reported sustained increases in peripheral catecholamine levels, increased sympathetic tone, decreased parasympathetic tone, and accompanying changes in heart rate, respiration, skin conductance, and other autonomic measures compared to controls under baseline conditions and in response to traumatic triggers (*7–14*). Yet interestingly, and inconsistent with the classic picture of stress, cortisol levels were not found to be elevated in chronic PTSD (*15,16*). Although not all studies have reported similar observations (reviewed in *17–19*), those in which cortisol levels were sampled regularly over a 24-h period under carefully controlled conditions found evidence of reduced cortisol levels as well as alterations in chronobiological parameters relating to cortisol release over the diurnal cycle (*20,21*).

The finding that cortisol levels were actually lower in PTSD, and dissociated from catecholamine levels, provided the first important lead in understanding the pathophysiology of PTSD. Certainly it could be reasoned that if the cortisol response to a stressor is muted, this could impede the reinstatement of physiological homeostasis and contribute to increased or prolonged activation of the SNS (*22,23*). Since the release of epinephrine also facilitates consolidation of the threat memory (*24*), failure to contain the SNS response may lead to more strongly encoded memories that are also more subjectively distressing. Indeed, a hallmark of PTSD is the presence of intrusive, distressing memories.

CORTISOL LEVELS IN PTSD

Initial data demonstrating low cortisol levels in the face of elevated catecholamines in combat veterans generated some early enthusiasm. It also generated skepticism and confusion. Following the observation of Mason and his colleagues (*15*), in the late 1980s there was a series of attempts to replicate and extend the findings; the series met with mixed results. Although there were disparate observations with respect to any of the biological parameters associated with PTSD that were measured concurrently and subsequently, including those reflecting SNS, brain, and cognitive functioning, the cortisol findings received particular scrutiny. Possibly this was because, unlike other emerging observations that did not contradict the essential biology of stress, there was no context for understanding why cortisol levels would be low in PTSD. Furthermore, as more observations were added to the field, it became apparent that CRF levels appeared to be increased in this disorder (25–27). Thus, it was difficult to understand the seemingly paradoxical combination of low cortisol and increased CRF.

PTSD was also found to be associated with an enhanced cortisol negative feedback inhibition, which seemed to result from increased responsiveness of GRs (19,28). The profile of neuroendocrine alterations was different from that observed in animal models of ongoing, chronic stress and from observations in depressed patients, in which elevated CRF resulted in increased cortisol levels, decreased GR responsiveness, and weaker cortisol negative feedback inhibition (29). Rather, the neuroendocrinology of PTSD suggested an increased sympathetic and central CRF activation in the face of reduced cortisol signaling—a constellation that had previously not been observed in relation to stress or psychiatric disorder.

It should also be mentioned that, as initial biological observations were being made, PTSD was a relatively new diagnosis and had not been fully characterized with respect to its prevalence, course, and risk factors. PTSD first appeared as a psychiatric diagnosis only in 1980. It was established to validate and legitimize the idea that extreme stress could result in long-term symptoms. The diagnosis did not enjoy immediate recognition as a legitimate clinical entity (e.g., some even referred to it as "compensation neurosis"). Thus, the idea of failing to confirm an established and known marker of stress (i.e., elevated cortisol levels) in PTSD may have been particularly challenging. Moreover, in the absence of epidemiologic data demonstrating the relative rareness of PTSD compared to the prevalence of trauma exposure, it was difficult to imagine that PTSD itself might not represent the quintessential normative response to extreme stress rather than a specific type of response to trauma that might be underpinned by specific alterations in the biology of stress. After establishing that PTSD is a disorder that is more likely not to develop following trauma exposure than to develop, it became plausible to consider biological alterations that deviated from those associated with normal stress as more central to PTSD pathophysiology than those that are consequences of trauma exposure.

COULD CORTISOL ALTERATIONS CONTRIBUTE TO PTSD RISK?

Observations of low cortisol levels in PTSD were initially interpreted as reflecting pathophysiology arising from trauma exposure. Yet, cross-sectional studies of chronic PTSD could not address the mechanisms underlying the neuroendocrine findings. In several (but not all) prospective, longitudinal studies, lower cortisol levels in the acute aftermath of trauma were associated with either the subsequent development of PTSD or with the risk factor of prior trauma exposure (30–34). These findings implied that reduced cortisol levels at the time of a trauma may compromise the inhibition of stress-induced biologic responses to trauma, resulting in prolonged physiological arousal and distress, leading to PTSD.

In rape victims, lower plasma cortisol levels (10) but higher levels of plasma 3-methoxy-4-hydroxyphenylglycol (MHPG) were associated with the risk factor of prior traumatization (31). Studies of motor vehicle accidents demonstrated that persons who subsequently developed PTSD had lower cortisol levels within hours after the accident than those who did not (31,34). In parallel studies of persons at risk for PTSD, lower cortisol and enhanced cortisol suppression following dexamethasone (DEX) were noted in the adult offspring of Holocaust survivors with, compared to those without, parental PTSD (35,36). Parental PTSD is a risk factor for PTSD because it produces a threefold increase in the prevalence of PTSD (but not trauma exposure) in offspring (37). Lower cortisol levels were also observed in the infant offspring of mothers who developed PTSD following exposure while pregnant to the World Trade Center attacks on 9/11 compared to those of mothers who did not develop PTSD (38). In both these "at risk" cohorts, neuroendocrine measures associated with severity of parental PTSD symptoms. This was true in the adult offspring of Holocaust survivors even after controlling for mood and anxiety in the offspring.

CIRCADIAN RHYTHM ALTERATIONS IN PTSD

As noted, there has been variability in the literature with respect to studies examining urinary free cortisol levels or plasma and salivary cortisol levels sampled at different times of the day. The majority of the studies reported that ambient cortisol concentrations in PTSD over a 24-h period are significantly lower (22,39–44) or not significantly different from those of normal volunteers (45,46), while a small percentage of studies reported cortisol levels in PTSD to be significantly higher (21,47,48). Interestingly, with very few exceptions, cortisol levels reported in the literature for persons with PTSD—whether significantly different from a nonpsychiatric comparison group or not—are within the normal endocrinologic range (15). That cortisol alterations are at best subtle and not easily differentiated from normal values may be one reason that it has been difficult to observe group differences in cortisol levels in small studies.

In addition, group differences in cortisol levels in PTSD may be obscured by other individual differences related to cortisol such as age, gender, body weight, height, metabolism, medical illness, mood, substance use (including alcohol and nicotine), and environmental stress. Studies that reported on cortisol levels in subjects homogeneous with these confounds or in which these variables were controlled for in statistical analyses have generally been more likely to observe significant differences in cortisol related to PTSD than those that have not (reviewed in Ref. *17*). One could make the argument for not controlling for all confounds since to be clinically meaningful the neuroendocrine "signal" associated with PTSD should be larger than the "noise." This would be the strategy of choice in examining relatively homogeneous groups with respect to gender, trauma type, age, and other important variables. The presence of individual differences also suggests that sample sizes need to be quite large, particularly in heterogeneous samples, to overcome the impact of confounding variables.

In contrast to studies obtaining integrated 24-h measures of urinary cortisol output (or assessing plasma or salivary cortisol at a few time points during the day), studies in which cortisol levels have been measured more carefully under controlled conditions (such as every hour or half hour via indwelling catheter in a clinical research center) have demonstrated overall reductions in cortisol levels across the diurnal cycle. More important, these studies have shown that, for large portions of the day and night, cortisol levels between persons with and without PTSD are not distinguishable (*41,44*). The assessment of cortisol at different time points throughout the day has the added advantage of providing information about circadian rhythmicity of cortisol.

An initial study of circadian parameters in PTSD was conducted by obtaining 49 consecutive blood samples from three groups of subjects—Vietnam combat veterans with PTSD, subjects (largely veterans) with major depression, and nonpsychiatric comparison subjects—every 30 min over a 24-h period under carefully controlled laboratory conditions. Lower mean basal cortisol levels, primarily in the late evening and early morning hours, were observed in PTSD compared to the other groups (*20*). The major difference between PTSD and non-PTSD groups was that cortisol levels were lower in the late night and very early morning and remained lower for a longer period of time in PTSD during hours when subjects are normally sleeping. By the time of awakening, the peak cortisol release was comparable in PTSD subjects and age-matched subjects. In a second study of women who had been sexually assaulted in childhood, cortisol levels were obtained every 15 min over a 24-h period. Significantly low cortisol levels were also observed in PTSD, this time in the afternoon and evening, but not morning, hours (*21*). It has been extremely difficult to evaluate true differences in circadian rhythm from studies using very few samples over the diurnal period because it is possible to miss the true peak and nadir of cortisol release.

RESULTS OF NEUROENDOCRINE CHALLENGES IN PTSD: FOCUS ON THE DEXAMETHASONE SUPPRESSION TEST

Neuroendocrine challenge studies have provided an important interpretive context for evaluating the significance of baseline cortisol levels in PTSD. PTSD is also associated with increased cortisol suppression in response to DEX administration in most (*49–62*), but not all (*63–65*), studies. More recently, the ACTH response to cortisol injection has also been found to be reduced (*66*). Both these effects likely result from increased responsiveness of central or peripheral GR (67–71). The profile of alterations in PTSD is clearly different from that observed in studies of acute and chronic stress and major depressive disorder, which have been associated with increased CRF, increased cortisol levels, and reduced cortisol suppression in response to DEX (72–74). The presence of these alterations has made it difficult to discount cortisol observations in the normal or low range. On the other hand, while the results of neuroendocrine challenge studies have provided support for the fact that there are alterations in the HPA axis in PTSD, when seen in the aggregate, they have not always presented a uniform understanding of PTSD. As with the findings of ambient hormone levels in PTSD, it is important to be able to critically evaluate the literature to know which conclusions can be made with more certainty than others. This involves the ability to evaluate whether a particular challenge test has been constructed and interpreted appropriately.

Results of studies using the low-dose dexamethasone suppression test (DST) perhaps provide the most consistent findings in PTSD, in part because the DST is a relatively straightforward test that has been applied in a consistent manner and in part because this test provides unambiguous information regarding negative-feedback inhibition. In contrast, results using CRF challenge testing have been conflicting, in part because these findings must be interpreted in the context of other HPA axis alterations. Studies using probes such as metyrapone have been inconclusive because of the disparate methodologies used. However, particularly problematic are cases in which interpretation is challenging because of the contradictory nature of the findings within one published report. An analysis of findings from these different challenge tests is presented to illustrate some of the interpretative issues that have arisen in trying to integrate the disparate observations.

Findings of the DST support the idea of increased glucocorticoid responsiveness. The DST provides a direct test of the effects of GR activation in the pituitary on ACTH secretion. Cortisol levels following DEX administration therefore provide an estimate of the strength of negative-feedback inhibition, provided that the adrenal response to ACTH is not altered. Nonsuppression of cortisol results from a reduced ability of DEX to exert negative-feedback inhibition on the release of CRF and ACTH (75). Thus, it is plausible that more extreme reductions in cortisol in response to DEX imply an enhanced negative-feedback inhibition. There are several hundred published studies reporting on the use of the DST in depression, all reporting that approximately 40–60% of patients with major depression demonstrate a failure to suppress cortisol levels below 5.0 µg/100 dL in response to 1.0 mg of DEX (76).

Initial studies using the DST in PTSD also used the 1.0-mg dose. Most of these studies failed to replicate the reduced negative-feedback inhibition observed in depression. In one of these studies, Halbreich et al. noted that post-DEX cortisol levels in the PTSD group were particularly lower than subjects with depression and even comparison subjects (75). This led our group to hypothesize that PTSD patients would show an enhanced, rather than reduced, cortisol suppression to

DEX and administered lower doses of DEX (0.50 and 0.25 mg) to examine this possibility (39,49). A hyperresponsiveness to low doses of DEX, as reflected by significantly lower post-DEX cortisol levels, was observed in combat Vietnam veterans compared to nonexposed subjects (77). The finding of an exaggerated suppression of cortisol in response to DEX was also observed in adult survivors of childhood sexual abuse (52,61), children who survived the Armenian earthquake (51), Gulf War soldiers who were still on active duty (53), Holocaust survivors (56), older combat veterans (56), depressed women with PTSD resulting from early childhood abuse (59), and survivors of domestic violence (62). Only two studies, one (64) using a mixed civilian group and one examining adolescents exposed to multiple traumatic events (65), failed to find cortisol differences in response to DEX. However, the main difference between these studies and others was in the use of saliva samples obtained at home rather than plasma samples obtained at confirmed standard intervals. Since the amount of free (active) cortisol is assessed preferentially in saliva, it may be that different findings relate to the higher fraction of bound cortisol in PTSD, a possibility further supported by the findings of increased cortisol-binding globulin (CBG) in PTSD (78).

GLUCOCORTICOID RESPONSIVENESS IN PTSD

Type II GRs are expressed in ACTH- and CRF-producing neurons of the pituitary, hypothalamus, and hippocampus and mediate most systemic glucocorticoid effects, particularly those related to stress responsiveness (79). The initial investigation of GRs in PTSD was based on knowledge that low circulating levels of a hormone or neurotransmitter could result in increased numbers of available receptors (80) that improve response capacity and facilitate homeostasis. Reciprocally, alterations in the number and sensitivity of both type I (mineralocorticoid) and type II GRs can significantly influence HPA axis activity and in particular can regulate hormone levels by mediating the strength of negative feedback. Either way, based on initial observations of low cortisol levels, it seemed important to focus on responsiveness of glucocorticoids by examining alterations in GRs.

The problem with this line of investigation has historically been a methodological one; it has been difficult to directly measure GRs in relevant tissue, and estimates of cytosolic (rather than nuclear or total) GR number only provide partial information about GR number and responsiveness. Yet, in view of the finding that lymphocyte and brain GRs were found to share similar regulatory and binding characteristics (81), an initial study was undertaken to examine peripheral cytosolic GR number in the lymphocytes. A greater number of 8:00 a.m., but not 4:00 p.m., type II GRs was reported in Vietnam veterans with PTSD compared to a normal comparison group (82). Subsequently, an inverse relationship was observed between 24-h urinary cortisol excretion and lymphocyte GR number in PTSD and depression (i.e., low cortisol and increased receptor levels were observed in PTSD, whereas in major depressive disorder, elevated cortisol and reduced receptor number were observed) (*22*).

Following the administration of a 0.25-mg dose of DEX, it was possible to observe that the cortisol response was accompanied by a concurrent decline in the number of cytosolic lymphocyte receptors (*56*). This finding contrasted the observation of a reduced decline in the number of cytosolic lymphocyte receptors in major depression, implying that the reduced cortisol levels following DEX administration may reflect an enhanced negative-feedback inhibition in PTSD (*83*).

The demonstration of increased glucocorticoid responsiveness in the live lymphocyte, as evidenced by the greater effects of DEX on lysozyme activity, is also noteworthy. Mononuclear leukocytes isolated from the blood of 26 men with PTSD and 18 men without PTSD were incubated with a series of concentrations of DEX to determine the rate of inhibition of lysozyme activity; a portion of cells was frozen for the determination of GRs. Subjects with PTSD showed evidence of greater sensitivity to glucocorticoids, as reflected by a significantly lower mean half maximal inhibitory concentration of dexamethasone for lysozyme activity (lysozyme $IC_{50\text{-}DEX}$). The lysozyme $IC_{50\text{-}DEX}$ was significantly correlated with age at exposure to the first traumatic event in subjects with PTSD, supporting the idea that enhanced GR responsiveness may be a risk factor for PTSD (*67*). Similarly, the recent finding that adult offspring of Holocaust survivors with PTSD demonstrated enhanced cortisol suppression on the DST is consistent with this notion (*43*). In the aggregate, the findings imply the presence of genetic or epigenetic changes in GR genes or genes regulating their activity, as has been demonstrated for FK506 binding protein 5 (FKBP5) (*83*).

PUTATIVE MODELS OF
HPA AXIS ALTERATIONS IN PTSD

Cortisol levels are often found to be lower than normal in PTSD but can also be similar to or greater than those in comparison subjects. Findings of changes in circadian rhythm suggest that there may be regulatory influences that result in a greater dynamic range of cortisol release over the diurnal cycle in PTSD. Studies using the DST have consistently demonstrated that there is enhanced negative-feedback inhibition of cortisol, at least at the level of the pituitary. An enhanced negative-feedback inhibition certainly explains why ambient cortisol levels may be normal or even lower in the face of hypothalamic CRF hypersecretion but, more important, is compatible with the idea that there may be transient elevations in cortisol. It would be expected that the regulatory influences responsible for enhancing negative-feedback inhibition (e.g., glucocorticoid responsiveness) would result in shorter-lived increases in cortisol due to a more efficient containment of ACTH release. In contrast to other models of endocrinopathy, which identify specific and usually singular primary alterations in endocrine organs or regulation, the explanation that enhanced negative-feedback inhibition explains other HPA alterations in PTSD is in large part descriptive and offers little explanation for why some individuals show such alterations of the HPA axis following exposure to traumatic experiences while others do not.

Another explanation for low cortisol levels in PTSD, and at least some of the other alterations observed, involves reduced adrenal output. This model certainly provides a reasonable explanation for why ambient cortisol levels would be lower than normal, and even for the relatively smaller magnitude of differences in ACTH relative to cortisol, but does not account for why basal ACTH levels are not significantly higher in PTSD than in comparison subjects, particularly in light of evidence of CRF hypersecretion. One of the challenges in elucidating a neuroendocrinology of PTSD is in being able to resolve the apparent paradox that cortisol levels are low when CRF levels appear to be elevated as well as to accommodate a dynamic process that accounts for observed diurnal fluctuations and potential responsivity to environmental cues. Heim, Newport, Bonsall, Miller, and Nemeroff again argued that in response to early trauma, CRF hypersecretion may result in downregulation of pituitary CRF receptors, leading to a decreased ACTH response (84). However, it is not quite clear according to this why in such cases CRF hypersecretion would lead to pituitary desensitization and low cortisol as opposed to the more classic model of HPA dysfunction articulated for major depressive disorder, in which the effect of hypothalamic CRF release on the pituitary would ultimately result in hypercortisolism. Furthermore, although findings of increased CRF levels in PTSD are important to the theory of enhanced negative-feedback inhibition in PTSD, they are not necessarily relevant to theories of adrenal insufficiency. That is, to the extent that there are increases in CRF, these would not necessarily occur as a direct response to reduced adrenal output but might have a different origin. Under conditions of reduced adrenal output, it is possible that compensatory changes in hypothalamic CRF might occur to the extent that there is weaker negative-feedback inhibition as a result of decreased cortisol output. But if this were occurring, it would be difficult to find an explanation for why the ACTH response to CRF and psychological stressors was augmented in relation to early traumatization.

Results of studies examining the cortisol response to DEX are compatible with both the enhanced negative-feedback inhibition model and adrenal insufficiency. However, in the latter case, one would not expect a reduced cortisol level to result from, or even be accompanied by change in, the GR but would reflect reduced adrenal output rather than an enhanced containment of ACTH. Findings of a blunted ACTH response to CRF are compatible with the enhanced negative-feedback model but not the adrenal insufficiency hypothesis. Adrenal insufficiency would not be expected to result in a blunted ACTH response to CRF. On the contrary, primary adrenal insufficiency is characterized by increased ACTH at baseline and in response to CRF. Findings demonstrating an augmented ACTH response to metyrapone are also consistent with enhanced negative-feedback inhibition but not adrenal insufficiency. Adrenal insufficiency is also not compatible with findings showing greater activation of cortisol in the context of reduced ACTH responses to pituitary challenges.

There are other possible explanations that have not yet been carefully considered. Differences in glucocorticoid production in the adrenals and glucocorticoid degradation in a variety of target tissue are also likely to be relevant to the neuroendocrine alterations in PTSD. These have not yet been carefully investigated. Furthermore, heterologous influences on the HPA axis, such as regulation of the pituitary ACTH or adrenal cortisol by other neuropeptides and factors, must also be considered and studied. Regardless of which model proves to be more explanatory, it appears clear that the majority of findings support the idea of an increased cortisol-signaling capacity so that lower levels of cortisol efficiently suppress HPA function. Such an alteration could conceivably lead to a situation in which afferent pathways in at least some tissues are exposed to reduced levels of cortisol, which may in turn result in increased sympathetic activation, also noted in PTSD (*22,23,85,86*).

FUTURE DIRECTIONS:
THE POTENTIAL RELEVANCE OF EPIGENETICS

Findings suggesting that cortisol levels might have been low prior to exposure to a focal trauma as well as those indicating that the most severe abnormalities of adult glucocorticoid metabolism are seen with earliest age of trauma exposure suggest that alterations are present as a result of developmental factors that then serve as regulators of long-term HPA axis dynamics. The recent observation that some cortisol-related alterations are observed in the infant (*38*) and adult (*87*) offspring of parents with PTSD also implies the possibility of transgenerational transmission relating to early glucocorticoid programming (*88*). Glucocorticoid programming has been shown to occur both pre- and postnatally and implicates epigenetic changes in association with HPA alterations in PTSD (*89*).

Epigenetics refers to a transgenerationally transmissible functional change in the genome that can be altered by environmental events and does not involve an alteration of DNA sequence (*90,91*). Several mechanisms of stable epigenetic gene regulation have been described in different organisms, of which the best characterized in the mammalian genome is DNA methylation at the cytosine site in CpG dinucleotides(*92,93*). Methylation of polymerase II promoters is an efficient way of gene silencing and accordingly provides a concrete molecular mechanism through which genetic-environmental interactions occur (*93*). Interest in epigenetics is sparked both by the general need to develop molecular markers that reflect the impact of the environment on gene activity and by the realization that such mechanisms are certainly likely to be important with respect to PTSD. There is good evidence that DNA methylation is a mechanism operative in programming the activity of genes regulating HPA activity by early life events (i.e., differences in maternal care) (*94,95*), paralleling observations that early life events are associated with the development of both PTSD (*96–98*) and the HPA axis alterations (*17*) described in this condition. Such changes in the rat pups result in permanent changes in hippocampal GR expression and HPA function (*99*) and provide a clear molecular link between early environment and gene expression and function. Interestingly, the alterations observed are in the same direction as those described in PTSD (i.e., increased GR sensitivity, enhanced cortisol response to DEX, lower cortisol levels), offering proof of principle that environmental exposures can result in such changes.

Although it is not immediately obvious what the similarities between effects of "positive" maternal behaviors (i.e., increased licking and grooming) and PTSD risk might be (i.e., prima facie, the latter would be expected to be associated with deprivation), in all other aspects the possibility of defining the pathways by which environmental risk factors might directly alter GR expression appears to constitute an extremely relevant finding to PTSD. This may form a basis for identifying individual differences in endocrine function and, perhaps, vulnerability in PTSD. The parallels are indeed striking. In theory, different cells and tissues are particularly sensitive to changes in methylation at different times during development, although in some instances, such as the development of cancer (100), DNA methylation appears to be central for the process throughout life. This is entirely congruent with findings in PTSD that point to a greater prevalence of PTSD following events occurring at specific developmental stages, although this disorder can develop throughout one's lifetime (101).

The GRs may be a particularly relevant target of epigenetic regulation based on the observations that this receptor is subject to programming by early life events that results in permanent changes in physiology throughout life in rats (102,103). A similar process in humans may likely be relevant for the development of PTSD. Furthermore, such changes are capable of being transmitted intergenerationally (104,105), which also fits with recent observations of HPA axis alterations in both infants and adult offspring of parents with PTSD. For obvious reasons, genetic analyses will simply not detect environment-gene activity connections, and although endocrine studies can in principle detect them, endocrine activities often are determined by more recent life events that may obfuscate the impact of earlier events (106). One of the major limitations of studying endocrine aspects of PTSD has been the inability to know for certain whether what is being measured constitutes a change associated with PTSD pathophysiology, the trauma that produced it, or the earlier risk factor. Although we have suggested that neuroendocrine aspects of PTSD may be somewhat stable, it is inarguable that the pattern of DNA methylation is far more stable and is more likely to reflect earlier life events rather than the cumulative effects of stress.

CONCLUSIONS

The HPA axis alterations in PTSD support the idea that different HPA axis alterations may be associated with different aspects of PTSD, including risk for the development of this disorder. Clearly, there is evidence that some features of the HPA axis may be altered prior to the exposure to a focal trauma. Understanding that components of the HPA axis are not uniformly regulated (e.g., circadian rhythm patterns, tonic cortisol secretion, negative-feedback inhibition, and the cortisol response to stress are differentially mediated) is critical in the integration of disparate findings, as is an appreciation for the fact that the HPA axis is a fundamentally dynamic system that may show transient increases or hyperresponsivity under certain environmental conditions.

The disparate observations observed in the neuroendocrinology of PTSD underscore the important observation of Mason et al. that HPA axis response patterns in PTSD are fundamentally in the normal range and do not reflect endocrinopathy (*16*). In endocrinologic disorders, for which there is usually a lesion in one or more target tissues or biosynthetic pathways, endocrine methods can usually isolate the problem with the appropriate tests and then obtain rather consistent results. In psychiatric disorders, neuroendocrine alterations may be subtle; therefore, when using standard endocrine tools to examine these alterations, there is a high probability of failing to observe all the alterations consistent with a neuroendocrine explanation of the pathology in tandem. It is hoped the next-generation studies will be able to apply more rigorous tests of neuroendocrinology of PTSD based on the appropriate developmental issues and in consideration of the longitudinal course of the disorder and the individual differences that affect these processes. No doubt such studies will require a closer examination of a wide range of biologic responses, including the genetic, cellular, and molecular mechanisms involved in adaptation to stress.

ACKNOWLEDGMENTS

This work was supported by National Institute of Mental Health, Department of Defense, and Veterans Affairs MERIT funding. I gratefully acknowledge Janelle Wohltmann for her assistance.

REFERENCES

1. Munck, A., Guyre, P. M., and Holbrook, N. J. (1984) Physiological functions of glucocorticoids in stress and their relation to pharmacological actions. Endocr Rev 5, 25–44.
2. McEwen, B. S. (1979) Influences of adrenocortical hormones on pituitary and brain function. Monogr Endocrinol 12, 467–92.
3. de Kloet, E. R., Reul, J. M., de Ronde, F. S., Bloemers, M., and Ratka, A. (1986) Function and plasticity of brain corticosteroid receptor systems: action of neuropeptides. J Steroid Biochem 25, 723–31.
4. Kardiner, A. (1941) The Traumatic Neuroses of War. New York: Hoeber.
5. Meakins, J. C., and Wilson, R. M. (1918) The effect of certain sensory stimulations of respiratory and heart rate in cases of so-called "irritable heart." Heart 7, 17–22.
6. Fraser, F., and Wilson, R. M. (1918) The sympathetic nervous system and the "irritable heart of soldiers." Br Med J.
7. Kosten, T. R., Mason, J. W., Giller, E. L., Ostroff, R. B., and Harkness, L. (1987) Sustained urinary norepinephrine and epinephrine elevation in post-traumatic stress disorder. Psychoneuroendocrinology 12, 13–20.
8. Yehuda, R., Southwick, S., Giller, E. L., Ma, X., and Mason, J. W. (1992) Urinary catecholamine excretion and severity of PTSD symptoms in Vietnam combat veterans. J Nerv Ment Dis 180, 321–25.

9. Southwick, S. M., Krystal, J. H., Bremner, J. D., Morgan, C. A. 3rd, , Nicolaou, A. L., Nagy, L. M., Johnson, D. R., Heninger, G. R., and Charney, D.S. (1997) Noradrenergic and serotonergic function in posttraumatic stress disorder. Arch Gen Psychiatry 54, 749–58.

10. Yehuda, R., Resnick, H. S., Schmeidler, J., Yang, R. K., and Pitman, R. K. (1998) Predictors of cortisol and 3-methoxy-4-hydroxyphenylglycol responses in the acute aftermath of rape. Biol Psychiatry 43, 855–59.

11. Buckley, T. C., and Kaloupek, D. G. (2001) A meta-analytic examination of basal cardiovascular activity in posttraumatic stress disorder. Psychosom Med 63, 585–94.

12. Mellman, T. A., Knorr, B. R., Pigeon, W. R., Leiter, J. C., and Akay, M. (2004) Heart rate variability during sleep and the early development of posttraumatic stress disorder. Biol Psychiatry 55, 953–56.

13. O'Donnell, T., Hegadoren, K. M., and Coupland, N. C. (2004) Noradrenergic mechanisms in the pathophysiology of post-traumatic stress disorder. Neuropsychobiology 50, 273–83.

14. Bryant, R. A. (2006) Longitudinal psychophysiological studies of heart rate: mediating effects and implications for treatment. Ann N Y Acad Sci 1071, 19–26.

15. Mason, J. W., Giller, E. L., Kosten, T. R., Ostroff, R. B., and Podd, L. (1986) Urinary free-cortisol levels in posttraumatic stress disorder patients. J Nerv Ment Dis 174, 145–49.

16. Mason, J. W., Giller, E. L., Kosten, T. R., and Harkness, L. (1988) Elevation of urinary norepinephrine/cortisol ratio in posttraumatic stress disorder. J Nerv Ment Dis 176, 498–502.

17. Yehuda, R. (2002) Current status of cortisol findings in post-traumatic stress disorder. Psychiatr Clin North Am 25, 341–68.

18. Yehuda, R. (2005) Neuroendocrine aspects of PTSD. Handb Exp Pharmacol 169, 371–403.

19. Yehuda, R. (2006) Advances in understanding neuroendocrine alterations in PTSD and their therapeutic implications. Ann N Y Acad Sci 1071, 137–66.

20. Yehuda, R., Teicher, M. H., Trestman, R. L., Levengood, R. A., and Siever, L. J. (1996) Cortisol regulation in posttraumatic stress disorder and major depression: a chronobiological analysis. Biol Psychiatry 40, 79–88.

21. Bremner, J. D., Vythilingam, M., Anderson, G., Vermetten, E., McGlashan, T., Heninger, G., Rasmusson, A., Southwick, S. M., and Charney, D. S. (2003) Assessment of the hypothalamic-pituitary-adrenal axis over a 24-hour diurnal period and in response to neuroendocrine challenges in women with and without childhood sexual abuse and posttraumatic stress disorder. Biol Psychiatry 54, 710–18.

22. Yehuda, R. (2002) Current status of cortisol findings in post-traumatic stress disorder. Psychiatr Clin North Am 25, 341–68, vii.

23. de Kloet, C. S., Vermetten, E., Geuze, E., Kavelaars, A., Heijnen, C. J., and Westenberg, H. G. (2006) Assessment of HPA-axis function in posttraumatic stress disorder: pharmacological and non-pharmacological challenge tests, a review. J Psychiatr Res 40, 550–67.

24. McGaugh, J. L., and Roozendaal, B. (2002) Role of adrenal stress hormones in forming lasting memories in the brain. Curr Opin Neurobiol 12, 205–10.

25. Bremner, J. D., Licinio, J., Darnell, A., Krystal, J. H., Owens, M. J., Southwick, S. M., Nemeroff, C. B., and Charney, D. S. (1997) Elevated CSF corticotropin-releasing factor concentrations in posttraumatic stress disorder. Am J Psychiatry 154, 624–29.

26. Sautter, F. J., Bissette, G., Wiley, J., Manguno-Mire, G., Schoenbachler, B., Myers, L., Johnson, J. E., Cerbone, A., and Malaspina, D. (2003) Corticotropin-releasing factor in posttraumatic stress disorder (PTSD) with secondary psychotic symptoms, nonpsychotic PTSD, and healthy control subjects. Biol Psychiatry 54, 1382–88.

27. Kasckow, J. W., Baker, and D., and Geracioti T. D., J (2000) Corticotropin-releasing hormone in depression and post-traumatic stress disorder. Peptides 22, 845–51
28. Yehuda, R.(2002) Post-traumatic stress disorder. N Engl J Med 346, 108–14.
29. Holsboer, F. (2003) Corticotropin-releasing hormone modulators and depression. Curr Opin Investig Drugs 4, 46–50.
30. Resnick, H. S., Yehuda, R., Pitman, R. K., and Foy, D. W. (1995) Effect of previous trauma on acute plasma cortisol level following rape. Am J Psychiatry 152, 1675–77.
31. Yehuda, R., McFarlane, A. C., and Shalev, A. Y. (1998) Predicting the development of posttraumatic stress disorder from the acute response to a traumatic event. Biol Psychiatry 44, 1305–13.
32. Anisman, H., Griffiths, J., Matheson, K., Ravindran, A. V., and Merali, Z. (2001) Post-traumatic stress symptoms and salivary cortisol levels. Am J Psychiatry 158, 1509–11.
33. Delahanty, D. L., Raimonde, A. J., and Spoonster, E. (2000) Initial posttraumatic urinary cortisol levels predict subsequent PTSD symptoms in motor vehicle accident victims. Biol Psychiatry 48, 940–47.
34. Delahanty, D. L., Raimonde, A. J., Spoonster, E., and Cullado, M. (2003) Injury severity, prior trauma history, urinary cortisol levels, and acute PTSD in motor vehicle accident victims. J Anxiety Disord 17, 149–64.
35. Yehuda, R., Teicher, M. H., Seck, J. R., Grossman, R. A., Morris, A., and Bierer, L. M. (2007) Parental posttraumatic stress disorder as a vulnerability factor for low cortisol trait in offspring of holocaust survivors. Arch Gen Psychiatry 64, 1040–48.
36. Yehuda, R., Blair, W., Labinsky, E., and Bierer, L. M. (2007) Effects of parental PTSD on the cortisol response to dexamethasone administration in their adult offspring. Am J Psychiatry 164, 163–66.
37. Yehuda, R., Halligan, S. L., and Bierer, L. M. (2001) Relationship of parental trauma exposure and PTSD to PTSD, depressive and anxiety disorders in offspring. J Psychiatr Res 35, 261–70.
38. Yehuda, R., Engel, S. M., Brand, S. R., Seckl, J., Marcus, S. M., and Berkowitz, G. S. (2005) Transgenerational effects of posttraumatic stress disorder in babies of mothers exposed to the World Trade Center attacks during pregnancy. J Clin Endocrinol Metab 90, 4115–18.
39. Yehuda, R., Southwick, S. M., Nussbaum, G., Wahby, V., Giller, E. L., Jr., and Mason, J. W. (1990) Low urinary cortisol excretion in patients with posttraumatic stress disorder. J Nerv Ment Dis 178, 366–69.
40. Yehuda, R., Boisoneau, D., Mason, J. W., and Giller, E. L. (1993) Glucocorticoid receptor number and cortisol excretion in mood, anxiety, and psychotic disorders. Biol Psychiatry 34, 18–25.
41. Yehuda, R., Kahana, B., Binder-Brynes, K., Southwick, S. M., Mason, J. W., and Giller, E. L. (1995) Low urinary cortisol excretion in Holocaust survivors with posttraumatic stress disorder. Am J Psychiatry 152, 982–86.
42. Yehuda, R., Teicher, M. H., Trestman, R. L., Levengood, R. A., and Siever, L. J. (1996) Cortisol regulation in posttraumatic stress disorder and major depression: a chronobiological analysis. Biol Psychiatry 40, 79–88.
43. Heim, C., Ehlert, U., Hanker, J. P., and Hellhammer, D. H. (1998) Abuse-related posttraumatic stress disorder and alterations of the hypothalamic-pituitary-adrenal axis in women with chronic pelvic pain. Psychosom Med 60, 309–18.
44. Glover, D. A., and Poland, R. E. (2002) Urinary cortisol and catecholamines in mothers of child cancer survivors with and without PTSD Psychoneuroendocrinology 27, 805–19.
45. Maes, M., Lin, A., Bonaccorso, S., van Hunsel, F., Van Gastel, A., Delmeire, L., Biondi, M., Bosmans, E., Kenis, G., and Scharpé, S. (1998) Increased 24-hour urinary cortisol excretion

in patients with post-traumatic stress disorder and patients with major depression, but not in patients with fibromyalgia. Acta Psychiatr Scand 98, 328–35.

46. Baker, D. G., West, S. A., Nicholson, W. E., Ekhator, N. N., Kasckow, J. W., Hill, K. K., Bruce, A. B., Orth, D. N., and Geracioti, T. D., Jr. (1999) Serial CSF corticotropin-releasing hormone levels and adrenocortical activity in combat veterans with posttraumatic stress disorder Am J Psychiatry 156, 585–588.

47. Pitman, R. K., and Orr, S. P. (1990) Twenty-four hour urinary cortisol and catecholamine excretion in combat-related posttraumatic stress disorder. Biol Psychiatry 27, 245–47.

48. Lemieux, A. M., and Coe, C. L. (1995) Abuse-related posttraumatic stress disorder: evidence for chronic neuroendocrine activation in women. Psychosom Med 57, 105–15.

49. Yehuda, R., Southwick, S. M., Krystal, J. H., Bremner, D., Charney, D. S., and Mason, J. W. (1993) Enhanced suppression of cortisol following dexamethasone administration in posttraumatic stress disorder. Am J Psychiatry 150, 83–86.

50. Yehuda, R., Boisoneau, D., Lowy, M. T., and Giller, E. L., Jr. (1995) Dose-response changes in plasma cortisol and lymphocyte glucocorticoid receptors following dexamethasone administration in combat veterans with and without posttraumatic stress disorder. Arch Gen Psychiatry 52, 583–93.

51. Goenjian, A. K., Yehuda, R., Pynoos, R. S., Steinberg, A. M., Tashjian, M., Yang, R. K., Najarian, L. M., and Fairbanks, L. A. (1996) Basal cortisol, dexamethasone suppression of cortisol, and MHPG in adolescents after the 1988 earthquake in Armenia. Am J Psychiatry 153, 929–34.

52. Stein, M. B., Yehuda, R., Koverola, C., and Hanna, C. (1997) Enhanced dexamethasone suppression of plasma cortisol in adult women traumatized by childhood sexual abuse. Biol Psychiatry 42, 680–86.

53. Kellner, M., Baker, D. G., and Yehuda, R. (1997) Salivary cortisol and PTSD symptoms in Persian Gulf War combatants. Ann N Y Acad Sci 821, 442–43.

54. Grossman, R., Yehuda, R., New, A., Schmeidler, J., Silverman, J., Mitropoulou, V., Sta Maria, N., Golier, J., and Siever, L. (2001) Dexamethasone suppression test findings in subjects with personality disorders: associations with posttraumatic stress disorder and major depression. Am J Psychiatry 160, 1291–98.

55. Rinne, T., de Kloet, E. R., Wouters, L., Goekoop, J. G., DeRijk, R. H., and van den Brink, W. (2002) Hyperresponsiveness of hypothalamic-pituitary-adrenal axis to combined dexamethasone/corticotropin-releasing hormone challenge in female borderline personality disorder subjects with a history of sustained childhood abuse. Biol Psychiatry 52, 1102–12.

56. Yehuda, R., Halligan, S. L., Grossman, R., Golier, J. A., and Wong, C. (2002) The cortisol and glucocorticoid receptor response to low dose dexamethasone administration in aging combat veterans and holocaust survivors with and without posttraumatic stress disorder. Biol Psychiatry 52, 393–403.

57. Lange, W., Wulff, H., Berea, C., Beblo, T., Saavedra, A. S., Mensebach, C., Wingenfeld, K., and Driessen, M. (2005) Dexamethasone suppression test in borderline personality disorder-effects of posttraumatic stress disorder. Psychoneuroendocrinology 30, 919–23.

58. Duval, F., Crocq, M. A., Guillon, M. S., Mokrani, M. C., Monreal, J., Bailey, P., and Macher, J. P. (2004) Increased adrenocorticotropin suppression following dexamethasone administration in sexually abused adolescents with posttraumatic stress disorder. Psychoneuroendocrinology 29, 1281–89.

59. Yehuda, R., Halligan, S. L., Golier, J. A., Grossman, R., and Bierer, L. M. (2004) Effects of trauma exposure on the cortisol response to dexamethasone administration in PTSD and major depressive disorder. Psychoneuroendocrinology 29, 389–404.

60. Yehuda, R., Golier, J. A., Halligan, S. L., Meaney, M., and Bierer, L. M. (2004) The ACTH response to dexamethasone in PTSD. Am J Psychiatry 161, 1397–1403.
61. Newport, D. J., Heim, C., Bonsall, R., Miller, A. H., and Nemeroff, C. B. (2004) Pituitary-adrenal responses to standard and low-dose dexamethasone suppression tests in adult survivors of child abuse. Biol Psychiatry 55, 10–20.
62. Griffin, M. G., Resick, P. A., and Yehuda, R. (2005) Enhanced cortisol suppression following dexamethasone administration in domestic violence survivors. Am J Psychiatry 162, 1192–99.
63. Lindley, S. E., Carlson, E. B., and Benoit, M. (2004) Basal and dexamethasone suppressed salivary cortisol concentrations in a community sample of patients with posttraumatic stress disorder. Biol Psychiatry 55, 940–45
64. Atmaca, M., Kuloglu, M., Tezcan, E., Onal, S., and Ustundag, B. (2002) Neopterin levels and dexamethasone suppression test in posttraumatic stress disorder. Eur Arch Psychiatry Clin Neurosci 252, 161–65.
65. Lipschitz, D. S., Rasmusson, A. M., Yehuda, R., Wang, S., Anyan, W., Gueoguieva, R., Grilo, C. M., Fehon, D. C., and Southwick, S. M. (2003) Salivary cortisol responses to dexamethasone in adolescents with posttraumatic stress disorder. J Am Acad Child Adolesc Psychiatry 42, 1310–17.
66. Yehuda, R., Yang, R. K., Buchsbaum, M. S., and Golier, J. A. (2006) Alterations in cortisol negative feedback inhibition as examined using the ACTH response to cortisol administration in PTSD. Psychoneuroendocrinology 31, 447–51.
67. Rohleder, N., Joksimovic, L., Wolf, J. M., and Kirschbaum, C. (2004) Hypocortisolism and increased glucocorticoid sensitivity of pro-Iinflammatory cytokine production in Bosnian war refugees with posttraumatic stress disorder. Biol Psychiatry 55, 745–51.
68. Coupland, N. J., Hegadoren, K. M., and Myrholm, J. (2003) Increased beclomethasone-induced vasoconstriction in women with posttraumatic stress disorder. J Psychiatr Res 37, 221–28.
69. Yehuda, R., Golier, J. A., Yang, R. K., and Tischler, L. (2004) Enhanced sensitivity to glucocorticoids in peripheral mononuclear leukocytes in posttraumatic stress disorder. Biol Psychiatry 55, 1110–16.
70. Gotovac, K., Sabioncello, A., Rabatic, S., Berki, T., and Dekaris, D. (2003) Flow cytometric determination of glucocorticoid receptor (GCR) expression in lymphocyte subpopulations: lower quantity of GCR in patients with post-traumatic stress disorder (PTSD). Clin Exp Immunol 131, 335–9.
71. Yehuda, R., Lowy, M. T., Southwick, S. M., Shaffer, D., and Giller, E. L., Jr. (1991) Lymphocyte glucocorticoid receptor number in posttraumatic stress disorder. Am J Psychiatry 148, 499–504.
72. Strohle, A., and Holsboer, F. (2003) Stress responsive neurohormones in depression and anxiety. Pharmacopsychiatry 36(suppl 3), S207–14.
73. Holsboer, F. (2003) Corticotropin-releasing hormone modulators and depression. Curr Opin Investig Drugs 4, 46–50.
74. Holsboer, F. (2000) The corticosteroid receptor hypothesis of depression. Neuropsychopharmacology 23, 477–501.
75. Halbreich, U., Olympia, J., Carson, S., Glogowski, J., Yeh, C. M., Axelrod, S., and Desu, M. M. (1989) Hypothalamo-pituitary-adrenal activity in endogenously depressed post-traumatic stress disorder patients. Psychoneuroendocrinology 14, 365–70.
76. Dinan, T. G., Barry, S., Yatham, L. N., Mobayed, M., and Brown, I. (1990) A pilot study of a neuroendocrine test battery in posttraumatic stress disorder. Biol Psychiatry 28, 665–72.

77. Kosten, T. R., Wahby, V., Giller, E., Jr., and Mason, J. (1990) The dexamethasone suppression test and thyrotropin-releasing hormone stimulation test in posttraumatic stress disorder. Biol Psychiatry 28, 657–64.
78. Yehuda, R., Levengood, R. A., Schmeidler, J., Wilson, S., Guo, L. S., and Gerber, D. (1996) Increased pituitary activation following metyrapone administration in post-traumatic stress disorder. Psychoneuroendocrinology 21, 1–16.
79. Lowy, M. T. (1989) Quantification of type I and II adrenal steroid receptors in neuronal, lymphoid and pituitary tissues. Brain Res 503, 191–97.
80. Gormley, G. J., Lowy, M. T., Reder, A. T., Hospelhorn, V. D., Antel, J. P., and Meltzer, H. Y. (1985) Glucocorticoid receptors in depression: relationship to the dexamethasone suppression test. Am J Psychiatry 142, 1278–84.
81. Kellner, M., Baker, D. G., Yassouridis, A., Bettinger, S., Otte, C., Naber, D., and Wiedemann, K. (2002) Mineralocorticoid receptor function in patients with posttraumatic stress disorder. Am J Psychiatry 159, 1938–40.
82. Gotovac, K., Sabioncello, A., Rabatic, S., Berki, T., and Dekaris, D. (2003) Flow cytometric determination of glucocorticoid receptor (GCR) expression in lymphocyte subpopulations: lower quantity of GCR in patients with post-traumatic stress disorder (PTSD). Clin Exp Immunol 131, 335–39.
83. Binder, E. B., Bradley, R. G., Liu, W., Epstein, M. P., Deveau, T. C., Mercer, K. B., Tang, Y., Gillespie, C. F., Heim, C. M., Nemeroff, C. B., Schwartz, A. C., Cubells, J. F., and Ressler, K. J. (2008) Association of FKBP5 polymorphisms and childhood abuse with risk of posttraumatic stress disorder symptoms in adults. JAMA 299, 1291–1305.
84. Heim, C., Newport, D. J., Bonsall, R., Miller, A. H., and Nemeroff, C. B. (2001) Altered pituitary-adrenal axis responses to provocative challenge tests in adult survivors of childhood abuse. Am J Psychiatry 158, 575–81.
85. Yehuda, R., and LeDoux, J. (2007) Response variation following trauma: a translational neuroscience approach to understanding PTSD. Neuron 56, 19–32.
86. Raison, C. L., and Miller, A. H. (2003) When not enough is too much: the role of insufficient glucocorticoid signaling in the pathophysiology of stress-related disorders. Am J Psychiatry 160, 1554–65.
87. Yehuda, R., Halligan, S. L., and Bierer, L. M. (2002) Cortisol levels in adult offspring of Holocaust survivors: relation to PTSD symptom severity in the parent and child. Psychoneuroendocrinology 27, 171–80.
88. Seckl, J. R. (2004) Prenatal glucocorticoids and long-term programming. Eur J Endocrinol 151(suppl 3), U49–U62.
89. Seckl, J. R., and Meaney, M. J. (2004) Glucocorticoid programming. Ann N Y Acad Sci 1032, 63–84.
90. Novik, K. L., Nimmrich, I., Genc, B., Maier, S., Piepenbrock, C., Olek, A., and Beck, S. (2002) Epigenomics: genome-wide study of methylation phenomena. Curr Issues Mol Biol 4, 111–28.
91. Nakao, M. (2001) Epigenetics: interaction of DNA methylation and chromatin. Gene 278, 25–31.
92. Holliday, R. (1989) DNA methylation and epigenetic mechanisms. Cell Biophys 15, 15–20.
93. Sutherland, J. E., and Costa, M. (2003) Epigenetics and the environment. Ann NY Acad Sci 983, 151–60.
94. Weaver, I. C., Szyf, M., and Meaney, M. J. (2002) From maternal care to gene expression: DNA methylation and the maternal programming of stress responses. Endocr Res 28, 699.

95. Weaver, I. C., Cervoni, N., Champagne, F. A., D'Alessio, A. C., Sharma, S., Seckl, J. R., Dymov, S., Szyf, M., and Meaney, M. J. (2004) Epigenetic programming by maternal behavior. Nat Neurosci 7, 847–54.
96. Nishith, P., Mechanic, M. B., and Resick, P. A. (2000) Prior interpersonal trauma: the contribution to current PTSD symptoms in female rape victims. J Abnorm Psychol 109, 20–25.
97. Epstein, J. N., Saunders, B. E., and Kilpatrick, D. G. (1997) Predicting PTSD in women with a history of childhood rape. J Trauma Stress 10, 573–88.
98. Andrews, B., Brewin, C. R., Rose, S., and Kirk, M. (2000) Predicting PTSD symptoms in victims of violent crime: the role of shame, anger, and childhood abuse. J Abnorm Psychol 109, 69–73.
99. Liu, D., Tannenbaum, B., Caldji, C., Francis, D., Freedman, A., Sharma, S., Pearson, D., Plotsky, P. M., and Meaney, M. J. (1997) Maternal care, hippocampal glucocorticoid receptors, and hypothalamic-pituitary-adrenal responses to stress. Science 277, 1659–62.
100. Esteller, M. (2005) Aberrant DNA methylation as a cancer-inducing mechanism. Annu Rev Pharmacol Toxicol 45, 629–56.
101. Kessler, R. C., Sonnega, A., Bromet, E., Hughes, M., and Nelson, C. B. (1995) Posttraumatic stress disorder in the National Comorbidity Survey. Arch Gen Psychiatry 52, 1048–1060.
102. Francis, D. D., Champagne, F. A., Liu, D., and Meaney, M. J. (1999) Maternal care, gene expression, and development of individual differences in stress reactivity. Ann N Y Acad Sci 896, 66–84.
103. Francis, D. D., and Meaney, M. J. (1999) Maternal care and the development of stress responses. Curr Opin Neurobiol 9, 128–34.
104. Champagne, F., and Meaney, M. J. (2001) Like mother, like daughter: evidence for non-genomic transmission of parental behavior and stress responsivity. Prog Brain Res 133, 287–302.
105. Francis, D., Diorio, J., Liu, D., and Meaney, M. J. (1999) Nongenomic transmission across generations of maternal behavior and stress responses in the rat. Science 286, 1155–58.
106. Selye, H. (1985) The nature of stress. Basal Facts 7, 3–11.

13 Low Basal Cortisol and Startle Responding as Possible Biomarkers of PTSD: The Influence of Internalizing and Externalizing Comorbidity

Mark W. Miller, Erika J. Wolf,
Laura Fabricant, and Nathan Stein

CONTENTS

INTRODUCTION
THE INTERNALIZING AND EXTERNALIZING MODEL
  OF PSYCHIATRIC COMORBIDITY
INTERNALIZING AND EXTERNALIZING PTSD SUBTYPES
RELATIONSHIP BETWEEN PTSD AND CORTISOL AND
  THE MODERATING INFLUENCE OF INTERNALIZING
  AND EXTERNALIZING COMORBIDITY
EVIDENCE FOR THE LINK BETWEEN INTERNALIZING
  DISORDERS AND ELEVATED CORTISOL
EVIDENCE FOR THE LINK BETWEEN EXTERNALIZING
  DISORDERS AND LOW CORTISOL
THE STARTLE RESPONSE
EFFECTS OF COMORBIDITY ON BASELINE AND OVERALL
  STARTLE AMPLITUDE
CONCLUSIONS AND DIRECTIONS FOR FUTURE RESEARCH
REFERENCES

From: *Post-Traumatic Stress Disorder: Basic Science and Clinical Practice*
Edited by: P. J. Shiromani et al., DOI: 10.1007/978-1-60327-329-9_13
© Humana Press, a part of Springer Science+Business Media, LLC 2009

Abstract

Comorbidity presents significant problems to investigators engaged in the search for biomarkers of post-traumatic stress disorder (PTSD) because it means that multiple overlapping psychiatric phenotypes may be present in any PTSD sample. This chapter reviews research on an internalizing/externalizing model of post-traumatic psychopathology and discusses its relevance to the search for PTSD biomarkers. It focuses on two candidate biomarkers that have been studied extensively in relation to PTSD—basal cortisol level and startle reflex amplitude—but have yielded complicated and mixed results. Our review of the cortisol literature finds evidence for links between disorders of the internalizing spectrum and elevated levels of cortisol and links between externalizing psychopathology and low levels of cortisol. The review of the startle reflex literature reveals an association between exaggerated startle and fear-related disorders of the internalizing spectrum. These findings illustrate how individual differences in internalizing and externalizing comorbidity may moderate associations between these measures and PTSD diagnostic status. The chapter concludes with a discussion of the advantages of studying latent dimensions of comorbidity in future PTSD biomarker research.

Key Words: Comorbidity, cortisol, heterogeneity, internalizing, externalizing, startle.

INTRODUCTION

Post-traumatic stress disorder (PTSD) is the product of an environmental pathogen (i.e., a traumatic stressor) operating on a variety of individual diatheses or predispositions. These diatheses span the spectrum of human variation in vulnerability to psychopathology and result in extensive heterogeneity in the phenotypic expression of the disorder. One manifestation of this is a diverse pattern of diagnostic comorbidity associated with PTSD. Brown et al. *(1)* assessed the co-occurrence of current and lifetime *Diagnostic and Statistical Manual of Mental Disorders*, fourth edition (DSM-IV) anxiety and unipolar mood disorders in 1,126 community outpatients and found that, of all the disorders assessed, PTSD showed the most prevalent and varied pattern of comorbidity. Of individuals with a current diagnosis of PTSD, 92% met criteria for another current Axis I disorder, with the most frequent being major depressive disorder (77%), generalized anxiety disorder (38%), and alcohol abuse/dependence (31%). Similarly, in studies of veterans receiving clinical services, 82% of those with a current diagnosis of PTSD met criteria for another Axis I disorder *(2)*, and the National Vietnam Veterans Readjustment Study showed that 50% of veterans with PTSD had an additional Axis I diagnosis *(3)*.

Comorbidity presents significant problems to investigators engaged in the search for biomarkers of PTSD. It undermines the assumption that PTSD is a discrete syndrome that is qualitatively and mechanistically distinct from other DSM-IV disorders. It also means that multiple overlapping psychiatric phenotypes may be present in any PTSD sample, which can obscure the search for markers that reliably distinguish cases from controls. The aims of this chapter are to review research on an internalizing/externalizing model of the phenotypic heterogeneity (i.e., clinical presentations) among individuals with PTSD and to discuss the relevance of this model for the search for PTSD biomarkers. We review the literature on two measures that have been the focus of extensive PTSD biomarker research—basal cortisol levels and startle reflex amplitude—and illustrate how individual differences in internalizing and externalizing comorbidity may moderate associations between these measures and PTSD diagnostic status.

THE INTERNALIZING AND EXTERNALIZING MODEL OF PSYCHIATRIC COMORBIDITY

The internalizing/externalizing model of psychiatric comorbidity proposes that patterns of behavioral disturbance and psychiatric symptoms among common mental disorders cohere along two underlying, or latent, dimensions. It is rooted in over 30 years of research in the area of childhood behavior disorders (cf.*4,5*) and has recently come to the fore in the adult psychopathology literature as the result of a series of influential factor-analytic studies of the structure of adult mental illness *(6–12)*. Krueger, Kendler, Kessler, and others have shown that comorbid disorders tend to cohere along these dimensions, with the alcohol and substance-related disorders and antisocial personality disorder loading on the externalizing dimension and the unipolar mood and anxiety disorders falling on the internalizing dimension. In several studies, the latter has been subdivided into correlated factors termed *anxious-misery* (defined by major depression, dysthymia, generalized anxiety disorder) and *fear* (comprised of panic and phobic disorders; *8,12–14)*. This structure has demonstrated invariance across genders and multiple samples drawn at random from a larger sample *(6,8)* and has also been shown to account for patterns of diagnostic comorbidity in combat veterans *(15)*. Twin and adoption studies have implicated genetic factors in the etiology of the externalizing and internalizing latent factors *(16,17)*, and the magnitude of these genetic effects increases with the severity of the behavior problems on a given dimension *(18)*.

The externalizing/internalizing model is consistent with other major models of comorbidity that posit that the co-occurrence of disorders among broad classes (e.g., the anxiety and unipolar mood disorders) is due largely to the fact that they emerge from a common diathesis (e.g., *19,20)*. This concept is supported by evidence suggesting that whereas much overlap exists in terms of the predisposing factors within a given spectrum of psychopathology, the manifestations of these diatheses differ considerably as a function of exposure to various environmental factors (e.g., trauma exposure, other life stressors, or developmental experiences). In other words, the different manifestations of these shared vulnerability dimensions are represented by the various DSM-IV diagnoses. This concept is in accord with a leading theoretical explanation for the high rate of co-occurrence of disorders within a spectrum of psychopathology (i.e., "Disorders A and B co-occur because they are both influenced by another underlying or causal factor C"; cf. *21*), although further empirical work is needed to explore the influence of other possibilities (e.g., disorder A predisposes or causes disorder B; disorders A and B are associated because they share overlapping definitional criteria; disorders A and B should not be considered comorbid because they can be subsumed into a larger category that has been artificially split by the classification system).

INTERNALIZING AND
EXTERNALIZING PTSD SUBTYPES

Recent studies suggest that the internalizing/externalizing model may also be relevant to the understanding of patterns of comorbidity (i.e., phenotypic heterogeneity) among individuals with PTSD and their links to underlying biologic mechanisms and biomarkers *(15,22–24)*. Specifically, through a series of cluster analytic studies of personality inventories completed by individuals with PTSD, Miller and colleagues found evidence of internalizing and externalizing subtypes of PTSD in both male and female samples totaling over 1,000 subjects. Summarizing across these three studies, Miller et al. found that one subtype, termed *externalizing*, was characterized by the tendency to express post-traumatic distress outwardly through antagonistic interactions with others and conflict with societal norms and values. Individuals in this subgroup had elevated rates of antisocial personality and substance-related disorders, endorsed high levels of anger and aggression, and produced personality inventory profiles defined by high disconstraint (i.e., impulsivity) coupled with high negative emotionality. They described themselves as easily upset, chronically stressed, and prone to act impulsively with little regard for the consequences of their actions. On measures of personality disorder features, they described themselves as tending toward exhibitionistic, manipulative, and unconventional behavior. In both studies of veterans in which data on premilitary characteristics were available, externalizers reported elevated rates of premilitary delinquency, suggesting that these characteristics may reflect the influence of externalizing personality traits that were present prior to the trauma.

In contrast, the *internalizing* subtype was characterized by tendencies to direct post-traumatic distress inwardly through shame, self-defeating/deprecating and anxious processes, avoidance, depression, and withdrawal. Across these three studies, individuals in this subtype were characterized by high rates of comorbid major depression and panic disorder, schizoid and avoidant personality disorder features, and personality profiles defined by high negative emotionality combined with low positive emotionality. Individuals in this subtype further described themselves as unenthusiastic, uninspired, easily fatigued, and lacking interests, but like externalizers, prone to experiencing frequent and intense negative emotions. They reported having few friends, feeling aloof and distant from others, and preferring to spend time alone. In contrast with the externalizers, internalizers reported that they tended to be self-effacing and humble and did not feel particularly special, admirable, or talented. They endorsed a restricted range of emotions in interpersonal settings and feelings of social inhibition, inadequacy, and hypersensitivity to negative evaluation.

These findings suggest that the internalizing/externalizing model of psychopathology, originally developed to account for covariation among broad classes of mental disorders *(9; c.f.11)*, is relevant to the understanding of the heterogeneity of PTSD comorbidity. Moreover, similar patterns that can now be interpreted as reflecting individual differences in internalizing and externalizing processes were described in earlier cluster analytic studies of U.S. and Australian veterans with PTSD *(25–27)*. Taken together, these findings suggest that the internalizing/externalizing model may be a useful heuristic for studying the influence of comorbidity on the relationship between PTSD and candidate biomarkers.

RELATIONSHIP BETWEEN PTSD AND CORTISOL AND THE MODERATING INFLUENCE OF INTERNALIZING AND EXTERNALIZING COMORBIDITY

The hypothalamic-pituitary-adrenal (HPA) axis is a key neurobiological substrate of the stress response, and abnormalities in its functioning have long been implicated in the pathophysiology of PTSD (for reviews, *see* Refs. *28–30*). Activity of this system is initiated by the release of corticotropin-releasing hormone (CRH) from the paraventricular nucleus of the hypothalamus. CRH acts as a neuropeptide in the production of adrenocorticotropic hormone (ACTH) in the pituitary and as a neurotransmitter in an elaborate network of interconnected neurons in the limbic system, brain stem, and cortex that are reactive to exogenous challenge and endogenous distress (for a review, *see* Ref. *31*). Once CRH is released from the paraventricular nucleus into the hypophyseal portal blood of the median eminence, it is transported to the anterior lobe of the pituitary, where it stimulates the secretion of ACTH. ACTH in turn enters the general circulation and triggers the adrenal cortex to begin the synthesis of cortisol from low-density lipoprotein (LDL) cholesterol.

Cortisol has many peripheral effects on metabolic and immune processes. Centrally, it plays an important role in negative-feedback control of HPA axis activity by binding to glucocorticoid receptors of the hypothalamus and pituitary, which inhibits the release of CRH and ACTH, respectively *(32,33)*. There is also evidence that adrenalectomy, which leads to a loss of negative feedback from peripheral cortisol, results in greatly increased numbers of CRH-containing storage vesicles in the central nucleus of the amygdala and bed nucleus of the stria terminalis, suggesting that cortisol also exerts inhibitory effects on CRH production in a variety of extrahypothalamic regions *(34)*.

Cortisol has been the most commonly studied component of the HPA axis as a potential biomarker for PTSD because it is easily sampled, can be measured in urine, plasma, or saliva, and is a well-established marker of the body's response to stress. Unfortunately, 20 years of clinical studies that have examined the relationship between cortisol levels and PTSD have yielded complicated and mixed results.

Many investigations have found lower levels of cortisol under baseline or non-stressful conditions using both urinary *(35,36)* and plasma samples *(37–40)* in individuals with PTSD compared to controls. Investigators have also reported evidence for a reduced rise in salivary cortisol on awakening in PTSD *(41,42)*, and patients with PTSD have been found in many studies to respond to dexamethasone administration with enhanced cortisol suppression, suggesting a heightened sensitivity to cortisol in PTSD *(38,41,43,44)*. These findings are not uniform, however. Other studies have found higher levels of cortisol in individuals with PTSD compared to controls in cerebral spinal fluid (CSF; *45)*, urine *(46–48)*, plasma *(49)*, and saliva *(50)*. Still others have shown no significant differences in salivary cortisol between groups differing in PTSD diagnostic status *(51,52)*.

In an effort to integrate these discrepant findings, investigators have focused primarily on demographic differences between samples (e.g., age, sex, chronicity of PTSD, type of trauma) and variability in the methods used to assess cortisol, such as the time of day of sample collection, the source of the sample (e.g., plasma, urine, saliva, or CSF), or the conditions under which the sample was collected (baseline vs. pre- or post-psychological or physical stress). These factors account for a large proportion of variation in cortisol levels, and a recent meta-analysis of over 100 studies linking stress to HPA axis function showed that such factors contribute significantly to differential findings across studies *(53)*. Results of that analysis also showed that, across studies, PTSD was associated with significantly lower daily levels of cortisol (Cohen's $d = -0.34$) and lower levels of cortisol post-dexamethasone administration (Cohen's $d = -0.25$) compared to control subjects exposed to the same stress.

One explanation for variation in study findings that has received little direct attention to date is the hypothesis that internalizing and externalizing comorbidity moderates the association between PTSD and cortisol levels. In many studies, the influence of comorbid disorders has not been well assessed or examined in the data analyses. When comorbidity has been factored into study designs or analyses, the focus has generally been on major depressive disorder because it is highly comorbid with PTSD and in non-PTSD samples generally associated with *hyper-* as opposed to *hypo*-cortisolism. In the section that follows, we review the literature on the differential relations between internalizing and externalizing psychopathology and cortisol levels to illustrate the moderating influences that these dimensions of comorbid psychopathology may have on the relationship between cortisol and PTSD.

EVIDENCE FOR THE LINK BETWEEN
INTERNALIZING DISORDERS AND ELEVATED CORTISOL

Research on childhood behavior disorders has been the source of considerable evidence for a link between internalizing symptoms and elevated cortisol. Internalizing symptoms, such as social withdrawal and anxiety, have been associated with greater salivary cortisol levels under baseline conditions *(54)* and in response to a social stressor in children and adolescents *(55,56)*. Behavioral inhibition, a trait related to shyness, withdrawal, and anxiety, evidences a similar association *(57,58)*, and infants whose mothers have panic disorder have been found to have higher salivary cortisol levels compared to controls *(59)*. Greater salivary cortisol reactivity in response to a social stressor has also been shown to prospectively predict the development of subsequent anxiety disorders *(60)*.

Studies with adult participants have paralleled these findings. Specifically, adults with panic disorder have been found to exhibit higher levels of baseline plasma *(61,62)* and urinary and salivary *(63)* cortisol compared to controls. Numerous studies have linked basal hypercortisolism and dexamethasone nonsuppression to major depression (for a review, *see* Ref.*64)*, and Miller, Chen, and Zhou's *(53)* meta-analysis estimated that the size of the depressed versus control group difference in postdexamethasone cortisol levels to be large ($d = 1.13$). Similar effects have been observed in individuals with generalized anxiety disorder *(65,66)*. Taken together, these studies provide strong evidence for a link between disorders of the internalizing spectrum and elevated levels of cortisol.

EVIDENCE FOR THE LINK BETWEEN EXTERNALIZING DISORDERS AND LOW CORTISOL

A contrasting body of research suggests an association between disorders of the externalizing spectrum and abnormally low levels of cortisol. Theorists have long conjectured that the neural substrate for externalizing disorders involves diminished arousal *(67–69)*, and since cortisol secretion is thought to partially reflect the arousal state of the organism, many investigators have focused on cortisol as a potential biomarker for this class of psychopathology. For example, Vanyukov et al., *(70)* found that young boys with antisocial fathers had lower levels of baseline salivary cortisol compared to controls, and their total number of conduct disorder symptoms was inversely correlated ($r = -.20$) with their cortisol levels. Similarly, investigators have reported associations between low basal cortisol concentrations and aggression toward peers *(71)*, hostility to the teacher *(72)*, and conduct disorder severity *(70)*. Finally, salivary *(73)* and serum *(74)* cortisol has been shown to be inversely associated with psychopathic traits (i.e., callousness, lack of remorse) in older male adolescents/young adults.

Similar effects have also been observed in research with adults with externalizing disorders. For example, King, Jones, Scheuer, Curtis, and Zarcone *(75)* found that inpatient adults with substance use diagnoses exhibited lower baseline levels of plasma cortisol than controls. Interestingly, in that sample no participants met criteria for major depressive disorder, while in a second study of substance users with comorbid depression, elevated serum cortisol levels were found *(76)*. There is also evidence that trait impulsivity, which is the personality dimension thought to underlie propensities toward externalizing disorders, may be inversely associated with cortisol levels. For example, Wang et al. *(77)* found that novelty seeking (a personality construct closely related to impulsivity) was inversely associated with urinary cortisol ($r = -.43$) in male Vietnam veterans with PTSD. King et al. *(75)* reported similar findings in a community sample control group. In sum, considerable evidence suggests that children and adults with problems in the externalizing domain exhibit low basal cortisol, and these findings align with theories that emphasize the role of hypo-arousal in the etiology of disorders in this spectrum (e.g., *69).* On the other hand, high levels of basal cortisol have often been found in association with disorders of the anxious-misery spectrum (e.g., major depression and generalized anxiety disorder) and problems in the domain of excessive behavioral inhibition.

THE STARTLE RESPONSE

Like basal cortisol, the startle response has been the focus of extensive research as a possible biomarker for PTSD. Exaggerated startle responding has been recognized as a core symptom of PTSD since the earliest descriptions of combat soldiers suffering adverse effects of exposure to the stress of combat. Many individuals with PTSD report extreme reactions to startling events in the environment. They may report flinching or recoiling in response to an unexpected touch or springing awake in response to an unexpected noise in the night and being unable to fall back to sleep. Combat veterans describe "hitting the dirt" or "ducking for cover" at the sound of a car backfiring. In each instance, the initial startle response may be followed by a cascade of anxious arousal symptoms, with recovery taking minutes to hours.

From a psychophysiological perspective, the startle response is a constellation of reflexive motor movements, phasic autonomic responses, and voluntary orienting responses that occur in response to any sudden, intense change in stimulus intensity. The reflexive component of the reaction begins with an eyeblink between 20 and 50 ms after the onset of a startle-eliciting stimulus (e.g., car backfiring) and spreads distally throughout the body. In humans, it is measured via electromyography (EMG) recordings of the contraction of the orbicularis oculi muscle, which closes the eyelid. Startle-eliciting stimuli are typically loud noises presented over headphones, and the magnitude of the muscle contraction is the primary measure of interest. Secondary, longer latency autonomic responses include heart rate acceleration and skin conductance increases. These begin within a second after the onset of a startling stimulus and typically peak several seconds later.

The startle response has attracted considerable attention as a potential PTSD biomarker. Exaggerated startle is unique among the PTSD symptoms in terms of the degree of correspondence between the clinical symptom that occurs in humans and the behavioral analogue that can studied in the clinical psychophysiology lab or using animal models. Perhaps because of this, more is known about the neurocircuitry and neuromodulators of startle than for any other symptom of the disorder. Two primary systems in the brain have been implicated as possible mechanisms for the symptom of exaggerated startle in PTSD: the locus coeruleus/norepinephrine system and the hypothalamic/CRH system. Evidence for these links includes studies showing that lesions of the locus coeruleus and drugs that inhibit its activity decrease startle reactivity, whereas drugs that increase locus coeruleus activity have the opposite effect *(78)*. Likewise, CRH administration produces a pronounced, dose-dependent enhancement of startle that can be blocked by pretreatment with a CRH receptor antagonist (e.g., *79,80)*.

Although these findings point to the promise of the startle response as a possible biomarker of PTSD, clinical laboratory studies have yielded mixed findings regarding the validity of exaggerated startle as a symptom of PTSD. Pole *(81)* recently conducted a meta-analysis of 20 studies that compared samples of individuals with and without PTSD on measures of startle responding and found that the effect size for the eyeblink reflex, weighted to control for sample size differences, was significant but modest ($r = .13$). Of those 20 studies, approximately half showed significant positive group differences in eyeblink startle amplitude, with some showing quite large effects (i.e., $r > .50$; *82,83)*. These findings suggest that there may be one or more important moderating variables that have not been consistently addressed by procedures used in past startle studies.

One variable that has received considerable research attention in studies of startle in PTSD is contextual anxiety, with the idea being that exaggerated startle in PTSD is a context- or state-dependent phenomenon related to anxiety processes *(84,85)*. This hypothesis follows from the seminal research of Michael Davis and colleagues (e.g., *86,87)* on the neurobiology of fear, anxiety, and startle, which showed that the amplitude of the startle response is potentiated by both exposure to contextual threat (i.e., anxiety; as in returning to the location of previous aversive conditioning) and explicit threat (i.e., fear; as in exposure to a conditioned stimulus signaling imminent shock). In line with this, a growing body of clinical research with PTSD patients suggests that differences between PTSD and non-PTSD groups are most reliably observed under test conditions involving the distal anticipation of an aversive stimulus and are not observed under conditions involving proximal threat (for a review, *see* Ref. *88)*. For example, Grillon et al. *(85)* examined startle responses in veterans with and without PTSD during an initial laboratory session that involved no aversive manipulation followed several days later by startle testing during an aversive conditioning procedure that involved anticipation of a mild shock. Significant group differences in baseline startle amplitude were observed only during session 2, suggesting that group effects were linked to the anxiogenic context in which the shock conditioning took place. Consistent with the possibility that exaggerated startle in PTSD is linked exclusively to the neurobiological system underlying contextual anxiety and not to the system underlying fear, no group differences in the fear response to presentation of conditioned threat cues (i.e., a CS+) were found.

EFFECTS OF COMORBIDITY ON BASELINE
AND OVERALL STARTLE AMPLITUDE

Comorbidity may also serve a moderating role in the relationship between PTSD and amplitude of the startle response. Several studies have found exaggerated startle responding in samples of individuals with other anxiety disorders, which raises questions about the specificity of the measure as a possible biomarker of PTSD. For example, exaggerated baseline startle has been observed in several studies of patients with panic disorder (89–93). Grillion and colleagues (94) examined startle as a possible vulnerability marker among offspring of parents with anxiety disorders or alcoholism and found that the magnitude of baseline startle was greater in children with a parental history of anxiety than in children without a parental history of anxiety. Similar findings were observed in a sample of individuals at risk for depression by virtue of their parents' depression diagnoses (95). In addition, Cuthbert et al. (96) reported that baseline startle responses were significantly larger among anxiety disorder patients with depression than for anxiety patients without depression, suggesting an additive effect of internalizing comorbidity on startle amplitude.

Other studies suggested that startle amplitude may tap individual differences in level of trait fearfulness. For example, rats that differ in fearfulness can be distinguished on the basis of their behavioral reactions to startling stimuli, with fearful rats exhibiting more extreme responses (97). In humans, individuals who score high on Cloninger's measure of harm avoidance (i.e., "a heritable tendency to respond intensely to aversive stimuli and to learn to avoid punishment, novelty and non-reward passively"; 98) exhibit larger overall startle response amplitudes compared to their counterparts who score low on the measure (99). Together, these findings suggest a link between exaggerated startle and psychopathology of the internalizing spectrum broadly and fear-related disorders more specifically.

CONCLUSIONS AND DIRECTIONS
FOR FUTURE RESEARCH

Comorbidity of PTSD presents problems on multiple levels for clinicians and researchers alike. In the clinical arena, individuals with comorbid Axis I or II disorders have been shown to have more severe PTSD symptoms (e.g., 100–102) and poorer responses to treatment (e.g.,103,104). For researchers, PTSD comorbidity often represents a nuisance variable addressed through post hoc statistical controls or challenging (and arguably ill-advised) efforts to select "pure" PTSD cases from highly comorbid samples. The heterogeneity within PTSD also means that there is potential for multiple overlapping phenotypes to occur within any sample of individuals with the disorder. As the foregoing literature review suggests, the diagnostic composition of any sample and the proportion of cases with predominantly internalizing versus externalizing comorbidity can have a substantial influence on associations between candidate biomarkers and measures of PTSD.

PTSD is not alone among psychiatric disorders in this regard. Psychiatric epidemiology studies suggest that similar heterogeneity exists in some, but not all, mental disorders with the determining factor being the breadth of comorbidity associated with the index disorder. PTSD shows a particularly severe and diverse pattern of diagnostic comorbidity with frequently co-occurring conditions ranging from those of the internalizing spectrum to the externalizing spectrum. Certain other disorders, such as alcohol abuse/dependence, show similar patterns of comorbidity. Cloninger *(98)* emphasized this when he advanced a two-class typology of alcohol dependence. In his model, type I alcoholics (i.e., an internalizing type) were defined as individuals who use alcohol in association with heightened negative affectivity to avoid, dampen, or escape those states. In type II alcoholism (i.e., an externalizing type), alcohol problems were thought to stem from propensities toward sensation seeking and risky or uninhibited behavior. On the other hand, other psychiatric disorders with a narrower range of comorbidity—and more distinct and circumscribed phenotypes—rarely co-occur with each other. For example, Kessler and colleagues *(7)* reported that the internalizing spectrum disorders obsessive-compulsive disorder and separation anxiety disorder were negatively correlated with the externalizing syndromes drug dependence and conduct disorder. Generalizing from this, one would not expect to find large numbers of externalizers among samples composed of individuals with protoypic internalizing diagnoses, especially those related to pathological fear or vice versa (e.g., antisocial personality disorder is not a problem commonly found among individuals with simple phobia).

The foregoing literature review suggests that exaggerated startle, low basal cortisol, and perhaps any candidate biomarkers for PTSD are *pleiotropic*, meaning that the same marker may relate to the occurrence of several different diagnostic phenotypes. We know that psychiatric disorders do not co-occur by chance but rather cohere along latent dimensions of psychopathology. By extension, we should expect most psychiatric biomarkers to correlate with disorders within a spectrum of psychopathology rather than with individual diagnoses, as basal cortisol and startle appear to. In future studies, it may be advantageous to model associations between biomarkers and phenotypes using analytic approaches that better map onto the complex nature of these associations. Latent variable methods would be well suited for the study of pleiotropic biomarkers because they can be used to model the common factor underlying a broad class of disorders as well as the unique factors that predict individual disorders. This permits the investigator to examine separately (1) the strength of associations between the candidate biomarker and the common factor underlying a set of diagnostic indicators and (2) the strength of the association between the biomarker and individual diagnostic indicators. Furthermore, the latent factors underlying co-occurring diagnoses can be conceptualized as *endophenotypic traits*, which represent purer, error-free measures of the dimension underlying the diagnoses of interest. As a result, one can expect latent dimensions of psychopathology to map more directly and completely onto their biologic substrate and yield substantially increased predictive power for biomarker association analyses compared to analyses that focus on identifying biomarkers of individual disorders.

REFERENCES

1. Brown, T. A., Campbell, L. A., Lehman, C. L., Grisham, J. R., and Mancill, R. B. (2001) Current and lifetime comorbidity of the DSM-IV anxiety and mood disorders in a large clinical sample. J Abnorm Psychol 110, 585–99.
2. Orsillo, S. M., Weathers, F. W., Litz, B. T., Steinberg, H. R., Huska, J. A., and Keane, T. M. (1996) Current and lifetime psychiatric disorders among veterans with war zone-related posttraumatic stress disorder. J Nerv Ment Dis 184, 307–13.
3. Kulka, R. A., Schlenger, W. E., Fairbank, J. A., Hough, R. L., Jordan, B. K., Marmar, C. R., and Weiss, D. S. (1990). Trauma and the Vietnam War Generation: Report on the Findings from the National Vietnam Veterans Readjustment Study. New York: Brunner/Mazel.
4. Achenbach, T. M., and Edelbrock, C. S. (1978) The classification of child psychopathology: a review and analysis of empirical efforts. Psychol Bull 85, 1275–1301.
5. Achenbach, T. M., and Edelbrock, C. S. (1984) Psychopathology of childhood. Annu Rev Psychol 35, 227–56.
6. Kendler, K. S., Prescott, C. A., Myers, J., and Neale, M. C. (2003) The structure of genetic and environmental risk factors for common psychiatric and substance use disorders in men and women. Arch Gen Psychiatry 60, 929–37.
7. Kessler, R. C., Chiu, W. T., Demler, O., Merikangas, K. R., and Walters, E. E. (2005) Prevalence, severity, and comorbidity of 12-month DSM-IV disorders in the National Comorbidity Survey Replication. Arch Gen Psychiatry 62, 617–27.
8. Krueger, R. F. (1999) The structure of common mental disorders. Arch Gen Psychiatry 56, 921–26.
9. Krueger, R. F., Caspi, A., Moffitt, T. E., and Silva, P. A. (1998) The structure and stability of common mental disorders (DSM-III-R): a longitudinal-epidemiological study. J Abnorm Psychol 107, 216–27.
10. Krueger, R. F., Chentsova-Dutton, Y. E., Markon, K. E., Goldberg, D., and Ormel, J. (2003) A cross-cultural study of the structure of comorbidity among common psychopathological syndromes in the general health care setting. J Abnorm Psychol 112, 437–47.
11. Krueger, R. F., McGue, M., and Iacono, W. G. (2001) The higher-order structure of common DSM mental disorders: internalization, externalization, and their connections to personality. Pers Indiv Differ 30, 1245–59.
12. Vollebergh, W. A. M., Idema, J., Bijl, R. V., de Graaf, R., Smit, F., and Ormel, J. (2001) The structure and stability of common mental disorders: the NEMESIS Study. Arch Gen Psychiatry 58, 597–603.
13. Cox, B. J., Clara, I. P., and Enns, M. W. (2002) Posttraumatic stress disorder and the structure of common mental disorders. Depress Anxiety 15, 168–71.
14. Slade, T., and Watson, D. (2006) The structure of common DSM-IV and ICD-10 mental disorders in the Australian general population. Psychol Med 36, 1593–1600.
15. Miller, M. W., Fogler, J. M., Wolf, E. J., Kaloupek, D. G., and Keane, T. M., (2008) The internalizing and externalizing structure of psychiatric comorbidity in combat veterans. J Trauma Stress 21, 58–65.
16. Krueger, R. F., Hicks, B. M., Patrick, C. J., Carlson, S. R., Iacono, W. G., and McGue, M. (2002) Etiologic connections among substance dependence, antisocial behavior and personality: modeling the externalizing spectrum. J Abnorm Psychol 111, 411–24.
17. Deater-Deckard, K., and Plomin, R. (1999) An adoption study of the etiology of teacher and parent reports of externalizing behavior problems in middle childhood. Child Dev 70, 144–54.

18. Gjone, H., Stevenson, J., and Sundet, J. M. (1996) Genetic influence on parent-reported attention-related problems in a Norwegian general population twin sample. J Am Acad Child Adolesc Psychiatry 35, 588–96.
19. Barlow, D. H., Chorpita, B. F., and Turovsky, J. (1996) Fear, panic, and disorders of emotion. In D. A. Hope, ed., Current Theory and Research in Motivation. Nebraska Symposium on Motivation 43. Lincoln: University of Nebraska Press.
20. Clark, D. A., Steer, R. A., and Beck, A. T. (1994) Common and specific dimensions of self-reported anxiety and depression: implications for the cognitive and tripartite models. J Abnorm Psychol 103, 645–54.
21. Frances, A. J., Widiger, T. A., and Fyer, M. R. (1990) The influence of classification methods on comorbidity. In J. D. Maser and C. R. Cloninger, , Comorbidity of Mood and Anxiety Disorders (pp. 41–59). Washington, DC: American Psychiatric Association.
22. Miller, M. W., Greif, J. L., and Smith, A. A. (2003) Multidimensional Personality Questionnaire profiles of veterans with traumatic combat exposure: internalizing and externalizing subtypes. Psychol Assessment 15, 205–15.
23. Miller, M. W., Kaloupek, D. G., Dillon, A. L., and Keane, T. M. (2004) Externalizing and internalizing subtypes of combat-related PTSD: a replication and extension using the PSY-5 Scales. J Abnorm Psychol 113, 636–45.
24. Miller, M. W., and Resick, P. A. (2007) Internalizing and externalizing subtypes of female sexual assault survivors: implications for the understanding of complex PTSD. Behav Ther 38, 58–71.
25. Forbes, D., Creamer, M., Allen, N., Elliott, P., McHugh, T., Debenham, P., and Hopwood, M. (2003) MMPI-2 based subgroups of veterans with combat-related PTSD. J Nerv Ment Dis 191, 531–537.
26. Hyer, L., Davis, H., Albrecht, W., Boudewyns, P., and Woods, G. (1994) Cluster analysis of MCMI and MCMI-II on chronic PTSD victims. J Clin Psychol 50, 502–15.
27. Piekarski, A. M., Sherwood, R., and Funari, D. J. (1993) Personality subgroups in an inpatient Vietnam veteran treatment program. Psychol Rep 72, 667–74.
28. Yehuda, R. (2001) Biology of posttraumatic stress disorder. J Clin Psychiat 62, 41–46.
29. Yehuda, R. (1997) Sensitization of the hypothalamic-pituitary-adrenal axis in posttraumatic stress disorder. Ann NY Acad Sci 821, 57–75.
30. Kaskow, J. W., Baker, D., and Geracioti, T. D. (2001) Corticotropin-releasing hormone in depression and post-traumatic stress disorder. Peptides 22, 845–51.
31. Lovallo, W. R., and Thomas, T. L. (2000) Stress hormones in psychophysiological research. In J. T. Cacioppo, L. G. Tassinary, and G. G. Bernston, , Handbook of Psychophysiology. 2nd ed. New York: Cambridge University Press.
32. McCann, S. M. (1988) The anterior pituitary and hypothalamus. In J. E. Griffin and S. R. Ojeda, eds. Textbook of Endocrine Physiology. New York: Oxford University Press.
33. Orth, D. N., Kovacs, W. J., and DeBold, C. R. (1992) The adrenal cortex. In J. D. and Wilson D. W. Foster,. ed., Textbook of Endocrinology. Philadelphia: Saunders.
34. Merchenthaler, I. (1984) Corticotropin-releasing factor (CRF)-like immunoreactivity in the rat central nervous system: extrahypothalamic distribution. Peptides 5, 53–69.
35. Yehuda, R., Soutwick, S. M., Nussbaum, G., Wahby, V., Giller, E. L., and Mason, J. W. (1990) Low urinary cortisol excretion in patient with posttraumatic stress disorder. J Nerv Ment Dis 178, 366–69.
36. Yehuda, R., Kahana, B., Binder-Brynes, K., Southwick, S. M., Mason, J. W., and Giller, E. L. (1995) Low urinary cortisol excretion in Holocaust survivors with posttraumatic stress disorder. Am J Psychiatry 152, 982–86.

37. Boscarino, J. A. (1996) Posttraumatic stress disorder, exposure to combat, and lower plasma cortisol among Vietnam veterans: findings and clinical impressions. J Consult Clin Psychol 64, 191–201.

38. Griffin, M. G., Resick, P. A., and Yehuda, R. (2005) Enhanced cortisol suppression following dexamethasone administration in domestic violence survivors. Am J Psychiatry 162, 1192–99.

39. Olff, M., Güzelcan, Y., de Vries, G. -J., Assies, J., and Gersons, B. P. R. (2006) HPA- and HPT-axis alterations in chronic posttraumatic stress disorder. Psychoneuroendocrinology 31, 1220–30.

40. Yehuda, R., Teicher, M. H., Trestman, R. L., Levengood, R. A., and Siever, L. J. (1996) Cortisol regulation in posttraumatic stress disorder and major depression: a chronobiological analysis. Biol Psychiatry 40, 79–88.

41. de Kloet, C. S., Vermetten, E., Heijnen, C. J., Geuze, E., Lentjes, E. G. W. M., and Westenberg, H. G. M. (2007) Enhanced cortisol suppression in response to dexamethasone administration in traumatized veterans with and without posttraumatic stress disorder. Psychoneuroendocrinlogy 32, 215–26.

42. Wessa, M., Rohleder, N., Kirschbam, C., and Flor, H. (2006) Altered cortisol awakening response in posttraumatic stress disorder. Psychoneuroendocrinology 31, 209–15.

43. Stein, M. B., Yehuda, R., Koverola, C., and Hanna, C. (1997) Enhanced dexamethasone suppression of plasma cortisol in adult women traumatized by childhood sexual abuse. Biol Psychiatry 42, 680–86.

44. Yehuda, R., Southwick, S. M., Krystal, J. M., Charney, D. S., and Mason, J. W. (1993) Enhanced suppression of cortisol following dexamethasone administration in combat veterans with posttraumatic stress disorder and major depressive disorder. Am J Psychiatry 150, 83–86.

45. Baker, D. G., Ekhator, N. N., Kasckow, J. W., Dashevsky, B., Horn, P. S., Bednarik, L., and Geracioti, T. D. (2005) Higher levels of basal serial CSF cortisol in combat veterans with posttraumatic stress disorder. Am J Psychiatry 162, 992–94.

46. Lemieux, A. M., and Coe, C. L. (1995) Abuse-related posttraumatic stress disorder: evidence for chronic neuroendocrine activation in women. Psychosom Med 57, 105–15.

47. Maes, M., Lin, A., Bonaccorso, S., van Hunsel, F., Van Gastel, A., Delmeire, L., Biondi, M., Bosmans, E., Kenis, G., and Scharpe, S. (1998) Increased 24-hour urinary cortisol excretion in patients with post-traumatic stress disorder and patients with major depression, but not in patients with fibromyalgia. Acta Psychiatr Scand 98, 328–35.

48. Pitman, R. K., and Orr, S. P. (1990) Twenty-four hour urinary cortisol and catecholamine excretion in combat-related posttraumatic stress disorder. Biol Psychiatry 27, 245–47.

49. Liberzon, I., Abelson, J. L., Flagel, S. B., Raz, J., and Young, E. A. (1999) Neuroendocrine and psychophysiologic responses in PTSD: a symptom provocation study. Neuropsychopharmacology 21, 40–50.

50. Lindley, S. E., Carlson, E. B., and Benoit, M. (2004) Basal and dexamethasone suppressed salivary cortisol concentrations in a community sample of patients with posttraumatic stress disorder. Biol Psychiatry 55, 940–45.

51. Young, E. A., and Breslau, N. (2004) Cortisol and catecholamines in posttraumatic stress disorder: an epidemiologic community study. Arch Gen Psychiatry 61, 394–401.

52. Young, E. A., and Breslau, N. (2004) Saliva cortisol in posttraumatic stress disorder: a community epidemiologic study. Biol Psychiatry 56, 205–9.

53. Miller, G. E., Chen, E., and Zhou, E. S. (2007) If it goes up, must it come down? Chronic stress and the hypothalamic-pituitary-adrenocortical axis in humans. Psychol Bull 133, 24–45.

54. Greaves-Lord, K., Ferdinand, R. F., Oldehinkel, A. J., Sondeijker, F. E. P. L., Ormel, J., and Verhulst, F. C. (2007) Higher cortisol awakening response in young adolescents with persistent anxiety problems. Acta Psychiatr Scand 116, 137–44.

55. Klimes-Dougan, K., Hastings, P. D., Granger, D. A., Usher, B. A., and Zahn-Waxler, C. (2001) Adrenocortical activity in at-risk and normally developing adolescents: individual differences in salivary cortisol basal levels, diurnal variation, and responses to social challenges. Dev Psychopathol 13, 695–719.

56. Granger, D. A., Weisz, J. R., and Kauneckis, D. (1994) Neuroendocrine reactivity, internalizing behavior problems, and control-related cognitions in clinic-referred children and adolescents. J Abnorm Psychol 103, 267–76.

57. Kagan, J., Reznick, J. S., and Snidman, N. (1988) Biological bases of childhood shyness. Science 240, 167–71.

58. Schmidt, L. A., Fox, N. A., Rubin, K. H., Sternberg, E. M., Gold, P. W., Smith, C. C., and Schulkin, J. (1997) Behavioral and neuroendocrine responses in shy children. Dev Psychobiol 30, 127–140.

59. Warren, S. L., Gunnar, M. R., Kagan, J., Anders, T. F., Simmens, S. J., Rones, M., Wease, S., Aron, E., Dahl, R., and Sroufe, A. (2003) Maternal panic disorder: infant temperament, neurophysiology, and parenting behaviors. J Am Acad Child Adolesc Psychiatry 42, 814–25.

60. Granger, D. A., Weisz, J. R., McCracken, J. T., Ikeda, S. G., and Douglas, P. (1996) Reciprocal influences among adrenocortical activation, psychosocial processes, and the behavioral adjustment of clinic-referred children. Child Dev 67, 3250–62.

61. Abelson, J. L., Khan, S., Liberzon, I., and Young, E. A. (2007) HPA axis activity in patients with panic disorder: review and synthesis of four studies. Depress Anxiety 24, 66–76.

62. Marshall, R. D., Blanco, C., Printz, D., Liebowitz, M. R., Klein, D. F., and Coplan, J. (2002) A pilot study of noradrenergic and HPA axis functioning in PTSD vs. panic disorder. Psychiatry Res 110, 219–30.

63. Bandelow, B., Wedekind, D., Sandvoss, V., Broocks, A., Hajak, G., Pauls, J., Peter, H., and Rüther, E. (2000) Diurnal variation of cortisol in panic disorder. Psychiatry Res 95, 245–50.

64. Holsboer, F. (2000) The corticosteroid receptor hypothesis of depression. Neuropsychopharmacology 23, 477–501.

65. Schweizer, E. E., Swenson, C. M., Winokur, A., Rickels, K., and Maislin, G. (1986). The dexamethasone suppression test in generalised anxiety disorder. Br J Psychiatry 149, 320– 22.

66. Tiller, J. W., Biddle, N., Maguire, K. P., and Davies, B. M. (1988) The dexamethasone suppression rest and plasma dexamethasone in generalized anxiety disorder. Biol Psychiatry 23, 261–70.

67. Quay, H. C. (1965) Psychopathic personality as pathological stimulation-seeking. Am J Psychiatry 122, 180–83.

68. Hare, R. D. (1970) Psychopathy: Theory and Research. New York: Wiley.

69. Zuckerman, M. (1999) Vulnerability to Psychopathology: A Biosocial Model. Washington, DC: American Psychiatric Press.

70. Vanyukov, M. M., Moss, H. B., Plail, J. A., Blackson, T., Mezzich, A. C., and Tarter, R. E. (1993) Antisocial symptoms in preadolescent boys and their parents: associations with cortisol. Psychiatry Res 46, 9–17.

71. Tennes, K., Kreye, M., Avitable, N., and Wells, R. (1986) Behavioral correlates of excreted catecholamines and cortisol in second-grade children. J Am Acad Child Adolesc Psychiatry 25, 764–70.

72. Tennes, K., and Kreye, M. (1985) Children's adrenocortical responses to classroom activities and tests in elementary school. Psychosom Med 47, 451–60.
73. Burke, J. D., Loeber, R., and Lahey, B. B. (2007) Adolescent conduct disorder and interpersonal callousness as predictors of psychopathy in young adults. J Clin Child Adolesc Psychol 36, 334–46.
74. Holi, M., Auvinen-Lintunen, L., Lindberg, N., Tani, P., and Virkkunen, M. (2006) Inverse correlation between severity of psychopathic traits and serum cortisol levels in young adult violent male offenders. Psychopathology 39, 102–4.
75. King, R. J., Jones, J., Scheuer, J. W., Curtis, D., and Zarcone, V. P. (1990) Plasma cortisol correlates of impulsivity and substance abuse. Pers Indiv Differ 11, 287–91.
76. Wisniewski, A. B., Brown, T. T., John, M., Cofranceso, J., Golub, E. T., Ricketts, E. P., Wand, G., and Dobs, A. S. (2006) Cortisol levels and depression in men and women using heroin and cocaine. Psychoneuroendocrinology 31, 250–55.
77. Wang, S., Mason, J., Charney, D., Yehuda, R., Riney, S., and Southwick, S. (1997) Relationships between hormonal profile and novelty seeking in combat-related posttraumatic stress disorder. Biol Psychiatry 41, 145–51.
78. Davis, M., Redmond, D. E., Jr., and Baraban, J. M. (1979) Noradrenergic agonists and antagonists: effects on conditioned fear as measured by the potentiated startle paradigm. Psychopharmacology 65, 111–18.
79. Swerdlow, N. R., Britton, K. T., and Koob, G. F. (1989) Potentiation of acoustic startle by corticotropin-releasing factor (CRH) and by fear are both reversed by a-helical CRH(9–41). Neuropsychopharmacology 2, 285–92.
80. Risbrough V. B., Hauger, R. L., Roberts, A. J., Vale, W. W., and Geyer, M. A. (2004) Corticotropin-releasing factor receptors CRF1 and CRF2 exert both additive and opposing influences on defensive startle behavior. J Neurosci 24, 6545–52.
81. Pole, N. (2007). The psychophysiology of posttraumatic stress disorder: a meta-analysis. Psychol Bull 137, 725–46.
82. Morgan, C. A., Grillon, C., Southwick, S. M., Davis, M., and Charney, D. S. (1995) Fear-potentiated startle in posttraumatic stress disorder. Biol Psychiatry 38, 378–85.
83. Morgan, A., Grillon, C. A., Southwick, S. M., Davis, M., and Charney, D. S. (1996) Exaggerated acoustic startle reflex in Gulf War veterans with posttraumatic stress disorder. Am J Psychiatry 153, 64–68.
84. Grillon, C., and Morgan, C. A. (1999) Fear-potentiated startle conditioning to explicit and contextual cues in Gulf War veterans with posttraumatic stress disorder. J Abnorm Psychol 108, 134–42.
85. Grillon, C., Morgan, C. A., Davis, M., and Southwick, S. M. (1998) Effect of darkness on acoustic startle in Vietnam veterans with PTSD. Am J Psychiatry 155, 812–17.
86. Davis, M., Walker, D. L., and Lee, Y. (1997) Role of the amygdala and bed nucleus of the stria terminalis in fear and anxiety measured with the acoustic startle reflex. Ann N Y Academy of Sci 821, 305–33.
87. Davis, M. Walker, D. L., and Lee, Y. (1999) Neurophysiology and neuropharmacology of startle and its affective modification. In M. Dawson, A. Schell, and M. Bohmelt, eds., Startle Modification: Implications for Neuroscience, Cognitive Science, and Clinical Science (pp. 95–113). Cambridge: Cambridge University Press.
88. Orr, S. P., Metzger, L. J., Miller, M. W., and Kaloupek, D. G. (2004) Psychophysiological assessment of posttraumatic stress disorder. In J. P. Wilson and T. M. Keane, eds., Assessing Psychological Trauma and PTSD. 2nd ed., pp. 289–343. New York: Guilford.
89. Buhlmann, U., Wilhelm, S., Deckersbach, T., Rauch, S. L., Pitman, R. K., and Orr, S. P. (2007) Physiologic responses to loud tones in individuals with obsessive-compulsive disorder. Psychosom Med 69, 166–72.

90. Kumai, V., Kaviani, H., Raven, P. W., Gray, J. A., and Checkley, S. A. (2001) Enhanced startle reactions to acoustic stimuli in patients with obsessive-compulsive disorder. Am J Psychiatry 158, 134–36.
91. Grillon, C., Ameli, R., Goddard, A., Woods, S. W., and Davis, M. (1994) Baseline and fear-potentiated startle in panic disorder patients. Biol Psychiatry 35, 431–39.
92. Ludewig, S., Geyer, M. A., Ramseier, M., Vollenweider, F. X., Rechsteiner, E., and Cattapan-Ludewig, K. (2005) Information-processing deficits and cognitive dysfunction in panic disorder. J Psychiatry Neurosci 30, 37–43.
93. Melzig, C. A., Weike, A. I., Zimmerman, J., and Hamm, A. O. (2007) Startle reflex modulation and autonomic responding during anxious apprehension in panic disorder patients. Psychophysiology 44, 846–54.
94. Grillon, C., Dierker, L., and Merikangas, K. R. (1997) Startle modulation in children at risk for anxiety disorders and/or alcoholism. J Am Acad Child Adolesc Psychiatry 36, 925–32.
95. Grillon, C., Warner, V., Hille, J., Merikangas, K. R., Bruder, G. E., Tenke, C. E., Nomura, Y., Leite, P., and Weissman, M. M. (2005) Families at high and low risk for depression: a three-generation startle study. Biol Psychiatry 57, 953–60.
96. Cuthbert, B. N., Lang, P. J., Strauss, C., Drobes, D., Patrick, C. J., Bradley, M. M., (2003) The psychophysiology of anxiety disorder: fear memory imagery. Psychophysiology 40, 407–22.
97. Plappert, C. F., Pilz, P. K. D., and Schnitzler, H., (1993) Acoustic startle response and habituation in freezing and nonfreezing rats. Behav Neurosci 107, 981–87.
98. Cloninger, C. R. (1987) Neurogenetic adaptive mechanisms in alcoholism. Science 236, 410–16.
99. Corr, P. J., Kumari, V., Wilson, G. D., Checkley, S., and Gray, J. A. (1997) Harm avoidance and affective modulation of the startle reflex: a replication. Pers Indiv Differ 22, 591–93.
100. Back, S. E., Sonne, S. C., and Killeen, T. (2003) Comparative profiles of women with PTSD and comorbid cocaine or alcohol dependence. Am J Drug Alcohol Abuse 29, 169–89.
101. Brady, K. T., and Clary, C. M. (2003) Affective and anxiety comorbidity in post-traumatic stress disorder treatment trials of sertraline. Compr Psychiatry 44, 360–69.
102. Zayfert, C., Becker, C. B., Unger, D. L., and Shearer, D. K. (2002) Comorbid anxiety disorders in civilians seeking treatment for posttraumatic stress disorder. J Trauma Stress 15, 31–38.
103. Zlotnick, C., Warshaw, M., Shea, M. T., Allsworth, J. Pearlstein, T., and Keller, M. B. (1999) Chronicity in posttraumatic stress disorder (PTSD) and predictors of course of comorbid PTSD in patients with anxiety disorders. J Trauma Stress 12, 89–100.
104. Cloitre, M., and Koenen, K. C. (2001) The impact of borderline personality disorder on the effectiveness of group treatment for women with PTSD related to childhood sexual abuse. Int J Group Psychother 53, 379–98.

Brain Imaging in Post-Traumatic Stress Disorder

14 Functional Neuroimaging in Post-Traumatic Stress Disorder

Israel Liberzon and Sarah N. Garfinkel

CONTENTS

INTRODUCTION
NEUROIMAGING STUDIES IN PTSD
THE MEDIAL PREFRONTAL CORTEX AND PTSD
SUMMARY AND FUTURE DIRECTIONS
REFERENCES

Abstract

Neuroimaging provides a powerful means to understand the mechanisms that mediate emotional processing in healthy individuals as well as the dysregulation of these processes in post-traumatic stress disorder (PTSD). Reviewed are neuroimaging findings in PTSD, with a focus on studies utilizing symptom provocation, cognitive activation, and functional connectivity. These studies highlight the role of the medial prefrontal cortex (mPFC), insula, amygdala, sublenticular extended amygdala (SLEA), and hippocampus in mediating symptom formation in PTSD. In addition, new and emerging foci in neuroimaging research relevant to PTSD involve psychological processes like fear conditioning, habituation, extinction recall; cognitive-emotional interactions; and self-related and social-emotional processing. Findings linking neurocircuitry subserving these processes to the abnormalities associated with PTSD are highlighted, suggesting that the mPFC is implicated in a number of these processes. It is proposed that the mPFC plays a role in the "contextualization" of stimuli, and dysregulation of contextualization processes might play a key role in the generation of PTSD symptoms.

Key Words: Contextualization, emotional appraisal, fear conditioning, fMRI, mPFC, neuroimaging, PTSD, self-related processing,

From: *Post-Traumatic Stress Disorder: Basic Science and Clinical Practice*
Edited by: P. J. Shiromani et al., DOI: 10.1007/978-1-60327-329-9_14
© Humana Press, a part of Springer Science+Business Media, LLC 2009

INTRODUCTION

Inspired by basic animal research and a growing number of human neuroimaging studies, the year since 1995 saw the emergence of neurocircuitry models of post-traumatic stress disorder (PTSD) (1–3). These models conceptualize PTSD as a state of heightened responsivity to threatening stimuli or a state of insufficient inhibitory control over exaggerated threat sensitivity. They emphasize the centrality of threat-related processing in the pathophysiology of PTSD and hence account for the "hypersensitivity to threat" that is highly characteristic of PTSD (such as hypervigilence and hyperarousal). It is becoming increasingly apparent, however, that the hypersensitivity-to-threat models do not fully capture the full complexity of PTSD or the complexity of changes associated with vulnerability, trauma exposure, and PTSD development. For instance, important phenomena associated with PTSD, such as intrusive thoughts and memories, avoidance and numbing, generalization, vulnerability and resilience factors, and chronicity and comorbidities of PTSD, all need to be further understood in terms of underlying psychological mechanisms and their neurobiological substrates.

There is presently a growing appreciation that additional mechanisms, other than hyperresponsivity to threat, must be involved in PTSD pathophysiology. Lines of research have begun exploring neurobiological and psychological processes seemingly relevant to the development, maintenance, or recovery of PTSD, including conditioning, habituation, stimulus generalization, extinction resistance, and (impaired) extinction recall. In addition, processes (and underlying neurocircuitry) involving higher-order cognitive-emotional interactions, appraisal, reappraisal, and meta-awareness; finally, social, self-related, and self-referent processing may also play an important role in PTSD vulnerability, pathophysiology, and resilience. In recent years, a growing body of literature has examined these processes in both healthy and PTSD subjects.

This chapter first reviews what is currently known on the basis of functional neuroimaging in PTSD, with a particular emphasis on symptom provocation studies, cognitive activation studies, and functional connectivity analyses. The second part of the chapter focuses on specific psychological processes that have been implicated in PTSD symptom generation or pathophysiology. These include neuroimaging studies of fear-conditioning phenomena (with a particular emphasis on extinction and extinction recall); cognitive-emotional interactions; and self-related and social-emotional processing. The chapter concludes with a brief discussion of the threat-related processing model of PTSD, and a modified and updated model is proposed in which a core process of PTSD involves impairments in the circuits that mediate the "contextualization" of stimuli. Finally, potential future directions for PTSD research are discussed.

NEUROIMAGING STUDIES IN PTSD

Neuroimaging studies in PTSD encompass a number of different imaging modalities, including single-photon emission tomography (SPECT), positron emission tomography (PET), and functional magnetic resonance imaging (fMRI); many of these are covered in this chapter, with a particular emphasis on fMRI.

Symptom Provocation Studies

Symptom provocation studies were the first studies to emerge, were also the first to provide relatively stable and replicable findings, and are still the most common studies in the PTSD functional neuroimaging literature. These often employ autobiographical stimuli that are trauma related (e.g., narrative scripts of personal trauma) or alternatively are more general in nature, employing generally evocative but not necessarily autobiographically relevant pictures and sounds. In one of the first functional imaging symptom provocation studies, Rauch and colleagues (4) used individualized trauma scripts and [^{15}O]H$_2$O PET in a small and heterogeneous group of eight PTSD subjects. They demonstrated increased regional cerebral blood flow (rCBF) in anterior paralimbic (right posterior medialorbito frontal cortex [OFC], insular, anterior temporal polar, and medial temporal cortex) and limbic structures (amygdala) in the provoked versus control contrast. In a following study, the same group then used combat-related, emotionally negative, and neutral pictures paired with verbal descriptions (imagery) in combat veterans with and without PTSD. Combat veterans with PTSD had increased rCBF in the ventral anterior cingulated cortex (ACC) and right amygdala when generating mental images of combat-related pictures but had deceased rCBF in the ACC in the combat image-viewing versus neutral image-viewing contrast (5). Although these early studies had methodological limitations, such as a small and heterogeneous sample size as well as a lack of adequate control groups that limited the generalization of their findings, they set the stage for more detailed studies into the neural substrate of the symptomatic PTSD state.

In an ensuing study, our group exposed three groups of subjects (14 combat PTSD subjects, 11 combat-exposed subjects without PTSD, and 11 combat-unexposed healthy subjects) to combat sounds or white noise in two counterbalanced sessions and studied rCBF with ^{99m}Tc hexamethylpropyleneamineoxime (HMPAO) SPECT. Only the PTSD group showed increased rCBF in the left amygdaloid region (6). Another study using combat-related pictures and sounds and PET in 10 combat veterans with and 10 without PTSD revealed decreased blood flow in the medial prefrontal cortex (mPFC) (area 25) and other areas in response to traumatic pictures and sounds in PTSD patients, while non-PTSD control subjects activated the anterior cingulate (area 24) to a greater degree than PTSD patients (7). The same group also studied childhood sexual abuse (CSA) subjects (22 women, 10 of whom had PTSD) with exposure to traumatic and neutral scripts and PET. The PTSD group showed rCBF increases in posterior cingulate (area 31) and superior and middle frontal gyri bilaterally, Brodmann areas 9 and 10. The PTSD group also showed deactivation in the subcallosal anterior cingulate (area 25) and decreased activation in an adjacent portion of anterior cingulate (area 32) (7). Using PET and script-driven imagery in 16 subjects with CSA (8 with PTSD), Shin and colleagues also reported deactivation of the medial prefrontal and as well as left inferior frontal (Broca's) areas in the PTSD group (8).

Lanius and colleagues reported two fMRI studies in which they used a script-driven symptom provocation paradigm. They also observed significantly decreased BOLD signal in the ventral ACC (Brodmann's area 32) and the thalamus in the PTSD group to both the traumatic and nontraumatic emotional state conditions, suggesting that the earlier neuroimaging findings related to these areas in PTSD may not be specific to traumatic stimuli *(9,10)*. Hendler, Rotshtein, and Hadar studied processing of repeated versus novel visual presentations in an fMRI study of combat veterans with and without PTSD. Repeated presentations resulted in less decrease in blood-oxygen-level dependent (BOLD) signal in the lateral occipital cortex in PTSD subjects, interpreted as impaired visual habituation to trauma-related stimuli *(11)*. A more recent PET script-driven imagery study of 17 Vietnam veterans with PTSD and 19 without PTSD replicated rCBF decreases in the medial frontal gyrus in the PTSD group. This activity was inversely correlated with rCBF changes in the left amygdala and the right amygdala-periamygdaloid cortex. Interestingly, only the male subgroup showed increased rCBF in the left amygdala *(12)*. We reported the results of a $[^{15}O]$ H_2O PET, script-driven imagery study of emotionally evocative and neutral autobiographic events in 16 combat veterans with PTSD (PTSD patients [PP]), 15 combat veterans without PTSD (combat controls [CC]), and 14 healthy, age-matched, control subjects (noncombat controls [NC]), which allowed isolation of changes that are trauma related (PP vs. NC and CC vs. NC) and PTSD specific (PTSD vs. CC). While all subjects deactivated the mPFC and activated the insula for traumatic scripts, PTSD patients deactivated the rostral anterior cingulate cortex (rACC) more than both control groups (CC and NC) but did not demonstrate ventromedial PFC (vmPFC) deactivation observed in controls. The findings observed only in the PTSD group (deactivation of the rACC and higher vmPFC activity) may reflect neural substrates specific to PTSD *(13)*.

To date, only limited studies have been performed in children or adolescents with PTSD to investigate the neural correlates induced by symptom provocation. One small study examined brain responses during visual perception and imaginary recollection of traumatic reminders of adolescents (aged 12–14 years) who developed PTSD versus those who did not after experiencing an earthquake *(14)*. Sample size was limited (five with PTSD vs. six trauma exposed PTSD-negative individuals). During earthquake imagery (as compared with neural imagery), the PTSD group was found to have activation in the bilateral visual cortex, bilarteral cerebellum, and left parahippocampal gyrus relative to the control group. During earthquake perception relative to neutral perception, the control group showed activation of the anterior cingulate, but the PTSD group did not. Additional analyses demonstrated that intergroup differences were significant, providing preliminary evidence that neurobiological alternations of PTSD in adolescence are reminiscent of those occurring in adult PTSD populations *(14)*.

Correlation with Cross-Sectional Symptom Severity

Several investigators have used correlational approaches to neuroimaging data in an attempt to understand the phenomenology of symptom genesis in PTSD (the correlation of imaging findings with measures of symptom severity). Osuch and colleagues correlated rCBF response with flashback intensity in a personalized, script-driven imagery PET paradigm in eight chronic PTSD subjects. The rCBF correlated directly with flashback intensity in the brain stem, insula, and hippocampus and inversely in the prefrontal, right fusiform, and medial temporal cortices (15). Similarly, in an fMRI study, Lanius and colleagues reported that seven CSA subjects with PTSD and concomitant dissociative responses to symptom provocation by scripts had increased activation in the ACC, mPFC, and several other cortical areas compared to ten control subjects (16). However, none of these activations correlated with either dissociative or flashback intensity. The small sample sizes and significant comorbidity limit the interpretation of these findings. In a script-driven imagery and PET study (8), Shin and colleagues reported that symptom severity in the PTSD group (as measured by the total score on the Clinician-Administered PTSD Scale [CAP]) was positively related to rCBF in the right amygdala and negatively related to rCBF in the medial frontal gyrus after controlling for depression severity score. In a recent block design fMRI study, investigators examined the time course of amygdala responses to trauma-relevant negative words, panic-relevant negative words (negative control condition), positive/safety words, and neutral words in 9 predominantly sexual assault PTSD patients and 14 healthy controls (17). The PTSD group showed an increased left amygdala response to trauma-relevant negative versus neutral stimuli compared to controls in the first two (but not last two) runs, and this response correlated with the symptom severity (CAPS total score). Healthy controls showed the opposite pattern.

In summary, symptom provocation studies have implicated anterior paralimbic and limbic structures in generation of PTSD symptoms, including the posterior medial OFC, the insula, and the medial temporal cortex (Fig. 1). One of the more consistent and reliable findings is decrease or failure of activation in subregions of the mPFC and ACC, and this was demonstrated by a number of studies, although it was not universally found. Increased responsivity of the amygdala has been observed in some studies but has not been a consistent finding. Design or methodological factors may contribute to these divergent findings, including the method of symptom provocation (trauma imagery vs. external stimuli), experimental tasks (passive viewing vs. active recall), scanning methodology, and relatively small sample sizes, all of which may affect the ability to activate or detect amygdala response.

Cognitive Activation Studies

Cognitive activation studies utilize a neurocognitive task (a "probe") that is expected to selectively activate neural circuits implicated in task-related processing. Selectively activating a circuit without eliciting symptoms has a substantial advantage in that this overcomes the confound of eliciting a large number of more general or nonspecific trauma-related responses. Investigators have used cognitive activation strategies to further examine a number of regions implicated in PTSD by symptom provocation studies, such as the mPFC, amygdala, ACC, and hippocampus.

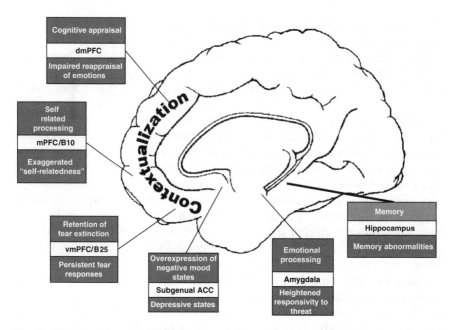

Fig. 1. Neural regions underlying core processes and post-traumatic stress disorder (PTSD) symptomatology. *ACC* anterior cingulate cortex. *dmPFC* dorsal medial prefrontal cortex, *mPFC* medial prefrontal cortex, *vmPFC* ventral medial prefrontal cortex

One region that has been implicated in PTSD in symptom provocation studies is the ACC, albeit as hypofunctioning or failing to activate as compared to unaffected controls. The ACC is a region that has been activated by many functional neuroimaging studies and has been implicated in different processes involving cognitive-emotional interactions. A variety of evidence supports the existence of functional subdivisions in the ACC, with the dorsal ACC supporting cognitive control and error-related processing, while the rACC is involved in the assessment of salience of emotional information and the regulation of emotional responses *(18)*. Bremner et al. *(19)* used the modified Stroop task (color Stroop, emotional Stroop, and control task) and [^{15}O] H$_2$O PET to probe ACC function in 12 women with early CSA-related PTSD and 9 CSA women without PTSD. The PTSD group demonstrated a relative decrease in ACC blood flow during the emotional but not the color Stroop task, which elicited increased rCBF in the ACC Brodmann area (BA) 24 and 32 in both groups *(19)*. Shin et al. *(20)* also investigated ACC functioning in 16 Vietnam combat veterans (8 with PTSD) using fMRI and an emotional counting Stroop paradigm. Subjects were asked to count the number of combat-related, generally negative, and neutral words while being scanned. In the comparison of combat-related to generally negative words, the non-PTSD group showed significant BOLD signal increases in rACC, but the PTSD group did not *(20)*.

Another region implicated in PTSD is the hippocampus, which plays a role in explicit memory processes as well as contextual learning *(21,22)*. A number of structural MRI studies reported decreased hippocampal volumes in individuals with PTSD *(23–27)*, and MRI studies have reported decreased *N*-acetylaspartate (NAA) levels in the hippocampus, interpreted as reflecting decreased neuronal integrity *(28,29)*. Reduced hippocampal volumes have ranged from 5% to 26% and have tended to be found bilaterally across studies *(30)*. It should be noted, however, that a number of studies have not replicated the finding of decreased hippocampal volumes in PTSD *(31–33)*. These discrepancies suggest that smaller hippocampi may be restricted to subgroups of PTSD or may be secondary to comorbid conditions or that hippocampal pathology may be subtle and not always detectable using standard morphometric MRI procedures *(30)*. Furthermore, it was not clear whether reported hippocampal changes are acquired signs of PTSD or potential predisposing factors. Gilbertson et al. *(34)* studied monozygotic twins discordant for trauma exposure, with and without PTSD, and found that both twins with PTSD and their trauma-unexposed twin had smaller hippocampi relative to trauma-exposed non-PTSD twins and their cotwins *(34)*. Moreover, the same group, both PTSD and trauma nonexposed cotwin, showed impaired hippocampus-mediated spatial processing using a cue configuration task *(35)*. These findings offer compelling evidence for reduced hippocampal size serving as a vulnerability or predisposing factor for PTSD. To investigate hippocampal function, Shin et al. *(12)* used PET in 16 firefighters (8 with PTSD) using a word stem completion task. Subjects completed a three-letter word stem with deeply encoded/high-recall and shallow-encoded/low-recall words learned during a preceding training session. Somewhat surprisingly, the PTSD group demonstrated greater rCBF in the hippocampi (bilateral) across conditions, and symptom severity was positively associated with rCBF in hippo-campus and parahippocampal gyrus. In the comparison of high- versus low-recall conditions, however, PTSD showed smaller rCBF increases in the left hippocampus. This was interpreted as potentially reflecting reduced efficiency of the hippocampus during the performance of an explicit memory task *(30)*.

Functional Connectivity Analyses

There is a growing appreciation that complicated cognitive and emotional processes rely on the orchestrated interactions of distributed brain networks rather than, or at least in addition to, activation of individual brain regions. Consequently, functional connectivity analysis, which refers to the application of specific statistical methods to functional neuroimaging data sets to identify correlated brain activity across various regions *(36,37)*, might be a particularly pertinent and useful technique.

Several studies have applied functional connectivity analysis to neuroimaging studies of PTSD. Gilboa et al. *(38)* studied, using symptom provocation (autobiographical trauma-related and neutral scripts) and [^{15}O] H$_2$O PET, 20 individuals with a history of civilian trauma (10 with PTSD). A multivariate analysis technique (partial least squares) was used to identify brain regions with activity that covaried with two reference ("seed") voxels, one in the right PFC (BA 10) and the other in the right amygdala. Amygdala activity was found to significantly influence activity in the visual cortex, subcallosal gyrus, and anterior cingulate in the PTSD subjects but not in the trauma-exposed controls (38). These findings indicate that blood flow measures reflect the influence of the amygdala on medial frontal regions in PTSD rather than a failure of mPFC inhibition of the amygdala. In addition, correlational analyses did not lend support for the failure of inhibition of the ACC over the amygdala.

Lanius et al. (39) used functional connectivity analyses on data gathered during fMRI script-driven symptom provocation experiments in 11 subjects with PTSD from sexual abuse/assault or motor vehicle accident (MVA) and 13 trauma-exposed subjects without PTSD. Connectivity maps for right ACC showed greater correlations in PTSD subjects (vs. controls) in the right posterior cingulate cortex (PCC) (BA 29), right caudate, right parietal lobe (BA 7 and 40), and right occipital lobe (BA 19). Subjects without PTSD had greater correlations of ACC with left superior frontal gyrus (BA 9), left anterior ACC (BA 32), left striatum (caudate), left parietal lobe (BA 40 and 43), and left insula (BA 13) (39). Although these findings are intriguing, our understanding of functional neural networks in both health and disease is still very limited. As methods for the analysis of functional connectivity continue to develop and the knowledge base regarding coordinated activation of brain regions grows, these approaches will likely play an increasingly important role in delineating functional relationships between regions implicated in the pathophysiology of PTSD.

Summary of Functional Neuroimaging Studies in PTSD

The studies reviewed involve different cohorts (combat and CSA-related PTSD), different paradigms (symptom provocation vs. cognitive activation), and different modalities (fMRI, PET, and SPECT). Taken together, they lend tentative support to a neurocircuitry model that emphasizes the role of dysregulation in threat-related processing in PTSD. According to this model, trauma exposure sets off a cascade of neural changes that culminates in a state of amygdala hyperresponsivity to trauma-reminiscent and other threat-related stimuli that mediates symptoms of hyperarousal and vigilance associated with PTSD. The model also proposes associated inadequate top-down control by the mPFC, which maintains and perpetuates the state of amygdala hyperresponsivity and helps mediate the failure to suppress attention to trauma-related stimuli. Consistent with this model, several studies have demonstrated reduced activation of the mPFC (BA 10 and 11) and ACC (BA 32) in PTSD subjects compared to traumatized controls (8–10,20,40). Other studies have reported increased responsivity of the amygdaloid region (4,41,42), although some have not (8,9,40). While the conceptualization of PTSD-related pathophysiology that emphasizes the role of threat-related processing has some empirical support, there is clearly a need for a broader conceptualization of the processes implicated in the disorder. This is because deficits in threat-related processing explain only some aspects of PTSD, and other significant manifestations of PTSD remain unexplained by this model. These include intrusive thoughts and memories, emotional numbing, vulnerability and resilience factors, and generalization of vigilance and avoidance from the initial traumatic event to other less closely related events. Thus, to understand these complex phenomena, additional relevant mechanisms that may assist in understanding the complex phenomenology of PTSD need to be explored. The following section includes a selective review of emerging neuroimaging research that focuses on a number of mechanisms that are potentially relevant to the pathophysiology of PTSD, including fear conditioning, cognitive-emotional interactions, and self-related and social-emotional processing.

THE MEDIAL PREFRONTAL CORTEX AND PTSD

Studies of Threat-Related Processing (Fear Conditioning, Habituation, and Extinction)

Studies using the fear-conditioning paradigm in rats since 1990 have helped outline specialized threat-related neurocircuitry with a number of functionally connected regions, including subregions of the PFC, the amygdala, and the hippocampus. A conceptual framework amalgamating their findings has been put forward, proposing the existence of two broad pathways in the processing of threat-related signals: a subcortical "fast" pathway that transmits features of the stimulus rapidly, but with poor specificity, and a cortical "slow" pathway that involves more integrated and detailed cognitive processing of stimulus characteristics *(43)*. Animal studies have identified the amygdaloid complex (central, lateral, and basolateral nuclei) as a crucial substrate in the formation of stimulus-response associations involved in the fear conditioning and aversive learning.

Functional neuroimaging studies have used PET and fMRI to examine fear conditioning in humans, confirming that similar regions identified in animal research subserve fear conditioning in humans *(44)*. These usually examined classical conditioning to aversive stimuli, typically aversive tones or mild electrical shocks. For example, Buchel, Dolan, Armony, and Friston used event-related fMRI to study the classical conditioning of faces paired with aversive tones in nine healthy right-handed volunteers *(45)*. Comparison of the CS+ condition (conditional stimulus reinforced with aversive tones) and CS-condition (conditioned stimulus not aversely reinforced) revealed greater activation of the ACC and greater activation in the amygdala only in early trials, suggesting a rapid habituation of the amygdala response in healthy volunteers. Interestingly, studies designed to investigate the time course for amygdala habituation demonstrated that individuals with PTSD failed to show the same patterns of habituation of amygdala responding to negative stimuli, suggesting a possible longer maintenance of fear responses in PTSD *(17)*.

Habituation and extinction are two neural processes that involve a time component that can modulate fear conditioning and aversive learning and might be highly relevant to PTSD. *Habituation* refers to the process by which repeated presentation of the same conditioned stimulus-unconditioned stimulus (CS-US) pairing leads to a decreasing conditioned response (CR), while extinction refers to a reduction and disappearance of a CR on account of learning about a new stimulus-response association (i.e., the CS is no longer associated with the US). These are adaptive processes for organisms as they provide the organism with flexibility to reallocate critical resources to threat-related stimuli in a constantly changing environment. The failure of habituation to trauma-related stimuli or the failure of extinction have been hypothesized to contribute to the development or maintenance of PTSD (i.e., trauma plays the role of the conditioning event).

These phenomena have been extensively studied in animals and behaviorally in humans, but these processes have only recently been the subject of neuroimaging investigations. A number of neuroimaging studies have found that presentation of emotionally expressive faces, presented both overtly as well as in a masked manner (fearful or happy faces masked with a neutral face such that subjects consciously perceive only the neutral face), activates the amygdala, and this response rapidly habituates with repeated presentation regardless of the mode of presentation (overt or masked) *(46,47)*. Several studies reviewed here in which a CS is repeatedly paired with an aversive US also found rapid habituation of the amygdala response *(45,48,49)*. One fMRI study suggested that repeated presentation of emotionally expressive faces may generate habituation in a regionally specific manner based on the valence of the facial stimulus. In this study, fearful and happy faces were repeatedly presented in two 2-min runs to eight right-handed healthy male subjects. Habituation was observed in the left dorsolateral prefrontal cortex (dlPFC) and premotor cortex and the right amygdala. The left dlPFC showed increased habituation to happy more than fearful faces, the right amygdala exhibited greater habituation to emotionally valenced stimuli, while the left amygdala responded significantly more to negatively versus positively valenced stimuli (relative to the right) *(50)*. Our laboratory has also demonstrated rACC habituation with repeated emotional picture (aversive minus neutral/blank) presentation *(51)*.

These studies provide evidence for habituation in the dlPFC, ACC, and the amygdala, with potentially differential habituation in prefrontal versus subcortical regions or lateralized specialization. Interestingly, the only study that has specifically addressed the time course of amygdala responses to trauma cues (trauma-relevant words) in PTSD patients and healthy controls found an increased left amygdala response to trauma-relevant negative versus neutral stimuli in the first two but not last two runs. This response correlated with the symptom severity (CAPS total score). However, while sensitization to non-trauma negative words was seen in the PTSD group, failure of habituation to trauma-related words was not seen *(17)*.

The process of extinction has also been the subject of neuroimaging studies, and it has been suggested that a failure to adequately extinguish fear responses is the mechanism underlying the maintenance of pathological fear in PTSD *(52)*. Phelps, Delgado, Nearing, and LeDoux *(53)* used a simple discrimination, partial reinforcement fear-conditioning paradigm with an event-related fMRI design. Colored squares were used for CS+ and CS− (blue and yellow), and the US was a mild wrist shock. The study was conducted in three phases: an acquisition phase in which subjects were exposed to reinforced presentations of the CS, followed by day 1 extinction and day 2 extinction, in which subjects were exposed to unreinforced presentations of the CS. The authors reported that right amygdala activation predicted the CR in the early acquisition (positive correlation) and day 1 extinction phase (negative correlation). The vmPFC (the subgenual anterior cingulate region of interest) response positively correlated with the CR magnitude during day 2 extinction *(53)*. Milad et al. *(54)* studied recall of fear extinction in healthy adults ($N = 17$). Context was manipulated, separating acquisition and extinction context, and the extinction recall took place the next day, in an extinction context. Significant bilateral activations in the vmPFC and left amygdala were identified during fear extinction, as were two distinct loci within the vmPFC and bilateral hippocampi during extinction recall *(54)*. Together, these findings appear to be consistent with those of animal research that implicates the amygdala in acquisition and extinction and the vmPFC in the retention and recall of the extinction learning process *(53,55–58)*. They are also intriguing in light of evidence reviewed from human neuroimaging studies of altered connectivity between medial frontal regions and amygdala in PTSD. Thus, the evidence from human neuroimaging studies implicates subregions of the mPFC and OFC, subdivisions of the ACC, the extended amygdala, the hippocampus, and nuclei of the thalamus in the processes of fear conditioning, habituation, and extinction. Neuroimaging studies of these processes in healthy humans and extending these studies to patients with PTSD are needed to better understand the roles of fear conditioning, habituation, and extinction in PTSD pathophysiology and symptom generation.

Cognitive-Emotional Interactions: Appraisal, Reappraisal, and Emotional Regulation

Emotion regulation refers to the set of mental processes by which people amplify, attenuate, or otherwise modulate emotion states *(59)*. Key features of PTSD, include emotional numbing and heightened and prolonged experience of fear, anxiety, and other negative affective states. While it is possible that abnormal threat processing drives some of these symptoms, it is also possible that poor emotion regulation plays a key or complimentary role in this disorder and contributes significantly to behavioral dysfunction. If threat detection is a "bottom-up" process, cognitive-emotional interaction can be seen as "top-down" regulation. Abnormalities in either one or both of these processing streams can lead to similar outcomes and in the case of PTSD to similar psychopathology. For the purposes of this discussion, emotion regulation is understood in terms of a number of component processes that operate over different timescales.

Appraisal refers to the cognitive interpretation of emotion-relevant stimuli by higher cortical centers. An increasing number of neuroimaging studies are providing evidence that cognitive appraisal can modulate emotional responses, which is reflected in changes in the activity of emotion-processing areas. *Cognitive reappraisal* is a form of emotion regulation that involves volitionally reinterpreting the meaning of a stimulus to change one's emotional response to it.

Cognitive Appraisal of Emotions

A number of studies have manipulated the extent to which subjects cognitively attend to aspects of emotion-relevant stimuli. These studies suggest that even the simple process of labeling or rating an emotion can reduce the activity in structures that are responsive when the emotional stimulus is passively viewed or experienced. Hariri, Bookheimer, and Mazziotta examined the cognitive modulation of emotions by comparing the BOLD response in healthy subjects as they performed three different tasks (match, label, and control). In the match task, subjects were asked to match the affect of one of two faces to that of a simultaneously presented target face (angry or fearful), whereas in the label task, they were asked to assign one of two simultaneously presented linguistic labels (angry or afraid) to a target face. Matching was associated with increased activation in both the right and left amygdala, whereas linguistically labeling the expression was associated with a decreased activation in the amygdala. In addition, right PFC activity was inversely correlated with left amygdala activity, interpreted as it being the neural substrate for the cognitive modulation of emotion *(60)*. This finding has been replicated using threatening and fearful pictures as well *(61)*.

In our laboratory, we examined rCBF response in healthy subjects, comparing a rating to a passive-viewing condition *(62)*. Subjects saw aversive and neutral pictures while they performed a passive viewing and rating task. During passive viewing, subjects activated right amygdala/insula and left insula, and rating was associated with increased activation of the dorsomedial prefrontal cortex (dmPFC) and the ACC and with reduced sadness and reduced activation of the right amygdala/insula and left insula. These findings demonstrate the involvement of the dmPFC and ACC in the cognitive rating task and suggest modulating effects of these structures on emotion-related structures, such as the amygdala and insula. These findings extend findings from animal studies that have demonstrated the inhibitory influence of the mPFC over the amygdala *(63)*. If indeed dmPFC/ACC dysfunction is present in PTSD, these findings could suggest one explanation for exaggerated emotional responses of PTSD patients as they are less effectively modulated by cognitive appraisal.

Cognitive Modulation of Emotions: Reappraisal

Cognitive reappraisal refers to volitional reinterpretion of the meaning of a stimulus to modify one's emotional response. Several groups have investigated the neural effects of reappraisal using functional neuroimaging methods. This line of work is likely very relevant to PTSD, for which an inability to reinterpret the meaning of ambiguous stimuli might contribute to emotional dysregulation. It is also of much interest in the investigation of brain mechanisms of cognitive-behavioral therapy, an effective treatment for some patients with PTSD. Ochsner, Bunge, Gross, and Gabrieli used an event-related fMRI design and aversive pictures to study cognitive reappraisal in healthy female subjects. Subjects were asked to attend (be aware of feelings elicited by the picture) or to reappraise (reinterpret the picture so that it no longer elicits a negative emotional response) while being scanned *(64)*. Reappraising (vs. attending) was associated with increased activation of the dorsal and ventral left lateral PFC, dmPFC, left temporal pole, right supramarginal gyrus (SMG), and left lateral occipital cortex. Greater activation in the right ACC and SMG correlated with greater decreases in negative affect (greater reappraisal success); left ventral PFC activation during reappraisal was inversely correlated with activity in the amygdala. Effective reappraisal resulted in increased activation in lateral PFC and mPFC regions and in decreased activation of medial OFC and amygdala.

Using a similar paradigm, Phan et al. *(65)* showed highly aversive and arousing pictures to healthy subjects, who were instructed to either "maintain" (feel naturally) or "suppress" (by positive reframing or rationalizing) negative affect. Successful reduction of negative affect was associated with increasing activation of the dmPFC, dorsal ACC, dlPFC, lateral OFC, and ventrolateral PFC/ inferior frontal gyrus and with decreasing activity in the left nucleus accumbens, left lateral PFC, and left extended amygdala. In addition, right dorsal ACC, right anterior insula, bilateral dlPFC, and bilateral ventrolateral PFC activity was inversely correlated with the intensity of negative affect. These studies provide evidence for the emotion-regulatory role of the lateral PFC, dmPFC, SMG, and ACC *(65)*. The observed difficulty among patients with PTSD to cognitively regulate their emotions can be hypothesized to be a result of dysfunctional cognitive-emotional processes (such as cognitive appraisal and reappraisal) subserved by some of these regions. The therapeutic mechanisms of cognitive-behavioral therapy in PTSD may also be related to these processes and structures. Therefore, there is a need to extend these innovative paradigms to the study of PTSD.

Self-Relatedness and Social-Emotional Processing

Healthy social functioning is pivotal to the survival of humans, and it makes intuitive sense that this important function be subserved by dedicated neural resources for the processing of social stimuli. Self-relatedness can be seen in the same context as a means to "map" social landscape. Some of the regions we discussed in the previous paragraphs have been implicated in processing social stimuli and self-relatedness. This might be of particular relevance to PTSD given that core manifestations of PTSD include a tendency to interpret or perceive stimuli as self-relevant, difficulties in interpersonal and social functioning, and the observation that interpersonal trauma results in the highest rates of PTSD *(66)*. Primate and human lesion studies have implicated the mPFC, OFC, superior temporal sulcus, amygdala, and other regions in processing social and related stimuli.

Our group has investigated the concept of self-relatedness in the context of emotional processing in a series of studies. In the first study, we used aversive, positive, and neutral International Affective Picture System (IAPS) pictures in a trial-related fMRI design to compare the neural substrates underlying the assessment of the emotional intensity of the pictures versus the self-relatedness of their content in healthy, right-handed volunteers *(67)*. Individualized subjective ratings over these two dimensions (obtained postscan) were correlated with brain activity in a parametric factorial analysis. The appraisal of self-relatedness specifically engaged the mPFC and recruited the dmPFC and insula as the extent of self-relatedness increased. In contrast, the amygdala activation was specific to affective judgment of emotional intensity. Both increasing emotional intensity and self-relatedness activated the nucleus accumbens. These findings suggest that appraisal of self-relatedness specifically recruits the mPFC.

We extended our investigation of the neural substrates of emotion to the processing of social versus nonsocial stimuli in 12 healthy, right-handed volunteers *(68)*. In a novel paradigm, subjects viewed short video segments that evoked positive or negative emotions that were categorized as "social" (humor, sadness) or "nonsocial" (appetite, physical disgust). Following the video, static frames extracted from the video were viewed for 30 s to help subjects maintain the emotions evoked by the video clip; during this period, fMRI images were acquired. Nonsocial and social-emotional experiences resulted in partially overlapping but somewhat separate neural patterns. Social-positive and social-negative conditions activated the amygdala/SLEA, superior temporal gyrus, hippocampus, and posterior cingulate, whereas nonsocial-positive and nonsocial-negative conditions activated insula and visual cortex. Additional activations depended on both social context and valence: amygdala (nonsocial negative); ACC (nonsocial positive and social negative); and OFC and nucleus accumbens (social positive).

In another study *(69)*, we explored the neural correlates of viewing messages that are more or less tailored to the characteristics of the viewer and thus are more or less "self-relevant." Active smokers were recruited and completed a baseline survey of their smoking habits. This survey was used to construct two sets of smoking cessation health messages; "high-tailored" messages incorporated information about the subject's personal smoking habits into the smoking cessation message, while "low-tailored" messages were linguistically comparable but lacked subject-specific information. In a mixed block and event-related fMRI design, subjects were presented with both high-tailored and low-tailored smoking cessation messages while fMRI images were acquired. Consistent with our hypothesis, preliminary data with nine subjects revealed greater activation in the vmPFC region when contrasting high-tailored events to low-tailored events. These studies, as well as a number of others performed by different groups *(70–72)*, independently replicate using different paradigms the involvement of mPFC and ACC regions in both self-relatedness and social cognition. Overall, these studies and findings highlight the roles of self-relatedness and of sociality linking these processes to activation of ventral regions of mPFC and of ACC as well as amygdala and other regions. The demonstrated link between ACC and mPFC function and PTSD in this context also raises an interesting possibility that abnormal functioning of these regions in PTSD might explain the well-documented deficit in social functioning in this condition.

The Failure of Stimulus Contextualization: A Core Process in PTSD?

The discussion covered a number of seemingly heterogeneous processes potentially involved in PTSD, including habituation, extinction, cognition-emotional interactions, and social and self-related processing. Intriguingly, all of these processes have been linked to activation of various regions in the medial wall of the prefrontal lobe, described as dorsal and ventral regions of the mPFC and ACC (Fig. 2). While it is possible that all these functions engage the medial wall of the prefrontal lobe independently, it might be worth formulating an

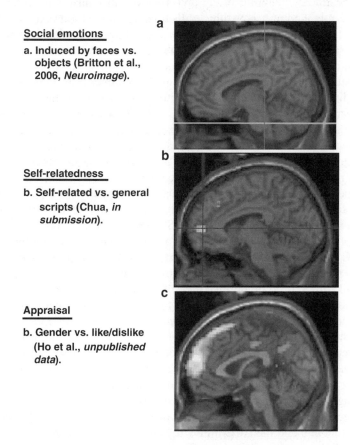

Social emotions

a. Induced by faces vs. objects (Britton et al., 2006, *Neuroimage*).

Self-relatedness

b. Self-related vs. general scripts (Chua, *in submission*).

Appraisal

b. Gender vs. like/dislike (Ho et al., *unpublished data*).

Fig. 2. Activation of the medial prefrontal cortex (mPFC) resulting from social emotions, self-relatedness, and emotional appraisal. **a.** Reference number 68, **b.** Reference number 69, and **c.** No reference number (*See Color Plates*)

integrating hypothesis regarding possible underlying themes that bring together these disparate processes in the hope of producing further insight into the fundamental pathophysiology of PTSD. One way of bringing together the preceding processes is to understand them as aspects of a larger process that might be labeled "contextualization." Complex organisms must be able to select the appropriate response to a particular stimulus from a large range of available alternatives. The same stimulus might represent different "values" that necessitate different responses depending on the context in which it appears. This task requires that the organism attend to the contextual cues in the environment, which includes cues present in the external environment as well as cues present in memory and even in the organism's internal metabolic/physiological milieu, that disambiguate which response is most appropriate given the particular situation.

Contextualization refers to the process by which key dimensions of the situational context are appraised, represented, and used to guide the selection of action. The studies reviewed in the preceding part of the chapter suggest that the mPFC might play a key role in contextualization. Extinction, cognitive-emotional interactions, reappraisal, social cognition, and self-relatedness are all processes that are based on contextualization. These processes all reassess the stimulus value based on new learning, cognitive information, context, social environment, or self-relatedness. Interestingly, a number of recent animal studies have linked mPFC regions to contextual modulation of cue value in rats *(73)*. Other findings that associate mPFC with reversal learning *(74)* are also highly consistent with the contextualization perspective on mPFC function since reversal learning can be understood as learning a new and different meaning in a new context. Thus, there appear to be at least three categories of contextual variables represented in mPFC: cognitive context, social context, and internal context, possibly represented along a caudal-rostral gradient in the mPFC. Cognitive context is established by processes that judge the relevance of stimuli to the organism's memories and strategic goals. Studies of cognitive control of emotion and reappraisal reviewed suggest that cognitive context is primarily represented in dmPFC as well as dlPFC. Social context, on the other hand, is established by processes that judge the extent to which stimuli are self-related, that is, whether they are like the self or are not like the self and to what degree. Studies of self-relatedness and of social emotions suggest that vmPFC and other regions of the mPFC represent information about the social context of stimuli. *Internal context* refers to the overall homeostatic state of the internal milieu, including the state of drives, metabolic states, and overall physiological load. A network of interrelated neocortical regions, especially the rostral anterior insula and OFC, are involved in interoceptive attention and assessing and representing the internal context *(75)* and are highly interconnected with the medial frontal wall.

If indeed the ACC and mPFC are involved in context-setting or contextualization function and the ACC/mPFC deficits are present in PTSD, this might shed new light on the specific deficits and processes of symptom generation in this disorder. This is an expansion of the prevailing model of PTSD that posits that mPFC deficits in PTSD lead to inadequate top-down control over the amygdala and persistent fear conditioning. The expanded contextualization model is based on the notion that mPFC circuitry has a much broader range of functions than merely providing inhibitory control over the amygdala. Indeed, animal *(76)* and neuroimaging data *(77)* demonstrate that the mPFC can have an activating or facilitating role with respect to the amygdala.

We propose that the mPFC plays a more complex role in contextualizing stimuli in terms of cognitive, social, and internal contexts, thus helping guide the selection of appropriate responses suited to particular features of the environment. It follows that dysfunction in the mPFC could produce a number of disparate problems, and these problems do in fact appear to be characteristic of PTSD. Failures in discriminating contextual cues might lead to the inappropriate expression of trauma-related memories and emotions, thus contributing to reexperiencing phenomena. Trauma cues are not perceived in the current context but rather independent of it—as if trauma is actually occurring. Poor contextual discrimination might also contribute to *emotional numbing*, the failure to experience emotions that are appropriate for a given context. Abnormal or dysregulated signals of internal milieu arising from the anterior insula and associated mPFC regions may give rise to anxiety, rumination, and avoidance behaviors *(78)*. Other deficits might include difficulties in social interactions due to inappropriate perception of stimuli as self-related. Overall, failure to contextualize might constitute a core process of PTSD, explaining a large number of features of the disorder that have eluded adequate explanation in the existing model, which emphasizes dysfunction in threat-related processing.

SUMMARY AND FUTURE DIRECTIONS

Neuroimaging studies of PTSD over the past decade have been based on a model that conceptualizes the disorder as a state of heightened responsivity to threatening stimuli or a state of insufficient inhibitory control over exaggerated threat sensitivity. Consistent with this model, several studies have demonstrated reduced activation of the mPFC (BA 10 and 11) and ACC (BA 32) in PTSD subjects compared to traumatized controls. Other studies have reported increased responsivity of the amygdaloid region, although findings were not always consistent (see Fig. 1 for a summary of neural regions implicated in PTSD). Findings may be influenced by several methodological issues, such as small sample sizes, heterogeneous populations, and varying imaging methods that limit broad generalization. Despite the progress made, existing models and findings are unable to fully capture the complexity of PTSD. Innovative paradigms being developed in cognitive and social neuroscience suggest novel directions for future work that can broaden our understanding of a range of pathophysiological processes in PTSD.

Future directions of research include neuroimaging studies of fear conditioning, habituation, and extinction as well as studies investigating emotion regulation processes and self-related and social-emotional processing. There is also a need for integrating different lines of inquiry, including genetic, neurochemical/receptor, hypothalamic-pituitary-adrenal (HPA) axis, and blood flow parameters in PTSD. This research holds the exciting promise of helping to identify neurobiological factors that may confer vulnerability or resilience to PTSD and offer meaningful clues to the pathophysiology of PTSD. This progress will be essential for the future development of effective prevention and treatment strategies for this disorder.

REFERENCES

1. Rauch SL, Shin LM. Functional neuroimaging studies in posttraumatic stress disorder. Ann N Y Acad Sci 1997; 821:83–98.
2. Pitman RK, Shin LM, Rauch SL. Investigating the pathogenesis of posttraumatic stress disorder with neuroimaging. J Clin Psychiatry 62 2001; (suppl 17):47–54.
3. Liberzon I, Phan KL. Brain-imaging studies of posttraumatic stress disorder. CNS Spectr 2003; 8(9):641–50.
4. Rauch SL, van der Kolk BA, Fisler RE, et al. A symptom provocation study of post-traumatic stress disorder using positron emission tomography and script-driven imagery. Arch Gen Psychiatry 1996; 53(5):380–87.
5. Shin LM, Kosslyn SM, McNally RJ, et al. Visual imagery and perception in posttraumatic stress disorder. A positron emission tomographic investigation. Arch Gen Psychiatry 1997;54(3):233–41.
6. Liberzon I, Britton JC, Phan KL. Neural correlates of traumatic recall in posttraumatic stress disorder. Stress 2003;6(3):151–56.
7. Bremner JD, Narayan M, Staib LH, Southwick SM, McGlashan T, Charney DS. Neural correlates of memories of childhood sexual abuse in women with and without posttraumatic stress disorder. Am J Psychiatry 1999;156(11):1787–95.
8. Shin LM, McNally RJ, Kosslyn SM, et al. Regional cerebral blood flow during script-driven imagery in childhood sexual abuse-related PTSD: a PET investigation. Am J Psychiatry 1999;156(4):575–84.
9. Lanius RA, Williamson PC, Densmore M, et al. Neural correlates of traumatic memories in posttraumatic stress disorder: a functional MRI investigation. Am J Psychiatry 2001;158(11):1920–22.
10. Lanius RA, Hopper JW, Menon RS. Individual differences in a husband and wife who developed PTSD after a motor vehicle accident: a functional MRI case study. Am J Psychiatry 2003;160(4):667–69.
11. Hendler T, Rotshtein P, Hadar U. Emotion-perception interplay in the visual cortex: "the eyes follow the heart." Cell Mol Neurobiol 2001;21(6):733–52.
12. Shin LM, Orr SP, Carson MA, et al. Regional cerebral blood flow in the amygdala and medial prefrontal cortex during traumatic imagery in male and female Vietnam veterans with PTSD. Arch Gen Psychiatry 2004;61(2):168–76.
13. Britton JC, Phan KL, Taylor SF, Fig LM, Liberzon I. Corticolimbic blood flow in posttraumatic stress disorder during script-driven imagery. Biol Psychiatry 2005;57(8):832–40.
14. Hsu CC, Chong MY, Yang P, Yen CF. Posttraumatic stress disorder among adolescent earthquake victims in Taiwan. J Am Acad Child Adolesc Psychiatry 2002;41(7):875–81.
15. Osuch EA, Benson B, Geraci M, et al. Regional cerebral blood flow correlated with flashback intensity in patients with posttraumatic stress disorder. Biol Psychiatry 2001;50(4):246–53.
16. Lanius RA, Williamson PC, Boksman K, et al. Brain activation during script-driven imagery induced dissociative responses in PTSD: a functional magnetic resonance imaging investigation. Biol Psychiatry 2002;52(4):305–11.
17. Protopopescu X, Pan H, Tuescher O, et al. Differential time courses and specificity of amygdala activity in posttraumatic stress disorder subjects and normal control subjects. Biol Psychiatry 2005;57(5):464–73.

18. Bush G, Luu P, Posner MI. Cognitive and emotional influences in anterior cingulate cortex. Trends Cogn Sci 2000;4(6):215–22.
19. Bremner JD, Vermetten E, Vythilingam M, et al. Neural correlates of the classic color and emotional Stroop in women with abuse-related posttraumatic stress disorder. Biol Psychiatry 2004;55(6):612–20.
20. Shin LM, Whalen PJ, Pitman RK, et al. An fMRI study of anterior cingulate function in posttraumatic stress disorder. Biol Psychiatry 2001;50(12):932–42.
21. Eichenbaum H. A cortical-hippocampal system for declarative memory. Nat Rev Neurosci 2000;1(1):41–50.
22. Corcoran KA, Maren S. Hippocampal inactivation disrupts contextual retrieval of fear memory after extinction. J Neurosci 2001;21(5):1720–2 6.
23. Bremner JD, Randall P, Scott TM, et al. MRI-based measurement of hippocampal volume in patients with combat-related posttraumatic stress disorder. Am J Psychiatry 1995;152(7):973–81.
24. Bremner JD, Randall P, Vermetten E, et al. Magnetic resonance imaging-based measurement of hippocampal volume in posttraumatic stress disorder related to childhood physical and sexual abuse—a preliminary report. Biol Psychiatry 1997;41(1):23–32.
25. Gurvits TV, Shenton ME, Hokama H, et al. Magnetic resonance imaging study of hippocampal volume in chronic, combat-related posttraumatic stress disorder. Biol Psychiatry 1996;40(11):1091–99.
26. Stein MB, Koverola C, Hanna C, Torchia MG, McClarty B. Hippocampal volume in women victimized by childhood sexual abuse. Psychol Med 1997;27(4):951–59.
27. Villarreal G, Hamilton DA, Petropoulos H, et al. Reduced hippocampal volume and total white matter volume in posttraumatic stress disorder. Biol Psychiatry 2002;52(2):119–25.
28. Schuff N, Neylan TC, Lenoci MA, et al. Decreased hippocampal N-acetylaspartate in the absence of atrophy in posttraumatic stress disorder. Biol Psychiatry 2001;50(12):952–59.
29. Villarreal G, Petropoulos H, Hamilton DA, et al. Proton magnetic resonance spectroscopy of the hippocampus and occipital white matter in PTSD: preliminary results. Can J Psychiatry 2002;47(7):666–70.
30. Shin LM, Shin PS, Heckers S, et al. Hippocampal function in posttraumatic stress disorder. Hippocampus 2004;14(3):292–300.
31. De Bellis MD, Keshavan MS, Clark DB, et al. A. E. Bennett Research Award. Developmental traumatology. Part II: Brain development. Biol Psychiatry 1999;45(10):1271–84.
32. Bonne O, Brandes D, Gilboa A, et al. Longitudinal MRI study of hippocampal volume in trauma survivors with PTSD. Am J Psychiatry 2001;158(8):1248–51.
33. Carrion VG, Weems CF, Eliez S, et al. Attenuation of frontal asymmetry in pediatric posttraumatic stress disorder. Biol Psychiatry 2001;50(12):943–51.
34. Gilbertson MW, Shenton ME, Ciszewski A, et al. Smaller hippocampal volume predicts pathologic vulnerability to psychological trauma. Nat Neurosci 2002;5(11):1242–47.
35. Gilbertson MW, Williston SK, Paulus LA, et al. Configural cue performance in identical twins discordant for posttraumatic stress disorder: theoretical implications for the role of hippocampal function. Biol Psychiatry 2007;62(5):513–20.
36. Friston KJ, Frith CD, Liddle PF, Frackowiak RS. Functional connectivity: the principal-component analysis of large (PET) data sets. J Cereb Blood Flow Metab 1993;13(1):5–14.
37. Friston KJ, Frith CD, Fletcher P, Liddle PF, Frackowiak RS. Functional topography: multidimensional scaling and functional connectivity in the brain. Cereb Cortex 1996;6(2):156–64.
38. Gilboa A, Shalev AY, Laor L, et al. Functional connectivity of the prefrontal cortex and the amygdala in posttraumatic stress disorder. Biol Psychiatry 2004;55(3):263–72.

39. Lanius RA, Williamson PC, Densmore M, et al. The nature of traumatic memories: a 4-T FMRI functional connectivity analysis. Am J Psychiatry 2004;161(1):36–44.
40. Bremner JD, Staib LH, Kaloupek D, Southwick SM, Soufer R, Charney DS. Neural correlates of exposure to traumatic pictures and sound in Vietnam combat veterans with and without posttraumatic stress disorder: a positron emission tomography study. Biol Psychiatry 1999;45(7):806–16.
41. Rauch SL, Whalen PJ, Shin LM, et al. Exaggerated amygdala response to masked facial stimuli in posttraumatic stress disorder: a functional MRI study. Biol Psychiatry 2000;47(9):769–76.
42. Liberzon I, Taylor SF, Amdur R, et al. Brain activation in PTSD in response to trauma-related stimuli. Biol Psychiatry 1999;45(7):817–26.
43. LeDoux JE. Emotion circuits in the brain. Ann Rev Neurosci 2000;23:155–84.
44. Buchel C, Dolan RJ. Classical fear conditioning in functional neuroimaging. Curr Opin Neurobiol 2000;10(2):219–23.
45. Buchel C, Dolan RJ, Armony JL, Friston KJ. Amygdala-hippocampal involvement in human aversive trace conditioning revealed through event-related functional magnetic resonance imaging. J Neurosci 1999;19(24):10869–76.
46. Breiter HC, Etcoff NL, Whalen PJ, et al. Response and habituation of the human amygdala during visual processing of facial expression. Neuron 1996;17(5):875–87.
47. Whalen PJ, Rauch SL, Etcoff NL, McInerney SC, Lee MB, Jenike MA. Masked presentations of emotional facial expressions amygdala activity without explicit knowledge. J Neurosci 1998;18:411–18.
48. Buchel C, Morris J, Dolan RJ, Friston KJ. Brain systems mediating aversive conditioning: an event-related fMRI study. Neuron 1998;20(5):947–57.
49. LaBar KS, Gatenby JC, Gore JC, LeDoux JE, Phelps EA. Human amygdala activation during conditioned fear acquisition and extinction: a mixed-trial fMRI study. Neuron 1998;20(5):937–45.
50. Wright CI, Fischer H, Whalen PJ, McInerney SC, Shin LM, Rauch SL. Differential prefrontal cortex and amygdala habituation to repeatedly presented emotional stimuli. Neuroreport 2001;12(2):379–83.
51. Phan KL, Liberzon I, Welsh RC, Britton JC, Taylor SF. Habituation of rostral anterior cingulate cortex to repeated emotionally salient pictures. Neuropsychopharmacology 2003;28(7):1344–50.
52. Charney DS, Deutch AY, Krystal JH, Southwick SM, Davis M. Psychobiologic mechanisms of posttraumatic stress disorder. Arch Gen Psychiatry 1993;50(4):295–305.
53. Phelps EA, Delgado MR, Nearing KI, LeDoux JE. Extinction learning in humans: role of the amygdala and vmPFC. Neuron 2004;43(6):897–905.
54. Milad MR, Wright CI, Orr SP, Pitman RK, Quirk GJ, Rauch SL. Recall of fear extinction in humans activates the ventromedial prefrontal cortex and hippocampus in concert. Biol Psychiatry 2007;62(5):446–54.
55. Falls WA, Miserendino MJ, Davis M. Extinction of fear-potentiated startle: blockade by infusion of an NMDA antagonist into the amygdala. J Neurosci 1992;12(3):854–63.
56. Morgan MA, Romanski LM, LeDoux JE. Extinction of emotional learning: contribution of medial prefrontal cortex. Neurosci Lett 1993;163(1):109–13.
57. Morgan MA, Schulkin J, LeDoux JE. Ventral medial prefrontal cortex and emotional perseveration: the memory for prior extinction training. Behav Brain Res 2003;146(1–2):121–30.
58. Morgan MA, LeDoux JE. Differential contribution of dorsal and ventral medial prefrontal cortex to the acquisition and extinction of conditioned fear in rats. Behav Neurosci 1995;109(4):681–88.

59. Gross JJ. Antecedent- and response-focused emotion regulation: divergent consequences for experience, expression, and physiology. J Pers Soc Psychol 1998;74(1):224–37.
60. Hariri AR, Bookheimer SY, Mazziotta JC. Modulating emotional responses: effects of a neocortical network on the limbic system. Neuroreport 2000;11(1):43–48.
61. Hariri AR, Mattay VS, Tessitore A, Fera F, Weinberger DR. Neocortical modulation of the amygdala response to fearful stimuli. Biol Psychiatry 2003;53(6):494–501.
62. Taylor SF, Phan KL, Decker LR, Liberzon I. Subjective rating of emotionally salient stimuli modulates neural activity. Neuroimage 2003;18(3):650–59.
63. Rosenkranz JA, Grace AA. Cellular mechanisms of infralimbic and prelimbic prefrontal cortical inhibition and dopaminergic modulation of basolateral amygdala neurons in vivo. J Neurosci 2002;22(1):324–37.
64. Ochsner KN, Bunge SA, Gross JJ, Gabrieli JD. Rethinking feelings: an FMRI study of the cognitive regulation of emotion. J Cogn Neurosci 2002;14(8):1215–29.
65. Phan KL, Fitzgerald DA, Nathan PJ, Moore GJ, Uhde TW, Tancer ME. Neural substrates for voluntary suppression of negative affect: a functional magnetic resonance imaging study. Biol Psychiatry 2005;57(3):210–19.
66. Kessler RC, Sonnega A, Bromet E, Hughes M, Nelson CB. Posttraumatic stress disorder in the National Comorbidity Survey. Arch Gen Psychiatry 1995;52(12):1048–60.
67. Phan KL, Taylor SF, Welsh RC, Ho SH, Britton JC, Liberzon I. Neural correlates of individual ratings of emotional salience: a trial-related fMRI study. Neuroimage 2004;21(2):768–80.
68. Britton JC, Phan KL, Taylor SF, Welsh RC, Berridge KC, Liberzon I. Neural correlates of social and nonsocial emotions: an fMRI study. Neuroimage 2006;31(1):397–409.
69. Chua FA, Liberzon I, Welsh, RC, Strecher, VJ. Neural correlates of message tailoring and self-relatedness in smoking cessation programming. Biol Psychiatry 65:165–168.
70. Mitchell JP, Banaji MR, Macrae CN. The link between social cognition and self-referential thought in the medial prefrontal cortex. J Cogn Neurosci 2005;17(8):1306–15.
71. Gusnard DA, Akbudak E, Shulman GL, Raichle ME. Medial prefrontal cortex and self-referential mental activity: relation to a default mode of brain function. Proc Natl Acad Sci U S A 2001;98(7):4259–64.
72. Pfeifer JH, Lieberman MD, Dapretto M. "I know you are but what am I?!": neural bases of self- and social knowledge retrieval in children and adults. J Cogn Neurosci 2007;19(8):1323–37.
73. Haddon JE, Killcross S. Prefrontal cortex lesions disrupt the contextual control of response conflict. J Neurosci 2006;26(11):2933–40.
74. Fellows LK, Farah MJ. Ventromedial frontal cortex mediates affective shifting in humans: evidence from a reversal learning paradigm. Brain 2003;126(pt 8):1830–37.
75. Craig AD. Human feelings: why are some more aware than others? Trends Cogn Sci 2004;8(6):239–41.
76. Sierra-Mercado D, Jr., Corcoran KA, Lebron-Milad K, Quirk GJ. Inactivation of the ventromedial prefrontal cortex reduces expression of conditioned fear and impairs subsequent recall of extinction. Eur J Neurosci 2006;24(6):1751–58.
77. Milad MR, Rauch SL, Pitman RK, Quirk GJ. Fear extinction in rats: implications for human brain imaging and anxiety disorders. Biol Psychol 2006;73(1):61–71.
78. Paulus MP, Stein MB. An insular view of anxiety. Biol Psychiatry 2006;60(4) 383–87.

15 The Amygdala in Post-Traumatic Stress Disorder

Lisa M. Shin

CONTENTS

INTRODUCTION
AMYGDALA FUNCTION
AMYGDALA VOLUMES AND RECEPTOR FUNCTION
MEDIAL PREFRONTAL CORTEX
AMYGDALA-MEDIAL PREFRONTAL INTERACTIONS
ANTERIOR CINGULATE CORTEX STRUCTURE
   AND NEUROCHEMISTRY
SUMMARY, LIMITATIONS, AND FUTURE DIRECTIONS
REFERENCES

Abstract

Over the past decade, neuroimaging studies have yielded important insights into the function of the amygdala in post-traumatic stress disorder (PTSD). The results of these studies are presented here. Because neurocircuitry models of PTSD also emphasize the role of the medial prefrontal cortex, findings regarding that brain region are discussed as well. The reviewed studies suggest that (1) the amygdala is hyperresponsive to both trauma-related and unrelated stimuli in PTSD, (2) amygdala activation is positively correlated with PTSD symptom severity and, in some studies, inversely correlated with medial prefrontal cortex function, (3) symptom reduction after treatment is associated with decreased amygdala activation and increased medial prefrontal cortex activation, and (4) medial prefrontal cortex is hyporesponsive in PTSD, perhaps reflecting diminished inhibitory control over the amygdala. All of this information suggests that the amygdala and medial prefrontal cortex play important roles in the pathogenesis or maintenance of this disorder. Limitations and future directions of this research are discussed.

From: *Post-Traumatic Stress Disorder: Basic Science and Clinical Practice*
Edited by: P. J. Shiromani et al., DOI: 10.1007/978-1-60327-329-9_15
© Humana Press, a part of Springer Science+Business Media, LLC 2009

Key Words: Amygdala, anterior cingulate cortex, fear conditioning, medial prefrontal cortex, neuroimaging.

INTRODUCTION

The amygdala is a medial temporal lobe brain structure that responds to potential threat or biologically relevant predictive ambiguity in the environment *(1–3)*. In healthy human participants, the amygdala activates in response to fearful facial expressions *(4–6)*, aversive photographs or films *(7,8)*, and aversively conditioned stimuli *(9–11)*. Furthermore, a greater degree of amygdala activation during the encoding of emotional stimuli is associated with better subsequent recollection of those stimuli *(12–15)*. (For a review, *see* Ref. *1*.) Although the amygdala generally performs a protective alerting function, it appears to be hyperresponsive in individuals with anxiety disorders, such as post-traumatic stress disorder (PTSD).

Current neurocircuitry models of PTSD posit that the amygdala is hyperresponsive, and that the medial prefrontal cortex is hyporesponsive and fails to exert inhibitory control over the amygdala *(16–20)*. Over the past decade, researchers have used neuroimaging techniques to assess amygdala function in PTSD and refine neurocircuitry models of this disorder. Findings from studies using functional magnetic resonance imaging (fMRI), positron emission tomography (PET), single-photon emission computed tomography (SPECT), and structural magnetic resonance imaging (MRI) to examine amygdala function and structure in PTSD are presented here. Although the main focus of this chapter is amygdala function in PTSD, to present a more complete picture of current neurocircuitry models, findings concerning the medial prefrontal cortex in this disorder are also reviewed. Finally, a discussion of the limitations and future directions of this research is offered.

AMYGDALA FUNCTION

Trauma-Related Stimuli

Several functional neuroimaging studies involving the presentation of trauma-related stimuli to participants in the scanner have reported amygdala hyperresponsivity in PTSD. In a SPECT study, Liberzon and colleagues *(21)* reported greater amygdala activation during the presentation of combat sounds versus white noise in combat veterans with PTSD relative to combat veterans without PTSD and healthy trauma-unexposed participants. Similarly, Pissiota et al. *(22)* found amygdala activation in response to combat sounds versus white noise in a group of veterans with PTSD. Furthermore, amygdala activation was positively correlated with subjective units of distress. Vermetten, Schmahl, Southwick, and Bremner *(23)* presented a combat-related smell (diesel fuel) to combat veterans with and without PTSD during PET scanning. The PTSD group reported greater distress and symptom severity in response to the diesel smell and exhibited greater amygdala activation than the combat veterans without PTSD. In a PET study, Shin and colleagues *(24)* reported amygdala activation during visual mental imagery of combat-related photographs in combat veterans with PTSD but not in combat veterans without PTSD. Using fMRI, Hendler et al. *(25)* found greater amygdala responses to combat-related photographs in combat veterans with PTSD versus combat veterans without PTSD. Protopopescu and colleagues *(26)* presented trauma-related, panic-related, positive, and neutral words to individuals with PTSD and trauma-unexposed healthy individuals during fMRI. The PTSD group exhibited relatively increased amygdala responses to the trauma-related words versus neutral words. In addition, amygdala activation was positively correlated with PTSD symptom severity. Interestingly, amygdala activation in the trauma versus neutral word comparison habituated over time in the PTSD group.

Several functional neuroimaging studies have implemented the use of idiographic trauma-related word cues or imagery scripts, which are narratives that describe the traumatic event and the participant's bodily sensations during the event. Although this early PET study included no comparison group, Rauch and colleagues *(27)* demonstrated amygdala activation in PTSD during traumatic as compared to neutral imagery scripts. In a PET study, Shin and colleagues *(28)* found greater amygdala activation in response to traumatic versus neutral scripts, but only in male Vietnam combat veterans with PTSD. Female nurses who served in Vietnam did not exhibit exaggerated amygdala activation relative to female nurse veterans without PTSD. However, in both male and female participants with PTSD, amygdala activation was positively correlated with PTSD symptom severity. Finally, Driessen and colleagues *(29)* found exaggerated amygdala activation during fMRI and the presentation of personalized trauma-related word cues to women with PTSD and borderline personality disorder.

It should be noted that several other studies employing idiographic imagery scripts have not found exaggerated amygdala activation in PTSD (e.g., *30–35*). Although a clear explanation of this discrepancy in the literature remains elusive, one possible account for the lack of amygdala hyperresponsivity in some studies might be related to the use of PET and SPECT as imaging techniques. PET has a relatively poor temporal resolution and requires a block design in which blood flow within a condition is typically averaged over a full minute. Amygdala responses may habituate within that time frame. Another explanation for the lack of exaggerated amygdala responses in some studies of PTSD may relate to the use of an imagery task. Amygdala responses have been shown to be smaller in response to internally generated stimuli as compared to externally presented stimuli *(8)*. Finally, variability both within and between studies in PTSD patients' symptom profiles (e.g., predominantly avoidance/numbing symptoms vs. reexperiencing symptoms), amygdala regulation by medial prefrontal cortex, or the presence of genetic variants (e.g., polymorphisms of the human serotonin transporter gene) *(36,37)* could explain the failure to replicate the finding of amygdala hyperresponsivity.

Trauma-Unrelated Stimuli

Exaggerated amygdala activation in PTSD has also occurred in response to some types of trauma-unrelated material, such as facial expressions. This fact suggests that amygdala hyperresponsivity may be a more general response to emotional (and occasionally even neutral) stimuli. In an fMRI study, Rauch and colleagues *(38)* examined amygdala responses to fearful and happy facial expressions that were "backwardly masked" (i.e., presented very rapidly immediately before neutral facial expressions such that participants did not report seeing the emotional expressions). Relative to the trauma-exposed comparison group, the PTSD group exhibited greater amygdala responses to the masked fearful versus happy faces. Furthermore, amygdala responses in the PTSD group were positively correlated with PTSD symptom severity. In an fMRI study of acute PTSD, Armony, Corbo, Clement, and Brunet *(39)* also reported a positive correlation between amygdala responses to masked fearful faces and PTSD symptom severity. Shin and colleagues *(40)* demonstrated exaggerated amygdala responses in PTSD using fMRI and unmasked (overtly presented) facial expressions. Relative to trauma-exposed comparison subjects without PTSD, individuals with PTSD showed exaggerated amygdala responses to fearful versus happy facial expressions. That study also reported a trend for less habituation to the fearful versus happy faces across repeated presentations in PTSD. Williams and colleagues *(41)* used fMRI and overtly presented fearful and neutral facial expressions to study participants with PTSD as compared to nontraumatized healthy participants. The PTSD group showed greater amygdala activation to fearful faces, especially in the later phase of stimulus presentation. At least one recent study has not found exaggerated amygdala activation in response to trauma-unrelated aversive photographs *(42)*.

Two studies by the same group reported a relationship between amygdala function and response to cognitive-behavioral therapy. Felmingham and colleagues *(43)* studied amygdala responses to fearful versus neutral facial expressions in PTSD before and after cognitive-behavioral therapy. The change in amygdala activation pre- versus posttreatment was correlated with symptomatic change, such that greater decreases in amygdala responses were associated with greater symptomatic improvement. Bryant et al. *(44)* reported that greater pretreatment amygdala activation to masked fearful versus neutral faces predicted a worse response to cognitive-behavioral therapy.

Given the important role of the amygdala in fear conditioning *(2)* as well as evidence for heightened acquisition of conditioned fear in PTSD *(45,46)*, researchers have become interested in studying amygdala function during fear conditioning and extinction in patients with this disorder *(47)*. Bremner and colleagues *(48)* have shown amygdala hyperresponsivity during the acquisition of fear conditioning in abuse survivors with PTSD as compared to healthy control subjects without abuse histories. Future studies will extend this work by using fMRI and trauma-exposed comparison groups without PTSD.

Interestingly, four recent studies have reported increased amygdala activation in PTSD in response to neutral stimuli or during the resting state. In an fMRI study described in the preceding section, Hendler et al. *(25)* found greater amygdala responses to combat-unrelated photographs in combat veterans with PTSD as compared to combat veterans without PTSD. Semple and colleagues *(49)* found higher amygdala blood flow during an auditory continuous performance task in a group of veterans with PTSD and comorbid substance abuse relative to a healthy comparison group. Using fMRI and an auditory oddball paradigm, Bryant and colleagues *(50)* found enhanced amygdala responses to targets in a PTSD group relative to a nontraumatized comparison group. Chung and colleagues *(51)* found greater amygdala perfusion during the resting state in PTSD as compared to a trauma-unexposed healthy control group. However, other PET and SPECT studies have not reported greater amygdala activation at rest in PTSD *(52–55)*.

AMYGDALA VOLUMES AND RECEPTOR FUNCTION

Relatively few studies have focused on examining amygdala volumes or receptor function in PTSD. Matsuoka, Yamawaki, Inagaki, Akechi, and Uchitomi *(56)* reported smaller amygdala volumes in breast cancer survivors with intrusive recollections compared to survivors without such recollections, although none of the participants met diagnostic criteria for PTSD. Two studies found trends for smaller left amygdala volumes in PTSD compared to trauma-unexposed healthy comparison groups *(57,58)* (*see also 59*). However, most other studies that have examined amygdala volumes have found no significant differences between PTSD and comparison groups *(60–66)*. Using PET and ^{11}C-carfentanil, Liberzon et al. *(67)* reported diminished mu-opioid receptor binding in the extended amygdala in trauma-exposed individuals with versus without PTSD. Additional research using larger cohorts and more uniform volumetric methodologies will be necessary before we can draw conclusions about amygdala structure in PTSD and how those measures might be related to amygdala function in this disorder.

MEDIAL PREFRONTAL CORTEX

A discussion of the functional neuroanatomy of PTSD would be incomplete without a brief description of the role of medial prefrontal cortical structures, such as the anterior cingulate cortex (ACC). These structures are interconnected with the amygdala *(68–70)* and are involved in the processing of emotional information *(71–74)* and in extinction and retention of extinction memories after fear conditioning *(75–79)*. Patients with PTSD exhibit attenuated extinction of conditioned fear responses in the laboratory *(45)*.

Previous functional neuroimaging studies of PTSD have reported decreased activation or failure to activate the ACC during the presentation of traumatic narratives *(30,32,33,35,80)*, traumatic pictures or sounds *(31,81,82)*, and negative, nontraumatic stimuli *(40–42,83,84)*. Relatively diminished activation of ACC in PTSD also has been shown during extinction after fear conditioning

(48), emotional Stroop interference *(85,86)*, emotional word retrieval *(87)*, non-emotional cognitive tasks *(49,50)*, and at rest *(49)*. Furthermore, PTSD symptom severity appears to be inversely associated with ACC activation, such that the greater the symptom severity, the lower the ACC activation *(40,41,88)*. Interestingly, increased medial prefrontal cortex activation following treatment has been positively associated with symptomatic improvement *(43,89*, but *see also 44)*. Most of the findings of diminished function in ACC have occurred in rostral or ventral portions of that structure. In contrast, dorsal portions of the ACC appear to show normal or possibly exaggerated responsivity in PTSD *(50,86,90)*, although additional research is needed to confirm this finding. Overall, relatively diminished medial prefrontal cortex function in PTSD is one of the most consistent findings in the literature *(91)*.

AMYGDALA-MEDIAL PREFRONTAL INTERACTIONS

Current neurocircuitry models emphasize a functional relationship between amygdala and medial prefrontal cortex, and researchers have just begun to assess these interregional relationships. Four studies have reported significant correlations between amygdala and medial prefrontal cortex activation *(28,40,41,92)*, although the findings are mixed with regard to the direction of this correlation.

In a script-driven imagery PET study, Shin et al. *(28)* found that in the PTSD group, regional cerebral blood flow (rCBF) changes in medial frontal gyrus were significantly inversely related to rCBF changes in bilateral amygdala. Similarly, in an fMRI study involving the presentation of unmasked fearful versus happy facial expressions, Shin et al. *(40)* reported an inverse correlation between amygdala responses and dorsal medial frontal gyrus responses in PTSD. In both studies, the inverse correlation remained even when participants with comorbid depression were removed from the analyses. Taken together, these two findings suggest a reciprocal relationship between medial prefrontal cortex and amygdala function in PTSD, although the direction of causality remains undetermined.

In contrast, two studies have provided evidence for a positive relationship between the amygdala and medial prefrontal cortex in PTSD. Using PET and script-driven imagery, Gilboa et al. *(92)* studied patients with PTSD and trauma-exposed individuals who never had PTSD. PET data were analyzed with partial least squares and structural equation modeling. Unlike the control group, the PTSD group exhibited a positive relationship among the amygdala, ACC, and posterior subcallosal cortex, among other regions. Williams et al. *(41)* presented fearful and neutral facial expressions during fMRI in participants with PTSD and a healthy trauma-unexposed comparison group. Positive correlations were found in the PTSD group between left ACC and right amygdala. However, which portion of the anterior cingulate was correlated with the amygdala was unclear. The amygdala might be expected to be positively correlated with dorsal portions of the ACC and negatively correlated with rostral portions of the ACC. In summary, there is preliminary evidence for a functional relationship between the amygdala and medial prefrontal structures in PTSD. Additional research will be required to confirm the direction of this relationship.

ANTERIOR CINGULATE CORTEX STRUCTURE AND NEUROCHEMISTRY

The findings of several studies suggest diminished cortical volumes or gray matter densities in the ACC in PTSD. Two studies that utilized MRI and cortical parcellation techniques reported smaller ACC volumes in individuals with PTSD as compared to trauma-exposed control groups (93,94), even after controlling for history of alcoholism (94). Three studies using MRI and voxel-based morphometry have reported diminished gray matter volumes in the ACC in participants with PTSD (95–97), although Corbo, Clement, Armony, Pruessner, and Brunet (95) speculated that shape differences in the anterior cingulate in PTSD may have driven their voxel-based morphometric findings. Smaller ACC volumes have been associated with greater PTSD symptom severity (94,97). In a study of monozygotic twins discordant for trauma exposure, Kasai and colleagues (96) found that diminished gray matter densities in pregenual ACC were not found in the identical twins of the PTSD participants, suggesting that such a gray matter density decrease is likely an acquired sign rather than a preexisting risk factor.

Reduced levels of the neuronal marker N-acetylaspartate (NAA) in the ACC have been reported in adolescents with PTSD (98,99) as well as in adults with PTSD (100,101), even after controlling for alcohol abuse and trauma exposure (102). NAA levels in the pregenual ACC have been negatively correlated with the severity of reexperiencing symptoms (100).

SUMMARY, LIMITATIONS, AND FUTURE DIRECTIONS

The literature reviewed suggests that (1) the amygdala is hyperresponsive to both trauma-related and unrelated stimuli in PTSD, (2) amygdala activation is positively correlated with PTSD symptom severity and, in some studies, inversely correlated with medial prefrontal cortex function, and (3) symptom reduction after treatment is associated with decreased amygdala activation and increased medial prefrontal cortex activation. Supplementing these observations, a study of focal lesions in combat veterans has shown that PTSD symptoms are significantly lower in patients with focal lesions in the amygdala as compared to patients with lesions elsewhere in the brain (103).

All of this information suggests that the amygdala plays an important role in the pathogenesis or maintenance of this disorder. However, whether the primary area of functional pathology lies in the amygdala is unknown. Given the well-replicated findings of structural abnormalities and diminished function in the medial prefrontal cortex in PTSD, perhaps the primary pathology lies in the medial prefrontal cortical structures, and the amygdala hyperresponsivity arises from diminished medial prefrontal inhibition. To distinguish between these alternatives, we will need to employ novel designs in the study of brain function.

For example, most functional neuroimaging studies of PTSD have involved patients with chronic forms of the disorder. Studies of acute PTSD will help determine whether functional abnormalities are detectable first in the amygdala, medial prefrontal cortex, or both. In addition, high-risk longitudinal studies (e.g., of military, police, or firefighter recruits) could help to reveal whether pretrauma functional abnormalities in amygdala, medial prefrontal cortex, or both can predict PTSD after trauma exposure. Studies of monozygotic twins discordant for trauma exposure may also help illuminate whether preexisting risk factors are observable in amygdala, medial prefrontal cortex, or both.

Despite the enormous amount of progress made over the last decade, functional neuroimaging studies of PTSD have been limited in several ways. First, as noted, most of the studies described involved chronic cases of PTSD. Whether the functional anatomy of acute PTSD is similar to that of chronic PTSD is unknown, and future studies ought to focus on acute PTSD or compare acute versus chronic PTSD.

Second, many studies have utilized healthy comparison groups of individuals who have never experienced traumatic events. In this type of design, any differences between PTSD and the healthy comparison group could be driven by trauma exposure or PTSD. Recent findings of exaggerated amygdala activation in trauma-exposed subjects *without* PTSD *(104)* underscore the importance of controlling for trauma exposure by using trauma-exposed healthy comparison subjects. Of course, the optimal (albeit more expensive) design might include both trauma-exposed and unexposed healthy comparison groups *(32)*; this would permit researchers to examine the effects of both trauma exposure and PTSD.

Third, whether functional abnormalities in the amygdala and medial prefrontal cortex in PTSD reflect familial risk factors or whether they are acquired characteristics of PTSD has not been fully examined, although twin studies are beginning to address this question *(96)*. In addition, recent evidence suggests that exaggerated amygdala function is found in healthy participants with a short allele variant of the serotonin transporter gene *(36,37)*. Thus, it remains possible that functional neuroimaging findings of amygdala hyperresponsivity in PTSD reflect a risk factor rather than a correlate of PTSD per se.

Fourth, the spatial resolution of functional neuroimaging techniques is limited, and researchers cannot clearly distinguish activations in different nuclei within the amygdala (although more broad distinctions, such as between dorsal vs. ventral amygdala can be made; *6,105*). Fifth, individuals with PTSD often have comorbid conditions, such as substance abuse/dependence and depression. Indeed, studies have found that groups of patients with PTSD and comorbid depression had different patterns of brain activation as compared to groups with PTSD only *(106,107)*. In future research, the issue of comorbidity must be addressed.

Finally, neuroimaging methodology, including data acquisition parameters, cognitive paradigms, and data analytic techniques, may vary widely across neuroimaging studies, sometimes making findings across studies difficult to reconcile. However, despite the variability in methodology, replication of some findings (e.g., diminished medial prefrontal cortex function in PTSD) has been quite impressive. Future studies are also expected to yield information that is potentially clinically relevant, such as whether pretreatment functional neuroimaging measures can assist the prediction of treatment response *(44)*.

REFERENCES

1. Davis, M. Whalen,, P. J., and (2001) The amygdala: vigilance and emotion. Mol Psychiatry 6, 13–34.
2. LeDoux, J. E. (2000) Emotion circuits in the brain. Annu Rev Neurosci 23, 155–84.
3. Whalen, P. J. (1998) Fear, vigilance, and ambiguity: initial neuroimaging studies of the human amygdala. Curr Direct Psychol Sci 6, 178–88.
4. Breiter, H. C., Etcoff, N. L., Whalen, P. J., Kennedy, W. A., Rauch, S. L., Buckner, R. L., Strauss, M. M., Hyman, S. E., and Rosen, B. R. (1996) Response and habituation of the human amygdala during visual processing of facial expression. Neuron 17, 875–87.
5. Morris, J. S., Frith, C. D., Perrett, D. I., Rowland, D., Young, A. W., Calder, A. J., and Dolan, R. J. (1996) A differential neural response in the human amygdala to fearful and happy facial expressions. Nature 383, 812–15.
6. Whalen, P. J., Rauch, S. L., Etcoff, N. L., McInerney, S. C., Lee, M. B., and Jenike, M. A. (1998) Masked presentations of emotional facial expressions modulate amygdala activity without explicit knowledge. J Neurosci 18, 411–18.
7. Irwin, W., Davidson, R. J., Lowe, M. J., Mock, B. J., Sorenson, J. A., and Turski, P. A. (1996) Human amygdala activation detected with echo-planar functional magnetic resonance imaging. Neuroreport 7, 1765–69.
8. Reiman, E. M., Lane, R. D., Ahern, G. L., Schwartz, G. E., Davidson, R. J., Friston, K. J., Yun, L. S., and Chen, K. (1997) Neuroanatomical correlates of externally and internally generated human emotion. Am J Psychiatry 154, 918–25.
9. Buchel, C., Morris, J., Dolan, R. J., and Friston, K. J. (1998) Brain systems mediating aversive conditioning: an event-related fMRI study. Neuron 20, 947–57.
10. Buchel, C., Dolan, R. J., Armony, J. L., and Friston, K. J. (1999) Amygdala-hippocampal involvement in human aversive trace conditioning revealed through event-related functional magnetic resonance imaging. J Neurosci 19, 10869–76.
11. LaBar, K. S., Gatenby, J. C., Gore, J. C., LeDoux, J. E., and Phelps, E. A. (1998) Human amygdala activation during conditioned fear acquisition and extinction: a mixed-trial fMRI study. Neuron 20, 937–45.
12. Cahill, L., Haier, R. J., Fallon, J., Alkire, M. T., Tang, C., Keator, D., Wu, J., and McGaugh, J. L. (1996) Amygdala activity at encoding correlated with long-term, free recall of emotional information. Proc Natl Acad Sci U S A 93, 8016–21.
13. Hamann, S. B., Ely, T. D., Grafton, S. T., and Kilts, C. D. (1999) Amygdala activity related to enhanced memory for pleasant and aversive stimuli. Nat Neurosci 2, 289–93.
14. Dolcos, F., LaBar, K. S., and Cabeza, R. (2004) Interaction between the amygdala and the medial temporal lobe memory system predicts better memory for emotional events. Neuron 42, 855–63.
15. Dolcos, F., LaBar, K. S., and Cabeza, R. (2005) Remembering one year later: role of the amygdala and the medial temporal lobe memory system in retrieving emotional memories. Proc Natl Acad Sci U S A 102, 2626–31.
16. Elzinga, B. M., and Bremner, J. D. (2002) Are the neural substrates of memory the final common pathway in posttraumatic stress disorder (PTSD)? J Affect Disord 70, 1–17.

17. Francati, V., Vermetten, E., and Bremner, J. D. (2007) Functional neuroimaging studies in posttraumatic stress disorder: review of current methods and findings. Depress Anxiety 24, 202–18.

18. Hamner, M. B., Lorberbaum, J. P., and George, M. S. (1999) Potential role of the anterior cingulate cortex in PTSD: review and hypothesis. Depress Anxiety 9, 1–14.

19. Layton, B., and Krikorian, R. (2002) Memory mechanisms in posttraumatic stress disorder. J Neuropsychiatry Clin Neurosci 14, 254–61.

20. Rauch, S. L., Shin, L. M., Whalen, P. J., and Pitman, R. K. (1998) Neuroimaging and the neuroanatomy of PTSD. CNS Spectrums 3(suppl. 2), 30–41.

21. Liberzon, I., Taylor, S. F., Amdur, R., Jung, T. D., Chamberlain, K. R., Minoshima, S., Koeppe, R. A., and Fig, L. M. (1999) Brain activation in PTSD in response to trauma-related stimuli. Biol Psychiatry 45, 817–26.

22. Pissiota, A., Frans, O., Fernandez, M., von Knorring, L., Fischer, H., and Fredrikson, M. (2002) Neurofunctional correlates of posttraumatic stress disorder: a PET symptom provocation study. Eur Arch Psychiatry Clin Neurosci 252, 68–75.

23. Vermetten, E., Schmahl, C., Southwick, S. M., and Bremner, J. D. (2007) Positron tomographic emission study of olfactory induced emotional recall in veterans with and without combat-related posttraumatic stress disorder. Psychopharmacol Bull 40, 8–30.

24. Shin, L. M., Kosslyn, S. M., McNally, R. J., Alpert, N. M., Thompson, W. L., Rauch, S. L., Macklin, M. L., and Pitman, R. K. (1997) Visual imagery and perception in posttraumatic stress disorder. A positron emission tomographic investigation. Arch Gen Psychiatry 54, 233–41.

25. Hendler, T., Rotshtein, P., Yeshurun, Y., Weizmann, T., Kahn, I., Ben-Bashat, D., Malach, R., and Bleich, A. (2003) Sensing the invisible: differential sensitivity of visual cortex and amygdala to traumatic context. Neuroimage 19, 587–600.

26. Protopopescu, X., Pan, H., Tuescher, O., Cloitre, M., Goldstein, M., Engelien, W., Epstein, J., Yang, Y., Gorman, J., Ledoux, J., Silbersweig, D., and Stern, E. (2005) Differential time courses and specificity of amygdala activity in posttraumatic stress disorder subjects and normal control subjects. Biol Psychiatry 57, 464–73.

27. Rauch, S. L., van der Kolk, B. A., Fisler, R. E., Alpert, N. M., Orr, S. P., Savage, C. R., Fischman, A. J., Jenike, M. A., and Pitman, R. K. (1996) A symptom provocation study of posttraumatic stress disorder using positron emission tomography and script-driven imagery. Arch Gen Psychiatry 53, 380–87.

28. Shin, L. M., Orr, S. P., Carson, M. A., Rauch, S. L., Macklin, M. L., Lasko, N. B., Marzol Peters, P., Metzger, L., Dougherty, D. D., Cannistraro, P. A., Alpert, N. M., Fischman, A. J., and Pitman, R. K. (2004) Regional cerebral blood flow in amygdala and medial prefrontal cortex during traumatic imagery in male and female Vietnam veterans with PTSD. Arch Gen Psychiatry 61, 168–76.

29. Driessen, M., Beblo, T., Mertens, M., Piefke, M., Rullkoetter, N., Silva-Saavedra, A., Reddemann, L., Rau, H., Markowitsch, H.J., Wulff, H., Lange, W., and Woermann, F. G. (2004) Posttraumatic stress disorder and fMRI activation patterns of traumatic memory in patients with borderline personality disorder. Biol Psychiatry 55, 603–11.

30. Bremner, J. D., Narayan, M., Staib, L. H., Southwick, S. M., McGlashan, T., and Charney, D. S. (1999) Neural correlates of memories of childhood sexual abuse in women with and without posttraumatic stress disorder. Am J Psychiatry 156, 1787–95.

31. Bremner, J. D., Staib, L. H., Kaloupek, D., Southwick, S. M., Soufer, R., and Charney, D. S. (1999) Neural correlates of exposure to traumatic pictures and sound in Vietnam combat veterans with and without posttraumatic stress disorder: a positron emission tomography study. Biol Psychiatry 45, 806–16.

32. Britton, J. C., Phan, K. L., Taylor, S. F., Fig, L. M., and Liberzon, I. (2005) Corticolimbic blood flow in posttraumatic stress disorder during script-driven imagery. Biol Psychiatry 57, 832–40.

33. Lanius, R. A., Williamson, P. C., Densmore, M., Boksman, K., Gupta, M. A., Neufeld, R. W., Gati, J. S., and Menon, R. S. (2001) Neural correlates of traumatic memories in posttraumatic stress disorder: a functional MRI investigation. Am J Psychiatry 158, 1920–22.

34. Lanius, R., Williamson, P., Boksman, K., Densmore, M., Gupta, M., Neufeld, R., Gati, J., and Menon, R. (2002) Brain activation during script-driven imagery induced dissociative responses in PTSD: a functional magnetic resonance imaging investigation. Biol Psychiatry 52, 305.

35. Shin, L. M., McNally, R. J., Kosslyn, S. M., Thompson, W. L., Rauch, S. L., Alpert, N. M., Metzger, L. J., Lasko, N. B., Orr, S. P., and Pitman, R. K. (1999) Regional cerebral blood flow during script-driven imagery in childhood sexual abuse-related PTSD: A PET investigation. Am J Psychiatry 156, 575–84.

36. Hariri, A. R., Drabant, E. M., Munoz, K. E., Kolachana, B. S., Mattay, V. S., Egan, M. F., and Weinberger, D. R. (2005) A susceptibility gene for affective disorders and the response of the human amygdala. Arch Gen Psychiatry 62, 146–52.

37. Pezawas, L., Meyer-Lindenberg, A., Drabant, E. M., Verchinski, B. A., Munoz, K. E., Kolachana, B. S., Egan, M. F., Mattay, V. S., Hariri, A. R., and Weinberger, D. R. (2005) 5-HTTLPR polymorphism impacts human cingulate-amygdala interactions: a genetic susceptibility mechanism for depression. Nat Neurosci 8, 828–34.

38. Rauch, S. L., Whalen, P. J., Shin, L. M., McInerney, S. C., Macklin, M. L., Lasko, N. B., Orr, S. P., and Pitman, R. K. (2000) Exaggerated amygdala response to masked facial stimuli in posttraumatic stress disorder: a functional MRI study. Biol Psychiatry 47, 769–76.

39. Armony, J. L., Corbo, V., Clement, M. H., and Brunet, A. (2005) Amygdala response in patients with acute PTSD to masked and unmasked emotional facial expressions. Am J Psychiatry 162, 1961–63.

40. Shin, L. M., Wright, C. I., Cannistraro, P. A., Wedig, M. M., McMullin, K., Martis, B., Macklin, M. L., Lasko, N. B., Cavanagh, S. R., Krangel, T. S., Orr, S. P., Pitman, R. K., Whalen, P. J., and Rauch, S. L. (2005) A functional magnetic resonance imaging study of amygdala and medial prefrontal cortex responses to overtly presented fearful faces in posttraumatic stress disorder. Arch Gen Psychiatry 62, 273–81.

41. Williams, L. M., Kemp, A. H., Felmingham, K., Barton, M., Olivieri, G., Peduto, A., Gordon, E., and Bryant, R. A. (2006) Trauma modulates amygdala and medial prefrontal responses to consciously attended fear. Neuroimage 29, 347–57.

42. Phan, K. L., Britton, J. C., Taylor, S. F., Fig, L. M., and Liberzon, I. (2006) Corticolimbic blood flow during nontraumatic emotional processing in posttraumatic stress disorder. Arch Gen Psychiatry 63, 184–92.

43. Felmingham, K., Kemp, A., Williams, L., Das, P., Hughes, G., Peduto, A., and Bryant, R. (2007) Changes in anterior cingulate and amygdala after cognitive behavior therapy of posttraumatic stress disorder. Psychol Sci 18, 127–29.

44. Bryant, R. A., Felmingham, K., Kemp, A., Das, P., Hughes, G., Peduto, A., and Williams, L. (2008) Amygdala and ventral anterior cingulate activation predicts treatment response to cognitive behaviour therapy for post-traumatic stress disorder. Psychol Med, 38, 555–61.

45. Orr, S. P., Metzger, L. J., Lasko, N. B., Macklin, M. L., Peri, T., and Pitman, R. K. (2000) De novo conditioning in trauma-exposed individuals with and without posttraumatic stress disorder. J Abnorm Psychol 109, 290–98.

46. Peri, T., Ben-Shakhar, G., Orr, S. P., and Shalev, A.Y. (2000) Psychophysiologic assessment of aversive conditioning in posttraumatic stress disorder. Biol Psychiatry 47, 512–19.

47. Rauch, S. L., Shin, L. M., and Phelps, E. A. (2006) Neurocircuitry models of posttraumatic stress disorder and extinction: human neuroimaging research—past, present, and future. Biol Psychiatry 60, 376–82.

48. Bremner, J. D., Vermetten, E., Schmahl, C., Vaccarino, V., Vythilingam, M., Afzal, N., Grillon, C., and Charney, D. S. (2005) Positron emission tomographic imaging of neural correlates of a fear acquisition and extinction paradigm in women with childhood sexual-abuse-related post-traumatic stress disorder. Psychol Med 35, 791–806.

49. Semple, W. E., Goyer, P. F., McCormick, R., Donovan, B., Muzic, R.F., Jr., Rugle, L., McCutcheon, K., Lewis, C., Liebling, D., Kowaliw, S., Vapenik, K., Semple, M. A., Flener, C. R., and Schulz, S. C. (2000) Higher brain blood flow at amygdala and lower frontal cortex blood flow in PTSD patients with comorbid cocaine and alcohol abuse compared with normals. Psychiatry 63, 65–74.

50. Bryant, R. A., Felmingham, K. L., Kemp, A. H., Barton, M., Peduto, A. S., Rennie, C., Gordon, E., and Williams, L. M. (2005) Neural networks of information processing in posttraumatic stress disorder: a functional magnetic resonance imaging study. Biol Psychiatry 58, 111–18.

51. Chung, Y. A., Kim, S. H., Chung, S. K., Chae, J. H., Yang, D. W., Sohn, H. S., and Jeong, J. (2006) Alterations in cerebral perfusion in posttraumatic stress disorder patients without re-exposure to accident-related stimuli. Clin Neurophysiol 117, 637–42.

52. Bonne, O., Gilboa, A., Louzoun, Y., Brandes, D., Yona, I., Lester, H., Barkai, G., Freedman, N., Chisin, R., and Shalev, A. Y. (2003) Resting regional cerebral perfusion in recent posttraumatic stress disorder. Biol Psychiatry 54, 1077–86.

53. Mirzaei, S., Knoll, P., Keck, A., Preitler, B., Gutierrez, E., Umek, H., Kohn, H., and Pecherstorfer, M. (2001) Regional cerebral blood flow in patients suffering from posttraumatic stress disorder. Neuropsychobiology 43, 260–4.

54. Pavic, L., Gregurek, R., Petrovic, R., Petrovic, D., Varda, R., Vukusic, H., and Crnkovic-Markovic, S. (2003) Alterations in brain activation in posttraumatic stress disorder patients with severe hyperarousal symptoms and impulsive aggressiveness. Eur Arch Psychiatry Clin Neurosci 253, 80–83.

55. Sachinvala, N., Kling, A., Suffin, S., Lake, R., and Cohen, M. (2000) Increased regional cerebral perfusion by 99mTc hexamethyl propylene amine oxime single photon emission computed tomography in post-traumatic stress disorder. Mil Med 165, 473–79.

56. Matsuoka, Y., Yamawaki, S., Inagaki, M., Akechi, T., and Uchitomi, Y. (2003) A volumetric study of amygdala in cancer survivors with intrusive recollections. Biol Psychiatry 54, 736–43.

57. Bremner, J. D., Randall, P., Vermetten, E., Staib, L., Bronen, R. A., Mazure, C., Capelli, S., McCarthy, G., Innis, R. B., and Charney, D. S. (1997) Magnetic resonance imaging-based measurement of hippocampal volume in posttraumatic stress disorder related to childhood physical and sexual abuse—a preliminary report. Biol Psychiatry 41, 23–32.

58. Wignall, E. L., Dickson, J. M., Vaughan, P., Farrow, T. F., Wilkinson, I. D., Hunter, M. D., and Woodruff, P. W. (2004) Smaller hippocampal volume in patients with recent-onset posttraumatic stress disorder. Biol Psychiatry 56, 832–36.

59. Karl, A., Schaefer, M., Malta, L. S., Dorfel, D., Rohleder, N., and Werner, A. (2006) A meta-analysis of structural brain abnormalities in PTSD. Neurosci Biobehav Rev 30, 1004–31.

60. Bonne, O., Brandes, D., Gilboa, A., Gomori, J. M., Shenton, M. E., Pitman, R. K., and Shalev, A. Y. (2001) Longitudinal MRI study of hippocampal volume in trauma survivors with PTSD. Am J Psychiatry 158, 1248–51.

61. De Bellis, M. D., Hall, J., Boring, A. M., Frustaci, K., and Moritz, G. (2001) A pilot longitudinal study of hippocampal volumes in pediatric maltreatment-related posttraumatic stress disorder. Biol Psychiatry 50, 305–9.

62. De Bellis, M. D., Keshavan, M. S., Shifflett, H., Iyengar, S., Beers, S. R., Hall, J., and Moritz, G. (2002) Brain structures in pediatric maltreatment-related posttraumatic stress disorder: a sociodemographically matched study. Biol Psychiatry 52, 1066–78.

63. Fennema-Notestine, C., Stein, M. B., Kennedy, C. M., Archibald, S. L., and Jernigan, T. L.(2002) Brain morphometry in female victims of intimate partner violence with and without posttraumatic stress disorder. Biol Psychiatry 52, 1089–101.

64. Gilbertson, M. W., Shenton, M. E., Ciszewski, A., Kasai, K., Lasko, N. B., Orr, S. P., and Pitman, R. K. (2002) Smaller hippocampal volume predicts pathologic vulnerability to psychological trauma. Nat Neurosci 5, 1242–47.

65. Gurvits, T. V., Shenton, M. E., Hokama, H., Ohta, H., Lasko, N. B., Gilbertson, M. W., Orr, S. P., Kikinis, R., Jolesz, F. A., McCarley, R. W., and Pitman, R. K. (1996) Magnetic resonance imaging study of hippocampal volume in chronic, combat-related posttraumatic stress disorder. Biol Psychiatry 40, 1091–99.

66. Lindauer, R. J., Vlieger, E. J., Jalink, M., Olff, M., Carlier, I. V., Majoie, C. B., den Heeten, G. J., and Gersons, B. P. (2004) Smaller hippocampal volume in Dutch police officers with posttraumatic stress disorder. Biol Psychiatry 56, 356–63.

67. Liberzon, I., Taylor, S. F., Phan, K. L., Britton, J. C., Fig, L. M., Bueller, J. A., Koeppe, R. A., and Zubieta, J. K. (2007) Altered central micro-opioid receptor binding after psychological trauma. Biol Psychiatry 61, 1030–38.

68. Aggleton, J. P., Burton, M. J., and Passingham, R. E. (1980) Cortical and subcortical afferents to the amygdala of the rhesus monkey (Macaca mulatta). Brain Res 190, 347–68.

69. Chiba, T., Kayahara, T., and Nakano, K. (2001) Efferent projections of infralimbic and prelimbic areas of the medial prefrontal cortex in the Japanese monkey, Macaca fuscata. Brain Res 888, 83–101.

70. Ghashghaei, H. T., and Barbas, H. (2002) Pathways for emotion: interactions of prefrontal and anterior temporal pathways in the amygdala of the rhesus monkey. Neuroscience 115, 1261–79.

71. Bush, G., Luu, P., and Posner, M. I. (2000) Cognitive and emotional influence in anterior cingulate cortex. Trends Cogn Sci 4, 215–22.

72. Mayberg, H. S., Brannan, S. K., Mahurin, R. K., Jerabek, P. A., Brickman, J. S., Tekell, J. L., Silva, J. A., McGinnis, S., Glass, T. G., Martin, C. C., and Fox, P. T. (1997) Cingulate function in depression: a potential predictor of treatment response. Neuroreport 8, 1057–61.

73. Mayberg, H. S. (1997) Limbic-cortical dysregulation: a proposed model of depression. J Neuropsychiatry Clin Neurosci 9, 471–81.

74. Whalen, P. J., Bush, G., McNally, R. J., Wilhelm, S., McInerney, S. C., Jenike, M. A., and Rauch, S. L. (1998) The emotional counting Stroop paradigm: a functional magnetic resonance imaging probe of the anterior cingulate affective division. Biol Psychiatry 44, 1219–28.

75. Milad, M. R., and Quirk, G. J. (2002) Neurons in medial prefrontal cortex signal memory for fear extinction. Nature 420, 70–74.

76. Milad, M. R., Wright, C. I., Orr, S. P., Pitman, R. K., Quirk, G. J., and Rauch, S. L. (2007) Recall of fear extinction in humans activates the ventromedial prefrontal cortex and hippocampus in concert. Biol Psychiatry 62, 446–54.

77. Morgan, M. A., Romanski, L. M., and LeDoux, J. E. (1993) Extinction of emotional learning: contribution of medial prefrontal cortex. Neurosci Lett 163, 109–13.

78. Phelps, E. A., Delgado, M. R., Nearing, K. I., and LeDoux, J. E. (2004) Extinction learning in humans: role of the amygdala and vmPFC. Neuron 43, 897–905.

79. Quirk, G. J., Russo, G. K., Barron, J. L., and Lebron, K. (2000) The role of ventromedial prefrontal cortex in the recovery of extinguished fear. J Neurosci 20, 6225–31.

80. Lindauer, R. J., Booij, J., Habraken, J. B., Uylings, H. B., Olff, M., Carlier, I. V., den Heeten, G. J., van Eck-Smit, B. L., and Gersons, B. P. (2004) Cerebral blood flow changes during script-driven imagery in police officers with posttraumatic stress disorder. Biol Psychiatry 56, 853–61.

81. Hou, C., Liu, J., Wang, K., Li, L., Liang, M., He, Z., Liu, Y., Zhang, Y., Li, W., and Jiang, T. (2007) Brain responses to symptom provocation and trauma-related short-term memory recall in coal mining accident survivors with acute severe PTSD. Brain Res 1144, 165–74.

82. Yang, P., Wu, M. T., Hsu, C. C., and Ker, J. H. (2004) Evidence of early neurobiological alternations in adolescents with posttraumatic stress disorder: a functional MRI study. Neurosci Lett 370, 13–18.

83. Lanius, R. A., Williamson, P. C., Hopper, J., Densmore, M., Boksman, K., Gupta, M. A., Neufeld, R. W., Gati, J. S., and Menon, R. S. (2003) Recall of emotional states in posttraumatic stress disorder: an fMRI investigation. Biol Psychiatry 53, 204–10.

84. Kim, M. J., Chey, J., Chung, A., Bae, S., Khang, H., Ham, B., Yoon, S. J., Jeong, D. U., and Lyoo, I. K. (2008) Diminished rostral anterior cingulate activity in response to threat-related events in posttraumatic stress disorder. J Psychiatr Res 42, 268–77.

85. Bremner, J. D., Vermetten, E., Vythilingam, M., Afzal, N., Schmahl, C., Elzinga, B., and Charney, D. S. (2004) Neural correlates of the classic color and emotional Stroop in women with abuse-related posttraumatic stress disorder. Biol Psychiatry 55, 612–20.

86. Shin, L. M., Whalen, P.J., Pitman, R. K., Bush, G., Macklin, M. L., Lasko, N. B., Orr, S. P., McInerney, S. C., and Rauch, S. L. (2001) An fMRI study of anterior cingulate function in posttraumatic stress disorder. Biol Psychiatry 50, 932–42.

87. Bremner, J. D., Vythilingam, M., Vermetten, E., Southwick, S. M., McGlashan, T., Staib, L. H., Soufer, R., and Charney, D. S. (2003) Neural correlates of declarative memory for emotionally valenced words in women with posttraumatic stress disorder related to early childhood sexual abuse. Biol Psychiatry 53, 879–89.

88. Hopper, J. W., Frewen, P. A., van der Kolk, B. A., and Lanius, R. A. (2007) Neural correlates of reexperiencing, avoidance, and dissociation in PTSD: symptom dimensions and emotion dysregulation in responses to script-driven trauma imagery. J Trauma Stress 20, 713–25.

89. Seedat, S., Warwick, J., van Heerden, B., Hugo, C., Zungu-Dirwayi, N., Van Kradenburg, J., and Stein, D. J. (2004) Single photon emission computed tomography in posttraumatic stress disorder before and after treatment with a selective serotonin reuptake inhibitor. J Affect Disord 80, 45–53.

90. Shin, L. M., Bush, G., Whalen, P. J., Handwerger, K., Cannistraro, P. A., Wright, C. I., Martis, B., Macklin, M. L., Lasko, N. B., Orr, S. P., Pitman, R. K., and Rauch, S. L. (2007) Dorsal anterior cingulate function in posttraumatic stress disorder. J Trauma Stress 20, 701–12.

91. Etkin, A., and Wager, T. D. (2007) Functional neuroimaging of anxiety: a meta-analysis of emotional processing in PTSD, social anxiety disorder, and specific phobia. Am J Psychiatry 164, 1476–88.

92. Gilboa, A., Shalev, A. Y., Laor, L., Lester, H., Louzoun, Y., Chisin, R., and Bonne, O. (2004) Functional connectivity of the prefrontal cortex and the amygdala in posttraumatic stress disorder. Biol Psychiatry 55, 263–72.

93. Rauch, S. L., Shin, L. M., Segal, E., Pitman, R. K., Carson, M. A., McMullin, K., Whalen, P. J., and Makris, N. (2003) Selectively reduced regional cortical volumes in post-traumatic stress disorder. Neuroreport 14, 913–16.

94. Woodward, S. H., Kaloupek, D. G., Streeter, C. C., Martinez, C., Schaer, M., and Eliez, S. (2006) Decreased anterior cingulate volume in combat-related PTSD. Biol Psychiatry 59, 582–87.

95. Corbo, V., Clement, M. H., Armony, J. L., Pruessner, J. C., and Brunet, A. (2005) Size versus shape differences: contrasting voxel-based and volumetric analyses of the anterior cingulate cortex in individuals with acute posttraumatic stress disorder. Biol Psychiatry 58, 119–24.

96. Kasai, K., Yamasue, H., Gilbertson, M. W., Shenton, M. E., Rauch, S. L., and Pitman, R. K. (2008) Evidence for acquired pregenual anterior cingulate gray matter loss from a twin study of combat-related posttraumatic stress disorder. Biol Psychiatry 63, 550–56.

97. Yamasue, H., Kasai, K., Iwanami, A., Ohtani, T., Yamada, H., Abe, O., Kuroki, N., Fukuda, R., Tochigi, M., Furukawa, S., Sadamatsu, M., Sasaki, T., Aoki, S., Ohtomo, K., Asukai, N., and Kato, N. (2003) Voxel-based analysis of MRI reveals anterior cingulate gray-matter volume reduction in posttraumatic stress disorder due to terrorism. Proc Natl Acad Sci U S A 100, 9039–43.

98. De Bellis, M. D., Keshavan, M. S., Spencer, S., and Hall, J. (2000) N-Acetylaspartate concentration in the anterior cingulate of maltreated children and adolescents with PTSD. Am J Psychiatry 157, 1175–77.

99. De Bellis, M. D., Keshavan, M. S., and Harenski, K. A. (2001) Anterior cingulate N-acetylaspartate/creatine ratios during clonidine treatment in a maltreated child with posttraumatic stress disorder. J Child Adolesc Psychopharmacol 11, 311–16.

100. Ham, B. J., Chey, J., Yoon, S. J., Sung, Y., Jeong, D. U., Ju Kim, S., Sim, M. E., Choi, N., Choi, I. G., Renshaw, P. F., and Lyoo, I. K. (2007) Decreased N-acetyl-aspartate levels in anterior cingulate and hippocampus in subjects with post-traumatic stress disorder: a proton magnetic resonance spectroscopy study. Eur J Neurosci 25, 324–29.

101. Mahmutyazicioglu, K., Konuk, N., Ozdemir, H., Atasoy, N., Atik, L., and Gundogdu, S. (2005) Evaluation of the hippocampus and the anterior cingulate gyrus by proton MR spectroscopy in patients with post-traumatic stress disorder. Diagn Interv Radiol 11, 125–29.

102. Schuff, N., Neylan, T. C., Fox-Bosetti, S., Lenoci, M., Samuelson, K. W., Studholme, C., Kornak, J., Marmar, C. R., and Weiner, M. W. (2008) Abnormal N-acetylaspartate in hippocampus and anterior cingulate in posttraumatic stress disorder. Psychiatry Res 162, 147–57.

103. Koenigs, M., Huey, E. D., Raymont, V., Cheon, B., Solomon, J., Wassermann, E. M., and Grafman, J. (2008) Focal brain damage protects against post-traumatic stress disorder in combat veterans. Nat Neurosci 11, 232–37.

104. Ganzel, B., Casey, B. J., Glover, G., Voss, H. U., Temple, E. (2007) The aftermath of 9/11: effect of intensity and recency of trauma on outcome. Emotion 7, 227–38.

105. Whalen, P. J., Shin, L. M., Mcinerney, S. C., Fischer, H., Wright, C. I., and Rauch, S. L. (2001) A functional MRI study of human amygdala responses to facial expressions of fear versus anger. Emotion 1, 70–83.

106. Kemp, A. H., Felmingham, K., Das, P., Hughes, G., Peduto, A. S., Bryant, R. A., and Williams, L. M. (2007) Influence of comorbid depression on fear in posttraumatic stress disorder: an fMRI study. Psychiatry Res 155, 265–69.
107. Lanius, R. A., Frewen, P. A., Girotti, M., Neufeld, R. W., Stevens, T. K., and Densmore, M. (2007) Neural correlates of trauma script-imagery in posttraumatic stress disorder with and without comorbid major depression: a functional MRI investigation. Psychiatry Res 155, 45–56.

Treatment Strategies

16 Pharmacologic Treatment of PTSD

Murray A. Raskind

CONTENTS

HISTORICAL OVERVIEW: PROGRESS AND DISCONNECTS
ANTIADRENERGICS
ANTICONVULSANTS
ATYPICAL ANTIPSYCHOTICS
BENZODIAZEPINES
SELECTIVE SEROTONIN REUPTAKE INHIBITORS AND
    SEROTONIN NOREPINEPHRINE REUPTAKE INHIBITORS
OTHER ANTIDEPRESSANTS
MISCELLANEOUS DRUGS
CONCLUSION
REFERENCES

Abstract

There has been a welcome increase of pharmacologic randomized controlled trials (RCTs) for post-traumatic stress disorder (PTSD) during the past two decades. Progress clearly has been made toward a rational psychopharmacology of PTSD, but recommendations of authoritative practice guidelines as well as prescribing patterns, especially for military veterans with chronic PTSD, often appear disconnected from evidence obtained from these RCTs. Furthermore, an Institute of Medicine assessment found the existing evidence inadequate to determine efficacy of any drug or drug class for PTSD. This chapter reviews data from the more informative PTSD drug RCTs, the rationale for potential efficacy of the drug classes evaluated, and the implications of the evidence available for clinicians who must decide how to prescribe for the patients in their practices.

From: *Post-Traumatic Stress Disorder: Basic Science and Clinical Practice*
Edited by: P. J. Shiromani et al., DOI: 10.1007/978-1-60327-329-9_16
© Humana Press, a part of Springer Science+Business Media, LLC 2009

Key Words: Antiadrenergic, anticonvulsant, antipsychotic, benzodiazepine, pharmacologic, PTSD, selective serotonin reuptake inhibitor.

HISTORICAL OVERVIEW: PROGRESS AND DISCONNECTS

Post-traumatic stress disorder (PTSD) was formally defined by the American Psychiatric Association (APA) as an anxiety disorder in 1980. The major impetus for this recognition came from the numerous Vietnam War veterans who continued to suffer distress and disability from this disorder for many years after returning home *(1,2)*. Epidemiologic studies subsequently demonstrated that PTSD caused by civilian trauma was highly prevalent in the general population *(3,4)*. For the first decade after its definition, PTSD pharmacologic treatment rationale was largely derivative. Drug selection relied on the substantial symptom overlap between some PTSD symptoms and those of other psychiatric disorders; the urgent need to relieve patients' and their significant others' distress from discrete PTSD symptoms such as severe sleep disruption and anger outbursts; and efforts to reduce comorbid anxiety and depression. Despite the lack of data from randomized controlled trials (RCTs), generically available antidepressant, antianxiety, and sedative hypnotic drugs demonstrated effective for other behavioral symptoms and disorders became widely prescribed "off label" to treat PTSD.

Since 1990, and particularly since 2000, there has been a welcome increase in data available from PTSD placebo-controlled trials. Although results of RCTs have been inconsistent, some progress has been made toward a rational PTSD psychopharmacology. Yet, prescribing practices for PTSD (particularly for American military veterans), and even the recommendations of authoritative practice guidelines *(5,6)*, sometimes appear disconnected from, or contrary to, evidence obtained from RCTs. Differential RCT results between studies performed in civilian trauma PTSD samples and American veteran PTSD samples have been particularly troublesome *(7)*. Another contributor to these disconnects may be that the outcome focus of most RCTs is improvement of PTSD as an overall disorder, whereas the outcome focus of individual prescribers often appears to be improvement in specific target symptoms *(8)*. Furthermore, the pharmacology of drugs chosen for evaluation in PTSD RCTs (with the exception of drugs that reduce central nervous system [CNS] adrenergic activity; see next section) has often lacked grounding in available knowledge about the neurobiology of PTSD. Confusion for practitioners has increased since the publication of a prestigious Institute of Medicine report commissioned by the Department of Veterans Affairs (VA) to assess the evidence on PTSD treatment modalities as of 2007 *(9)*. This report concluded that for all drug classes reviewed, the evidence is inadequate to determine efficacy in the treatment of PTSD.

This chapter discusses progress made in pharmacologic treatment of PTSD as well as the frequent disconnects between the data generated from clinical trials and prescribing practices. The available data from the most informative RCTs for each psychotropic drug class is reviewed in the order used in the Institute of Medicine report with some modification of nomenclature. Discussion of each drug class will include the neurobiologic rationale (or lack thereof) for choosing the drug class for treatment of PTSD.

ANTIADRENERGICS

Neurobiologic and Phenomenologic Rationale

The central and peripheral adrenergic systems prominently contribute to mammalian adaptive responses to traumatic stress. Excess CNS adrenergic activity produces hyperarousal, anxiety, startle, sleep disruption, and other "fight-or-flight" responses *(10,11)*. The phenomenologic similarities between the behaviors elicited by increased CNS adrenergic activity and many symptoms of PTSD are clear. Studies performed largely (but not exclusively) in veterans with chronic PTSD consistently have demonstrated increased CNS adrenergic activity at both presynaptic and postsynaptic levels. For example, there are elevated concentrations of norepinephrine and its metabolites at rest and in response to stress in cerebrospinal fluid (CSF) *(12)* and in peripheral compartments coregulated with the CNS adrenergic system *(13)*. These results are consistent with increased CNS presynaptic adrenergic outflow from the locus ceruleus contributing to PTSD symptomatology, particularly at night *(14)*.

Increased behavioral and cardiovascular responses to psychologic and pharmacologic stimulation of adrenergic outflow are consistent with increased responsiveness of postsynaptic adrenoreceptors (the α1-adrenoreceptor or the β-adrenoreceptor) also contributing to clinical expression of PTSD *(15–17)*. In addition to its possible involvement in PTSD symptom expression, preclinical and clinical studies suggest the postsynaptic β-adrenoreceptor may be involved in PTSD pathogenesis by mediating consolidation of emotionally arousing memories *(18)*.

The postsynaptic α1-adrenergic receptor is a particularly attractive treatment target in PTSD. Several neurobiologic systems likely involved in PTSD pathophysiology are under stimulatory regulation by α1-adrenergic receptors. These include (1) components of sleep architecture relevant to emergence of trauma nightmares *(19,20)*; (2) CNS release of corticotropin-releasing factor *(21)*, a neuropeptide that generates anxiety and fear *(22)*; and *(3)* prefrontal neocortex systems that favor primitive fear and alarm cognitions *(23)*.

Lipid-soluble antiadrenergic drugs that are CNS active when administered peripherally are available to reduce CNS adrenergic activity by several mechanisms *(24)*. Presynaptic CNS norepinephrine outflow can be reduced with agonists for the inhibitory presynaptic α2-adrenoreceptor such as guanfacine and clonidine. The CNS postsynaptic β-adrenoreceptor is antagonized by propranolol. The CNS postsynaptic α1-adrenoreceptor is antagonized by prazosin. Originally introduced in the 1970s to treat hypertension, these inexpensive generic antiadrenergic drugs have been widely and safely used in general medicine *(25–27)*.

Randomized Controlled Trials

α-2-Adrenoreceptor Agonists: Clonidine and Guanfacine

The α2-adrenoreceptor agonist clonidine was reported in open-label case series to reduce PTSD trauma nightmares and improve sleep in Cambodian refugees (28) and improve PTSD symptoms in veterans (29). Improved sleep in one open-label study was accompanied by improved sleep physiology objectively demonstrated with polysomnography (30). Despite these encouraging anecdotal reports from experienced PTSD clinicians, there have been no clonidine RCTs for PTSD.

Guanfacine is a well-tolerated α2-adrenoreceptor agonist pharmacologically similar to clonidine that has been evaluated in two recent multisite RCTs in American veterans with chronic PTSD. In the first study, 63 veterans were randomized to guanfacine (mean dose 2.4 mg/day) or placebo for 8 weeks (31). Improvements in Clinician Administered PTSD Scale (CAPS) (32) total score (-4.4 vs. -6.1, p = .8), and other changes in the outcome measures were almost identical in the active medication and placebo groups. A second trial of guanfacine for PTSD in predominantly male combat veterans also was negative (33). That reducing overall norepinephrine outflow with guanfacine has not been effective for PTSD suggests that adrenergic contributions to PTSD pathophysiology are complex and may involve differential responsiveness of postsynaptic adrenoreceptor subtypes.

β-Adrenergic Antagonist: Propranolol

Elevated heart rate following trauma predicts subsequent development of PTSD (34), and persons with PTSD compared to controls have an enhanced heart rate response to adrenergic stimulation (15,16). These findings are consistent with increased β-adrenoreceptor responsiveness in PTSD. Because propranolol is the most lipid soluble of available β-adrenoreceptor antagonists (and thus crosses easily from blood to brain) and is nonselective among β-adrenoreceptor subtypes (24), it is a rational choice for evaluation in PTSD. Despite an early anecdotal report of beneficial propranolol effects on chronic PTSD symptoms in veterans (29), there have been no RCTs of propranolol for chronic PTSD reported in the literature. This lack of propranolol RCTs may reflect the general problem of finding resources to support adequately powered RCTs of already clinically available generic drugs for a potential new behavioral indication. The absence of patent protection effectively eliminates the possibility of pharmaceutical industry support. That propranolol can produce vivid dreams as an adverse effect (34) may exacerbate trauma nightmares in PTSD (unpublished observations).

Propranolol has been evaluated as potential pharmacotherapy to prevent development of PTSD following a traumatic event. Forty-one traumatized persons recruited in a hospital emergency department were randomized to a 10-day course of propranolol 40 mg tid (three times a day) or placebo within 6 h of trauma (35). At 1-month follow-up, CAPS total scores of the 11 propranolol completers (28 ± 16) did not differ significantly from the 20 placebo completers (36 ± 22). However, physiologic responses to script-driven imagery 3 months afterward suggested possible benefit of the propranolol treatment. In a subsequent study *(36)*, 48 persons recruited in a surgical trauma center were randomized to begin within 48 h of trauma a 14-day course of propranolol 40 mg tid, the anticonvulsant gabapentin 400 mg tid, or placebo. Neither propranolol nor gabapentin compared to placebo showed any effect on reducing PTSD symptoms or other psychopathology at follow-up.

α1-Adrenoreceptor Antagonist: Prazosin

Of the pharmacologic approaches to reducing CNS adrenergic activity in PTSD, only antagonizing the α1-adrenoreceptor with prazosin has been demonstrated clearly effective for reducing core PTSD symptoms. Prazosin is the most lipid soluble of available α1-adrenoreceptor antagonists *(24)*. Peripherally administered prazosin specifically blocks CNS α1-adrenoreceptors *(37)* and suppresses CNS α1-mediated hyperexcitability and stress-induced anxiety *(38)*.

In each of the three RCTs evaluating prazosin for PTSD, drug was administered as a single evening dose specifically to target persistent and distressing trauma-related nightmares and sleep disruption as primary outcome measures. These distressing nighttime symptoms are the most common chief complaint of combat veterans seeking treatment for PTSD (unpublished observation). Measures of global clinical change also were assessed to determine the impact of nightmare reduction and sleep improvement on sense of well-being and ability to function. Because prazosin duration of action is only 7 to 10 h *(24)*, the single evening dose regimen was not designed to test prazosin effects on the daytime PTSD symptoms that comprise the large majority of PTSD symptoms assessed by the CAPS. That said, each study also assessed prazosin effects on total PTSD symptomatology using either the CAPS (in the two veteran sample studies) or the PTSD Checklist Civilian version (PCL-C) *(39)* in the civilian sample study.

A double-blind, placebo-controlled crossover study was performed in ten Vietnam combat veterans *(40)*, all of whom were receiving disability compensation for PTSD. Because nightmares return within a few days of discontinuing prazosin, even after years of successful treatment (unpublished observations), the "carryover effect" that makes a crossover design inappropriate for many psychotropics is not an issue with prazosin. Because of the possibility of "first-dose" hypotension if α1-adrenoreceptor antagonists are initiated at a high dose *(34)*, prazosin was titrated to an apparently effective dose beginning at an initial dose of 1 mg 1 h before bedtime. Both active drug and placebo were then increased during a 3-week dose titration phase that was followed by a 6-week maintenance dose phase. At a mean achieved maintenance dose of 9.6 mg given an hour before bedtime, prazosin was significantly and substantially superior to placebo for reducing nightmares (CAPS "recurrent distressing dreams" item) and sleep disturbance (CAPS "sleep difficulty" item) and improving global clinical status (Clinical Global Impression of Change [CGIC]) *(41)*. All Cohen's d effect sizes were large, greater than 1.0. Change in total CAPS score and all three CAPS clusters (reexperiencing, avoidance, and hyperarousal) also significantly favored prazosin. The large beneficial effects of evening prazosin on trauma nightmares, sleep disturbance, and global clinical status were confirmed and extended in a parallel group placebo-controlled trial of 40 veterans with chronic PTSD, most of whom experienced combat trauma in the Vietnam War *(42)*. A 4-week dose titration of prazosin or placebo was followed by 8 weeks of maintenance medication (13.3 mg mean maintenance evening prazosin dose). Prazosin again was significantly and substantially superior to placebo for reducing nightmares and sleep disturbance and improving global clinical status. Effect sizes again were large (Cohen's d all > 0.9). Ratings of dream characteristics demonstrated a change from trauma nightmares to normal dreaming during prazosin treatment. Adverse effects were minimal. Although there was a numerically greater reduction in total CAPS score with prazosin than placebo, differences in this trial did not reach statistical significance.

The third prazosin study is unique among all PTSD RCTs in that it measured effects of drug on an objective measure of sleep physiology *(43)*. Thirteen civilian trauma PTSD participants with trauma nightmares and sleep disturbance were randomized to prazosin or placebo in a double-blind crossover trial. Prazosin or placebo was rapidly titrated to 3 mg in the evening during each 3-week treatment period. In the final three nights of each treatment condition, total sleep time, rapid eye movement (REM) sleep time, and sleep latency were recorded at home with the portable REMView device. Total sleep time was 94 min longer in the prazosin than in the placebo condition (374 ± 86 min vs. 280 ± 105 min, $p < .01$, Cohen's d = 0.98). Sleep latency was not significantly different in the prazosin and placebo conditions and actually was several minutes longer in the prazosin conditions. This is consistent with the nonsedating nature of prazosin, which normalizes and extends sleep once sleep is achieved but is not initially "hypnotic." Both REM time and mean REM period duration increased as well, suggesting reduced disruption of REM sleep. Such disruption of REM sleep by inappropriate bursts of CNS adrenergic activity may contribute to the genesis of trauma nightmares *(43,44)*. Clinical outcome measures also favored prazosin in this study, with significantly greater reductions during prazosin treatment of trauma nightmares and PCL-C quantification of total PTSD symptoms, as well as significantly greater improvement in global clinical status.

These studies suggest a specific role for increased α1-adrenoreceptor responsiveness in the pathophysiology of PTSD. A VA multisite cooperative study of prazosin for combat trauma PTSD began randomizing subjects in summer 2008. This study includes both morning and evening doses to enable evaluation of prazosin's effects on both daytime and sleep-associated symptoms.

Several types of psychotropic drugs used clinically in the treatment of PTSD also have substantial α1-adrenergic antagonist activities among their pharmacologic properties *(45,46)*. These drugs include all the atypical antipsychotic drugs (e.g., risperidone, olanzapine, and quetiapine) (discussed separately here), the original tricyclic antidepressants (e.g., imipramine and amitriptyline), and the novel antidepressants trazodone and nefazodone. It is possible that this α1-adrenoreceptor antagonist property contributes to the potential usefulness of these traditional psychotropic drugs in PTSD treatment.

In clinical practice, the beneficial effects of prazosin once achieved usually continue for years with little or no development of tolerance (unpublished observation). In addition, chronic prazosin treatment modifies blood lipids in a beneficial direction by reducing harmful LDL cholesterol and triglycerides and increasing protective HDL cholesterol *(24)*. Beneficial effects of prazosin on blood lipids and absence of effects on weight and blood sugar are in marked contrast to the increased risk of weight gain, hyperglycemia, dyslipidemia, and metabolic syndrome development during chronic treatment with many of the atypical antipsychotic drugs *(47)*.

Prazosin also has reduced alcohol abuse and dependence, an important comorbidity of PTSD in veterans who "self-medicate" with alcohol to alleviate sleep disturbance and other hyperarousal PTSD symptoms (unpublished observations). Prazosin reduces alcohol consumption in animal models of alcohol dependence *(48,49)* and has reduced alcohol consumption in a recent RCT in alcohol-dependent persons *(50)*.

ANTICONVULSANTS

Phenomenological and Neurobiological Rationale

The stereotyped repetitive nature of reexperiencing symptoms in PTSD has suggested similarity to epileptic phenomena such as temporal lobe seizures. Reduced activity of the widely distributed inhibitory neurotransmitter γ-aminobutyric acid (GABA) has been proposed as a mechanism contributing to PTSD pathophysiology. Increasing CNS GABA activity is an important mechanism of action of anticonvulsant drugs such as divalproex, tiagabine, and topiramate *(51–53)*. Low plasma GABA concentrations following trauma have been associated with subsequent emergence of PTSD *(54)*. Several neuroimaging studies *(55,56)* (but not all; *57)* suggest decreased brain GABA receptor binding in PTSD. Some anticonvulsants also have antikindling effects. Such "kindling" has been postulated to cause limbic brain regions involved in emotional memory to become hypersensitive after traumatic events and reexperiencing phenomena, possibly by repetitive noradrenergic stimulation from the locus ceruleus *(58)*.

Unfortunately, recent well-designed, industry-supported RCTs have failed to confirm efficacy of anticonvulsants in chronic PTSD. Divalproex is an effective anticonvulsant and antimanic drug that increases brain GABA levels *(51)*. Eighty-five American veterans were randomized to divalproex (mean dose 2,309 mg/day) or placebo for 8 weeks *(59)*. Reductions in CAPS total scores did not differ between divalproex and placebo (15.1 vs. 16.5 points, nonsignificant *p* value not reported). Reductions on the primary outcomes measure, the CAPS hyperarousal symptom cluster, did not differ between divalproex and placebo (5.9 vs. 4.8 points).

Tiagabine is an anticonvulsant that selectively inhibits GABA reuptake and may have antianxiety activity *(52)*. Two hundred thirty-two people with chronic PTSD (including 9% with combat trauma PTSD) were randomized to tiagabine (mean dose 11.2 mg/day) or placebo for 12 weeks *(60)*. Reduction in total CAPS score did not differ between tiagabine and placebo groups (30.7 vs. 30.2 points, $p = .85$).

Topiramate is an effective anticonvulsant that may have antikindling effects and enhances inhibitory effects of GABA *(52)*. Thirty-eight civilian trauma patients (30 women) with chronic PTSD were randomized to topiramate (mean dose 150 mg/day) or placebo for 12 weeks *(61)*. There were large reductions of CAPS total scores in both treatment groups, but these reductions did not differ between topiramate and placebo (52.7 vs. 42.0 points, $p = .23$).

These negative RCTs make it unlikely that anticonvulsants are effective for core symptoms of PTSD. Together with absence of benzodiazepine effects on core PTSD symptoms (see below Benzodiazepine), these results argue against an important role for GABA in PTSD pathophysiology. The nonspecific sedative effect of many of the anticonvulsant drugs may be subjectively helpful for some PTSD patients but deleterious for others (unpublished observations).

ATYPICAL ANTIPSYCHOTICS

Phenomenological and Neurobiological Rationale

The presence of positive psychotic symptoms is associated with more severe PTSD symptomatology and decreased responsiveness to conventional treatments *(62)*. Flashbacks, a core reexperiencing symptom of PTSD in which the patient transiently but vividly perceives himself or herself experiencing the traumatic event, can mimic psychosis and be difficult to distinguish from complex hallucinations. The presence of comorbid psychotic-like symptoms, the phenomenologic resemblance of intense "flashback" reexperiencing symptoms to psychosis, the sedating property of several atypical antipsychotics, and their ability to reduce cognitive and perceptual distortions in psychosis have been cited as rationale for evaluating atypical antipsychotic drugs as treatment for PTSD. Pseudoparkinsonian adverse effects of first-generation antipsychotics such as haloperidol are much less prevalent with the atypical antipsychotics (risperidone, olanzapine, and quetiapine) that have been used to treat PTSD *(46)*.

The neurobiologic basis of the effects of atypical antipsychotics in psychotic disorders such as schizophrenia is believed to involve antagonism of the dopamine type 2 (D2) and the serotonin type 2 ($5HT_2$) receptors *(46)*. There is no clear evidence implicating abnormal responsiveness of these receptors in the pathophysiology of PTSD. Less widely appreciated is that the atypical antipsychotics all are $\alpha 1$-adrenoreceptor antagonists. Their binding affinities for the $\alpha 1$-adrenoreceptor are equivalent to (and for quetiapine substantially exceed) their binding affinities for the D2 and $5HT_2$ receptors *(46)*. Risperidone has the strongest affinity for the $\alpha 1$-adrenoreceptor among the atypical anticonvulsants that have been evaluated for PTSD *(46)*. This high affinity of atypical antipsychotics for the $\alpha 1$-adrenoreceptor has generally been considered a nuisance cause of orthostatic hypotension as an adverse effect in the treatment of psychotic illnesses. However, this $\alpha 1$-adrenoreceptor antagonist property increases the likelihood that atypical antipsychotics could reduce PTSD reexperiencing and hyperarousal symptoms (see antiadrenergic drugs discussion). Some atypical antipsychotics (e.g., olanzapine and quetiapine) also strongly antagonize the histamine type 1 (H1) receptor *(46)*, a property that likely contributes to their sedative effects. H1 histamine receptor antagonism and α1-adrenoreceptor antagonism are particularly prominent for quetiapine *(46)*, an atypical antipsychotic that is widely used for the sleep disturbance of PTSD in veterans and active duty military personnel (unpublished observation).

A Note of Caution

Although the atypical antipsychotics are much less likely than first-generation antipsychotics to produce extrapyramidal adverse effects, their ability to induce substantial weight gain, dyslipidemia, elevated blood glucose, and the metabolic syndrome is increasingly recognized as a major public health problem *(47)*. Increased risk for the metabolic syndrome must be taken into account in deciding if and when atypical antipsychotics are appropriate for the long-term treatment that often is necessary for chronic PTSD. The atypical antipsychotics aripiprazole and ziprasadone that do not induce the metabolic syndrome unfortunately have not been evaluated for treatment of PTSD.

Randomized Controlled Trials

Two trials have evaluated olanzapine for PTSD. Fifteen subjects (14 women) with PTSD caused predominantly by military sexual trauma and civilian sexual abuse or other violence were randomized to olanzapine (14 mg/day) or placebo for 10 weeks *(63)*. Reduction in PTSD symptoms measured by the Structured Interview for PTSD did not differ significantly between olanzapine (−20.5) and placebo (−28.9). A troublesome adverse effect was an 11.5-lb weight gain over the 10-week trial in the olanzapine group versus only a 0.9-lb weight gain in the placebo group. In another olanzapine PTSD study, 19 male veterans with combat-related PTSD and pronounced sleep problems but no psychotic symptoms were randomized to 8 weeks augmentation with olanzapine (15 mg/day) or placebo *(64)*. All subjects had been only minimally responsive to 12 weeks of selective serotonin reuptake inhibitor (SSRI) treatment that was continued unaltered during the trial. Reduction of PTSD symptoms by total CAPS score was significantly greater with olanzapine (−14.8) than with placebo (−2.2). The investigators suggested that enhanced sleep accounted for much of the reported improvement. Again, weight gain was a prominent adverse effect. Olanzapine subjects gained 13.2 lb over the 8-week trial compared to a loss of 3.0 lb in the placebo subjects.

Risperidone has received the greatest research attention among the atypical antipsychotics. There have been three adjunctive risperidone RCTs in American veterans with combat trauma PTSD and two adjunctive and one monotherapy risperidone studies in civilian trauma PTSD. Forty combat veterans with chronic PTSD who reported psychotic symptoms (hallucinations, delusions, thought disorder) but did not meet criteria for a primary psychotic disorder (e.g., schizophrenia) were randomized to risperidone (mean dose 2.5 mg/day) or placebo for 5 weeks *(65)*. The risperidone group compared to the placebo group showed a modest but significantly greater reduction in psychotic symptoms but not in PTSD symptoms by the total CAPS or CAPS subscales. However, there was a trend-level effect on the CAPS reexperiencing subscale (which includes flashbacks among its symptoms). Weight change was not reported. That psychotic symptoms included phenomena that were referable to the original combat trauma (e.g., hearing gunfire or soldiers screaming, visual hallucinations of enemy soldiers) raises the possibility that some of these drug-responsive psychotic symptoms may have been intense flashbacks.

In an interesting study extending anecdotal observations that atypicals may reduce irritability/anger outbursts in PTSD, 16 combat veterans were administered low-dose risperidone (mean dose 0.57 mg/day) or placebo for 6 weeks as adjunctive therapy. Specifically targeted as outcome measures were irritability and aggressive behavior *(66)*. These behaviors were measured with the Overt Aggression Scale–Modified for Outpatients (OAS-M). Active drug was significantly more effective for irritability (but not for aggression) than placebo. Low-dose risperidone also was effective for intrusive PTSD symptoms. Weight change was not reported. The majority of veterans in both treatment groups were receiving maintenance trazodone or nefazodone, two novel antidepressants with substantial α1-adrenoreceptor antagonist activity *(45)*. A possible explanation for the observed therapeutic effect of low-dose risperidone augmentation in this study is that the atypical antipsychotics added enough α1-adrenoreceptor antagonist activity to that of the novel antidepressants to achieve beneficial effects on intrusive and hyperarousal symptoms.

In a larger 16-week study, 65 veterans with severe PTSD despite maintenance psychotropic medication regimens were randomized to adjunctive risperidone (mean CAPS total at baseline = 102 ± 12) or placebo (mean CAPS total at baseline = 99 ± 16) *(67)*. Risperidone was initiated at 1 mg at bedtime and increased to 3 mg at bedtime while subjects were receiving inpatient psychiatric care. Reduction in total CAPS score (−14.3 vs. −4.6) and CAPS hyperarousal cluster score (−5.5 vs. −1.1) were significantly greater in risperidone versus placebo groups. This study is one of the few to have reported change scores in the 17 individual CAPS items. These results demonstrated greater reduction in risperidone than placebo for psychological distress to trauma reminders, detachment, and restricted affect. There were significant changes over time within the risperidone group for physiologic reaction to trauma reminders, thought avoidance, disturbed sleep, irritability/anger outburst, and hypervigilance. End study weight (214 vs. 213 lb) did not differ between groups, but change in weight from baseline was not reported.

Risperidone has been evaluated in three studies in women with civilian trauma PTSD. Twenty women with PTSD related to sexual assault and domestic abuse were randomized to risperidone monotherapy (mean dose 2.6 mg) or placebo for 10 weeks *(68)*. There was a modest numeric advantage of risperidone compared to placebo on the reduction in CAPS total score, but this did not approach statistical significance. Twenty-one women with PTSD related to childhood abuse were randomized to risperidone (mean dose 1–4 mg/day) or placebo for 8 weeks with other psychotropics held constant during the study *(69)*. CAPS total score reduction at end of study was greater in the risperidone group (−30 ± 32) than placebo group (±19 ± 12). Weight gain did not differ between risperidone and placebo groups (2.5 ± 4.1 lb vs. 3.0 ± 6.2 lb). In a third study, 25 civilian trauma PTSD subjects, predominantly women, who had an incomplete response to an 8-week open-label trial of sertraline were randomized for an additional 8 weeks to risperidone (2.1 mg/day) or placebo *(70)*. There was no difference in total CAPS score reduction (23 ± 13 vs. 24 ± 20 points) among the 21 completers between risperidone and placebo groups. However, there was a greater reduction in CAPS sleep difficulty item favoring risperidone at a trend significance ($p = .09$) level. Trend significance differences favoring risperidone for reductions on the positive symptoms and paranoia scales of the positive and negative syndrome scale (PANSS) were interpreted as consistent with beneficial effects of risperidone on anger and hypervigilance symptoms in these nonpsychotic patients. There also was a trend for more participants in the risperidone group to terminate study participation ($p = .10$). Weight changes were not reported.

Quetiapine

Among the atypical antipsychotics, quetiapine has particularly strong H1 antihistaminic and substantial $\alpha1$-adrenergic receptor antagonist effects *(46)*. Because sedating antihistaminics (e.g., diphenhydramine) induce sleep and the CNS-active $\alpha1$-adrenoreceptor antagonist prazosin reduces sleep disruption and distressing trauma nightmares (see prazosin section), there is rationale for evaluation of quetiapine for the sleep difficulty that is so troublesome for many persons with PTSD. To date, there are no reported quetiapine RCTs for PTSD. An open-label trial in combat veterans with PTSD suggested subjective benefit of quetiapine for sleep latency and duration *(71)*. An RCT of quetiapine for PTSD is under way currently, and results soon will be available (M. Hamner, March 2008, personal communication). The increased risk for weight gain and metabolic syndrome with quetiapine may limit its utility for long-term treatment of chronic PTSD. Although the prominent sedating quality of quetiapine taken at bedtime can be useful for difficulty falling asleep, "hangover" into the subsequent day can interfere with daytime activities that require alertness and vigilance (unpublished observation). This daytime sedation can be troublesome for active duty soldiers and others who need a high level of alertness to perform their jobs successfully.

Taken together, these atypical antipsychotic PTSD trials suggest potential benefits of this drug class for PTSD sleep difficulty, irritability/anger outburst, intense flashbacks, and comorbid psychotic symptoms in both veterans and civilian trauma patients. The consistent very large weight gain in the two olanzapine trials likely will limit the potential usefulness of this drug. Results of ongoing multicenter risperidone and quetiapine PTSD trials will help clarify the efficacy and safety of these atypical antipsychotics in PTSD.

BENZODIAZEPINES

Phenomenological and Neurobiological Rationale

Phenomenological similarities between symptoms of several anxiety disorders and several symptoms of PTSD are clear. There is also some neurobiologic rationale for potential benzodiazepine efficacy in PTSD *(72)*. The antianxiety mechanism of benzodiazepines likely is enhancement of $GABA_A$ receptor function *(73)*. As reviewed in the anticonvulsant section (and benzodiazepines also are effective anticonvulsants; *73)*, reduced GABA concentrations and reduced $GABA_A$ benzodiazepine-binding activity have been demonstrated in PTSD in some studies *(54–56)*. Arguing against major benzodiazepine/ $GABA_A$ receptor involvement in PTSD pathophysiology is a study in which the benzodiazepine receptor antagonist flumazanil did not increase anxiety or other PTSD symptoms in Vietnam combat veterans *(74)*.

Results of RCTs

Only one benzodiazepine RCT has directly addressed PTSD core symptom reduction. In a placebo-controlled crossover study in 16 subjects, including 6 with combat trauma *(75)*, the antianxiety benzodiazepine alprazolam failed to demonstrate efficacy for core PTSD reexperiencing and avoidance symptoms. There was some improvement in anxiety and sleep, but rebound anxiety also was observed. Other benzodiazepine trials either have addressed post-trauma PTSD prevention or have specifically targeted PTSD sleep disturbance and nightmares. Although low post-trauma GABA plasma levels were associated with subsequent development of PTSD *(52)*, treatment with alprazolam or clonazepam started within 1 week of trauma in persons selected for substantial post-trauma distress had no effect on development of PTSD symptoms, anxiety, or depression *(76)*. In other small trials targeting sleep disturbance, benzodiazepines were ineffective in improving sleep disturbance, particularly nightmares, in combat veterans *(77,78)*.

Despite these negative benzodiazepine studies and guideline recommendations against using benzodiazepines to treat PTSD *(6)*, benzodiazepines are widely prescribed to veterans with PTSD. Of the more than 220,000 veterans with a PTSD diagnosis prescribed any psychotropic in 2004 in the VA, 24% were prescribed a benzodiazepine *(8)*. The percentage increased to 31% in veterans seen in mental health clinics. Clinical experience suggests that benzodiazepines are prescribed to veterans with PTSD for comorbid anxiety symptoms and for sleep initiation.

SELECTIVE SEROTONIN REUPTAKE INHIBITORS AND SEROTONIN NOREPINEPHRINE REUPTAKE INHIBITORS

Phenomenological and Neurobiological Rationale

The phenomenologic similarity of many PTSD core and comorbid symptoms to those of depression and the anxiety disorders for which SSRIs and serotonin norepinehprine reuptake inhibitors (SNRIs) have been demonstrated effective are the major cited rationale for their evaluation in PTSD. This rationale together with patent protection for then newly approved compounds generated large-scale pharmaceutical industry support for multicenter PTSD trials of these drugs.

A few neurobiologic studies suggested possible involvement of serotonergic systems in PTSD pathophysiology. An H^3 paroxetine-binding study in platelets revealed decreased receptor number and increased receptor affinity in Vietnam combat veterans with PTSD (79). In a clinical study, the mixed serotonergic agonist/antagonist meta-chlorophenylpiperazine (m-CPP) provoked PTSD symptoms in some veterans with PTSD (80). Whether and how CNS serotonergic systems neurobiologically contribute to PTSD remains unclear.

Results of RCTs

The SSRIs were first evaluated for PTSD in multicenter trials of sertraline and paroxetine in samples predominantly of women with civilian trauma PTSD. In each of two sertraline studies (81,82), total CAPS scores decreased significantly more in sertraline than placebo groups (−33 vs. −26 points and −33 vs. −23 points, respectively), but effect sizes were modest. Sertraline-versus-placebo differences reached statistical significance for the CAPS avoidance/numbing symptom cluster and the CAPS hyperarousal symptom cluster but not for the CAPS reexperiencing/intrusion cluster. Also, insomnia was a common sertraline adverse effect in both studies. In the two paroxetine studies (83,84), significantly greater CAPS-2 decreases with drug versus placebo were similar in magnitude to those in the sertraline studies (−38 vs. −23 points and −36 vs. −26 points, respectively). In contrast to the sertraline studies (81,82) (and perhaps suggesting potential advantage for paroxetine), paroxetine-versus-placebo differences were significant for all three CAPS clusters, and insomnia was not a common adverse effect.

These positive results, albeit with modest effect sizes, from the SSRI studies performed in civilian trauma PTSD samples led to Food and Drug Administration (FDA) approval for the then-proprietary SSRIs sertraline (Zoloft) and paroxetine (Paxil) in 2002. SSRIs soon were recommended as the "first-line" drugs for PTSD. The American Psychiatric Association practice guidelines recommended the SSRIs for PTSD with "substantial clinical confidence" (5). Although SSRI RCTs in American veterans consistently have been negative (see Interventions: PTSD Pharmacotherapy), the VA/Department of Defense (DoD) *Clinical Practice Guideline(6)* classified the SSRIs as being "of significant benefit" for PTSD and "strongly recommended" them as monotherapy. As of 2004, SSRIs were prescribed to 85% of the more than 220,000 veterans with a PTSD diagnosis given any psychotropic drug prescription by the VA (8). It is likely that these drugs are widely prescribed for PTSD in the general population as well.

Overall, this progression from results of earlier SSRI RCTs to widespread SSRI use in clinical practice, at least in nonveterans, is consistent with principles of evidence-based medicine. But, there remain questions about the role of SSRIs and SNRIs in PTSD psychopharmacology. The first question is whether SSRIs are as effective (or effective at all) for combat trauma-induced PTSD in military veterans. Ironically, although PTSD was first delineated as a clinical disorder in military veterans, the large majority of multicenter PTSD RCTs have recruited predominantly women with PTSD caused by civilian trauma. In contrast to the mostly positive results of RCTs in civilian trauma PTSD, four of five SSRI RCTs in combat trauma PTSD have been negative. All three performed in American veterans, including the only large multicenter SSRI trial in this population (7), have been negative.

In a pioneering and still instructive study, 31 veteran outpatients with chronic PTSD were randomized to fluoxetine (average dose 40 mg/day) for 5 weeks (85). Change in total PTSD scores as measured by the CAPS did not differ between fluoxetine and placebo. The authors concluded: "Most VA patients on fluoxetine treatment showed little change: only 1 of the VA patients on fluoxetine had a robust change in his CAPS score, while 2 on placebo did." Fluoxetine was significantly superior to placebo for their comorbid depression symptoms. In contrast to the clear absence of fluoxetine benefit for PTSD symptoms in these veterans, fluoxetine was effective for PTSD symptoms in a sample of predominantly women with civilian trauma PTSD studied concurrently and reported in the same publication (85). In a second single-site SSRI study in veterans, 12 Vietnam War veterans were randomized to fluoxetine (mean dose 48 mg/day) or placebo for 12 weeks (86). Mean improvement on the Davidson Trauma Scale (87) actually favored placebo (9 points) compared to fluoxetine (3 points), but differences were not significant. Only one of the fluoxetine subjects as compared to two of the placebo subjects was rated as globally "very much improved."

The third study in American veterans, a large multicenter RCT of the subsequently FDA approved (for PTSD) SSRI sertraline, was performed in 169 outpatients recruited from 10 VA medical centers between May 1994 and September 1996 (7). Results unfortunately confirmed and extended the negative results of the two smaller fluoxetine trials in American veterans. Following a 1-week placebo run-in period, veterans were randomized to 12 weeks of flexibly dosed sertraline (mean dose 156 mg/day among completers) or placebo. PTSD symptom reduction as measured by the CAPS total score did not differ between sertraline (-13.1 ± 3.0) and placebo (-15.4 ± 3.1) groups. Although sertraline was fairly well tolerated, discontinuation rate due to adverse effects tended to be greater in the sertraline group than in the placebo group. For both sertraline and placebo groups, combat-related PTSD was associated with relatively poorer outcome than non-combat-related PTSD. In contrast to the first fluoxetine study in American veterans (85), this multicenter trial failed even to show significant beneficial sertraline effects for comorbid depressive symptoms. In another sertraline RCT, 42 Israeli male combat veterans with chronic PTSD were randomized to sertraline (mean achieved dose 120 ± 60 mg/day) or placebo (88). There were no significant differences in change in CAPS total PTSD symptom scores or any of the three CAPS cluster scores between sertraline and placebo groups. However, there were trends for greater benefit of sertraline for global clinical status and depression symptoms. Also, a post hoc analysis among completers demonstrated a significant effect of sertraline on the CAPS "irritability/anger outburst" item.

Taken together, these four SSRI RCTs in American and Israeli veterans with chronic PTSD provide little rationale for their use for PTSD per se in this population (8), and they do not justify VA/DoD practice guidelines recommending SSRIs as the first-line monotherapy for PTSD. Their widespread use in the VA, however, suggests that clinicians detect symptomatic benefit from SSRIs in their chronic PTSD patients. Clinical observations supported by some study results suggest that PTSD "irritability/low anger threshold" and comorbid depression and anxiety symptoms are among the symptoms that appear most likely to benefit.

The sole positive SSRI study in combat-related PTSD evaluated fluoxetine in 143 men (and 1 woman) recruited at eight sites in Bosnia-Herzegovina, Croatia, and Yugoslavia *(89)*. Subjects were randomized to fluoxetine ($n = 110$) or placebo ($n = 34$) for 12 weeks. The mean dose of 65 ± 18 mg achieved at week 12 was relatively high but was well tolerated in this sample. Fluoxetine was significantly superior to placebo for PTSD as measured by reductions in total CAPS and CAPS cluster scores. Fluoxetine was also effective for depression symptoms as measured by the Montgomery Asberg Depression Rating Scale *(90)*, for anxiety symptoms, and for global clinical status. Several factors may have contributed to the positive findings in this study compared to the other negative SSRI studies in Vietnam and Israeli veterans. These Balkan war veterans were somewhat younger (mean age 36 years) and somewhat more recently traumatized (although PTSD was still chronic with mean time since traumatic event 6 to 7 years) than veterans in the other studies. They also likely had received less treatment of any type for their chronic PTSD. Given the phenotypic similarity between some symptoms of depression and PTSD, the similar reductions with fluoxetine treatment in Montgomery Asberg Depression Rating Scale (MADRS) total score (35%) and CAPS total score (39%), and the similarity of a number of items between these depression and PTSD rating scales raises the possibility that antidepressant effects of fluoxetine contributed in part to the reduction in total CAPS score. An analysis of the 17 individual CAPS symptom items could clarify this possibility. Finally, nonobvious differences between study populations or methods may have contributed importantly to this unique positive finding among RCTs for combat trauma PTSD.

The second question is whether the effect sizes of SSRIs and SNRIs in RCTs in the general population warrant the enthusiasm with which they are recommended in clinical guidelines. Recently published SSRI and SNRI multicenter PTSD trials have shown smaller effect sizes than earlier trials or lack of efficacy altogether. A recent large ($n = 411$) multicenter RCT of fluoxetine for predominantly civilian trauma PTSD failed to demonstrate separation of the SSRI from placebo *(91)*. Mean total PTSD symptoms (measured by the CAPS) decreased 43, 43, and 37 points in the 20 mg fluoxetine, 40 mg fluoxetine, and placebo groups, respectively. A large multicenter PTSD RCT of the SNRI venlafaxine that included a sertraline group showed a disappointingly small effect size for both medications *(92)*. Five hundred thirty-eight PTSD outpatients at 59 U.S. sites were randomized to venlafaxine (mean dose 64 mg/day), sertraline (mean dose 110 mg/day), or placebo for 12 weeks. CAPS total scores decreased 42, 39, and 34 points in the venlafaxine, sertraline, and placebo groups, respectively. Although venlafaxine was significantly superior to placebo ($p = .015$), effect size was small (0.26). Sertraline difference from placebo did not reach statistical significance ($p = .08$) and effect size was only 0.19.

The trials in which specific PTSD symptom responses to SSRIs or the SNRI venlafaxine have been examined individually *(93–95)* suggest some benefit for the majority of daytime PTSD symptoms, but they demonstrate little or no benefit for trauma-related nightmares and sleep disturbance. This lack of SSRI and SNRI benefits for sleep disturbance are consistent with unpublished results from the original large multicenter sertraline trials that were positive for total PTSD symptoms (81,82). Unpublished analyses of the individual CAPS items measuring trauma nightmares (item 2, "recurrent distressing dreams") and disturbed sleep (item 13, "difficulty falling or staying asleep") demonstrated no significant separation of sertraline from placebo (personal communication). The overall lack of benefit of SSRIs (and the SNRI venlafaxine) for PTSD nightmares and sleep disturbance is consistent with their disrupting REM sleep and intensifying dreaming when administered to normal persons (96,97).

The preponderance of SSRI RCTs support small-to-moderate efficacy with variable response rate for daytime PTSD symptoms in civilian trauma victims. However, SSRIs are not effective for most core PTSD symptoms in veterans, at least not in older Vietnam War veterans, despite being widely prescribed to this population. SSRIs also do not appear to prevent PTSD when administered soon after trauma (98). Whether SSRIs will be effective for core PTSD symptoms in more recently traumatized veterans returning from conflicts in Iraq and Afghanistan is a question deserving careful study. I agree with the thoughtful minority opinion to the Institute of Medicine report by committee member Thomas Mellman: "The evidence is suggestive but not sufficient to conclude efficacy of SSRIs in the general population. The available evidence is further suggestive that SSRIs are not effective in populations consisting of predominantly male veterans with chronic PTSD" (9, p. 210).

OTHER ANTIDEPRESSANTS

Almost a decade after the formal recognition of PTSD as a disorder, results from a few small-to-moderate-size single-site RCTs of generically available antidepressants performed in American military veterans began to appear in the literature. A small RCT demonstrated modest efficacy for the tricyclic antidepressant (TCA) amitriptyline (99). A larger RCT demonstrated modest efficacy for the TCA imipramine and more robust efficacy for the monoamine oxidase inhibitor (MAOI) phenelzine (100). Perhaps because of concerns about potential (albeit rare; 101) adverse effects of MAOIs and dietary restrictions recommended with their use (45) or because these generic antidepressant drugs were without industry marketing support, the generally positive studies of TCAs and MAOIs for PTSD in veterans failed to generate either clinical enthusiasm or research support for large RCTs. For whatever reason, MAOIs and TCAs are infrequently prescribed to treat PTSD, at least among American veterans (8).

The sedating generically available antidepressants trazodone and nefazodone are commonly prescribed to veterans with PTSD (e.g., 66), particularly for sleep difficulty (unpublished observation). There have been anecdotal reports (102) but no RCTs of trazodone for PTSD, perhaps because it has long been generic. An RCT of nefazodone in veterans showed modest but statistically superior reduction of CAPS total score for nefazodone versus placebo

(19.1 vs. 13.5 points) *(103)*. That these related compounds both have substantial α1-adrenoreceptor antagonist activity and are sedating may be relevant to their frequent prescription for nighttime PTSD symptoms. Mirtazapine is a very sedating antidepressant that has shown some benefit in one PTSD trial *(104)* but can produce troublesome daytime sedation and weight gain *(45)*.

MAOIs and TCAs remain rational options for PTSD patients, particularly those with prominent depression and panic symptoms. Given that some RCTs of amitriptyline, imipramine, and phenelzine have been positive for PTSD in American veterans whereas SSRI RCTs in this population have been consistently negative, it remains unclear why SSRIs are far more frequently prescribed to veterans within VA than are these other antidepressants *(8)*.

MISCELLANEOUS DRUGS

Several molecules with neurobiologic roles in memory have been proposed as possible therapeutic agents in PTSD. D-Cycloserine is a partial agonist of the *N*-methyl D-aspartate (NMDA) receptor associated glycine site *(105)* that has been proposed to facilitate psychotherapeutic reduction of the deleterious effects of trauma memories. D-Cycloserine has adjunctive benefit in psychotherapy of several anxiety disorders *(106)*. In a small RCT for PTSD, 11 persons with chronic civilian trauma PTSD received D-cycloserine (50 mg/day) and placebo in a double-blind, random-order crossover design study *(107)*. Small reductions in CAPS total score in both groups did not differ significantly ($p = .5$). However, D-cycloserine continues under active investigation as a potential adjunct to exposure-based psychotherapy. Oxytocin is a hypothalamic neuropeptide demonstrated in rodents to impair consolidation and retrieval of aversive memory *(108)*. Although oxytocin has not been evaluated therapeutically in PTSD, an elegant study demonstrated that single-dose oxytocin administered intranasally to Vietnam veterans reduced physiologic responding to personal combat imagery *(109)*. If memory-active neuropeptides or antagonists to the α1-adrenoreceptor-mediated anxiogenic neuropeptide corticotrophin-releasing factor *(110)* could be administered safely in preparations reliably able to cross from blood into brain, they would be interesting candidates for evaluation in PTSD trials. Cyproheptadine, a sedating antihistamine with complex pharmacologic properties, was demonstrated not more effective than placebo for trauma nightmares and sleep difficulty in veterans *(111)*.

CONCLUSION

Resolving the logical and practical discrepancies among the current evidence from available RCTs, the discouraging interpretation of this evidence by the Institute of Medicine committee that no drug has established efficacy for PTSD and clinicians' widespread prescription of pharmacologic treatment for their distressed patients suffering from PTSD is a challenging task. The high prevalence of PTSD among the millions of men and women who have participated in the war on terrorism in Iraq and Afghanistan (not to mention that of the many severely traumatized civilians) makes resolving these discrepancies even more pressing. This task requires both short- and long-term approaches.

One potentially helpful approach is to reconceptualize what is meant by "effective treatment" of PTSD. If the "gold standard" efficacy outcome measure is disorder focused and limited to the sum score of all 17 PTSD symptoms listed in the CAPS, and these items are assumed to be equally weighted regarding impact on patients' lives, then clinically important therapeutic drug effects on particularly distressing individual symptoms may be obscured. Commenting on their finding a disconnect between the widespread prescription of multiple psychotropic drug classes for PTSD in American veterans and the RCT-derived data base *(8)*, Mohamed and Rosenheck stated: "A new type of efficacy research may be needed to determine symptom responses to psychotropic medications as well as disorder responses." Such target symptoms in PTSD research ideally would focus on those symptoms most distressing to patients and to their families.

A related issue is the failure of most drug RCTs to report active treatment-versus-placebo effects on individual PTSD symptoms. Such reporting of effects on all 17 CAPS items by Bartzokis, Lu, Turner, Mintz, and Saunders *(67)* is unique among published RCTs and enhanced the clinical value of their risperidone augmentation trial. Even relying on the three CAPS symptom clusters is not adequate to avoid potentially obscuring valuable information about individual symptom responses to treatment.

A powerful long-term approach to developing additional effective drug treatments for PTSD is an enhanced research effort to unravel the complex neurobiology of PTSD. Studies in animal models can help. Clinicians and patients need studies to determine efficacy of generic drugs widely prescribed for PTSD (e.g., trazodone and benzodiazepines) that will not be supported by pharmaceutical company funds. And, the likely complex interactions between pharmacotherapy and psychotherapy need to be addressed in carefully designed trials.

REFERENCES

1. Kulka, R., Fairbank, J., Jordan, K. B., and Weiss, D. (1990) Trauma and the Vietnam War Generation: Report of Findings from the National Vietnam Veterans Readjustment Study. New York: Routledge.
2. Neylan, T. C., Marmar, C. R., Metzler, T. J., Weiss, D. S., Zatzick, D. F., Delucchi, K. L., et al. (1998) Sleep disturbances in the Vietnam generation: findings from a nationally representative sample of male Vietnam veterans. Am J Psychiatry 155:929–33.
3. Breslau, N., Davis, G. C., Andreski, P., and Peterson, E. (1991) Traumatic events and posttraumatic stress disorder in an urban population of young adults. Arch Gen Psychiatry 48:216–22.
4. Kessler, R. C., Sonnega, A., Bromet, E., Hughes, M., and Nelson, C. B. (1995) Posttraumatic stress disorder in the National Comorbidity Survey. Arch Gen Psychiatry 52:1048–60.
5. American Psychiatric Association. (2004) Practice Guideline for the Treatment of Patients with Acute Stress Disorder and Posttraumatic Stress Disorder. Washington, DC: American Psychiatric Press.
6. VA (Veterans Affairs), DoD (Department of Defense), Management of Post-Traumatic Stress Working Group. (2004) VA/DoD Clinical Practice Guideline for the Management

of Posttraumatic stress. Version 1.0. Washington, DC: Department of Veterans Affairs and Department of Defense.

7. Friedman, M. J., Marmar, C. R., Baker, D. G., Sikes, C. R., and Farfel, G. M. (2007) Randomized, double-blind comparison of sertraline and placebo for posttraumatic stress disorder in a Department of Veterans Affairs Setting. J Clin Psychiatry 68:711–20.

8. Mohamed, S., and Rosenheck, R. (2008) Pharmacotherapy of PTSD in the U.S. Department of Veterans Affairs: diagnostic- and symptom-guided drug selection. J Clin Psychiatry 69:959–65.

9. Institute of Medicine. (2008) Treatment of Posttraumatic Stress Disorder: An Assessment of the Evidence. Washington, DC: National Academies Press.

10. Glavin, G. B. (1985) Stress and brain noradrenaline: a review. Behav Neurosci Rev 9:233–43.

11. Yehuda, R., Southwick, S., Giller, E. L., Ma, X., and Mason, J. W. (1992) Urinary catecholamine excretion and severity of PTSD symptoms in Vietnam combat veterans. J Nerv Ment Dis 180:321–25.

12. Geracioti, T. D., Jr., Baker, D. G., Ekhator, N. N., West, S. A., Hill, K. K., Bruce, A. B., Schmidt, D., Rounds-Kugler, B., Yehuda, R., Keck, P. E., Jr., and Kasckow, J. W. (2001) CSF norepinephrine concentrations in posttraumatic stress disorder. Am J Psychiatry 158:1227–30.

13. Liberzon, I., Abelson, J. L., Flagel, S. B., Raz, J., and Young, E. A. (1999) Neuroendocrine and psychophysiologic responses in PTSD: a symptom provocation study. Neuropsychopharmacology 21:40–50.

14. Mellman, T. A., Kumar, A., Kulick-Bell, R., Kumar, M., and Nolan, R. (1995) Nocturnal/daytime urine noradrenergic measures and sleep in combat-related PTSD. Biol Psychiatry 38:174–79.

15. McFall, M. E., Murburg, M. M., Ko, G. N., and Veith, R. C. (1990) Autonomic responses to stress in Vietnam combat veterans with posttraumatic stress disorder. Biol Psychiatry 27:1165–75.

16. Pitman, R. K., Orr, S. P., Forgue, D. F., deJong, J. B., and Claiborn, J. M. (1987) Psychophysiologic assessment of posttraumatic stress disorder in Vietnam combat veterans. Arch Gen Psychiatry 44:970–75.

17. Southwick, S. M., Krystal, J. H., Morgan, A., Johnson, D., Nagy, L. M., Nicolaou, A., Heninger, G. R., Charney, D. S. (1993) Abnormal noradrenergic function in posttraumatic stress disorder. Arch Gen Psychiatry 50:266–74.

18. Reist, C., Duffy, J. G., Fujimoto, K., and Cahill, L. (2001) β-Adrenergic blockade and emotional memory in PTSD. Int J Neuropsychopharmacol 4:377–83.

19. Woodward, S. H., Arsenault, N. J., Murray, C., and Bliwise, D. L. (2000) Laboratory sleep correlates of nightmare complaint in PTSD inpatients. Biol Psychiatry 48:1081–87.

20. Mallick, B. N., Majumdar, S., Faisal, M., Yadav, V., Madan, V., and Pal, D. (2002) Role of norepinephrine in the regulation of rapid eye movement sleep. J Biosci 27:539–51.

21. Vythilingam, M., Anderson, G. M., Owens, M. J., Halaszynski, T. M., Bremner, J. D., Carpenter, L. L., Heninger, G. R., Nemeroff, C. B., and Charney, D. S. (2000) Cerebrospinal fluid corticotrophin-releasing hormone in healthy humans: effects of yohimbine and naloxone. J Clin Endocrinol Metab 85:4138–45.

22. Koob, G. F. (1999) Corticotropin-releasing factor, norepinephrine, and stress. Biol Psychiatry 46:1167–80.

23. Birnbaum, S., Gobeske, K. T., Auerbach, J., Taylor, J. R., and Arnsten, A. F. (1999) A role for norepinephrine in stress-induced cognitive deficits: alpha-1 adrenoreceptor mediations in the prefrontal cortex. Biol Psychiatry 46:1266–74.

24. Westfall, T. C., and Westfall, D. P. (2006) Adrenergic agonists and antagonists. In: Goodman and Gilman's The Pharmacological Basis of Therapeutics. 11th ed. New York: McGraw-Hill, pp. 237–95.
25. Cleland, J. G. (2003) β-Blockers for heart failure: why, which, when, and where. Med Clin North Am 87:339–71.
26. Cooper, K. L., McKiernan, J. M., and Kaplan, S. A. (1999) α-Adrenoreceptor antagonists in the treatment of benign prostatic hyperplasia. Drugs 57:9–17.
27. MacMillan, L. B., Hein, L., Smith, M. S., Piascik, M. T., and Limbird, L. E. (1996) Central hypotensive effects of the α_{2A}-adrenergic receptor subtype. Science 273:801–3.
28. Kinzie, J. D., and Leung, P. (1989) Clonidine in Cambodian patients with posttraumatic stress disorder. J Nerv Ment Dis 177:546–50.
29. Kolb, L. C., Burris, B. C., and Griffiths, S. (1984) Propranolol and clonidine in the treatment of posttraumatic stress disorders of war. In: van der Kolk, B. A., ed., Posttraumatic Stress Disorder: Psychological and Biological Sequelae. Washington, DC: American Psychiatric Press, pp. 98–105.
30. Kinzie, J. D., Sacks, R. L., and Riley, C. M. (1994) The polysomnographic effects of clonidine on sleep disorders in posttraumatic stress disorders: a pilot study with Cambodian patients. J Nerv Ment Dis 182:585–87.
31. Neylan, T. C., Lenoci, M., Samuelson, K. W., Metzler, T. J., Henn-Haase, C., Hierholzer, R. W., Lindley, S. E., Otte, C., Schoenfeld, F. B., Yesavage, J. A., and Marmar, C. A. (2006) No improvement of posttraumatic stress disorder symptoms with guanfacine treatment. Am J Psychiatry 163:2186–88.
32. Blake, D. D., Weathers, F. W., Nagy, L. M., Kaloupek, D. G., Gusman, F. D., Charney, D. S., and Keane, T. M. (1995) The development of a clinician administered PTSD scale. J Trauma Stress 8:75–90.
33. Davis, L. L., Ward, C., Rasmusson, A., Newell, J. M., Frazier, E., and Southwick, S. M. (2008) A placebo-controlled trial of guanfacine for the treatment of posttraumatic stress disorder in veterans. Psychopharm Bull 41:8–18.
34. Medical Economics Company. (2008) Physicians Desk Reference. 62nd ed. Montvale, NJ: Medical Economics.
35. Pitman, R. K., Sanders, K. M., Zusman, R. M., Healy, A. R., Cheema, F., Lasko, N. B., Cahill, L., and Orr, S. P. (2002) Pilot study of secondary prevention of posttraumatic stress disorder with propranolol. Biol Psychiatry 51:189–92.
36. Stein, M. B., Kerridge, C., Dimsdale, J. E., and Hoyt, D. B. (2007) Pharmacotherapy to prevent PTSD: results from a randomized controlled proof-of-concept trial in physically injured patients. J Trauma Stress 20:923–32.
37. Menkes, D. B., Baraban, J. M., and Aghajanian, G. K. (1981) Prazosin selectively antagonizes neuronal responses mediated by alpha-1 adrenoreceptors in brain. Naunyn Schmiedebergs Arch Pharmacol 317:273–75.
38. Cecchi, M., Khoshbouei, H., Javors, M., and Morilak, D. A. (2002) Modulatory effects of norepinephrine in the lateral bed nucleus of the stria terminalis on behavioral and neuroendocrine response to acute stress. Neuroscience 112:13–21.
39. Weathers, F. W., Litz, B. T., Herman, J. A., Huska, J. A., and Keane, T. M. (1993) The PTSD Checklist: reliability, validity, and diagnostic utility. Presented at the annual meeting of the International Society for Traumatic Stress Studies, San Antonio, TX, October 24–27.
40. Raskind, M. A., Peskind, E. R., Kanter, E. D., Petrie, E. C., Radant, A., Thompson, C. E., Dobie, D. J., Hoff, D., Rein, R. J., Straits-Tröster, K., Thomas, R. G., and McFall, M. E. (2003) Reduction in nightmares and other PTSD symptoms in combat veterans by prazosin: a placebo-controlled study. Am J Psychiatry 160:371–73.

41. Guy, W. (1976) Assessment Manual for Psychopharmacology. Washington, DC: U.S. Department of Health, Education and Welfare. Publication (ADM) 76-338 NIMH, pp. 218–22.
42. Raskind, M. A., Peskind, E. R., Hoff, D. J., Hart, K. L., Holmes, H. A., Warren, D., Shofer, J., O'Connell, J., Taylor, F., Gross, C., Rohde, K., and McFall, M. E. (2007) A parallel group placebo controlled study of prazosin for trauma nightmares and sleep disturbance in combat veterans with posttraumatic stress disorder. Biol Psychiatry 61:928–34.
43. Taylor, F. B., Martin, P., Thompson, C., Williams, J., Mellman, T. A., Gross, C., Peskind, E. R., and Raskind, M. A. (2008) Prazosin effects on sleep measures and clinical symptoms in civilian trauma posttraumatic stress disorder: a placebo-controlled study. Biol Psychiatry 63:629–32.
44. Mellman, T. A., Knorr, B. R., Pigeon, W. R., Leiter, J. C., and Akay, M. (2004) Heart rate variability during sleep and the early development of posttraumatic stress disorder. Biol Psychiatry 55:953–56.
45. Baldessarini, R. J. (2006) Drug therapy of depression and anxiety disorders. In: Goodman and Gilman's The Pharmacological Basis of Therapeutics. 11th ed. New York: McGraw-Hill, pp. 429–59.
46. Baldessarini, R. J., and Tarazi, F. I. (2006) Pharmacotherapy of psychosis and mania. In: Goodman and Gilman's The Pharmacological Basis of Therapeutics. 11th ed. New York: McGraw-Hill, pp. 461–500.
47. American Diabetes Association. (2004) Consensus development conference on antipsychotic drugs and obesity in diabetes. Diabetes Care 27:596–601.
48. Rasmussen, D.A., Alexander, L.L., Raskind, M.A., and Froehlich, J.C. (Submitted). The α1-adrenergic receptor antagonist, prazosin, reduces alcohol drinking in alcohol-preferring (P) rats. Alcoholism Clin Exp Res (In press).
49. Walker, B. M., Rasmussen, D. D., Raskind, M. A., and Koob, G. F. (2008) The effects of α1-noradrenergic receptor antagonism on dependence-induced increases in responding for ethanol. Alcohol 42:91–97.
50. Simpson, T. L., Meredith, C. W., Gross, C. A., Raskind, M. A., and Saxon, A. J. (2007) Pilot trial of prazosin for treatment of alcohol dependence. Alcohol Clin Exp Res 31 (suppl):60A.
51. Loscher, W. (1999) Valproate: a reappraisal of its pharmacodynamic properties and mechanism of action. Prog Neurobiol 58:31–59.
52. Pollack, M. H., Roy-Byrne, P. P., Van Ameringen, M., et al. (2005) The selective GABA reuptake inhibitor tiagabine for the treatment of generalized anxiety disorder: results of a placebo-controlled study. J Clin Psychiatry 66:1401–8.
53. Herrero, A. I., Olmo, N., Gonzales-Escalada, J. R., et al. (2002) Two new actions of topiramate: inhibition of depolarizing GABA(A)-mediated responses and activation of a potassium conductance. Neuropharmacology 42:210–20.
54. Vaiva, G., Thomas, P., Ducrocq, F., Fontaine, M., Boss, V., Devos, P., Rascle, C., Cottencin, O., Brunet, A., Laffargue, P., and Goudemand, M. (2004) Low posttrauma GABA plasma levels as a predictive factor in the development of acute posttraumatic stress disorder. Biol Psychiatry 55:250–54.
55. Bremner, J. D., Innis, R. B., Southwick, S. M., Staib, L., Zoghbi, S., and Charney, D. S. (2000) Decreased benzodiazepine receptor binding in prefrontal cortex in combat-related posttraumatic stress disorder. Am J Psychiatry 157:1120–26.
56. Geuze, E., van Berckel, B. N. M., Lammertsma, A. A., Boellard, R., de Kloet, C. S., Vermetten, E., and Westenberg, H. G. M. (2008) Reduced GABAA benzodiazepine receptor binding in veterans with posttraumatic stress disorder. Mol Psychiatry 13:74–83.
57. Fujita, M., Southwick, S. M., Denucci, C. C., Zoghbi, S. S., Dillon, M. S., Baldwin, R. M., et al. (2004) Central type benzodiazepine receptors in Gulf War veterans with posttraumatic stress disorder. Biol Psychiatry 56:95–100.

58. Post, R. M., Ballenger, J. C., Putnam, F. M., and Bunney, W. F. (1983) Carbamazepine in alcohol withdrawal syndromes. J Clin Psychopharmacol 3:204–5.

59. Davis, L. L., Davidson, J. R. T., Ward, C., Bartolucci, A., Bowden, C. L., and Petty, F. (2008) Divalproex in the treatment of posttraumatic stress disorder: a randomized, double-blind, placebo-controlled trial in a veteran population. J Clin Psychopharmacol 28:84–88.

60. Davidson, J. R. T., Brady, K., Mellman, T. A., Stein, M. B., and Pollack, M. H. (2007) The efficacy and tolerability of tiagabine in adult patients with posttraumatic stress disorder. J Clin Psychopharmacol 27:85–88.

61. Tucker, P., Trautman, R. P., Wyatt, D. B., Thompson, J., Wu, S.-C., Capece, J. A., and Rosenthal, N. R. (2007) Efficacy and safety of topiramate monotherapy in civilian post-traumatic stress disorder: a randomized, double-blind, placebo-controlled study. J Clin Psychiatry 68:201–6.

62. Davis, D., Kutcher, G. S., Jackson, E. I., and Mellman, T. A. (1999) Psychotic symptoms in combat-related posttraumatic stress disorder. J Clin Psychiatry 60:29–32.

63. Butterfield, M. I., Becker, M. E., Connor, K. M., Sutherland, S., Churchill, L. E., and Davidson, J. R. T. (2001) Olanzapine in the treatment of posttraumatic stress disorder: a pilot study. Int Clin Psychopharmacol 16:197–203.

64. Stein, M. B., Kline, N. A., and Matloff, J. L. (2002) Adjunctive olanzapine for SSRI-resistant combat-related PTSD: a double-blind, placebo-controlled study. Am J Psychiatry 159:1777–79.

65. Hamner, M. B., Faldowski, R. A., Ulmer, H. G., Frueh, B. C., Huber, M. G., and Arana, G. W. (2003). Adjunctive risperidone treatment in posttraumatic stress disorder: a preliminary controlled trial in effects on comorbid psychotic symptoms. Int Clin Psychopharmacol 18:1–8.

66. Monnelly, E. P., Ciraulo, D. A., Knapp, C., and Keane, T. (2003) Low-dose risperidone as adjunctive therapy for irritable aggression in posttraumatic stress disorder. J Clin Psychopharmacol 23:193–96.

67. Bartzokis, G., Lu, P. H., Turner, J., Mintz, J., and Saunders, C. S. (2004) Adjunctive risperidone in the treatment of chronic combat-related posttraumatic stress disorder. Biol Psychiatry 57:474–79.

68. Padala, P. R., Madison, J., Monnahan, M., Marcil, W., Price, P., Ramaswamy, S., Din, A. U., Wilson, D. R., Petty, F. (2006) Risperidone monotherapy for posttraumatic stress disorder related to sexual assault and domestic abuse in women. Int Clin Psychopharmacol 21:275–80.

69. Reich, D. B., Winternitz, S., Hennen, J., Watts, T., and Stanculescu, C. (2004) A preliminary study of risperidone in the treatment of posttraumatic stress disorder related to childhood abuse in women. J Clin Psychiatry 65:1601–6.

70. Rothbaum, B. O., Killeen, T. K., Davidson, J. R. T., Brady, K. T., Connor, K. M., and Heekin, M. H. (2008) Placebo-controlled trial of risperidone augmentation for selective serotonin reuptake inhibitor-resistant civilian posttraumatic stress disorder. J Clin Psychiatry February 13:e1–e6, Epub ahead of print.

71. Robert, S., Hamner, M. B., Chose, S., et al. (2005) Quetiapine improves sleep disturbances in combat trauma veterans with PTSD: sleep data from a prospective open-label study. J Clin Psychopharmacol 25:387–88.

72. Medina, J. H., Novas, M. L., Wolfman, C. N., Levi de Stein, M., and De Robertis, E. (1983) Benzodiazepine receptors in rat cerebral cortex and hippocampus undergo rapid and reversible changes after acute stress. Neuroscience 9:331–35.

73. Charney, D. S., Mihic, S. J., and Harris, R. A. Hypnotics and sedatives. In: Goodman and Gilman's The Pharmacological Basis of Therapeutics. 11th ed. New York: McGraw-Hill, pp. 401–27.

74. Randall, P. K., Bremner, D., Krystal, J. H., Nagy, L. M., Heninger, G. R., Nicolau, A. L., and Charney, D. S. (1995) Effects of the benzodiazepine antagonist flumazenil in PTSD. Biol Psychiatry 38:319–24.

75. Braun, P. D., Greenberg, D., Dasberg, H., and Lerer, B. (1990) Core symptoms of posttraumatic stress disorder unimproved by alprazolam treatment. J Clin Psychiatry 51:236–38.

76. Gelpin, E., Bonne, O., Peri, T., Brandes, D., and Shalev, A. Y. (1996) Treatment of recent trauma survivors with benzodiazepines: a prospective study. J Clin Psychiatry 57:390–94.

77. Cates, M. E., Bishop, M. H., Davis, L. L., and Woolley, T. W. (2004) Clonazepam for treatment of sleep disturbances associated with combat-related posttraumatic stress disorder. Ann Pharmacother 38:1395–99.

78. Davidson, J. R. T. (2004) Use of benzodiazepines in social anxiety disorder, generalized anxiety disorder, and posttraumatic stress disorder. J Clin Psychiatry 65(suppl 5): 29–33.

79. Arora, R. C., Fichtner, C. G., O'Connor, F., and Crayton, J. W. (1993) Paroxetine binding in the blood platelets of posttraumatic stress disorder patients. Life Sci 53:919–28.

80. Southwick, S. M., Krystal, J. H., Bremner, D., Morgan, C. A., Nicolaou, A. L., Nagy, L. M., Johnson, D. R., Heninger, G. R., and Charney, D. S. (1997) Noradrenergic and serotonergic function in posttraumatic stress disorder. Arch Gen Psychiatry 54:749–58.

81. Brady, K., Pearlstein, T., Asnis, G. M., Baker, D., Rothbaum, B., Sikes, C. R., Farfel, G. M. (2002) Efficacy and safety of sertraline treatment of posttraumatic stress disorder. JAMA 283:1837–44.

82. Davidson, J. R.T., Rothbaum, B. O., van der Kolk, B. A., Sikes, C. R., and Farfel, G. M. (2001) Multicenter, double-blind comparison of sertraline and placebo in the treatment of posttraumatic stress disorder. Arch Gen Psychiatry 58:485–92.

83. Marshall, R. D., Beebe, K. L., Oldham, M., and Zaninelli, R. (2001) Efficacy and safety of paroxetine treatment for chronic PTSD: a fixed-dose, placebo-controlled study. Am J Psychiatry 158:1982–88.

84. Tucker, P., Zaninelli, R., Yehuda, R., Ruggiero, L., Dillingham, K., and Pitts, C. D. (2001) Paroxetine in the treatment of chronic posttraumatic stress disorder: results of a placebo-controlled, flexible-dosage trial. J Clin Psychiatry 62:860–68.

85. Van der Kolk, B. A., Dreyfuss, D., Michaels, M., Shera, D., Berkowitz, R., Fisler, R., and Saxe, G. (1994) Fluoxetine in posttraumatic stress disorder. J Clin Psychiatry 55:517–22.

86. Hertzberg, M. A., Feldman, M. E., Beckham, J. C., Kudler, H. S., and Davidson, J. R. T. (2000) Lack of efficacy for fluoxetine in PTSD: a placebo controlled trial in combat veterans. Ann Clin Psychiatry 12:101–5.

87. Davidson, J. R., Book, S. W., Colket, J. T., Tupler, L. A., Roth, S., David, D., Hertzberg, M., Mellman, T., Beckham, J. C., Smith, R. D., Davison, R. M., Katz, R., and Feldman, M. E. (1997) Assessment of a new self-rating scale for posttraumatic stress disorder. Psychol Med 27:153–60.

88. Zohar, J., Amital, D., Miodownik, C., Kotler, M., Bleich, A., Lane, R. M., and Austin, C. (2002) Double-blind placebo-controlled study of sertraline in military veterans with posttraumatic stress disorder. J Clin Psychiatry 22:190–95.

89. Martenyi, F., and Soldatenkova, V. (2006) Fluoxetine in the acute treatment and relapse prevention of combat-related posttraumatic stress disorder: analysis of the veteran group of a placebo-controlled, randomized clinical trial. Eur Neuropsychopharmacol 16:340–49.

90. Montgomery, S. A., and Asberg, M. (1979) A new depression scale designed to be sensitive to change. Br J Psychiatry 134:382–89.

90. Montgomery, S. A., and Asberg, M. (1979) A new depression scale designed to be sensitive to change. Br J Psychiatry 134:382–89.

92. Davidson, J., Baldwin, D., Stein, D. J., Kuper, E., Benattia, I., Ahmed, S., Pedersen, R., and Musgnung, J. (2006) Treatment of posttraumatic stress disorder with venlafaxine extended release. Arch Gen Psychiatry 63:1158–65.
93. Davidson, J. R. T., Landerman, L. R., Farfel, G. M., and Clary, C. M. (2002) Characterizing the effects of sertraline in posttraumatic stress disorder. Psychol Med 32:661–70.
94. Meltzer-Brody, S., Connor, K. M., Churchill, E., and Davidson, J. R. T. (2000) Symptom-specific effects of fluoxetine in posttraumatic stress disorder. Int Clin Psychopharmacol 15:227–31.
95. Stein, D. J., Pederson, R., Rothbaum, B. O., Baldwin, D. S., Ahmed, S., Musgnung, J., and Davidson, J. (2008) Onset of activity and time to response on individual CAPS-SX17 items in patients treated for posttraumatic stress disorder with venlafaxine ER: a pooled analysis. Int J Neuropscychopharmacol 11:1–9.
96. Obendorfer, S., Saletu-Zyhlarz, G., and Saletu, B. (2000) Effects of selective serotonin reuptake inhibitors on objective and subjective sleep quality. Pharmacopsychiatry 42:69–81.
97. Hamilton, M. S., and Opler, L. A. (1992) Akathisia, suicidality, and fluoxetine. J Clin Psychiatry 53:401–6.
98. Shalev, A. (2007) A randomized controlled study of the efficacy of prolonged exposure, cognitive therapy and an SSRI in the prevention of PTSD. Presented at the 23rd International Society for Traumatic Stress Studies Annual Meeting, Baltimore, MD.
99. Davidson, J., Kudler, H., Smith, R., Mahorney, S. L., Lipper, S., Hammett, E., Saunders, W. B., and Cavenar, J. O. (1990) Treatment of posttraumatic stress disorder with amitriptyline and placebo. Arch Gen Psychiatry 47:259–66.
100. Kosten, T. R., Frank, J. B., Dan, E., McDougle, C. J., and Giller, E. L., Jr. (1991) Pharmacotherapy for posttraumatic stress disorder using phenelzine or imipramine. J Nerv Ment Dis 179:366–70.
101. Schuckit, M., Robins, E., and Feighner, J. (1971) Tricyclic antidepressants and monoamine oxidase inhibitors. Arch Gen Psychiatry 24:509–14.
102. Hertzberg, M. A., Feldman, M. E., Beckham, J. C., and Davidson, J. R. T. (1996) Trial of trazodone for posttraumatic stress disorder using a multiple baseline group design. J Clin Psychopharmacol 16:294–98.
103. Davis, L. L., Jewell, M. E., Ambrose, S., Farley, J., English, B., Bartolucci, A., and Petty, F. (2004) A placebo-controlled study of nefazodone for the treatment of chronic posttraumatic stress disorder. J Clin Psychopharmacol 24:291–97.
104. Davidson, J. R., Weisler, R. H., Butterfield, M. I., Casat, C. D., Connor, M., Barnett, S., and van Meter, S. (2003) Mirtazapine vs. placebo in posttraumatic stress disorder: a pilot trial. Biol Psychiatry 53:188–91.
105. Thompson, L. T., Moskal, J. R., and Disterhoft, J. F. (1992) Hippocampus-dependent learning facilitated by a monoclonal antibody or D-cycloserine. Nature 356:638–41.
106. Rothbaum, B. O. (2008) Critical parameters for D-cycloserine enhancement of cognitive-behavioral therapy for obsessive-compulsive disorder. Editorial. Am J Psychiatry 165:293–96.
107. Heresco-Levy, U., Kremer, I., Javitt, D. C., Goichman, R., Reshef, A., Blanaru, M., and Cohen, T. (2002) Pilot-controlled trial of D-cycloserine for the treatment of posttraumatic stress disorder. Int J Neuropsychopharmacol 5:301–7.
108. Bohus, B., Kovacs, G. L., and De Wied, D. (1978) Oxytocin, vasopressin and memory: opposite effects on consolidation and retrieval processes. Brain Res 157:414–17.
109. Pitman, R. K., Orr, S. P., and Lasko, N. B. (1993) Effects of intranasal vasopressin and oxytocin on physiologic responding during personal combat imagery in Vietnam veterans with posttraumatic stress disorder. Psychiatry Res 48:107–17.

110. Jacobs-Rebhun, S., Schnurr, P. P., Friedman, M. J., Peck, R., Brophy, M., and Fuller, D. (2000) Posttraumatic stress disorder and sleep difficulty. Am J Psychiatry 157:1525–26.
111. Baker, D. G., West, S. A., Nicholson, W. E., Ekhator, N. N., Kasckow, J. W., Hill, K. K., Bruce, A. B., Orth, D. N., Geracioti, T. D., Jr (1999) Serial CSF corticotrophin-releasing hormone levels and adrenocortical activity in combat veterans with posttraumatic stress disorder. Am J Psychiatry 156:585–88.

17 Guided Imagery as a Therapeutic Tool in Post-Traumatic Stress Disorder

Jennifer L. Strauss, Patrick S. Calhoun, and Christine E. Marx

Contents

BACKGROUND
WHAT IS GUIDED IMAGERY?
WHAT GUIDED IMAGERY IS NOT
GIFT: GUIDED IMAGERY FOR TRAUMA
GIFT: OVERVIEW OF TREATMENT PROTOCOL
CONCEPTUAL FRAMEWORK FOR A SELF-MANAGEMENT
    INTERVENTION FOR PTSD
PILOT STUDY OF GIFT INTERVENTION IN WOMEN WITH
    PTSD RELATED TO MILITARY SEXUAL TRAUMA
CURRENT RESEARCH EFFORTS
REFERENCES

Abstract

Guided imagery is a behavioral technique used to direct individuals to effectively create and manipulate mental representations to produce therapeutic changes. A growing empirical literature supports the use of these techniques in a variety of physical and emotional conditions. The focus of our research program is on applying these techniques to the treatment of post-traumatic stress disorder (PTSD). We have developed and piloted a clinician-facilitated, self-management intervention for PTSD called guided imagery for trauma (GIFT). We describe the rationale for this approach, its conceptual framework, and the treatment protocol. We present preliminary findings in a sample of women with

From: *Post-Traumatic Stress Disorder: Basic Science and Clinical Practice*
Edited by: P. J. Shiromani et al., DOI: 10.1007/978-1-60327-329-9_17
© Humana Press, a part of Springer Science+Business Media, LLC 2009

PTSD related to military sexual trauma, which demonstrate feasibility, tolerability, and a large effect on PTSD symptoms. We also describe our current research efforts, including a randomized controlled trial of the GIFT intervention in women survivors of military sexual trauma, and the extension of this intervention to the treatment of combat-related PTSD.

Key Words: Guided imagery, post-traumatic stress disorder, self-administration, self-management, sexual trauma.

BACKGROUND

Broadly stated, guided imagery techniques encompass verbal instructions for creating mental representations for a variety of purposes. These mind-body techniques combine aspects of skills training, visualization, and meditation. Common applications include relaxation, improved mood, and enhanced concentration. Although the research base for this approach is currently limited, it is steadily growing. In this chapter, we describe this technique and how we have applied it to the treatment of post-traumatic stress disorder (PTSD).

WHAT IS GUIDED IMAGERY?

First and foremost, guided imagery is a tool. It is a means of engaging the patient's imagination to direct change. Guided imagery can include the full range of senses, including sounds, tastes, smells, and tactile sensations, as well as visual images. Guided by verbal instructions (delivered in person or via audio), individuals are directed to create mental representations that are personally meaningful and often symbolic and to manipulate these representations toward a desired goal.

A popular example is the use of guided imagery techniques by athletes, such as the runner whose coach helps her to paint a vivid, multisensory, mental picture of herself crossing the finish line in first place. The coach may begin by guiding the athlete through a series of imagery exercises to promote relaxation and mental focus prior to introducing performance-related material. Commonly used relaxation exercises include breathing relaxation, passive or progressive muscle relaxation, and mentally visualizing a relaxing scene or favorite place. Of course, in addition to preparing the athlete to imagine a victorious race, repeated practice of relaxation techniques has the added benefit of teaching the athlete highly generalizable and transportable skills that can be used to manage stress and anxiety.

Once the athlete is appropriately relaxed and able to focus attention on the primary goals of the exercise (to visualize winning an upcoming race, for example), the coach will shift the focus of the imagery. Again, drawing on as many of the senses as possible, the coach may direct the runner to imagine sensations associated with the experience of running: the staccato sound of her sneakers pounding the pavement, the scent of freshly cut grass, the saltiness of perspiration beading on her upper lip, the rush of wind in her face, the steady rhythm of her breathing, and the strain of her quadriceps as she pushes ahead of opponents. The goal, of course, is for the athlete to experience these sensations as fully and realistically as possible. Typically, such an exercise would also include suggestions about the runner's cognitive-emotional state: She feels confident and strong, trusts her body to carry her as far and as fast as she wants it to go, and believes in herself and her ability to win.

As the instructions progress, the athlete may be directed to visualize the finish line just ahead and to be aware of the increasingly distant sound of opponents' footsteps, trailing behind. The athlete gathers her strength and finally pushes forward to cross the finish line and win the race. The athlete vividly sees and feels herself proudly achieving her goal. Although certainly not a substitute for physical training, repeated use of these guided imagery exercises may enhance the athlete's performance by increasing motivation, focus, and self-confidence.

Although the research base for these techniques is still quite limited, small-scale studies suggest that guided imagery techniques may be applied to improve a broad variety of conditions, including cancer pain *(1,2)*, chemotherapy nausea and vomiting *(3)*, HIV-related symptoms *(4,5)*, postcardiac surgery pain *(1)*, and tension headaches and migraines *(6)*. Guided imagery may also change cortisol levels *(7)*, blood pressure, and pulse rate *(5)* and improve anxiety *(8,9)* and depression symptoms *(7)*. A common theme among these studies is the use of guided imagery techniques, typically delivered in a standardized, self-administered audio format, to provide patients with a means of self-managing and potentially improving a given condition.

Several studies have examined applications of guided imagery for trauma. An open trial of a group therapy intervention that included guided imagery showed reduced trauma symptoms in a sample of 139 adolescents in postwar Kosovo *(10)*. A randomized controlled trial was conducted in 168 women of a group therapy for PTSD-related nightmares that included an imagery component. Study results showed improved sleep and an average decrease of PTSD symptoms from the moderately severe to moderate range *(11)*. Half of participants also used imagery to manage daily problems and to improve mood, suggesting that imagery skills may generalize to manage routine stressors and difficulties. The focus of our ongoing research, described in this chapter, has been on the use of self-administered guided imagery in the treatment of PTSD. Finally, one of the guided imagery audios included in our treatment protocol has previously been piloted in 37 male combat veterans as part of anxiety management group treatment. Following a 1-month trial of daily home practice, veterans reported reduced anxiety and arousal and increased positive mood, self-esteem, concentration, and emotional management *(12)*.

WHAT GUIDED IMAGERY IS NOT

Contrary to some coverage it has received in the lay press, guided imagery is certainly not a cure-all or "magic bullet." For example, a quick Internet search of the term "guided imagery" yielded the following misinformation: "Although it isn't always curative, imagery is helpful in 90 percent of the problems that people bring to the attention of their primary care physicians" *(13)*. We are aware of no empirical support for this statement. For better *and* for worse, guided imagery has achieved popular appeal. The upside is that guided imagery has received initial recognition as a safe and well-tolerated intervention that may potentially be helpful as an adjunctive treatment for a number of disorders. The downside is that unsubstantiated claims abound. For this reason, we urge clinicians applying this technique to carefully educate their patients with regard to its strengths and limitations in the context of the existing scientific literature. The degree of popular attention received by guided imagery, however, perhaps does suggest that there is something about this approach that appeals to a broad audience, which may have important implications for treatment acceptance and retention.

In the context of treatments for PTSD, it is also important to distinguish applications of guided imagery from alternate techniques that make use of visual stimuli or visualization techniques. The application of guided imagery entails the manipulation of mental images that symbolize some aspect of oneself or one's goals. This process is quite distinct from the use of imagery to recall or reexperience past traumatic events (i.e., imaginal exposure), a core component of exposure-based therapies *(14)*. In exposure-based therapies, traumatic memories are activated for the purpose of confronting feared situations and modifying pathological aspects of these memories through habituation, extinction, and new learning *(15)*. The efficacy of cognitive-behavioral treatments such as prolonged exposure is well established, although some patients may have difficulty managing the strong emotions evoked by these techniques *(14)*. In contrast to the largely self-administered format of guided imagery, prolonged exposure is typically conducted in the context of intensive individual sessions with a therapist who has been well trained in these specialized techniques. Described in further detail in the next section of this chapter, we propose that guided imagery for PTSD may be a novel alternative to prolonged exposure and other cognitive-behavioral techniques.

GIFT: GUIDED IMAGERY FOR TRAUMA

Guided imagery for trauma (GIFT) is a manualized, clinician-facilitated, self-management intervention. In our protocol, each patient is paired with a clinician "facilitator" whose role is to support, via face-to-face meetings and telephone contact, the patients' use of the GIFT guided imagery audios over the course of the 12-week treatment period. The rationale for this approach is threefold. First, we initially designed this intervention for use by women survivors of sexual trauma receiving treatment at a Veteran Affairs (VA) medical center. Given resource limitations and treatment barriers that commonly challenge mental health delivery, a preliminary goal was to design an intervention that would require minimal clinical and financial resources. We initially considered developing a pure self-help intervention but opted not to pursue this idea following our early pilot work in this area (unpublished data) and review of prior reports of self-help approaches for PTSD *(16)*. Our own early work and the work of other investigators suggest (not surprisingly) that patients are more likely to both adhere to and apply self-help treatments when administered under clinical supervision. And certainly, the therapeutic relationship is a well-recognized change factor in therapy *(17–20)*. Thus, we decided to develop a transportable, facilitated, self-management intervention.

Second, our intervention design was informed by an appreciation for the feelings of helplessness, vulnerability, and disempowerment with which trauma survivors frequently struggle. For this reason, an important goal was to promote a sense of self-efficacy, mastery, and control and to increase patients' involvement in the treatment process. Inherent in this self-management design is the message to patients that there is a great deal that they can do to help themselves as active participants in their health care rather than be solely passive recipients of a clinician's efforts and treatment intervention. We strongly believe that this is a critical point to communicate to any patient population, particularly to those who have been victimized. The structure of the relationship between the patient and clinician facilitator in our intervention differs in important ways from a traditional psychotherapeutic relationship. By design, it is highly collaborative and provides a model for patients to become active participants in their own treatment and, by extension, in other relationships. Like many self-help approaches, our treatment model requires patients to set aside at least 30 minutes, five times a week, to complete the guided imagery exercises. Hence, we encourage patients to examine and address their own mental health needs and well-being and to prioritize, even if for only 30 minutes a day, their own self-care.

A third goal was to design an intervention that would be well tolerated and well accepted by patients. In this regard, guided imagery's gentle approach and popular appeal made it an attractive choice. Given the heightened sensitivity of those with PTSD to perceptual, sensory, and emotional cues, we hypothesized that such patients might respond particularly well to a technique that targets, and teaches patients to manipulate and direct, these experiences. Finally, recent reports indicated that only a small percentage of veterans returning from Iraq or Afghanistan who screen positively for PTSD receive help from a mental health provider, and that difficulty scheduling or reaching appointments and distrust of mental health providers are significant barriers to seeking services *(21)*. Relevant to these data, our pilot data support the acceptability of self-administered interventions. In a survey of 89 VA clinic users, 86% endorsed the belief that self-administered treatments could improve mental health, and 70% were willing to use self-help guided imagery for stress reduction (unpublished data). Thus, we predicted that an intervention that may be administered remotely and which encourages self-management would be well received and might improve access to care. Jointly, these goals dictated our design of the GIFT intervention.

GIFT: OVERVIEW OF TREATMENT PROTOCOL

Orientation Session

At the beginning of treatment, each patient attends a 50-minute session with the clinician facilitator. The primary objectives of this session are to focus, structure, and support the patient's use of the GIFT audios. Collaboratively, the patient and clinician identify specific treatment goals and develop a plan for the patient's independent use of the audios. In this and all clinical contact with the patient, an adaptation of motivational interviewing techniques is employed (22), such as posing open-ended questions about the patient's thoughts and feelings about the intervention and using reflective listening to increase support and trust. Use of these techniques is intended to capitalize on patients' motivation and to help patients overcome barriers they experience during the treatment. The patient is also provided with psychoeducation and handouts about sexual trauma and PTSD and instructions for use of the audio. We require each patient to listen to the audio once prior to leaving our clinic to ensure tolerability.

Telephone Coaching

Each patient receives weekly, 10-minute "coaching" calls, placed by the facilitator at a predetermined time. These semistructured calls include a review of treatment goals, audio use, and attempts to apply new skills. A solution-focused approach is employed to address any adherence issues. These calls also serve to provide emotional support and maintenance of treatment motivation and commitment.

Midpoint Consultation Session

Each patient returns to our clinic at week 8, the treatment midpoint, for a 50-minute consultation meeting with the clinician facilitator. During this session, the facilitator and patient work collaboratively to review and revise (as needed) treatment goals, to identify positive changes and treatment gains, to troubleshoot treatment adherence, and to reinforce treatment motivation. The importance of the patient's active involvement in the treatment process is emphasized.

Guided Imagery Audio Exercises

The 30-minute GIFT guided imagery audios were developed by our consultant, Belleruth Naparstek, LISW, a nationally recognized expert in guided imagery techniques. The first audio presents exercises for relaxation, stress management, and emotion regulation. It combines mental imagery with instructions for established techniques, including breathing and muscle relaxation. Consistent with many cognitive-behavioral interventions for PTSD, this audio is introduced early in treatment to bolster relaxation and emotion regulation skills prior to introducing trauma-focused content (15). The second audio provides instructions for creating positive mental imagery, beliefs, and feelings associated with surviving trauma. These imagery exercises are designed to increase self-confidence, motivation, and hope and to reduce feelings of shame, guilt, helplessness, and vulnerability. As noted, in contrast to some other approaches, the focus is on the patient's present experience and the impact of past experiences on current functioning; patients are *not* directed to remember of relive past traumas.

Self-Monitoring

Patients monitor their use of the audios to promote adherence and treatment self-management. Self-monitoring has been shown to enhance the effects of behavioral self-management interventions *(23)* and is often used in psychotherapy to increase awareness of treatment objectives and to monitor symptoms, use of new skills, and completion of "homework" assignments *(24,25)*.

CONCEPTUAL FRAMEWORK FOR A SELF-MANAGEMENT INTERVENTION FOR PTSD

Our intervention model is informed by each of the four "essential elements" identified by Von Korff and colleagues in their description of collaborative management interventions: (1) collaborative definition of problems; (2) targeting, goal setting, and planning; (3) self-management training and support services; and (4) active, sustained follow-up *(23)*. A focus on *collaborative definition of problems* acknowledges the different perspectives that providers and patients often bring to the table and targets improved communication, shared decision making, and attention to patient preferences. *Targeting* entails identifying specific problems to address as opposed to initiating numerous changes at once, which may increase the likelihood of nonadherence and demoralization. *Goal setting and planning* ensure that patients and providers agree on realistic and mutually endorsed treatment goals and strategies. The role of *self-management training and support services* is to enhance patients' capacity for self-care. Von Korff and colleagues suggest that self-management training be individualized, tailored to each patients' motivation and readiness, and aligned with priorities that have been mutually agreed on by the patient and provider. Finally, outcomes are best achieved through *active, sustained follow-up*. Von Korff and colleagues suggest that follow-up occur at planned intervals so that providers can obtain information about patients' functional status, identify obstacles or setbacks early in the process, check progress in implementing the treatment plan, make necessary modifications, and reinforce patients' efforts and progress. Of note, there is some evidence that telephone follow-up (as opposed to return office visits, mail, or electronic mail) may be particularly effective *(26–28)*.

The specific mechanisms through which guided imagery may exert its effects are currently unknown. Consistent with other cognitive-behavioral interventions, we have hypothesized that patients' self-administration of the GIFT guided imagery audios principally affects change through improved anxiety management and mastery. Through repeated practice of the guided imagery exercises, patients may learn to better manage both specific fears and the chronic hyperarousal that are among the defining characteristics of PTSD. The self-administered design of this intervention is also hypothesized to improve mastery and self-esteem. By completing the guided imagery exercises, patients learn that they can replace trauma-related emotions with positive imagery and healthier emotions, potentially leading to the reduction of PTSD symptoms.

PILOT STUDY OF GIFT INTERVENTION IN WOMEN WITH PTSD RELATED TO MILITARY SEXUAL TRAUMA

We have completed a feasibility trial of the GIFT intervention *(29,30)*. Fifteen women with PTSD related to military sexual trauma were enrolled from the Durham VA Medical Center's Women Veterans Mental Health Clinic. PTSD diagnosis was confirmed by administration of the Clinician-Administered PTSD Scale (CAPS) *(31)* at baseline by a rater who was blinded to treatment assignment; CAPS severity scores were our primary outcome variable. Our inclusion criteria were as follows: (1) PTSD diagnosis related to military sexual trauma; (2) no current suicidality, parasuicidality, homicidality, or domestic violence; and (3) no current substance abuse. Patients could continue psychiatric medications during the course of the trial if stabilized for longer than 3 months and could continue supportive individual or group therapies. However, we required that they not begin new psychiatric medications or change the doses of existing psychiatric medications during the course of the trial, or receive PTSD-specific psychological interventions (e.g., exposure therapy, cognitive processing therapy). In our sample, the average time since trauma was 27.73 years; 93% were taking psychotropic medications for PTSD, 80% were receiving supportive individual counseling, and 60% were receiving supportive group therapy. Hence, this was a sample of patients with long-standing trauma histories who were symptomatic despite ongoing services.

Of the 15 women enrolled, 10 completed the full 12-week intervention, 2 completed two-thirds of the intervention, 2 completed one-third of the intervention, and 1 was administratively withdrawn following a medication change. This completion rate is similar to rates reported in an analysis of 25 controlled studies of exposure-based and other cognitive-behavioral individual psychotherapies for PTSD (67.0–82.3%) *(32)*. We found a large, significant reduction in PTSD symptoms in the completer sample. The mean symptom change was 21.1 for the CAPS, $t(1,9) = 2.79$, $p = .02$. The mean symptom change was 15.1 for the PTSD Checklist (PCL) *(34)*, $t(1.9) = 2.79$, $p = .03$. These are large pre-post effect sizes as defined by Cohen's d (d = pretreatment score = posttreatment score/pretreatment SD); for CAPS, d = 1.08, and for PCL, d = 1.97. Significant symptom reductions were also observed in a preliminary intent-to-treat analysis; effect sizes were 0.72 for the CAPS and 1.43 for PCL. Although preliminary, these effect sizes are comparable to those reported for evidence-based therapies for PTSD and above those that would be expected for placebo alone *(32)*. There were no adverse events following this guided imagery intervention. These initial findings suggest that the self-directed format of GIFT can be feasibly administered and is well tolerated by women veterans with military sexual trauma. Qualitative data from follow-up interviews support patients' adherence and satisfaction:

- "I still listen to the guided imagery about four times a week. It keeps me going."
- "I am no longer a victim in my dreams."
- "I have not had an anxiety attack since beginning the guided imagery."
- "I feel this is a very positive way to heal the effects of trauma."

CURRENT RESEARCH EFFORTS

We are currently conducting a randomized controlled trial of this intervention in a similar sample of women veterans with PTSD related to military sexual trauma. In lieu of the GIFT intervention, those randomized to the control condition receive an audio of relaxing music rather than the guided imagery audio, and interactions with the clinician facilitator are limited to provision of psychoeducation and interpersonal support. In all other respects, the GIFT and control intervention groups are matched for length and frequency of audio use and clinical contact. In addition to examining clinical outcomes, we will be assessing the effects of this treatment on neurobiological markers relevant to PTSD. We have also recently begun a pilot study of this intervention (renamed self-management audio for recovery from trauma, or SMART) in veterans with combat-related PTSD. We hypothesize comparable effects to those seen in our pilot work and current trial of women veterans with PTSD related to military sexual trauma. Qualitative feedback gathered at posttreatment will be used to refine the protocol, as needed, to address the treatment concerns of the primarily male population who have experienced combat trauma. The long-term goal of this research program is to develop an effective self-management intervention for PTSD that is transportable and easily implemented, particularly within large health care systems.

ACKNOWLEDGEMENTS

We acknowledge assistance from the Department of Veteran Affairs Research Career Development Award (J. L. S.), Samueli Foundation/VET-HEAL Award (J. L. S.); National Institute of Mental Health R03 Award (J. L. S.), Department of Veteran Affairs Advanced Research Career Development Award (CEM), and Veterans Affairs Mid-Atlantic Mental Illness Research, Education, and Clinical Center. The views expressed are those of the authors and do not necessarily represent the views of the Department of Veterans Affairs. This chapter is presented in loving memory of Dr. Marian I. Butterfield, who died on June 26, 2006, after a courageous five-year battle with breast cancer. We wish to acknowledge her extensive contributions to the ideas and research presented and to celebrate her significant contributions to the field of psychiatry and to the care of our nation's veterans.

REFERENCES

1. Graffam, S., and Johnson, A. (1987) A comparison of two relaxation strategies for the relief of pain and its distress. J Pain Symptom Manage 2, 229–31.
2. Syrjala, K. L., Donaldson, G. W., Davis, M. W., and Kippes, M. E., and Carr, J. E. (1995) Relaxation and imagery and cognitive-behavioral training reduce pain during cancer treatment: a controlled clinical trial. Pain 63, 189–98.
3. Lyles, J. N., Burish, T. G., Krozely, M. G., and Oldham, R. K. (1982) Efficacy of relaxation training and guided imagery in reducing the aversiveness of cancer chemotherapy. J Consult Clin Psychol 50, 509–24.
4. Auerbach, J. E., Oleson, T. D., and Solomon, G. F. (1992) A behavioral medicine intervention as an adjunctive treatment for HIV-related illness. Psychol Health 6, 325–34.
5. Eller, L. S. (1995) Effects of two cognitive-behavioral interventions on immunity and symptoms in person with HIV. Ann Behav Med 17, 339–48.
6. Mannix, L. K., Chandurkar, R. S., Rybicki, L. A., Tusek, D. L., and Solomon, G. D. (1999) Effect of guided imagery on quality of life for patients with chronic tension-type headache. Headache 39, 326–34.
7. McKinney, C. H., Antoni, M. H., Kumar, M., Tims, F. C., and McCabe, P. M. (1997) Effects of guided imagery and music (GIM) therapy on mood and cortisol in healthy adults. Health Psychol 16, 390–400.
8. Hammer, S. E. (1996) The effects of guided imagery through music on state and trait anxiety. J Music Ther 33, 47–70.
9. Schandler, S. L., and Dana, E. R. (1983) Cognitive imagery and physiological feedback relaxation protocols applied to clinically tense young adults: a comparison of state, trait, and physiological effects. J Clin Psychol 39, 672–81.
10. Gordon, J. S., Staples, J. K., Blyta, A., and Bytyqi, M. (2004) Treatment of posttraumatic stress disorder in postwar Kosovo high school students using mind-body skills groups: a pilot study. J Trauma Stress 17, 143–47.
11. Krakow, B., Hollifield, M., Johnston, L., et al. (2001) Imagery rehearsal therapy for chronic nightmares in sexual assault survivors with posttraumatic stress disorder: a randomized controlled trial. JAMA 286, 537–45.
12. Root, L. P., Koch, E. I., Reyntjens, J. O., Alexander, S. K., and Gaughf, N. W. (2002) Trauma-specific guided imagery: a systematic evaluation of an adjunct intervention to group psychotherapy. Abstract presented at International Society for Traumatic Stress Studies annual meeting; Baltimore, MD; November.
13. Guided Imagery. Available at http://www.holisticonline.com/guided-imagery.htm.
14. Foa, E. B., Keane, T. M., and Friedman, M. J. (2000) Effective Treatments for PTSD: Practice Guidelines from the International Society for Traumatic Stress Studies. New York: Guilford Press.
15. Foa, E. B., and Rothbaum, B. O. (1998) Treating the Trauma of Rape: Cognitive-Behavioral Therapy for PTSD. New York: Guilford Press.
16. Ehlers, A., Clark, D. M., Hackmann, A., et al. (2003) A randomized controlled trial of cognitive therapy, a self-help booklet, and repeated assessments as early interventions for posttraumatic stress disorder. Arch Gen Psychiatry 60, 1024–32.
17. Horvath, A. O., and Bedi, R. P. (2002) The alliance. In: Norcross, J. C., Psychotherapy Relationships that Work: Therapist Contributions and Responsiveness to Patients. New York: Oxford University Press; pp. 37–69.
18. Horvath, A. O., and Symonds, B. D. (1991) Relation between working alliance and outcome in psychotherapy: a meta-analysis. J Counsel Psychol 38, 139–49.

19. Martin, D. J., Garske, J. P., and Davis, M. K. (2000) Relation of the therapeutic alliance with outcome and other variables: a meta-analytic review. J Consult Clin Psychol 68, 438–50.
20. Orlinsky, D. E., Grawe, K., and Parks, B. K. (1994) Process and outcome in psycho-therapy—noch einmal. In:Bergin, A. E., and Garfield, S. L., eds., Handbook of Psycho-therapy and Behavior Change. New York: Wiley; pp. 270–376.
21. Hoge, C. W., Castro, C. A., Messer, S. C., McGurk, D., Cotting, D. I., and Koffman, R. L. (2004) Combat duty in Iraq and Afghanistan, mental health problems, and barriers to care. N Engl J Med 351, 13–22.
22. Miller, W. R., and Rollnick, S. (2002) Motivational Interviewing: Preparing People for Change. 2nd ed. New York: Guilford Press.
23. Von Korff, M., Gruman, J., Schaefer, J., Curry, S. J., and Wagner, E. H. (1997) Collabo-rative management of chronic illness. Ann Intern Med 127, 1097–1102.
24. Barlow, D. H. (1993) Clinical Handbook of Psychological Disorders: A Step-by-Step Treatment Manual. 2nd ed. New York: Guilford Press.
25. Beck, A. T., Rush, A. J., Shaw, B. F., and Emery, G. (1979) Cognitive Therapy for Depression. New York: Wiley.
26. DeBusk, R. F., Miller, N. H., Superko, H. R., et al. (1994) A case-management system for coronary risk factor modification after acute myocardial infarction. Ann Intern Med 120, 721–29.
27. Rich, M. W., Beckham, V., Wittenberg, C., Leven, C. L., Freedland, K. E., and Carney, R. M. (1995) A multidisciplinary intervention to prevent the readmission of elderly patients with congestive heart failure. N Engl J Med 333, 1190–95.
28. Wasson, J., Gaudette, C., Whaley, F., Sauvigne, A., Baribeau, P., and Welch, H. G. (1992) Telephone care as a substitute for routine clinic follow-up. JAMA 267, 1788–93.
29. Strauss, J. L., Marx, C. E., Morey, R. A., et al. (2007) A brief, transportable intervention for women veterans with PTSD related to military sexual trauma. Paper presented at 10th Annual Force Health Protection Conference; Louisville, KY; August.
30. Strauss, J. L., Marx, C. E., Oddone, E. Z., O'Loughlin, S. H., and Butterfield, M. I. (2006) A transportable PTSD intervention shows promise for women veterans with military sexual trauma. Abstract presented at American Psychiatric Association Annual Meeting; Toronto, Canada; May.
31. Blake, D. D., Weathers, F. W., Nagy, L. M., Kaloupek, D. G., Charney, D. S., and Keane, T. M. (1998) Clinician-Administered PTSD Scale for DSM-IV. Boston: National Center for Posttraumatic Stress Disorder.
32. Bradley, R., Greene, J., Russ, E., Dutra, L., and Westen, D. (2005) A multidimensional meta-analysis of psychotherapy for PTSD. Am J Psychiatry 162, 214–27.
33. Blanchard, E. B., Jones-Alexander, J., Buckley, T. C., and Forneris, C. A. (1996) The psychometric properties of the PTSD Checklist (PCL). Behav Res Ther 34, 669–73

18 Virtual Reality Exposure Therapy for Combat-Related PTSD

Albert Rizzo, Greg Reger, Greg Gahm, JoAnn Difede, and Barbara O. Rothbaum

Contents

INTRODUCTION
VIRTUAL REALITY AND CLINICAL APPLICATIONS
EXPOSURE THERAPY FOR PTSD
CHALLENGES FOR TREATING ACTIVE DUTY SERVICE
    MEMBERS/VETERANS WITH PTSD
VIRTUAL REALITY EXPOSURE THERAPY
DESIGN AND DEVELOPMENT OF THE VIRTUAL IRAQ
    EXPOSURE THERAPY SYSTEM
STATUS OF CURRENT VIRTUAL IRAQ RESEARCH
CONCLUSIONS
REFERENCES

Abstract

War is one of the most challenging environments that a human can experience. The cognitive, emotional, and physical demands of a combat environment place enormous stress on even the best-prepared military personnel. The OEF-OIF (Operation Enduring Freedom-Operation Iraqi Freedom) combat theatre, with its ubiquitous battlefronts, ambiguous enemy identification, and repeated extended deployments, was anticipated to produce significant numbers of military personnel with post-traumatic stress disorder (PTSD) and other mental disorders. Recent studies are now confirming this expectation. Among the many approaches that have been used to treat PTSD, exposure therapy appears to have

From: *Post-Traumatic Stress Disorder: Basic Science and Clinical Practice*
Edited by: P. J. Shiromani et al., DOI: 10.1007/978-1-60327-329-9_18
© Humana Press, a part of Springer Science+Business Media, LLC 2009

the best-documented therapeutic efficacy. Such treatment typically involves the graded and repeated imaginal reliving of the traumatic event within the therapeutic setting and is believed to provide a low-threat context in which the patient can begin to therapeutically process trauma-relevant emotions as well as decondition the learning cycle of the disorder via a habituation/extinction process. While the efficacy of imaginal exposure has been established in multiple studies with diverse trauma populations, many patients are unwilling or unable to effectively visualize the traumatic event. To address this problem, researchers have recently turned to the use of virtual reality (VR) to deliver exposure therapy by immersing patients in simulations of trauma-relevant environments that allow for precise control of stimulus conditions. This chapter presents an overview of PTSD exposure therapy, a description of VR, and the rationale for how this technology has been applied as a tool to deliver exposure therapy along with a brief review of current research. We then provide a description of the current Virtual Iraq exposure therapy system and treatment protocol and present initial results from an open clinical trial with active duty military personnel and a brief case study. The chapter concludes with a summary of future directions in which VR technology can be further applied to more comprehensively address a range of PTSD-relevant issues.

Key Words: Clinical interface, exposure therapy, extinction, habituation, PTSD, virtual reality.

INTRODUCTION

War is perhaps one of the most challenging situations that a human being can experience. The physical, emotional, cognitive, and psychological demands of a combat environment place enormous stress on even the best-prepared military personnel. The high level of stress that is naturally experienced in combat typically results in a significant percentage of soldiers at risk for developing PTSD on the return home. Indeed, the Iraq/Afghanistan combat theatres, with their ubiquitous battlefronts, ambiguous enemy identification, and repeated extended deployments, have produced large numbers of returning American service members (SMs) reporting symptoms that are congruent with the diagnosis of post-traumatic stress disorder (PTSD) and other mental disorders. In the first systematic study of mental health problems due to these conflicts, "The percentage of study subjects whose responses met the screening criteria for major depression, generalized anxiety, or PTSD was significantly higher after duty in Iraq (15.6 to 17.1 percent) than after duty in Afghanistan (11.2 percent) or before deployment to Iraq (9.3 percent)" (1). These estimates were made before the violence escalated even further, and other reports since the original Hoge et al. (1) publication have indicated equivalent or higher numbers of returning military SMs and veterans reporting positive for PTSD and symptoms of other forms of mental disorders (2,3).

Among the many approaches that have been used to treat PTSD, exposure therapy appears to have the best-documented therapeutic efficacy (4–9). Such treatment typically involves the graded and repeated imaginal reliving of the traumatic event within the therapeutic setting. This approach is believed to provide a low-threat context in which the patient can begin to therapeutically process the emotions that are relevant to the traumatic event as well as decondition the learning cycle of the disorder via a habituation/extinction process. While the efficacy of imaginal exposure has been established in multiple studies with diverse trauma populations *(6–9)*, many patients are unwilling or unable to effectively visualize the traumatic event. In fact, avoidance of reminders of the trauma is inherent in PTSD and is one of the cardinal symptoms of the disorder. To address this problem, researchers have recently turned to the use of virtual reality (VR) to deliver exposure therapy by immersing clients in simulations of trauma-relevant environments that allow for precise control of stimulus conditions. The enthusiasm that is common among proponents of the use of VR for exposure-based treatment derives from the view that VR technology provides the capacity for clinicians to deliver specific, consistent, and controllable trauma-relevant stimulus environments that do not rely exclusively on the hidden world of the patient's imagination.

This chapter presents an overview of virtual reality exposure therapy (VRET) starting with a description of VR technology, a brief overview of its application in the assessment and treatment of clinical disorders, and following a discussion of traditional imaginal exposure therapy, providing a rationale for the use of VR as a tool to deliver exposure therapy for combat-related PTSD. Previous research in this area is then reviewed, followed by a description of the current Virtual Iraq exposure therapy system and treatment protocol, presentation of initial results from an open clinical trial with active duty military personnel, and a brief case study. The chapter concludes with a summary of future directions in which we feel VR technology can be further applied to more comprehensively address a range of PTSD-relevant issues.

VIRTUAL REALITY AND CLINICAL APPLICATIONS

Virtual reality (VR) has undergone a transition over the last 10 years that has taken it out of the realm of expensive toy and into that of functional technology. The unique match between VR technology assets and the needs of various clinical aims has been recognized by a number of authors and an encouraging body of research has emerged *(10–14)*. VR can be generally defined as "a way for humans to visualize, manipulate, and interact with computers and extremely complex data" *(15)*. This advanced form of human-computer interaction is achieved via the integration of computers, real-time graphics, visual displays, body-tracking sensors, and specialized interface devices that serve to immerse a participant in a computer-generated simulated world that changes in a natural way with head and body motion. The capacity of VR technology to create controllable, multisensory, interactive three-dimensional (3D) stimulus environments within which a person can become immersed and interact offers clinical assessment and intervention options that are not possible using traditional methods *(10,12)*. Much like an aircraft simulator serves to test and train piloting ability under a variety of controlled conditions, VR can be used to create context-relevant simulated environments where assessment and treatment of cognitive, emotional, and motor processes can take place. When used in this fashion, clinical VR can extend the skill of the clinician by allowing the clinician to precisely and systematically deliver complex, dynamic, and ecologically relevant stimulus presentations—within which sophisticated interaction, behavioral tracking, performance recording, and physiological monitoring can occur.

Virtual environments have been developed that are now demonstrating effectiveness in a number of areas in clinical psychology, neuropsychology, and rehabilitation. VR has been used with adults in many domains of psychological assessment and intervention, including exposure therapy for anxiety disorders such as fear of flying (16–20), fear of heights (21,22), and various other phobias (23–28). As well, VR has been usefully implemented with PTSD (29–32), addictive behaviors (33), and acute pain reduction (34) and for the assessment and rehabilitation of cognitive and motor impairments following stroke, brain injury, and other forms of neurological disorders (12,13,35,36). To do this, scientists have constructed VR airplanes, skyscrapers, spiders, battlefields, social events populated with virtual humans, fantasy worlds, and the mundane (but highly relevant) functional environments of the schoolroom, office, home, street, and supermarket. These initiatives give hope that in the 21st century, new and useful simulation tools will be developed that can advance clinical approaches that have long been mired in the methods of the past.

The VR environments discussed in this chapter primarily display computer graphics in a motion-tracked head-mounted display (HMD) and are augmented with vibration platforms, localizable 3D sounds within the VR space, physical props, and in some scenarios, scent delivery technology to facilitate an immersive experience for participants. In this format, the multisensory immersive nature of VR typically leads to a strong sense of *presence* or "being there" reported by those immersed in the virtual environment.

EXPOSURE THERAPY FOR PTSD

PTSD is a severe and often chronic, disabling anxiety disorder that develops in some persons following exposure to a traumatic event that involves actual or threatened injury to themselves or to others. Prospective studies indicate that most traumatized individuals experience symptoms of PTSD in the immediate aftermath of the trauma. In a prospective study of rape victims, 94% met symptom criteria for PTSD in the first week following the assault (37). Therefore, the symptoms of PTSD are part of the *normal reaction* to trauma. The majority of trauma victims naturally recover, as indicated by a gradual decrease in PTSD symptom severity over time. However, subsets of persons continue to exhibit severe PTSD symptoms long after a traumatic experience. Therefore, PTSD can be viewed as a failure of natural recovery that reflects in part a failure of fear extinction following trauma.

Consequently, several theorists have proposed that conditioning processes are involved in the etiology and maintenance of PTSD. These theorists invoke Mowrer's two-factor theory (38), which posits that both Pavlovian and instrumental conditioning are involved in the acquisition of fear and avoidance behavior. Through a generalization process, many stimuli may elicit fear and avoidance. Consistent with this hypothesis, emotional and physiological reactivity to stimuli resembling the original traumatic event, even years after the event's occurrence, is a prominent characteristic of PTSD and has been reliably replicated in the laboratory *(39,40)*. Further, cognitive and behavioral avoidance strategies are hypothesized to develop in an attempt to avoid or escape these distressing conditioned emotional reactions. The presence of extensive avoidance responses can also interfere with extinction by limiting the amount of exposure to the conditioned stimulus (CS) in the absence of the unconditioned stimulus (US).

Expert treatment guidelines for PTSD published for the first time in 1999 recommended that cognitive-behavioral treatment (CBT) with prolonged exposure (PE) should be the first-line therapy for PTSD *(41)*. PE is a form of individual psychotherapy based on Foa and Kozak's *(42)* emotional processing theory, which posits that PTSD involves pathological fear structures that are activated when information represented in the structures is encountered. These fear structures are composed of harmless stimuli that have been associated with danger *(43)* and are reflected in the belief that the world is a dangerous place. This belief then manifests itself in cognitive and behavioral avoidance strategies that limit exposure to potentially corrective information that could be incorporated into and alter the fear structure. Successful treatment requires emotional processing of the fear structures to modify their pathological elements so that the stimuli no longer invoke fear.

Emotional processing first requires accessing and activating the fear structure associated with the traumatic event and then incorporating information that is not compatible with it. PE accomplishes activation through imaginal and in vivo exposure exercises. Imaginal exposure entails engaging mentally with the fear structure through repeatedly revisiting the traumatic event in a safe environment. In practice, a person with PTSD typically is guided and encouraged by the clinician gradually to *imagine, narrate, and emotionally process* the traumatic event within the safe and supportive environment of the clinician's office. In vivo exposure requires approaching real situations such as driving a car or going to crowded public destinations that the patient has avoided since the traumatic event. The proposed mechanisms for symptom reduction involve activation and emotional processing of the traumatic memories, extinction/habituation of the anxiety, cognitive reprocessing of pathogenic meanings, the learning of new responses to previously feared stimuli, and ultimately an integration of corrective nonpathological information into the fear structure *(44,45)*. Such changes allow the survivor to tolerate memories of events without emotional flooding or rigid avoidance and to restore more realistic views of the self, others, and world *(42,43)*. PTSD patients can then begin to process emotional trauma memories adaptively as needed for successful coping and healing.

Strong evidence suggests that CBT is an efficacious treatment for PTSD *(44,46)*. Over 30 randomized controlled trials of psychotherapy for PTSD have been conducted, and many have specifically examined treatment approaches for combat veterans *(47)*. Two meta-analyses have synthesized this literature by examining PTSD outcomes following CBT. Both reported moderate-to-large effect sizes, indicating significant symptom improvements following CBT treatment *(8,48)*. Within the CBT literature, exposure therapy has received significant empirical support *(4,49,50)*. The comparative empirical support for exposure therapy was also recently documented in a review by the Institute of Medicine at the National Academies of Science (sponsored by the U.S. Department of Veterans Affairs [VA]) of 53 studies of pharmaceuticals and 37 studies of psychotherapies used in PTSD treatment *(6)*. The report concluded that although there is not enough reliable evidence to draw conclusions about the effectiveness of most PTSD treatments, there is sufficient evidence to conclude that exposure therapies are effective in treating people with PTSD.

CHALLENGES FOR TREATING ACTIVE DUTY SERVICE MEMBERS/VETERANS WITH PTSD

Although traditional exposure therapy is considered to be the only approach for which the evidence is sufficient to support its efficacy in the treatment of PTSD, there are several reasons why it may not be the most viable option for many active duty SMs and veterans. For example, avoidance and numbing of painful memories and emotions associated with the traumatic event are characteristic of PTSD and can limit a SM's ability to engage in treatment known to relieve symptoms. Imagery-based exposure therapy requires a level of emotional engagement in the imaginal reliving of the trauma that many patients are unable to obtain or tolerate *(5)*. Studies addressing treatment failures have shown that a failure to engage emotionally is the best predictor of a poor treatment outcome *(51–54)*. Foa, Riggs, Massie, and Yarczower *(53)* showed that female rape victim's fear expression (a sign of emotional engagement) during the first reliving of rape memories was strongly related to improvement at posttreatment. Jaycox, Foa, and Morral *(54)* found that while all participants in a study investigating the use of PE with female assault victims made treatment gains, those with therapeutic levels of engagement made significantly greater improvement.

Equally challenging is the fact that stigma and concerns about peer and leadership perceptions of treatment may have a significant impact on whether a SM or veteran will seek care. Hoge et al. *(1)* reported significant fear of treatment stigma among deployed SMs that was greatest among those most in need of help. Those who screened positive for a mental disorder were twice as likely to report concerns about treatment stigma. In another study, Britt *(55)* examined the perceived stigma of psychological versus medical problems in SMs returning from a peacekeeping mission to Bosnia and found that SMs felt more stigmatized when admitting a psychological than a medical problem. This was magnified for SMs returning with their units rather than alone, suggesting that subjective norms influence stigma perceptions. The challenges associated with emotionally engaging with the fear structures as required in PE and the stigma associated with traditional "talk therapies" are significant barriers to optimizing access to care that could be addressed via a VR approach.

VIRTUAL REALITY EXPOSURE THERAPY

Researchers have explored the use of VR to deliver exposure therapy by immersing participants in customized simulations of trauma-relevant environments in which the emotional intensity of the scenes can be precisely controlled by the clinician. In this fashion, VRET offers a way to circumvent the natural avoidance tendency by directly delivering multisensory and context-relevant cues that evoke the trauma without demanding that the patient actively try to access personal experience through effortful memory retrieval. Within a VR environment, the hidden world of the patient's imagination is not exclusively relied on, and this is particularly relevant with PTSD, for which avoidance of cues and reminders of the trauma are cardinal symptoms of the disorder. In addition, VRET may offer an appealing, nontraditional treatment approach that is perceived with less stigma by "digital generation" SMs and veterans who may be reluctant to seek out what they perceive as traditional talk therapies.

The first effort to apply VRET began in 1997 when researchers at Georgia Tech and Emory University began testing the Virtual Vietnam VR scenario with Vietnam veterans diagnosed with PTSD *(5)*. This occurred over 20 years after the end of the Vietnam War. During those intervening years, in spite of valiant efforts to develop and apply traditional psychotherapeutic and pharmacological treatment approaches to PTSD, the progression of the disorder in some veterans had a significant impact on their psychological well-being, functional abilities, and quality of life as well as that of their families and friends. This initial effort yielded encouraging results in a case study of a 50-year-old, male Vietnam veteran meeting *Diagnostic and Statistical Manual of Mental Disorders* (DSM) criteria for PTSD *(56)*. Results indicated post-treatment improvement on all measures of PTSD and maintenance of these gains at a 6-month follow-up, with a 34% decrease in clinician-rated symptoms of PTSD and a 45% decrease on self-reported symptoms of PTSD. This case study was followed by an open clinical trial with Vietnam veterans *(5)*. In this study, 16 male veterans with PTSD were exposed to two HMD-delivered virtual environments: a virtual clearing surrounded by jungle scenery and a virtual Huey helicopter, in which the therapist controlled various visual and auditory effects (e.g., rockets, explosions, day/night, shouting). After an average of 13 exposure therapy sessions over 5–7 weeks, there was a significant reduction in PTSD and related symptoms.

Similar positive results were reported by Difede and Hoffman *(30)* for PTSD that resulted from the attack on the World Trade Center; they used a case study using VRET with a patient who had failed to improve with traditional exposure therapy. This group has recently reported positive results from a wait-list controlled study using the same World Trade Center VR application *(57)*. The VR group demonstrated statistically and clinically significant decreases on the "gold standard" Clinician-Administered PTSD Scale (CAPS) relative to both pretreatment and to the wait-list control group with a between-group posttreatment effect size of 1.54. Seven of ten people in the VR group no longer carried the diagnosis of PTSD, while all of the wait-list controls retained the diagnosis following the waiting period, and treatment gains

were maintained at 6-month follow-up. Also noteworthy was the finding that five of
the ten VR patients had previously participated in imaginal exposure treatment with
no clinical benefit. Such initial results are encouraging and suggest that VR may be
a useful component within a comprehensive treatment approach for persons with
combat/terrorist attack-related PTSD.

There are also other research groups currently in the early stages of applying VR
to treat PTSD in survivors of war and terrorist attacks *(58–61)*. One research group
has reported "partial remission" of PTSD symptoms in four of six Iraq war SMs
using VR combined with meditation and attentional refocusing *(58)*. However, it
is difficult to draw any conclusions from this work as the authors did not provide a
clear specification or statistical analysis of the pre-/post-PTSD Checklist-Military
version (PCL-M) scores other than to report a baseline PCL-M mean of 47.3, which
is actually below the PTSD cutoff of 50 *(59)*. Another research group in Portugal,
where there are an estimated 25,000 survivors with PTSD from their 1961–1974
colonial wars in Mozambique, Angola, and Guiné, has constructed a VR exposure
scenario by modifying a common PC-based combat game *(60)*. This group has
reported an initial case study in which the patient did not complete treatment due
to experiencing a distressing flashback following the seventh session. While this is
rarely reported in the exposure literature, this report highlights the need for well-
trained clinicians with expertise in the delivery of exposure therapy at a rate that the
patient can effectively handle and process and in the sensitive monitoring of patient
status. Finally, in Israel, Josman et al. *(61)* are implementing a VR terrorist "bus
bombing" PTSD treatment scenario in which participants are positioned in an urban
cafe across the street from a site where a civilian bus may explode. This research
program has only recently commenced, and no clinical data are currently available.
However, analog pilot research by this group with non-PTSD participants is under
way to examine emotional reactivity across VR exposure levels to characterize the
evocative nature of the stimulus environment to inform future clinical use (Naomi
Josman, personal communication, December 4, 2007).

DESIGN AND DEVELOPMENT OF THE VIRTUAL IRAQ
EXPOSURE THERAPY SYSTEM

The University of Southern California's Institute for Creative Technologies
(ICT), in collaboration with us, have partnered on a project funded by the Office
of Naval Research (ONR); the U.S. Army Research, Development, and Engineering
Command (RDECOM); and the Telemedicine and Advanced Technology Research
Center (TATRC) to develop a series of VR exposure environments known as Virtual
Iraq. This VR treatment system was originally constructed by recycling virtual art
assets that were initially designed for the commercially successful X-Box game
and U.S. Army-funded combat tactical simulation trainer Full Spectrum Warrior. Other
existing and newly created art and technology assets available to ICT have been
integrated into this continually evolving application.

Virtual Iraq consists of Middle Eastern themed city and desert road environments
(see Figs. 1–4) and was designed to resemble the general contexts that most

Fig. 1-4. Virtual Iraq city and desert HUMVEE scenario scenes (*See Color Plates*)

Fig. 1-4. (continued)

SMs experience during deployment to Iraq. The 18-square-block "city" setting has a variety of elements, including a marketplace, desolate streets, old buildings, ramshackle apartments, warehouses, mosques, shops, and dirt lots strewn with junk. Access to building interiors and rooftops is available, and the backdrop surrounding the navigable exposure zone creates the illusion of being embedded within a section of a sprawling densely populated desert city. Vehicles are active in streets, and animated virtual pedestrians (civilian and military) can be added or eliminated from the scenes. The software has been designed such that users can be teleported to specific locations within the city based on a determination regarding which environments most closely match the patient's needs relevant to their individual trauma-related experiences.

The "desert road" scenario consists of a roadway through an expansive desert area with sand dunes, occasional areas of vegetation, intact and broken-down structures, bridges, battle wreckage, a checkpoint, debris, and virtual human figures. The user is positioned inside of a Humvee that supports the perception of travel within a convoy or as a lone vehicle with selectable positions as a driver, a passenger, or an individual in the more exposed turret position above the roof of the vehicle. The number of soldiers in the cab of the Humvee can also be varied as well as their capacity to become wounded during certain attack scenarios (e.g., improvised explosive devices [IEDs], rooftop and bridge attacks). Both the city and Humvee scenarios are adjustable for time of day or night, weather conditions, night vision, illumination, and ambient sound (wind, motors, city noise, prayer call, etc.).

Users can navigate in both scenarios via the use of a standard game pad controller, although we have recently added the option for a replica M4 weapon with a "thumb-mouse" controller that supports movement during the city foot patrol. This was based on repeated requests from Iraq-experienced SMs, who provided frank feedback indicating that to walk within such a setting without a weapon in hand was completely unnatural and distracting. However, there is no option for firing a weapon within the VR scenarios. It is our firm belief that the principles of exposure therapy are incompatible with the cathartic acting out of a revenge fantasy that a responsive weapon might encourage.

In addition to the visual stimuli presented in the VR HMD, directional 3D audio, vibrotactile, and olfactory stimuli can be delivered into the VR scenarios in real time by the clinician. The presentation of additive, combat-relevant stimuli in the VR scenarios can be controlled via a separate "Wizard of Oz" control panel, while the clinician is in full audio contact with the patient. This clinical "interface" is a key feature that provides a clinician with the capacity to customize the therapy experience to the individual needs of the patient. The patient can be placed by the clinician in VR scenario locations that resemble the setting in which the trauma-relevant events occurred and modify ambient light and sound conditions to match the patient's description of his or her experience. The clinician can then gradually introduce and control real-time trigger stimuli (visual, auditory, olfactory, and tactile), via the clinician's interface, as required to foster the anxiety modulation needed for therapeutic habituation and emotional processing in

386 Rizzo et al.

a customized fashion according to the patient's past experience and treatment progress. The clinician interface options have been designed with the aid of feedback from clinicians with the goal to provide a usable and flexible control panel system for conducting thoughtfully administered exposure therapy that can be readily customized to suit the needs of the patient. Such options for real-time stimulus delivery flexibility and user experience customization are key elements for these types of VR exposure applications.

The specification, creation, and addition of trigger stimulus options into the Virtual Iraq system has been an evolving process throughout the development of the application based on continually solicited patient and clinician feedback. We began this part of the design process by including options that have been reported to be relevant by returning soldiers and military subject matter experts. For example, the Hoge et al. (1) study of Iraq/Afghanistan SMs presented a listing of combat-related events that were commonly experienced in their sample. These events provided a useful starting point for conceptualizing how relevant trigger stimuli could be presented in a VR environment. Such commonly reported events included: "Being attacked or ambushed ..., receiving incoming artillery, rocket, or mortar fire, ... being shot at or receiving small-arms fire, ... seeing dead bodies or human remains" (p. 18).

From this and other sources, we began our initial effort to conceptualize what was both functionally relevant and technically possible to include as trigger stimuli. Thus far, we have created a variety of auditory trigger stimuli (e.g., incoming mortars, weapons fire, voices, wind, etc.) that are actuated by the clinician via mouse clicks on the clinical interface. We can also similarly trigger dynamic audiovisual events such as helicopter flyovers, bridge attacks, exploding vehicles and IEDs, and so on. The creation of more complex events that can be intuitively delivered in Virtual Iraq from the clinicians' interface while providing a patient with options to interact or respond in a meaningful manner is one of the ongoing focuses in this project. However, such trigger options require not only interface design expertise, but also clinical wisdom regarding how much and what type of exposure is needed to produce a positive clinical effect. These issues have been keenly attended to in our initial nonclinical user-centered tests with Iraq-experienced SMs and in the current clinical trials with patients. This feedback is essential for informed VR scenario design beyond what is possible to imagine from the "ivory tower" of the academic world.

Whenever possible, Virtual Iraq was designed to use off-the-shelf equipment to minimize costs and maximize the access and availability of the finished system. The minimum computing requirements for the current application are two Pentium 4 computers each with 1 GB RAM, and a 128-MB DirectX 9-compatible NVIDIA 3D graphics card. The two computers are linked using a null Ethernet cable, with one running the therapist's clinical interface, while the second one drives the simulation via the user's HMD and navigation interface (game pad or gun controller). The HMD that was chosen was the eMagin z800, with displays capable of 800 × 600 resolution within a 40° diagonal field of view (http://www.emagin.com/). The major selling point for using this HMD was the presence of a built-in head-tracking system. At under $1,500 per unit with built-in head tracking, this integrated display/tracking solution was viewed as the best option to minimize costs and maximize the access to this system. The simulation's real-time 3D scenes are presented using Numerical Design Limited's (NDL) Gamebryo rendering library. Preexisting art assets were integrated using Alias's Maya 6 and Autodesk 3D Studio Max 7, with new art created primarily in Maya.

We have also added olfactory and tactile stimuli to the experience of the environment. The Envirodine Incorporated Scent Palette is a USB (universal serial bus) device that uses up to eight smell cartridges, a series of fans, and a small air compressor to deliver scents to participants. The scents can also be controlled by mouse clicks on the clinical interface. Scents may be employed as direct stimuli (e.g., scent of smoke as a user walks by a burning vehicle) or as cues to help immerse users in the world (e.g., ethnic food cooking). The scents selected for this application include burning rubber, cordite, garbage, body odor, smoke, diesel fuel, Iraqi food spices, and gunpowder. Vibration is also used as an additional user sensory input. Vibration is generated through the use of a Logitech force-feedback game control pad and through low-cost (<$120) audio-tactile sound transducers (Aura Sound Inc.) located beneath the patient's floor platform and seat. Audio files are customized to provide vibration consistent with relevant visual and audio stimuli in the scenario. For example, explosions can be accompanied by a shaking floor, and in the Humvee scenario, the user experiences engine vibrations as the vehicle moves across the virtual terrain. This package of controllable multisensory stimulus options was included in the design of Virtual Iraq to allow a clinician the flexibility to engage users across a wide range of unique and highly customizable levels of exposure intensity. As well, these same features have broadened the applicability of Virtual Iraq as a research tool for studies that require systematic control of stimulus presentation within combat-relevant environments *(62)*.

STATUS OF CURRENT VIRTUAL IRAQ RESEARCH

The Virtual Iraq scenario is currently being implemented as an exposure therapy tool with active duty SMs and veterans at Madigan Army Medical Center (MAMC) at Fort Lewis, Washington; the Naval Medical Center–San Diego (NMCSD); Camp Pendleton; Emory University; Walter Reed Army Medical Center (WRAMC); the Weill Medical College of Cornell University; and at 14 other VA, military, and university laboratory sites for VRET research and a variety of other PTSD-related investigations. However, the user-centered design process for optimizing Virtual Iraq for clinical use is noteworthy and is briefly described before summarizing the status of the initial open clinical trial results.

User-Centered Feedback from Non-PTSD Service Members

User-centered tests with early prototypes of the Virtual Iraq application were conducted at the NMCSD and within an army combat stress control team in Iraq (see Fig. 5). This informal feedback provided by nondiagnosed Iraq-

Fig. 5. User Centered feedback on the Virtual Iraq application being collected by a U.S. Army Combat Stress Control team member (Reger), while in "real" Iraq (*See Color Plates*)

experienced military personnel provided essential information on the content, realism, and usability of the initial "intuitively designed" system that fed an iterative design process. More formal evaluation of the system took place at MAMC from late 2006 to early 2007 *(63,64)*. Ninety-three screened SMs (all non-PSTD) evaluated the Virtual Iraq scenarios shortly after returning from deployment in Iraq. SMs experienced the city and Humvee environments while exposed to scripted researcher-initiated VR trigger stimuli to simulate an actual treatment session. SMs then completed standardized questionnaires to evaluate the realism, sense of "presence" (the feeling of being in Iraq), sensory stimuli, and overall technical capabilities of Virtual Iraq. Items were rated on a scale from 0 (poor) to 10 (excellent). Qualitative feedback was also collected to determine additional required software improvements. The results suggested that the Virtual Iraq environment in its form at the time was realistic and provided a good sense of "being back in Iraq." Average ratings across environments were between adequate and excellent for all evaluated aspects of the virtual environments. Auditory stimuli realism (M = 7.9, SD = 1.7) and quality (M = 7.9, SD = 1.8) were rated higher than visual realism (M = 6.7, SD = 2.1) and quality (M = 7.0, SD = 2.0). Soldiers had high ratings of the computer's ability to update visual graphics during movement (M = 8.4, SD = 1.7). The HMD was reportedly very comfortable (M = 8.2, SD = 1.7), and the average ratings for the ability to move within the virtual environment was generally adequate or above (M = 6.1, SD = 2.5). These data, along with the collected qualitative feedback, were used to inform upgrades to the current version of Virtual Iraq that is now in clinical use, and this "design-collect feedback-redesign" cycle will continue throughout the life of the project.

Service Member Acceptance of VR in Treatment

The prior results indicated that the Virtual Iraq software was capable of producing the level of presence in Iraq-experienced SMs that was believed to be required for exposure therapy. However, successful clinical implementation also requires patients to accept the approach as a useful and credible behavioral health treatment. To address this issue, a survey study with 325 army SMs from the Fort Lewis deployment screening clinic was conducted to assess knowledge of current technologies and attitudes toward the use of technology in behavioral health care (65). One section of the survey asked these active duty SMs to rate on a 5-point scale how willing they would be to receive mental health treatment ("not willing at all" to "very willing") via traditional approaches (e.g., face-to-face counseling) and a variety of technology-oriented delivery methods (e.g., Web site, video teleconferencing, use of VR). Eighty-three percent of participants reported that they were neutral to very willing to use some form of technology as part of their behavioral health care, with 58% reporting some willingness to use a VR treatment program. Seventy-one percent of SMs were equally or more willing to use some form of technological treatment than solely talking to a therapist in a traditional setting. Most interesting is that 20% of SMs who stated they were not willing to seek traditional psychotherapy rated their willingness to use a VR-based treatment as neutral to very willing. One possible interpretation of this finding is that a subgroup of this sample of SMs with a significant disinterest in traditional mental health treatment would be willing to pursue treatment with a VR-based approach. It is also possible that these findings generalize to SMs who have disengaged from or terminated traditional treatment.

Preliminary Results from an Open Clinical Trial Using Virtual Iraq at the NMCSD

The Virtual Iraq system built from this user-centered design process is currently being tested in an open clinical trial with PTSD-diagnosed active duty SMs at NMCSD and Camp Pendleton. The ONR funded the initial system development of Virtual Iraq along with this initial trial to evaluate the feasibility of using VRET with active duty participants. The participants were SMs who recently redeployed from Iraq and who had engaged in previous PTSD treatments (e.g., group counseling, selective serotonin reuptake inhibitors [SSRIs], etc.) without benefit. The standard treatment protocol consisted of twice-weekly 90- to 120-min sessions over 5 weeks that also included physiological monitoring (heart rate [HR], Galvanic Skin Response [GSR], and respiration) as part of the data collection. However, in this open clinical trial, elements of the protocol were occasionally modified (i.e., adjusting the number and timing of sessions) to meet patient's needs; thus, these data represent an uncontrolled feasibility trial. The VRET exposure exercises followed the principles of graded behavioral exposure, and the pace was individualized and patient driven.

The first VRET session consisted of a clinical interview that identified the index trauma, provided psychoeducation on trauma and PTSD, and provided instruction on a deep-breathing technique for general stress management purposes. The second session provided instruction on the use of subjective units of distress (SUDs), the rationale for PE, including imaginal exposure and in vivo exposure. The participants also engaged in their first experience of imaginal exposure of the index trauma, and the in vivo hierarchy exposure list was constructed with the first item assigned as homework. Session 3 introduced the rationale for VRET, and the participant experienced the VR environment without recounting the index trauma narrative for approximately 25 min with no provocative trigger stimuli introduced. The purpose of not recounting the index trauma was to allow the participant to navigate Virtual Iraq in an exploratory manner and to function as a "bridge session" from imaginal alone to imaginal exposure combined with VR. Sessions 4 through 10 focused on the participant engaging in the VR while recounting the trauma narrative. Generally, when participants were putting on the HMD, they were instructed that they would be asked to recount their trauma in the first person, as if it were happening again, with as much attention to sensory detail as they could provide. Using clinical judgment, the therapist might prompt the patient with questions about their experience or provide encouraging remarks as deemed necessary to facilitate the recounting of the trauma narrative.

The treatment included homework, such as requesting the participant to listen to the audiotape of their exposure narrative from the most recent session. Listening to the audiotape several times over a week functioned as continual exposure for processing the index trauma to further enhance the probability for habituation to occur. In vivo hierarchy exposure items were assigned in a sequential fashion, starting with the lowest-rated SUD item. A new item was assigned once the participant demonstrated approximately a 50% reduction of SUDs ratings on the previous item. Self-report measures were obtained at baseline and prior to sessions 3, 5, 7, 9, and 10 and 1 week and 3 months posttreatment to assess in-treatment and follow-up symptom status. The measures used were the PCL-M, Beck Anxiety Inventory (BAI), and Patient Health Questionnaire-Depression (PHQ-9) (59,66–68).

As of the submission date for this chapter, initial analyses of our first 15 treatment completers (14 male, 1 female, mean age = 28, age range 21–51) have indicated positive clinical outcomes. For this sample, mean pre-/post-PCL-M scores decreased; mean (standard deviation) values went from 54.6 (10.4) to 35.8 (18.6). Paired pre/post t-test analysis showed these differences to be significant ($t = 5.28$, $df = 14, p < .0001$). Correcting for the PCL-M no-symptom baseline of 17 indicated a 50% decrease in symptoms, and 12 of the 15 completers no longer met DSM criteria for PTSD at posttreatment. Three participants in this group with PTSD diagnoses had pretreatment baseline scores below the cutoff value of 50 (prescores = 42, 36, 38) and reported decreased values at posttreatment (postscores = 22, 22, 24, respectively). Individual participant scores at baseline, posttreatment, and 3-month follow-up (for those available at this date) are in Fig. 6. For this same group, mean BAI scores significantly decreased 33% from 17.9 (9.5) to 11.6 (13.6), ($t = 2.4$, $df = 14, p < .03$) and mean PHQ-9 (depression) scores decreased 50% from 13.7 (4.5) to 6.9 (6.2) ($t = 3.2$, $df = 14$, $p < .006$). The average number of sessions for this sample was just under 12. Also, two of the successful treatment completers had documented mild and moderate traumatic brain injuries, which suggests that this form of exposure can be useful (and beneficial) for this population.

In spite of these initial positive results for treatment completers, challenges existed with dropouts from this active duty sample. Seven participants who were assessed and approved for the study failed to appear at the first session, six

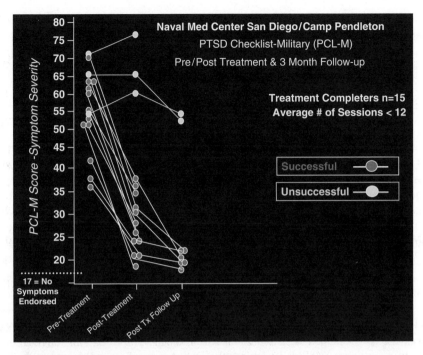

Fig. 6. Individual PTSD Checklist-military (PCL-M) from first 15 virtual reality exposure therapy (VRET) treatment completers. The average score pre- and posttreatment indicates a decline in scores. The scores remained low at 3-month follow-up. Three were unsuccessful (*See Color Plates*)

attended the first session and dropped out prior to formal commencement of VRET at session 4, and seven dropped out at various points following session 4. While some of these active duty participants left due to transfers and other reasons beyond their control, these dropout numbers are concerning, and we intend to examine all data gathered from this subset of the total sample to search for discriminating factors. This open trial will continue until we have 20 treatment completers, and at that point we intend to examine the dropout issue and to analyze the physiological data that we have logged throughout the course of this trial.

MAMC Case Study

The following case is included to illustrate the conduct and results from a course of treatment that did not follow the twice-a-week protocol used at NMCSD. With the demands placed on active duty SMs regarding training and transfers, it may not be realistic to expect that exposure sessions can be delivered within a consistently short time frame for all participants. The following case report was reviewed by the MAMC Department of Clinical Investigation, and explicit written consent from the patient for this case report was obtained on reviewing the text.

The patient was an active duty army SM in his 30s who presented with a mix of trauma-related anxiety symptoms associated with an index trauma experienced during a convoy in Iraq. At the time of referral, he reported intense emotional and physiological reactivity when he encountered reminders of his experience. He had multiple nightmares a week and reported increased irritability, exaggerated startle, and avoidance of crowds, congested traffic, and public places. He had experienced limited benefit from approximately one-and-a-half years of psychotherapy that did not involve exposure. Treatment options were reviewed with the patient, including Eye Movement Desensitization and Reprocessing [EMDR], imaginal PE, and VR exposure. After considering the potential risks and benefits, he selected VRET.

Prior to starting treatment, his PTSD symptoms were assessed with the PCL-M. His baseline score on the PCL-M before beginning VRET was 71, well above the recommended cut point for screening positive for PTSD. He completed 11 sessions of VR exposure across 7 months, interrupted intermittently by the SM's vacations and several crises necessitating clinical attention. During VR exposure, SUDs ratings were obtained every 5 min. Consistent with the theoretical assumption that the multisensory nature of VR facilitates increased activation of the trauma memory, emotional engagement during the initial VR exposure session was high, with an initial SUDs of 80 and a peak SUDs of 90. The SM reported that tearfulness during post-VR exposure discussion was the first time he cried about losses during the deployment. Over the course of VRET, the SM demonstrated high levels of emotional engagement, and at termination, the SM reported significant improvement in symptoms and functioning. He was actively socializing with groups in a variety of crowded public places, and nightmares were rare. Irritability had decreased, and he reported decreased anxiety on encountering cues and reminders of his experience. Consistent with his description of improvement, his posttreatment PCL-M was 38, demonstrating a substantial drop from his baseline of 71.

Case reports have numerous limitations, and the efficacy of VRET cannot be established without controlled clinical trials. Numerous factors may figure into outcomes that can only be determined from a larger sample in a controlled randomized trial that includes both "intent-to-treat" and "treatment completer" analyses. Nonetheless, this case illustrates the successful use of VRET with an active duty SM, albeit outside the typically recommended time course. Although exposure sessions are often conducted once or twice a week for 2 to 3 months, this patient benefited from sessions of much lower frequency. As an aside, it is also interesting to note that the SM discussed his therapy with some of his peers, one of whom inquired about the appropriateness of this form of treatment for his symptoms. For more information on this project, two case summaries from the NMCSD trial and a more detailed case report of a National Guardsman successfully treated at Emory University are now in print (69,70).

CONCLUSIONS

Results from such uncontrolled trials and case reports are difficult to generalize from, and we are cautious not to make excessive claims based on these early results. At the current time, we are encouraged by these early successes, and we continue to gather feedback from the patients regarding the therapy and the Virtual Iraq environment in order to continue our iterative system development process. We continue to update the Virtual Iraq system with added functionality that has its design "roots" from feedback acquired from these initial patients and the clinicians who have used the system thus far. We are using these initial results to develop, explore, and test hypotheses regarding how we can improve treatment and determine which patient characteristics may predict who will benefit from VRET and who may be best served by other approaches.

The current clinical treatment research program with the Virtual Iraq application is also providing important data needed to determine the feasibility of expanding the range of applications that can be created from this initial research-and-development program. In the course of the ongoing evolution of this system, our approach has always focused on the creation of a VR system/tool that could address *both* clinical and scientific PTSD research questions in a more comprehensive fashion. In this regard, we are expanding our research program using the Virtual Iraq system to

study the feasibility of assessing soldiers in advance of deployment to predict those who might have a higher likelihood of developing PTSD or other mental health difficulties based on physiological reactivity (and other measures) to a series of virtual combat engagements.

deliver "stress inoculation" training to better prepare military personnel for what might occur in real combat environments.

study the effectiveness of using VR as an assessment tool that is administered immediately on redeployment to determine who may be "at risk" for developing full-blown PTSD after an incubation period. Psychophysiological reactivity could figure well as a marker variable for this project, and a prospective longitudinal study is needed in this area. This is particularly important for maximizing the probability that a soldier at risk would be directed into appropriate treatment or programming before being sent on a second or third deployment.

study the impact of multiple traumatic events on the course of PTSD as may be relevant for the reintegration of military personnel into civilian settings following multiple deployments.

study the differences between national guard, reservist personnel, army/marine/air force standing military SMs and veterans in terms of their susceptibility for developing PTSD and if variations in the course of treatment would be required. This is also relevant for the study of PTSD treatment response differences due to age, gender, education, family support, and previous exposure to trauma (as in the case of a reservist who served in emergency services as a civilian in the police or fire department, where exposure to traumatic events commonly occurs).

evolve understanding of the neuroscience of PTSD via the use of brain-imaging protocols (e.g., functional magnetic resonance imaging [fMRI], diffusion tensor imaging); traditional physiological measurement (e.g., electroencephalography [EEG], electrocardiography [EKG], GSR, etc.); and other forms of body-based responses (e.g., eyeblink, startle response, and other motor behaviors) by leveraging the high controllability of stimulus events that is available with the Virtual Iraq application.

study the treatment efficacy of Virtual Iraq across a range of standard therapeutic issues (i.e., what rate of exposure is needed to optimally treat PTSD).

study the interaction between the use of VR exposure in combination with a host of pharmacological treatment strategies (e.g., D-cycloserine). Randomized controlled trials comparing VRET alone and VRET plus D-cycloserine are currently in progress at Emory University and at Weill Cornell Medical College after successful results were reported with VRET plus D-cycloserine for treating fear of heights *(71)*.

expand the functionality of our existing system based on the results of the ongoing and future research. This will involve refining the system in terms of the breadth of scenarios/trigger events, the audiovisual stimulus content, and the level of artificial intelligence of virtual human characters that "inhabit" the system.

One of the more foreboding findings in the Hoge et al. *(1)* report was the observation that, among Iraq/Afghanistan War veterans, "those whose responses were positive for a mental disorder, only 23 to 40 percent sought mental health care. Those whose responses were positive for a mental disorder were twice as likely as those whose responses were negative to report concern about possible stigmatization and other barriers to seeking mental health care" (p. 13). While military training methodology has better prepared soldiers for combat in recent years, such hesitancy to seek treatment for difficulties that emerge on return from combat, especially by those who may need it most, suggests an area of military mental health care that is in need of attention.

To address this concern, a VR system for PTSD treatment could serve as a component within a reconceptualized approach to how treatment is accessed by SMs and veterans returning from combat. Perhaps VR exposure could be embedded within the context of "postcombat reintegration training" by which the perceived stigma of seeking treatment could be lessened as the soldier would be simply involved in this "training" in similar fashion to other designated duties on redeployment stateside.

VRET therapy may also offer an additional attraction and promote treatment seeking by certain demographic groups in need of care. The current generation of young military personnel, having grown up with digital gaming technology, may actually be more attracted to and comfortable with participation in VRET as an alternative to what is viewed as traditional talk therapy (even though such talk therapy would obviously occur in the course of a multicomponent CBT approach for this disorder).

Finally, one of the guiding principles in our development work concerns how novel VR systems can extend the skills of a well-trained clinician. VR exposure therapy approaches are not intended to be automated treatment protocols that are administered in a "self-help" format. The presentation of such emotionally evocative VR combat-related scenarios, while providing treatment options not possible until recently, will most likely produce therapeutic benefits when administered within the context of appropriate care via a thoughtful professional appreciation of the complexity and impact of this disorder.

ACKNOWLEDGMENT

This research was funded by the Office of Naval Research, award N0014-05-1-0384 and the U.S. Army Research, Development, and Engineering Command/ Telemedicine and Advanced Technology Research Center, award 53-0821-2404. Any opinions, findings, and conclusions or recommendations expressed in this material are those of the authors and do not necessarily reflect the views of the ONR, RDECOM, or TATRC.

Disclosure: Dr. Rothbaum is a consultant to and owns equity in Virtually Better Incorporated, which is developing products related to the VR research described in this presentation. The terms of this arrangement have been reviewed and approved by Emory University in accordance with its conflict-of-interest policies.

REFERENCES

1. Hoge, C. W., Castro, C. A., Messer, S. C., McGurk, D., Cotting, D. I., and Koffman, R. L. (2004) Combat duty in Iraq and Afghanistan, mental health problems, and barriers to care. N Engl J Med 351(1), 13–22.
2. Seal, K. H., Bertenthal, D., Nuber, C. R., Sen, S., and Marmar, C. (2007) Bringing the war back home: mental health disorders among 103,788 U.S. veterans returning from Iraq and Afghanistan seen at Department of Veterans Affairs facilities. Arch Intern Med 167, 476–82.
3. Hoge, C. W., Auchterlonie, J. L., and Milliken, C. S. (2006) Mental health problems, use of mental health services, and attrition from military service after returning from deployment to Iraq or Afghanistan. JAMA 295(9), 1023–32.
4. Rothbaum, B. O., Meadows, E. A., Resick, P., and Foy, D. W. (2000) Cognitive-behavioral treatment position paper summary for the ISTSS Treatment Guidelines Committee. J Trauma Stress 13, 558–63.
5. Rothbaum, B., Hodges, L., Ready, D., Graap, K., and Alarcon, R. (2001) Virtual reality exposure therapy for Vietnam veterans with posttraumatic stress disorder. J Clin Psychiatry 62, 617–22.
6. National Academies of Science Institute of Medicine Committee on Treatment of Posttraumatic Stress Disorder. (2007) Treatment of posttraumatic stress disorder: an assessment of the evidence. Available at: http://www.nap.edu/catalog/11955.html (accessed October 24,2007).
7. Rothbaum, B. O., and Schwartz, A. (2002) Exposure therapy for posttraumatic stress disorder. Am J Psychother 56, 59–75.
8. Van Etten, M. L., and Taylor, S. (1998) Comparative efficacy of treatments of posttraumatic stress disorder: an empirical review. JAMA 268, 633–38.
9. Bryant, R. A. (2005) Psychosocial approaches of acute stress reactions. CNS Spectrums 10(2), 116–22.
10. Rizzo, A. A., Wiederhold, M., and Buckwalter, J. G. (1998) Basic issues in the use of virtual environments for mental health applications. In Riva, G., Wiederhold, B., and Molinari, E., Eds., Virtual Reality in Clinical Psychology and Neuroscience. Amsterdam, the Netherlands: IOS Press, pp. 21–42.
11. Glantz, K., Rizzo, A. A., and Graap, K. (2003) Virtual reality for psychotherapy: current reality and future possibilities. Psychother Theory Res Pract Train 40(1), 55–67.
12. Rizzo, A. A., Schultheis, M. T., Kerns, K., and Mateer, C. (2004) Analysis of assets for virtual reality applications in neuropsychology. Neuropsychol Rehab 14(1/2), 207–39.

13. Rose, F. D., Brooks, B. M., and Rizzo, A. A. (2005) Virtual reality in brain damage rehabilitation: review. CyberPsychol Behav 8(3), 241–62.

14. Rizzo, A. A., and Kim, G. (2005) A SWOT analysis of the field of virtual rehabilitation and therapy. Presence: Teleoperators and Virtual Environ 14(2),1–28.

15. Aukstakalnis, S., and Blatner, D. (1992) Silicon mirage: The Art and Science of Virtual Reality. Berkeley, CA: Peachpit Press.

16. Rothbaum, B. O., Hodges, L., Watson, B. A., Kessler, C. D. and Opdyke, D. (1996) Virtual reality exposure therapy in the treatment of fear of flying: a case report. Behav Res Ther 34(5–6), 477–81.

17. Rothbaum, B. O., Hodges, L., Smith, S., Lee, J. H., and Price, L. (2000) A controlled study of virtual reality exposure therapy for the fear of flying. J Consult Clin Psychol 68(6), 1020–26.

18. Rothbaum, B. O., Hodges, L., Anderson, P. L., Price, L. and Smith, S. (2002) Twelve-month follow-up of virtual reality and standard exposure therapies for the fear of flying. J Consult Clin Psychol 70(2), 428–32.

19. Smith, S. G., Rothbaum, B. O. and Hodges, L. (1999) Treatment of fear of flying using virtual reality exposure therapy: a single case study. Behav Ther 22(8), 154–58.

20. Rothbaum, B. O., Anderson, P., Zimand, E., Hodges, L., Lang, D. and Wilson, J. (2006) Virtual reality exposure therapy and standard (in vivo) exposure therapy in the treatment of fear of flying. Behav Ther 37(1), 80–90.

21. Rothbaum, B. O., Hodges, L. F., Kooper, R., Opdyke, D., Williford, J. S. and North, M. (1995) Effectiveness of computer-generated (virtual reality) graded exposure in the treatment of acrophobia. Am J Psychiatry 152(4), 626–28.

22. Emmelkamp, P. M., Krijn, M., Hulsbosch, A. M., de Vries, S., Schuemie, M. J., and van der Mast, C. A. (2002) Virtual reality treatment versus exposure in vivo: a comparative evaluation in acrophobia. Behav Res Ther 40(5), 509–16.

23. Anderson, P., Rothbaum, B. O. and Hodges, L. F. (2003) Virtual reality exposure in the treatment of social anxiety: two case reports. Cogn Behav Pract 10, 240–47.

24. Botella, C., Banos, R. M., Perpina, C., Villa, H., Alcaniz, M. and Rey, A. (1998) Virtual reality treatment of claustrophobia: a case report. Behav Res Ther 36(2), 239–46.

25. Carlin, A. S., Hoffman, H. G. and Weghorst, S. (1997) Virtual reality and tactile augmentation in the treatment of spider phobia: a case report. Behav Res Ther 35(2), 153–158.

26. Garcia-Palacios, A., Hoffman, H., Carlin, A., Furness, T. A., 3rd, and Botella, C. (2002) Virtual reality in the treatment of spider phobia: a controlled study. Behav Res Ther 40(9), 983–93.

27. Parsons, T. D. and Rizzo, A. A. (2008) Affective outcomes of virtual reality exposure therapy for anxiety and specific phobias: a meta-analysis. J Behav Ther Exp Psychiatry 39, 250–61.

28. Powers, M. B., and Emmelkamp, P. M. G. (2008) Virtual reality exposure therapy for anxiety disorders: a meta-analysis. J Anxiety Disord 22, 561–69.

29. Rothbaum, B., Hodges, L., Ready, D., Graap, K., and Alarcon, R. (2001) Virtual reality exposure therapy for Vietnam veterans with posttraumatic stress disorder. J Clin Psychiatry 62, 617–22.

30. Difede, J., and Hoffman, H. G. (2002) Virtual reality exposure therapy for World Trade Center post-traumatic stress disorder: a case report. Cyberpsychol Behav 5(6), 529–35.

31. Difede, J., Cukor, J., Patt, I., Goisan, C., and Hoffman, H. (2006) The application of virtual reality to the treatment of PTSD Following the WTC attack. Ann N Y Acad Sci 1071, 500–1.

32. Difede, J., Cukor, J., Jayasinghe, N., Patt, I., Jedel, S., Spielman, L., et-al. (2007) Virtual reality exposure therapy for the treatment of posttraumatic stress disorder following September 11, 2001. J Clin Psychiatry 68, 1639–47.

33. Bordnick, P., Graap, K., Copp, H., Brooks, J., and Ferrer, M. (2005) Virtual reality cue reactivity assessment in cigarette smokers. CyberPsychol Behav 8(5), 487–92.

34. Gold, J. I., Kim, S. H., Kant, A. J., and Rizzo, A. A. (2005) Virtual anesthesia: the use of virtual reality for pain distraction during acute medical interventions. Semin Anesth Periop Med Pain 24, 203–10.

35. Morrow, K., Docan, C., Burdea, G., and Merians, A. (2006) Low-cost virtual rehabilitation of the hand for patients post-stroke. In Proceedings of the 5th International Workshop on Virtual Rehabilitation, 6–10.

36. Stewart, J. C., Yeh, S. C., Jung, Y., Yoon, H., Whitford, M., Chen, S., Li, L., McLaughlin, M., Rizzo, A. A., and Winstein, C. J. (2007) Intervention to enhance skilled arm and hand movements after stroke: a feasibility study using a new virtual reality system. J Neuroeng Rehab 4(21), 1–18.

37. Rothbaum, B. O., Foa, E. B., Riggs, D., Murdock, T., & Walsh, W. (1992) A prospective examination of post-traumatic stress disorder in rape victims. J Trauma Stress 5, 455–75.

38. Mowrer, O. A. (1960) Learning and Behavior. New York: Wiley.

39. Pitman, R. K., Orr, S. P., Forgue, D. F., de Jong, J. B., & Claiborn, J. M. (1987) Psychophysiologic assessment of post-traumatic stress disorder imagery in Vietnam combat veterans. Arch Gen Psychiatry 44, 970–75.

40. Blanchard, E. B., Kolb, L. C., Gerardi, R. J., Ryan, D., and Pallmeyer, T. P. (1986) Cardiac response to relevant stimuli as an adjunctive tool for diagnosing post-traumatic stress disorder in Vietnam veterans. Behav Ther 17, 592–606.

41. Foa, E. B., Davidson, R. T., and Frances, A. (1999) Expert Consensus Guideline Series: treatment of posttraumatic stress disorder. American J Clin Psychiatry 60, 5–76.

42. Foa, E. B., and Kozak, M. J. (1986) Emotional processing of fear: exposure to corrective information. Psychol Bull 99(1), 20–35.

43. Foa, E. B., Steketee, G. S., and Rothbaum, B. O. (1989) Behavioral/cognitive conceptualizations of post-traumatic stress disorder. Behav Ther 20, 155–76.

44. Bryant, R. A., Moulds, M. L., Guthrie, R. M., Dang, S. T. and Nixon, R. D. (2003) Imaginal exposure alone and imaginal exposure with cognitive restructuring in treatment of posttraumatic stress disorder. J Consult Clin Psychol 71(4), 706–12.

45. Foa, E. B., and Hearst-Ikeda, D. (1996) Emotional dissociation in response to trauma: an information-processing approach. In Michelson, L.K., and Ray, W.J., eds., Handbook of Dissociation: Theoretical and Clinical Perspectives (pp. 207–22). New York: Plenum Press.

46. Foa, E. B., and Meadows, E. A. (1997) Psychosocial treatments for posttraumatic stress disorder: a critical review. Annu Rev Psychol 48, 449–80.

47. Carlson, J. G., Chemtob, C. M., Rusnak, K., Hedlund, N. L., and Muraoka, M. Y. (1998) Eye movement desensitization and reprocessing (EDMR) treatment for combat-related posttraumatic stress disorder. J Trauma Stress 11(1), 3–24.

48. Sherman, J. J. (1998) Effects of psychotherapeutic treatments for PTSD: a meta-analysis of controlled clinical trials. J Trauma Stress 11(3), 413–35.

49. Resick, P. A., Nishith, P., Weaver, T. L., Astin, M. C., and Feuer, C. A. (2002) A comparison of cognitive-processing therapy with prolonged exposure and a waiting condition for the treatment of chronic posttraumatic stress disorder in female rape victims. J Consult Clin Psychol 70(4), 867–79.

50. Wessa, M., and Flor, H. (2007) Failure of extinction of fear responses in posttraumatic stress disorder: evidence from second-order conditioning. Am J Psychiatry 164, 1684–92.

51. Cardena, E., and Spiegel, D. (1993) Dissociative reactions to the San Francisco Bay Area earthquake of 1989. Am J Psychiatry 150(3), 474–78.

52. Koopman, C., Classen, C., and Spiegel, D. (1994) Predictors of posttraumatic stress symptoms among survivors of the Oakland/Berkeley, Calif., firestorm. Am J Psychiatry 151(6), 888–94.

53. Foa, E. B., Riggs, D. S., Massie, E. D., and Yarczower, M. (1995) The impact of fear activation and anger on the efficacy of exposure treatment for PTSD. Behav Ther 26, 487–99.

54. Jaycox, L. H., Foa, E. B., and Morral, A. R. (1998) Influence of emotional engagement and habituation on exposure therapy for PTSD. J Consult Clin Psychol 66(1), 185–92.

55. Britt, T. W. (2000) The stigma of psychological problems in a work environment: Evidence from the screening of service members returning from Bosnia. J Appl Physiol 30(8), 1599–1618.

56. Rothbaum, B. O., and Hodges, L. F. (1999) The use of virtual reality exposure in the treatment of anxiety disorders. Behav Mod 23(4), 507–25.

57. Difede, J., Cukor, J., Jayasinghe, N., Patt, I., Jedel, S., Spielman, L., et-al. (2007) Virtual Reality exposure therapy for the treatment of posttraumatic stress disorder following September 11, 2001. J Clin Psychiatry 68, 1639–47.

58. Wood, D. P., Murphy, J. A., Center, K., Russ, C., McLay, R. N., et-al. (2008) Combat related post traumatic stress disorder: a multiple case report using virtual reality graded exposure therapy with physiological monitoring. In Medicine Meets Virtual Reality 16. Amsterdam, the Netherlands: IOS Press, pp. 556–561.

59. Weathers, F. W., Litz, B., Herman, D. S., Huska, J. A., and Keane, T. M. (1993) The PTSD Checklist (PCL): reliability, validity, and diagnostic utility. Paper presented at the Annual Meeting of International Society for Traumatic Stress Studies, San Antonio, TX; October.

60. Gamito, P., Oliveira, J., Morais, D., Saraiva, T., Rosa, P., et al. (2007) War PTSD: A VR pre-trial case study. Annu Rev Cyberther Telemed 191–98.

61. Josman, N., Somer, E., Reisberg, A., Weiss, P. L., Garcia-Palacios, A., and Hoffman, H. (2006) BusWorld: designing a virtual environment for PTSD in Israel: a protocol. Cyberpsychol Behav 9(2), 241–44.

62. Parsons, T. D., and Rizzo, A. A. (2008) Initial validation of a virtual environment for assessment of memory functioning: virtual reality cognitive performance assessment test. Cyberpsychol Behav 11(1), 16–24.

63. Reger, G. M., Gahm, G. A., Rizzo, A. A., Swanson, R. A., Etherage, J., and Reger, M. A. (2007) Virtual reality in operational and garrison psychology: a review of the applications of the VR Iraq at Fort Lewis. Paper presented at Cybertherapy 2007, Washington, DC.

64. Reger, G. M., Gahm, G. A., Rizzo, A. A., Swanson, R. A., and Duma, S. (2009) Soldier evaluation of the Virtual Reality Iraq. Telemedicine and e-health 15(1), 100–103.

65. Wilson, J. A. B., Onorati, K., Mishkind, M., Reger, M. A., and Gahm, G. A. (2008) Soldier attitudes about technology-based approaches to mental healthcare. Cyberpsychol Behav Nov 9. Epub ahead of print.

66. Blanchard, E. B., Jones-Alexander, J., Buckley, T. C., and Forneris, C. A. (1996) Psychometric properties of the PTSD Checklist (PCL). Behav Res Ther 34(8), 669–73.

67. Beck, A. T., Epstein, N., Brown, G., and Steer, R. A. (1988) An inventory for measuring clinical anxiety: psychometric properties. J Consult Clin Psychol 56(6), 893–97.

68. Kroenke, K., and Spitzer, R. L. (2002) The PHQ-9: A new depression and diagnostic severity measure. Psychiatr Ann 32, 509–21.

69. Rizzo, A. A., Graap, K., Perlman, K., Mclay, R. N., Rothbaum, B. O., Reger, G., Parsons, T., Difede, J., and Pair, J. (2008) Virtual Iraq: initial results from a VR exposure therapy application for OIF/OEF combat-related post traumatic stress disorder. In Westwood, J.D., et al., eds., Studies in Health Technology and Informatics. Amsterdam, the Netherlands: IOS Press, pp. 420–25.
70. Gerardi, M., Rothbaum, B. O., Ressler, K., Heekin, M., and Rizzo, A. A. (2008) Virtual reality exposure therapy using a Virtual Iraq: case report. J Trauma Stress 21(2), 1–5.
71. Ressler, K. J., Rothbaum, B. O., Tannenbaum, L., Anderson, P., Zimand, E., Hodges, L., and Davis, M. (2004) Facilitation of psychotherapy with D-cycloserine, a putative cognitive enhancer. Arch Gen Psychiatry 61, 1136–44.

Index

A

ACC. *See* Anterior cingulated cortex
Acetylcholine, 172, 189, 191, 192
ACTH. *See* Adrenocorticotropic hormone
Acute stress, 51, 52, 110, 116, 160, 161
Adrenalectomy, 281
Adrenal glucocorticoids. *See* Glucocoricoids
Adrenal insufficiency, 266
Adrenal steroids, 162, 163, 164, 165, 169, 170, 171
β-Adrenergic antagonist, 29, 340–341
Adrenocorticotropic hormone, 54, 140, 170, 258–259, 263, 265–267, 281
α2-Adrenoreceptor agonists, 340
α1-Adrenoreceptor antagonist, 341–343
Alcoholism, 325
Allostatic overload in animal/person, 159
Alprazolam, 348
Alterations in sleep, 246. *See also* Corticotropin-releasing hormone
Alzheimer's disease, 191
American Psychiatric Association (APA), 338
Amine modulatory systems, 27
γ-Aminobutyric acid, 28, 42, 52, 85, 167, 172, 189, 190, 191, 343, 344, 348
α-Amino-3-hydroxy-5-methyl-4-isoxazolepropionic acid (AMPA) binding, 169
Amitriptyline, 352, 353
AMPA receptor internalization, 58
Amygdala. *See also* Fear conditioning; Hippocampus
  electrolytic lesions, 172
  function
    trauma-related stimuli, 320–321
    trauma-unrelated stimuli, 322–323
  GABA-ergic system in, 167

impact of repeated stress, on, 158–159
implied in adaptive and pathological fear, 31
major input and output regions, 27–28
in modulating effects of stress on sleep, 243–246
pharmacological perturbations in, 172
protective role for corticosterone in, 170
role of, 24
seizure-like activity on, 59
sensory inputs, 26
synaptic signaling, 28–29
thalamic and cortical pathways, 26–27
two-roads model, of signal transmission, 27
volumes, 323
Amygdala-medial prefrontal interactions, 324–325
Animal models, 134
  on changes in neurobiological systems, 139–140
  changes in neurobiological systems, 139–140
  mechanism-based models, 136–139
  modeling additional factors, 140–143
  trauma-/stress-based models, 135–136
α$_2$-Antagonist yohimbine, 225
Anterior cingulated cortex, 299–302, 304, 305, 309, 311, 312, 323–325
Antiadrenergics, 339
Anticonvulsants, 343–344
Antidopamine-β-hydroxylase-saporin (DBH-sap), 195
Antikindling effects, 343
Antipsychotics, 342, 344–347
Anxiety diseases, 80
Anxiety disorders, 24, 80–83. *See also* Learned fear

Anxiety-like behavior, 170
Anxiolytics, 169
Anxious arousal symptoms, 284
Anxious-misery, 279
Approach and avoidance, 25
Arc/ARG3.1 pathway, 88
Astressin, 205, 247
Auditory fear conditioning, 25
Autobiographical memory, 106–107
    alterations in, 110–111
    overgeneral memory, mechanisms
        of, 108–110
    overgeneral nature of, 107–108
Avoidance symptoms, 2
Axis I disorder, 278

B
BAI. *See* Beck anxiety inventory
Basal forebrain, 188
    and acetylcholine, 191–192
    arousal triggers during sleep, 194–196
Basolateral amygdala. *See also* Amygdala
    dendritic lengthening, neurons in, 171
    effects of chronic stress, principal
        neurons of, 168
    excitability, neurochemical modulation
        dopamine (DA), 50–51
        neuromodulators, 52–54
        neuropeptides, 51–52
        norepinephrine (NE), 51
        serotonin (5HT), 48–50
    histamine, action on, 192
    β-receptors located within, 224
    spinogenesis, 160
Basolateral complex
    afferent input, 41
    depression of CS-evoked activity, 57
    interneurons, 43–44
    neuronal heterogeneity, 42–44
    projection neurons, 42
    reciprocal interactions, between PFC
        and, 40
    synaptic transmission, 44–48
BDNF. *See* Brain-derived neurotrophic
    factor
Beck anxiety inventory, 390
Bed nucleus of stria terminalis, 63, 172,
    205–207
Behavioral impairments, 166

Benzodiazepines, 53, 169, 347–348
BF. *See* Basal forebrain
Bipolar disorder, 40
BLA. *See* Basolateral amygdala
BLC. *See* Basolateral complex
BNST. *See* Bed nucleus of stria terminalis
Brain-derived neurotrophic factor, 29, 53,
    86, 94, 142, 160, 167, 168
Brain regions, 153–155
Brain temperature, 189
Brief stressors and delayed impact, 159–162

C
Calcium/calmodulin-dependent protein
    kinase II (CaMKII), 89
Calcium channels, 166
Cannabinoid agonist WIN55212-2, 53
Cannabinoid receptor 1 (CB1), 85
Carbon dioxide, 196
3(2-Carboxypiperazine-4-yl)propyl-1-
    phosphinic acid (CPP), 57
Catecholamines, 29, 214, 223, 259
CBT. *See* Cognitive-behavioral treatment
Central nucleus of amygdala (CeA),
    54, 172
Cerebral blood flow (rCBF), 299, 301, 302
Cerebral spinal fluid (CSF), 282
Cholecystokinin (CCK), 42, 43, 52
Cholineacetyltransferase (ChAT), 42, 195
Cholinergic neurons, 191
Chronic stress, 165, 166, 168
Circadian rhythm alterations, 261–262
Clinician-administered PTSD scale (CAPS),
    301, 340
Clonidine, 340
Cloninger's measure of harm avoidance, 286
Cognitive activation studies. *See*
    Neuroimaging studies
Cognitive-behavioral treatment, 379–380, 394
Cognitive-emotional interactions, 307–309
Cognitive function, 221
Cognitive reappraisal, 308
Collaborative management interventions,
    and guided imagery, 369
Combat environment, and PTSD risk, 376
Comorbidity, 278–279
    internalizing/externalizing model (*see
        also* Psychiatric comorbidity)
    startle amplitude, effect of, 286

Conditioned fear. *See also* Pavlovian fear
    conditioning
    and alterations in sleep, 236–242
    extinction of, 56–58
    Hcrt2-sap, abolishing cardiovascular and
        behavioral response, 191
Conditioned stimulus (CS), 24
Conditioned threat cues, 285
Contextualization, 312–313
Cortico-BLC pathway, 56
Corticosterone (CORT), 53, 140, 168,
    170, 171
Corticotrophin-releasing factor, 140, 202,
    258, 281
    hypersecretion, 265, 266
    receptor, 191
Corticotropin-releasing hormone, 170,
    246–248
    administration and startle response, 285
    antagonists, 247
Cortisol, 159, 170, 281
    circadian rhythmicity of, 261–262
    externalizing disorders, and low basal
        cortisol, 283–284
    internalizing disorders, and elevated
        cortisol level, 282–283
    levels, 259–261
    motor vehicle accidents and, 261
    rape victims and, 261
Cortisol-binding globulin (CBG), 264
CRF. *See* Corticotrophin-releasing factor
CRH. *See* Corticotropin-releasing hormone
CSA-related PTSD, 302
CST. *See* Cerebral spinal fluid
Cushing's disease, 170
Cutoff behavioral criteria approach,
    140–141
Cyclic adenosine monophosphate (cAMP),
    48, 86, 223
Cyclic adenosine monophosphate response
    element-binding (CREB), 28, 89, 163
Cycline-dependent kinase 5 (Cdk5), 89
Cyproheptadine, 353
Cytokines, 189

D

DA-containing ventral tegmental area
    (VTA) neurons, 60
D-cycloserine (DCS), 57, 353

Dentate gyrus, 165, 172
Detroit trauma survey, 10
Dexamethasone (DEX), 261–265
Dexamethasone suppression test, 54,
    262–265
Diagnostic and Statistical Manual of Mental
    Disorders, fourth edition (DSM-IV),
    278, 279
Differential contextual-odor conditioning
    (DCOC), 138
Divalproex, 343
DNA methylation, 267, 268
Dominant negative Cdk5 mutant
    (dnCdk5), 90
Dopamine (DA), 29, 50–51
Dopaminergic signaling, 87
Dopamine type 2 (D2) receptors, 344
DST. *See* Dexamethasone suppression test

E

Electromyography (EMG) recordings, 284
Emotion
    cognitive appraisal of, 308
    cognitive modulation of, 308–309
    regulation, 307
Emotional disorders, 80
Emotional memory formation, 40
Emotional numbing, 2
Endocannabinoids, 29
Endogenous cannabinoid receptor, 53
Envirodine incorporated scent
    palette, 387. *See also* Virtual Iraq
    system
Epigenetics, 267–268
Epinephrine, 159, 162, 223, 259
Erk1/2
    role of, 88–89
    signaling, 93
Etiological model, 6–7
Eustress, 215
Excitatory postsynaptic currents
    (EPSCs), 165
Excitatory synapses, plasticity, 165–166
Excitatory synaptic transmission, 164–165
Exposure therapy for, 378–380
Externalizing disorders and low cortisol,
    283–284
Extinction, 306–307
Extinction-deficit model, 59

Extreme behavioral response (EBR), 140, 141
Extreme distress, 2
Extreme shyness, 24
Eyeblink conditioning, 166
Eye movement desensitization and
    reprocessing (EMDR), 392

F
Familial psychopathology, 7–8
Fear and anxiety, neural mechanisms
    of, 24
Fear conditioning. *See also* Conditioned
    fear
  acquisition and extinction fear in, 82
  cellular hypothesis of, 29
  enhancement (*see also* Animal models)
  histamine, implicate in, 192
  unit oscillations and synchrony, 58
Fear, extinction of, 30–31
  associative and nonassociative
      mechanisms of, 84
  kinase signaling during, 86–93
  neurotransmitter systems, in, 83–86
  and sleep, 242–243
Fear learning, in human brain, 32
Fear memories, 29–30, 174
Fear motivating behaviors, 25
FKBP5 gene, 54, 265
Flashbacks, 344
Fluoxetine, 350–351
Functional connectivity analysis. *See*
    Neuroimaging studies
Functional magnetic resonance imaging
    (fMRI), 32, 298–299, 320

G
GABA. *See* γ-Aminobutyric acid
GABA$_A$ receptors, 46, 47, 51, 53, 59, 86,
    169, 348
GABA$_B$ receptors, 45, 46, 60
GABA-ergic modulation, by stress and
    stress hormones, 171
GABA-ergic neurons, 28, 59, 158, 189,
    190, 194
GABA-ergic transmission, 46, 53, 61, 85,
    86, 87, 167
Galanin, 189
Galvanic skin response (GSR), 389
Genetic background, contribution of, 142

GFP-positive GABA-ergic cortical
    interneurons, 190
GIFT. *See* Guided imagery for trauma
Glucocorticoid receptors, 53, 162, 163, 259,
    260, 264–265, 268
Glucocorticoids, 29, 165–167, 170, 267
GluR2-derived peptide, 58
Glutamate, 29, 44, 50, 60, 86, 163, 164,
    167, 169
  receptor, activation and plasticity, 171
  transporter Glt1a and Glt1b, 165
Green fluorescent protein (GFP), 190
GR gene polymorphisms, 54
GRs. *See* Glucocorticoid receptors
Guanfacine, 340
Guanosine triphosphatase (GTPase), 91
Guided imagery
  application in diseases, 365
  definition, 364
  as self-management intervention,
      369–370
  treatment protocol (*see also* Guided
      imagery for trauma)
  vs. alternate techniques, 366
Guided imagery for trauma (GIFT),
    366–367
  treatment protocol
    guided imagery audio exercises,
        368–369
    midpoint consultation session, 368
    military sexual trauma, 370–371
    orientation session, 368
    self-monitoring, 369
    telephone coaching, 368
  vs. alternate techniques, 366
  in women with PTSD related to military
      sexual trauma, 370–371

H
Habituation, 305–306
Hcrt2 receptor, 191
HDAC inhibitors, 94
Heart rate (HR), 389
Hebbian LTP, 171
α-Helical CRH$_{9-41}$ (α HelCRH), 247
Heritability factors, 7
High-frequency stimulation-dependent LTP
    (HFS-LTP), 56
Hippocampal LTP, impairment, 172–173

Hippocampal memory, 172
Hippocampal Rac-1 activity, 91
Hippocampus, 40
   activation of postsynaptic NMDA
      receptors in, 171
   in vivo electrophysiological recording
      and interaction, 174
   and PFC, effects of repeated stress on,
      155–157
   regions, 303
   stress-induced plasticity, 172
   voltage-gated calcium currents in, 166
Hippocampus-dependent spatial learning
   task, impairment, 166
Histamine, 189
   H1 and H2 receptors, 192
   neurons, 196
Histaminergic neurons, 192
Histamine type 1 (H1) receptor, 344–345
Histidine decarboxylase, 196
Histone-acetyl transferases (HATs), 94
Histone deacetylases (HDACs), 94
Histones acetylation, 94
Homeostasis, 155, 162, 169, 235, 236,
   258, 264
HPA axis alterations, 265–267
Hyperarousal symptoms, 2
Hypercortisolemia, 170, 282, 283
Hypervigilance for danger, 2
Hypo-cortisolism, 282
Hypocretin 1 (Hcrt1), 93, 191
Hypocretin 1 and hypocretin 2 (Hcrt1 and
   Hcrt2). See Hypocretin peptide
Hypocretin neurons, 192, 194
Hypocretin peptide, 190, 202–203
   to BF induces wakefulness, 191
   interaction with neural circuitry, 204–205
   role in arousal, 203
   and stress, 204
Hypothalamic-pituitary-adrenal (HPA) axis,
   53, 54, 139–140, 153, 162, 247, 258,
   263, 265–268, 281

I
ICU-related PTSD symptoms, 170
Immediate-early genes (IEGs), 221
Immobilization stress, 160
Immunoreactive interneurons, 43
Impaired cognitive function, 170

Impaired contextualization, 138–139
Impaired extinction, 137–138
Inbred mouse strains, post-traumatic stress
   behavioral responses, 142–143
Inhibitory postsynaptic potentials, 44, 45,
   56, 167
Inhibitory synaptic transmission, 167–169
Innate fear, 24
Intensive care units (ICUs), 170
Intercalated cells (ITCs), 26
Internalizing disorders and elevated cortisol,
   282–283
Intra-amygdala microcircuitry, of fear,
   25–28
IPSPs. See Inhibitory postsynaptic
   potentials

K
Kindling model, of epilepsy, 59–60

L
Lateral amygdala, signal transduction
   pathways, 29
Lateral dorsal tegmentum (LDT), 194, 203,
   206
LC. See Locus coeruleus
Learned fear, 80. See also Fear, extinction
Lewis rat strain, 161
Life adversity, 10
Life-threatening potential, perception of, 134
Locus coeruleus, 190
   arousal triggers during sleep, 194–196
   in stress-related disorders, 224–225
   neurons, 193, 244, 215, 216
Locus coeruleus-noradrenergic system
   arousal-enhancing actions of, 217–219
   modulating sensory information
      processing, 219–220
   modulatory actions
      on cognitive processes, 221–223
      on neuronal plasticity, 220–221
   plasticity in stress, 216–217
   sensitivity to appetitive stimuli, 217
Long-term potentiation (LTP), 136, 160, 168
Low-density lipoprotein (LDL)
   cholesterol, 281
L type voltage gated calcium channel
   (L-VGCC), 56
Lysine acetylation, 93

M

Madigan Army Medical Center (MAMC), 387
Maladaptive fear, 24
MAPK. *See* Mitogen-activated protein kinase MBR. *See* Minimal behavioral response
Medial amygdala (MeA), 172
Medial prefrontal cortex, 137, 159, 174, 299, 323–324
  activation of, 311
  cognitive-emotional interactions, 307–308
    cognitive appraisal of emotions, 308
    cognitive reappraisal, 308–309
  contextualizing stimuli, failure of, 311–313
  self-relatedness and social-emotional processing, 309–311
  threat-related processing, studies of, 305–307
Median preoptic area (MPOA), 188
MEK inhibitors, 87
Memory alterations, 106
Memory reconsolidation, 30
Messenger ribonucleic acid (mRNA) levels, 169, 221
meta-Chlorophenylpiperazine (m-CPP), 349
3-Methoxy-4-hydroxyphenylglycol (MHPG), 261
Metyrapone, 266
Military sexual trauma, 370
Mineralocorticoid receptors (MRs), 162, 164
Minimal behavioral response (MBR), 141
Mirtazapine, 353
Mitogen-activated protein kinase, 28, 87, 88
Modeling early life stress, 141–142
Monoamine xidase inhibitor (MAOI), 352–353
Montgomery Asberg Depression Rating Scale (MADRS), 351
Mowrer's two-factor theory, 378–379
mPFC. *See* Medial prefrontal cortex
MPOA neurons, 190
MR/GR ratios, 163
Multidrug resistance (MDR), 163
Muscimol, 172, 173, 243

N

N-acetylaspartate (NAA), 303, 325
Narcolepsy, 193–194, 203
National Comorbidity Survey (NCS), 3
National Comorbidity Survey Replication (NCS-R), 3
National Vietnam Veterans Readjustment Study (NVVRS), 4
Naval Medical Center–San Diego (NMCSD), 387
NE. *See* Norepinephrine
Nefazodone, 352–353
Network architectures, 172
Neural substrates, 155–159
Neurobiological system. *See* Animal model; HPA axis
Neuroendocrinology, 258–259
Neuroimaging studies. *See also* Amygdala; Medial prefrontal cortex
  cognitive activation studies, 301–303
  functional connectivity analyses, 303–304
  symptom provocation studies, 299–301
Neuronal network and wakefulness, 191–193
Neuronal nitric oxide synthase (nNOS), 190
Neuropeptides, 42, 51–52, 258, 267, 353
Neuropeptide Y (NPY), 29, 52, 61
Neurotoxins
  hypocretin 2 (Hcrt2)-saporin, 191
  lesions, 191
New learning impairments, 114–115
  neural and cognitive bases of, 115–117
  predisposition/consequence, 117–118
New learning, of emotional information, 118–120
Nitric oxide (NO), 28, 29, 53
NMDA- and non-NMDA receptor-mediated glutamatergic transmission, 59, 168
NMDA-dependent LTD of synapses, 166
NMDA-receptor-mediated EPSCs, 55
N-Methyl D-aspartate (NMDA) receptors, 163
  antagonism, 165
  receptor, 90
Non-REM sleep, 188, 190, 247
Noradrenaline, 29, 48, 51
Norepinephrine, 51, 159, 172, 189, 193, 215, 218, 221–225. *See also* Locus coeruleus-noradrenergic system

Norepinephrine-synthesizing enzyme, 196
Nuclear factor kappa B (NFκB), 163

O

Odor stimulus, 138
Olanzapine, 344, 345
Operation enduring freedom (OEF), 5
Operation iraqi freedom (OIF), 5
Opioid, 172
Orexin. *See* Hypocretin peptide
Overt aggression scale–modified (OAS-M)
    for outpatients, 346
Oxytocin, 353

P

Panic disorder, 40
Paraventricular nucleus (PVN), 259
Parental PTSD, 261
Paroxetine, 349
Parvalbumin (PARV), 43, 44
Patient health questionnaire-depression
    (PHQ-9), 390
Pavlovian fear conditioning, 24, 55–56
Paxil. *See* Paroxetine
Pedunculopontine tegmental (PPT) area,
    194, 203
People with PTSD, symptoms, 2–3
Perceived life threat, 13–14
Peritraumatic dissociation, 12–13
Peritraumatic emotional response, 11–12
pErk1/2, for learning and extinction, 88
p35 and p39 expression, 90
PFC. *See* Prefrontal cortex
Pharmacologic treatment, 338–339,
    352–353
    antiadrenergics, 339
        clonidine, 340
        guanfacine, 340
        prazosin, 341–343
        propranolol, 340–341
    anticonvulsants, 343–344
    antipsychotics, 344–347
    benzodiazepines, 347–348
    SSRIs and SNRIs, 348–352
Phenelzine, 352, 353
Phosphorylates p21-activated kinase 1
    (PAK-1), 91
Pituitary-adrenal axis, 214
Pituitary desensitization, 266

Positron emission tomography (PET),
    298, 320
Postsynaptic group II mGluRs in BLC
    projection neurons, 60
Post-trauma factors, 13
Prazosin, 341–343
Predator scent stress (PSS), 138
Predator stimuli potency, 135
Predator stress, 135
Predicted threat, 24
Prefrontal cortex, 40, 49, 61, 63, 137, 155,
    157, 159, 172, 174, 222, 309
Prevalence, 3
    in disaster contexts, 5–6
    refugees, 5
    U.S. combatants, 4–5
    U.S. population, 3–4
Primed-burst potentiation (PBP), 165, 166
Prior trauma, meta-analysis of, 10
Prolonged exposure (PE), and emotional
    processing theory, 379
Propranolol, 29, 225, 340–341
Protein kinase A (PKA), 28, 89
Protein kinase C (PKC), 28, 59, 89
Proteolysis, 165
Psychiatric comorbidity, internalizing and
    externalizing model, 279–280
Psychiatric disorder, 8, 41, 134, 260, 269,
    287, 338
PTSD Checklist-military (PCL-M),
    391, 392
PVN. *See* Paraventricular nucleus

Q

Quetiapine, 345, 347

R

R-α-methylhistamine (RAMH), 192
Randomized controlled trials (RCTs), 338
Rapid eye movement (REM) sleep, 188,
    193, 216, 232, 235, 246, 342
    c-Fos in response to, 190
    neurons regulating, 193–194
3-α- and 5-α Reductases, 163
Regional cerebral blood flow (rCBF),
    299–301, 324
REMView device, 342
Retention memory, 166
Rho/Rock pathway, 88

Risk factors
  demographic factors, 8–11
  post-trauma factors, 13
  priori factors, 7–8
  traumatic event itself, 11–13
Risperidone, 344–347
Rodents to predator stimuli, 135
Rostral anterior cingulate cortex (rACC),
    300, 302, 306

S
Salivary cortisol levels, 282–283
Saporin (sap), 191
Selective serotonin reuptake inhibitor
    (SSRI), 345, 348–352
Self-management intervention, 369–370
Self-relatedness, 309
SEM. See Structural equation modeling
Serotonin (5HT), 29, 48–50, 159, 171,
    189, 193
Serotonin norepinephrine reuptake
    inhibitors (SNRIs), 348–352
Serotonin type 2 (5HT$_2$) receptors, 344
Sertraline, 349–351
Service members (SMs), 376
Severe stress, 160, 162
Single-photon emission tomography
    (SPECT), 298, 320
Single prolonged stress (SPS), animal
    models, 138
Sleep-active neurons, 188–190
Sleep apnea, 196
Sleep deprivation, 190
Sleep disturbance, 187, 233–234
Sleep in animals, effects of stress, 234–235
Sleep neurons, 188–190
  electrophysiology studies, 188
  neuronal circuitry of, 189
Sleep pressure, 190
Sleep-related disturbances, 225
Social-emotional processing, 309–311
Somatostatin (SST), 42, 43, 52, 59
Spatiotemporal dynamics, of stress, 173–174
Spinogenesis, 160
Spontaneous miniature inhibitory
    postsynaptic currents (mIPSCs), 167
Sprague-Dawley (SD) rats, 161
Startle-eliciting stimuli, 284
Startle reflex amplitude, 279

Startle response, 284–285
11-β-Steroid dehydrogenase 1 and 2, 163
Stimulus contextualization failure, 311–313
Stress
  models of, 60–61
  neuroendocrinology, 258
  paradigms, in animals studies, 135
  sleep, and development of, 235–236
Stress hormones. See also Dexamethasone
    suppression test
  circadian rhythm alterations, 261–262
  cortisol levels, 259–261
  epigenetic changes, 267–268
  glucocorticoid responsiveness, 264–265
  HPA axis, 258–259, 265–267
Structural equation modeling (SEM), 13
Subjective units of distress (SUDs), 389,
    390, 392
Sustained arousal, 214
Sympathetic nervous system (SNS), 258
Symptom provocation studies. See
    Neuroimaging studies
Synaptic plasticity, 91
  in hippocampus, 166
  and molecules, 28–29
Synaptic signaling, 28–29, 170–171. See
    also Fear conditioning
Synchronized neuronal oscillations, 58

T
Temporal axis, 159
Temporal characteristics, of stress-induced
    structural plasticity, 160
Temporal lobe, 40
Terrorism, 2
Tetanic stimulation, 136
Tetrahydrocannabinol (THC), 53
Therapeutic strategies, 80
Threat-related processing, studies, 305–307
Tiagabine, 343
TMN. See Tuberomammillary nucleus
Topiramate, 343–344
Transcription factors, 163
Trauma memory, 111–114. See also
    Autobiographical memory
Trauma
  psychopathology, 10–11
  severity, 11
Trauma-related stimuli, 320–321

Trauma-unrelated stimuli, 322–323
Trazodone, 352
Tricyclic antidepressant (TCA), 352–353
Trimethylthiazoline, 135
Tuberomammillary nucleus, 190, 192, 194, 195, 196, 203
Type II GRs, 264

U
Unconditioned response (UR), 136
Unconditioned stimulus (US), 55
Underwater trauma, 135–136
Unipolar mood disorders, 278

V
Vasoactive intestinal peptide (VIP), 43
Vasopressin (AVP), 258
Venlafaxine, 351–352
Ventral lateral preoptic area (VLPO), 188, 190, 203
Vietnam era veterans (VEVs), 4
Vietnam theater veterans (VTVs), 4
Vietnam veteran twin registry, 7
Virtual environments, 378
Virtual Iraq system, 393–394
    current research
        MAMC case study, 391–392
        open clinical trial, at NMCSD, 389–391

service member acceptance, for treatment, 388–389
    user-centered feedback, 387–388
design and development of, 382–387
    desert road scenario, 385
    minimum computing requirements for, 386
    olfactory and tactile stimuli, use of, 387
Virtual reality exposure therapy (VRET), 381–382. *See also* Virtual Iraq system
Virtual reality (VR), and clinical applications, 377–378
VLPO neurons, 189, 190

W
Wake-active neurons, 189, 190
Wakefulness, 190. *See also* Acetylcholine; Histamine; Hypocretin peptide; Serotonin (5HT)
Walter Reed Army Medical Center (WRAMC), 387
Working memory, 222–223
World Trade Center (WTC), 2

Z
Zoloft, 349

Printed in the United States of America